S0-BYE-683

SIMMS INTEGRATED MATHEMATICS

A Modeling Approach Using Technology

Level 4, Third Edition

KENDALL/HUNT PUBLISHING COMPANY
4050 Westmark Drive Dubuque, Iowa 52002

CONTRIBUTORS

Masha Albrecht ■ Glenn Allinger ■ Byron Anderson ■ Staci Auck ■ Shirley Bagwell ■ Cliff Bara ■ Gary Bauer ■ Jack Beal ■ Patricia Bean ■ Glenn Blake ■ Kyle Boyce ■ Monty Brekke ■ Ruth Brocklebank ■ Lee Brown ■ Maurice Burke ■ Clay Burkett ■ Randy Carspecken ■ John Carter ■ William Chalgren ■ Terri Dahl ■ Ted Drieth ■ Wendy Driscoll ■ Bonnie Eichenberger ■ Todd Fife ■ Jerry Fisher ■ John Freal ■ John Gebhart ■ Kimberley Girard ■ Janet Higgins ■ James Hirstein ■ Sherry Horyna ■ Jeffrey Hostetter ■ Alexander Johnson ■ Danny Jones ■ Russ Killingsworth ■ John Knudson-Martin ■ Robbie Korin ■ Pam Koterba ■ Janet Kuchenbrod ■ Phillip Lieske ■ Satinee Lightbourne ■ Fred Longhart ■ Karen Longhart ■ Johnny W. Lott ■ Franklin Lund ■ Mike Lundin ■ Joy Lustgraaf ■ Mark Lutz ■ Peggy Lynn ■ Douglas Mack ■ Pat Mauch ■ Patty Mazurek ■ Anne Merrifield ■ Mary Ann Miller ■ Susan Moore ■ Mindy Obert ■ Laurie Paladichuk ■ Roger Patterson ■ Arthur Perleberg ■ Margaret Plouvier ■ Dean Preble ■ Darlene Pugh ■ Peter Rasmussen ■ Howard Reinhardt ■ Kate Riley ■ Todd Robbins ■ Dick Sander ■ Lisa Schlange ■ Verne Schlepp ■ Lisa Scott ■ Dick Seitz ■ Mike Sinclair ■ Ed Sisolak ■ Tim Skinner ■ David Stabio ■ Paul Swenson ■ Thomas Teegarden ■ David Thiel ■ Otis Thompson ■ Michael Trudnowski ■ Deanna Turley ■ Karen Umbaugh ■ Sharon Walen ■ Anne Watkins ■ Marcia Weinhold ■ Daniel West ■ Teri Willard ■ James Williamson ■ Lisa Wood ■ Mike Wood ■ Steve Yockim

SERIES EDITOR

Terry A. Souhrada

TECHNICAL EDITOR

Peter W. Fong

This material is based upon work supported by the National Science Foundation under Cooperative Agreement No. OSR 9150055. Any opinions, findings, conclusions or recommendations expressed in this material are those of the author(s) and do not necessarily reflect the views of the National Science Foundation.

Cover Credits:
© Photodisc: top left ride, top right gears, bottom right Ferris wheel
© Flat Earth: bottom left roller coaster

ISBN 13: 978-0-7575-2034-1
ISBN 10: 0-7575-2034-0

Printed in the United States of America.

1 2 3 4 5 6 7 8 9 10 10 09 08 07 06

Contents

Preface

In recent years, many voices have called for the reform of mathematics education. The concerns cited include international test scores in mathematics, the retention of students in mathematical and scientific career paths, and the production of mathematically literate adults. Attempts to identify the root causes of these concerns have targeted not only the methods used to instruct and assess students, but also the nature of the mathematics that students learn and the manner in which they are expected to learn.

The Systemic Initiative for Montana Mathematics and Science (SIMMS) began as a five-year, cooperative enterprise of the state of Montana and the National Science Foundation. Funded through the Montana Council of Teachers of Mathematics, and led by mathematics and science teachers from around the state, SIMMS had an ambitious list of objectives, including redesigning the 9–12 mathematics curriculum using an integrated, interdisciplinary approach for *all* students; incorporating the use of technology in all facets and at all levels of mathematics and science; and developing and publishing curriculum and assessment materials for grades 9–16.

With additional funding from the National Science Foundation and the support of teachers, students, and the Kendall/Hunt Publishing Company, these curricular objectives have continued for more than a decade.

What Is Integrated Mathematics?

An integrated mathematics program "consists of topics chosen from a wide variety of mathematical fields . . . . [It] emphasizes the relationships among topics within mathematics as well as between mathematics and other disciplines" (Beal, et al., 1992; Lott and Reeves, 1991).

In its 2000 document, *Principles and Standards for School Mathematics,* the National Council of Teachers of Mathematics addressed curricular reform with these recommendations:

> Mathematics comprises different topical strands, such as algebra and geometry, but the strands are highly interconnected. The interconnection should be displayed prominently in the curriculum and in instructional materials and lessons. A coherent curriculum effectively organizes and integrates important mathematical ideas so that students can see how the ideas build on, or connect with, other ideas, thus enabling them to develop new understandings and skills . . . .
>
> Big ideas encountered in a variety of contexts should be established carefully, with important elements such as terminology, definitions, notation, concepts, and skills emerging in the process . . . .

> In addition, the curriculum should offer experiences that allow students to see that mathematics has powerful uses in modeling and predicting real-world phenomena. (pp. 15–16)

SIMMS *Integrated Mathematics* offers this coherent curriculum, built around big ideas in a variety of contexts, while providing experiences that allow students to model and predict phenomena.

In order to create innovative and accessible materials, a diverse group of more than 80 secondary teachers of mathematics and science, mathematicians, and mathematics educators contributed their skills as writers and reviewers. The SIMMS *Integrated Mathematics* curriculum is expressly designed for use in heterogeneous classrooms, and seeks to encourage the participation of underrepresented groups in mathematics.

Each academic year of SIMMS *Integrated Mathematics* includes algebra, geometry, probability, statistics, and discrete mathematics. Essential mathematical concepts are explored more than once, each time at a slightly higher level—in different settings and in different years—to help students build both vital connections and critical competencies. Students investigate mathematics in the context of crucial social and environmental issues—such as population growth, oil spills, and earthquake damage—along with other real-world topics including mapmaking, business inventory, digital animation, and automobile insurance.

Technology in the Classroom

SIMMS *Integrated Mathematics* focuses on the future needs of mathematically literate adults. Because of this commitment, the use of technology is a fundamental part of curriculum.

In *Principles and Standards for School Mathematics*, the Council noted that "Technology is essential in teaching and learning mathematics; it influences the mathematics that is taught and enhances students' learning" (p. 24). Nearly all current research on the appropriate use of technology in the classroom indicates that students using technology become better problem solvers, without suffering a decline in their more traditional skills.

SIMMS *Integrated Mathematics* works best when students have access to a word processor, spreadsheet, graphing utility, geometry utility, statistics package, and computer algebra system. (Many reasonably priced graphing calculators now include all of these features, with the exception of word processing.)

Student Performance

During the development of SIMMS *Integrated Mathematics*, researchers conducted periodic assessments of student performances in pilot schools. After the publication of the first edition, a four-year longitudinal case study was completed. In these studies, two basic measures—a selection of open-ended mathematical tasks and the PSAT—were administered to experimental and control populations.

On the test of open-ended tasks, technology was made available to both groups. In a comparative analysis, SIMMS *Integrated Mathematics* students were more likely to provide justification for their solutions and made more and better use of graphs, charts, and diagrams. They also demonstrated a greater variety of problem-solving strategies and were more willing to attempt difficult problems.

For the PSAT, technology was not allowed for either group. Student mathematics scores indicated no significant differences in achievement. In other words, although SIMMS *Integrated Mathematics* students were denied access to the technology typically available for classroom work, their performance on the PSAT matched that of their peers.

A summary of the pilot study, as well as a larger National Science Foundation study involving students in selected U.S. cities, is now in print (Senk and Thompson, 2003).

A Look to the Future

Once again in *Principles and Standards for School Mathematics,* the Council argues that:

> When students can connect mathematical ideas, their understanding is deeper and more lasting. They can see mathematical connections in the rich interplay among mathematical topics, in contexts that relate mathematics to other subjects, and in their own interests and experience. Through instruction that emphasizes the interrelatedness of mathematical ideas, students not only learn mathematics, they also learn about the utility of mathematics. (p. 64)

This deep and lasting understanding is what all teachers desire for their students. The third edition of SIMMS *Integrated Mathematics* builds on reform middle-school curricula, and is designed to replace all currently offered secondary mathematics courses, with the possible exception of Advanced Placement Calculus.

—Johnny W. Lott, former co-director of The SIMMS Project and past president of the National Council of Teachers of Mathematics

References

Beal, J., D. Dolan, J. Lott and J. Smith. *Integrated Mathematics: Definitions, Issues, and Implications; Report and Executive Summary.* ERIC Clearinghouse for Science, Mathematics, and Environmental Education. The Ohio State University, Columbus, OH: ED 34701, January 1990, 115 pp.

Lott, J., and A. Reeves. "The Integrated Mathematics Project." *Mathematics Teacher* 84 (April 1991): 334–35.

National Council of Teachers of Mathematics. *Curriculum and Evaluation Standards for School Mathematics.* Reston, VA; NCTM, 1989.

———. *Principles and Standards for School Mathematics.* Reston, VA: NCTM, 2000.

Senk, S., and D. Thompson (eds.). *Standards-Based School Mathematics Curricula: What Are They? What Do Students Learn?* Mahwah, NJ: Lawrence Erlbaum Associates, 2003.

The SIMMS Project. *Monograph I: Philosophies.* Missoula, MT: The Montana Council of Teachers of Mathematics, 1993.

Souhrada, T. "Secondary school mathematics in transition: A comparative study of mathematics curricula and student results." *Dissertation Abstracts International* 62.4 (October 2001): 1355A.

Introduction

When the first edition of SIMMS *Integrated Mathematics: A Modeling Approach Using Technology* was published more than a decade ago, it provided an innovative approach to teaching and learning high school mathematics. The third edition maintains this standard while representing a significant revision of previous versions.

SIMMS *Integrated Mathematics* now includes four levels, offering a comprehensive alternative to traditional secondary mathematics courses. Each year-long level contains 15 modules. All modules are divided into activities, typically including an exploration, a discussion, warm-up problems, a set of homework assignments, and a research project.

Assessment materials—including alternative assessments that emphasize writing and logical argument—are an integral part of the curriculum. Each activity includes one or more suggested assessment items, identified in the Teacher Edition, while each module closes with an open-ended summary assessment. A more traditional assessment, for use at the teacher's discretion, appears in the Teacher Resources, along with short quizzes and review problems, as well as blackline masters for classroom handouts.

Level 1: A First-Year Course

Level 1 concentrates on the knowledge and understanding that students need to become mathematically literate citizens, while providing the necessary foundation for those who wish to pursue careers involving mathematics and science. Each module presents the relevant mathematics in an applied context. These contexts include human nutrition, the properties of reflected light, population growth, structural physiology, and topographic maps, among others. Mathematical content includes data collection, presentation and interpretation; linear, quadratic, and exponential functions; probability; trigonometric ratios; and an introduction to graph theory.

Level 2: A Second-Year Course

Level 2 continues to build on the mathematics that students need to become mathematically literate citizens. While retaining an emphasis on the presentation and interpretation of data, Level 2 also introduces such topics as matrix operations, elementary polynomials, combinatorics, statistics, and fair division. Students investigate traditional geometry, including proof, within the context of home building. They explore transformational geometry through cartoon animation. Other contexts include genetics, business inventory, radioactive decay, and carnival games.

Level 3: A Third-Year Course

This level continues to build mathematical understanding and logical reasoning, based on the first two years of work. Students expand their knowledge of data analysis, algebraic functions, geometric proof, probability, and graph theory. Contexts include map coloring, logarithmic scales, navigation, and quality control, among others. Specific mathematical topics include trigonometric functions, the normal curve, spherical geometry, parametric equations, basic topology, and an introduction to limits.

Level 4: A Fourth-Year Course

For some students, this course represents the end of a high-school mathematical career. For others, this course represents a stepping-stone to advanced placement courses. Because of these different needs, this course is both mathematically and contextually challenging and engaging. Students explore complex numbers, conic sections, hypothesis testing, finite geometry, mathematical induction, and derivatives. Applied contexts include cartography, automobile insurance, and compound interest, among others.

The Student Edition

The third edition of SIMMS *Integrated Mathematics* contains all of the basic elements found in previous editions, along with some new features. For example, each activity now offers an additional problem set, designed to hone mathematical skills before students encounter more complicated assignments. Several individual modules were substantially revised, presenting fresh approaches to geometric proof, hypothesis testing, compositions of functions, and other topics.

Explorations

Nearly all activities contain at least one exploration, giving students a hands-on opportunity to develop their own understandings of mathematical concepts. To facilitate the exchange of ideas and strategies, explorations are designed for work in a variety of instructional formats, including small groups.

Discussions

Discussions give students a structured forum for sharing insights and communicating mathematical ideas, and give teachers a setting for assessing comprehension and reinforcing essential concepts.

Mathematics Notes

Mathematics Notes formally summarize the mathematics students are expected to understand and apply. Each typically includes a definition or explanation, a description of the appropriate notation, and an example or graph.

Warm-Ups

These problem sets—a new feature in the third edition—are designed to review essential mathematical skills and vocabulary before students proceed to the Assignment. Warm-up problems typically do not invoke a real-world context.

Assignments

As in previous editions, most assignment problems present mathematics in applied contexts. Some extend previously learned concepts to other mathematical settings. Students are encouraged to justify their solutions and describe their reasoning.

Research Projects

Many modules contain a Research Project, offering students an opportunity for further study of contemporary or historical mathematics.

Summary Assessment

Summary Assessments typically ask students to demonstrate their problem-solving skills in the same context used in the module. They are often project-oriented and suitable for collaborative work.

Module Summary

At the end of every module, a Module Summary repeats the important mathematics from each activity.

Glossary

The Glossary offers an alphabetical list of definitions for all of the terms and concepts in an entire level (also included in the Teacher Edition).

Selected References

This list provides a helpful compilation of print and other resources for the entire level (also included in the Teacher Edition).

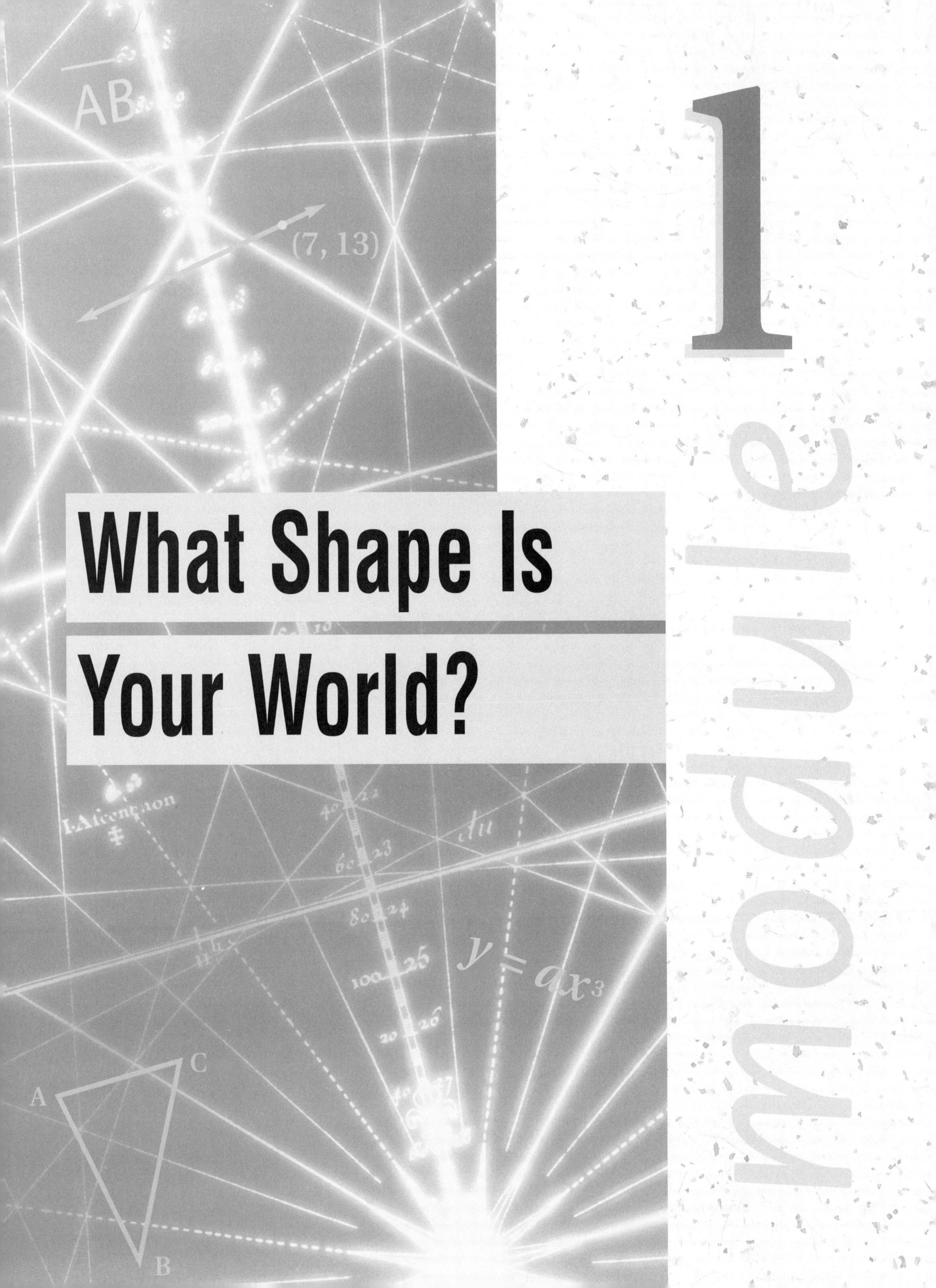

module 1

What Shape Is Your World?

Introduction

Cartography, the science of mapmaking, dates back at least to the time of the ancient Greeks. Humans are travelers, and travelers have always needed directions. Historically, most maps have been drawn on a flat surface, despite the approximately spherical shape of the earth. Over short distances, this projection of a three-dimensional surface onto two dimensions is relatively accurate. However, when mapping large regions covering thousands of square kilometers, some distortion is inevitable.

For example, each map of Greenland shown below was created using a different mapping technique. The map in Figure **1-1a** was made using a **stereographic projection,** a projection whose center is at one of the earth's poles. The map in Figure **1-1b** was made using a **cylindrical projection,** a projection with its center at the earth's center.

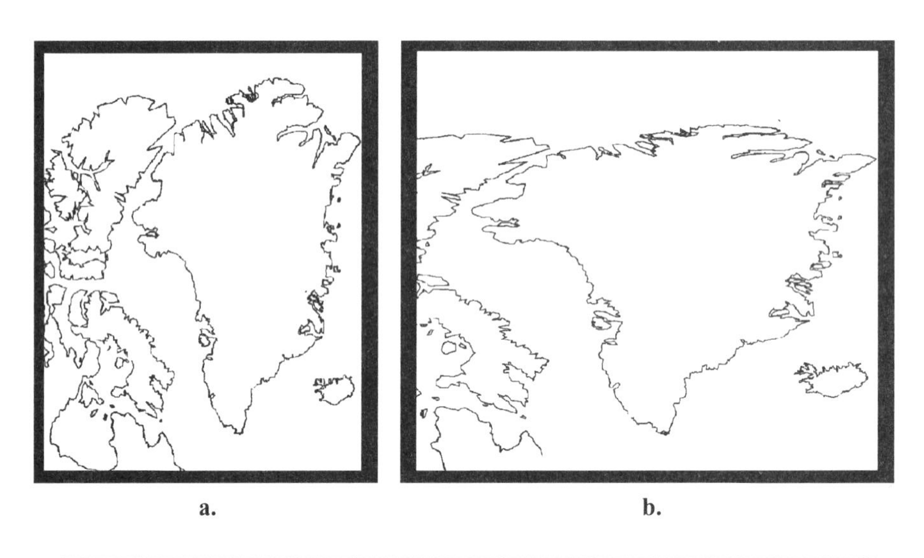

Figure 1-1 Two maps of Greenland made using different projections.

Distortions can make flat paper maps somewhat misleading, but such maps have been quite useful in the past, and certainly will remain so in the future. In the following activities, you investigate some of the inconsistencies and distortions that might result from representing a three-dimensional surface on a flat sheet of paper.

Exploration

a. Obtain two sheets of centimeter graph paper from your teacher. Also get the templates of the two maps in Figure **1-1.** Use each of the templates to make an estimate of Greenland's area, in square kilometers.

b. 1. Compare your two estimates with those of your classmates.

   2. Use the class estimates to find a mean value for Greenland's area on each template.

c. Determine which template of Greenland more closely resembles the shape and proportional size of Greenland on a globe.

Discussion

a. What differences did you observe in the two maps of Greenland?

b. 1. The actual area of Greenland is about 2,175,600 km^2. How does this compare to the two values you obtained in Part **b** of the exploration?

   2. What might account for any differences between your estimates and the actual area?

c. How do you think that geographers determined the actual area of Greenland?

d. Despite the distortions in flat maps of Greenland, what useful information still may be obtained from them?

e. Do you think a map of Greenland on a globe is more accurate than the maps in Figure **1-1**? Explain your response.

One method of giving directions from a starting place to a destination involves specifying a distance east or west, followed by a distance north or south. In other words, the destination is described as a pair of distances along perpendicular lines beginning from a point of origin. This task can be accomplished using a rectangular (Cartesian) coordinate system.

Another method of giving directions involves specifying the distance "as the crow flies" from the starting point to the destination, along with an angle measured from a fixed ray. This task can be accomplished using a **polar coordinate system.** In this activity, you use polar coordinate systems to identify locations on different types of maps.

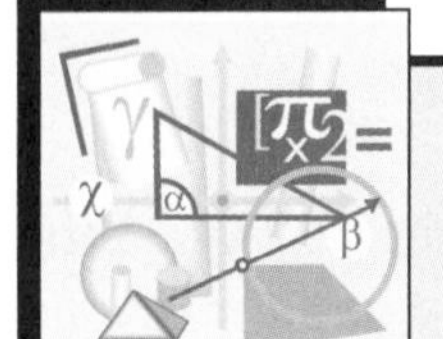

mathematics note

A **polar coordinate system** describes the location of a point P in a plane using an ordered pair consisting of a **radius** r and a **polar angle** θ.

The plane containing a polar coordinate system is the **polar plane.** The polar angle is an angle measured from a fixed ray, called the **polar axis.** The endpoint of the polar axis is the **pole.** The distance from the pole to point P, measured in the polar plane, is r.

To establish a polar coordinate system, a point in the plane is designated as the pole O. Any ray with endpoint O can be designated as the polar axis for the plane. In a standard polar coordinate system, the pole corresponds to the origin of a rectangular coordinate system, while the polar axis corresponds to the positive x-axis, as shown in Figure **1-2.**

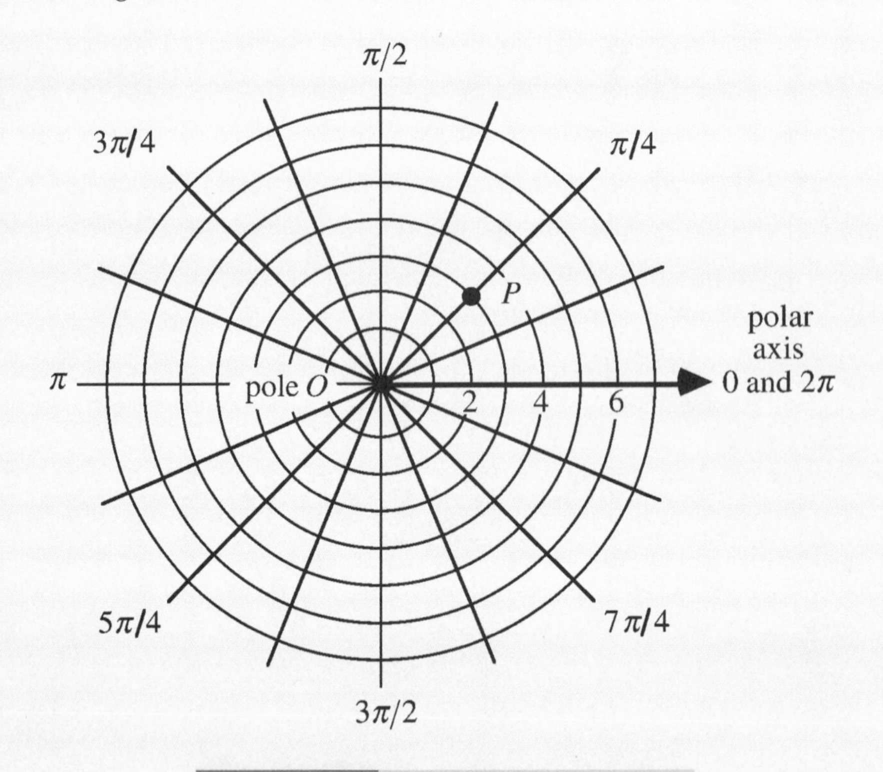

FIGURE 1-2 **A polar coordinate system.**

In this system, any point P in the plane may be represented as an ordered pair (r, θ). The variable r represents the distance between O and P, while θ represents the directed measure of the angle formed by the polar axis and $\overrightarrow{OP}$. The measure of the polar angle may be given in either radians or degrees.

In Figure **1-2,** for example, the coordinates of point P may be given as $(3,45^\circ)$ using degrees or as $(3,\pi/4) \approx (3,0.79)$ using radians.

Exploration 1

Figure **1-3** shows a map of a popular hiking area. In this exploration, you use a polar coordinate system to describe some of the destinations on the map.

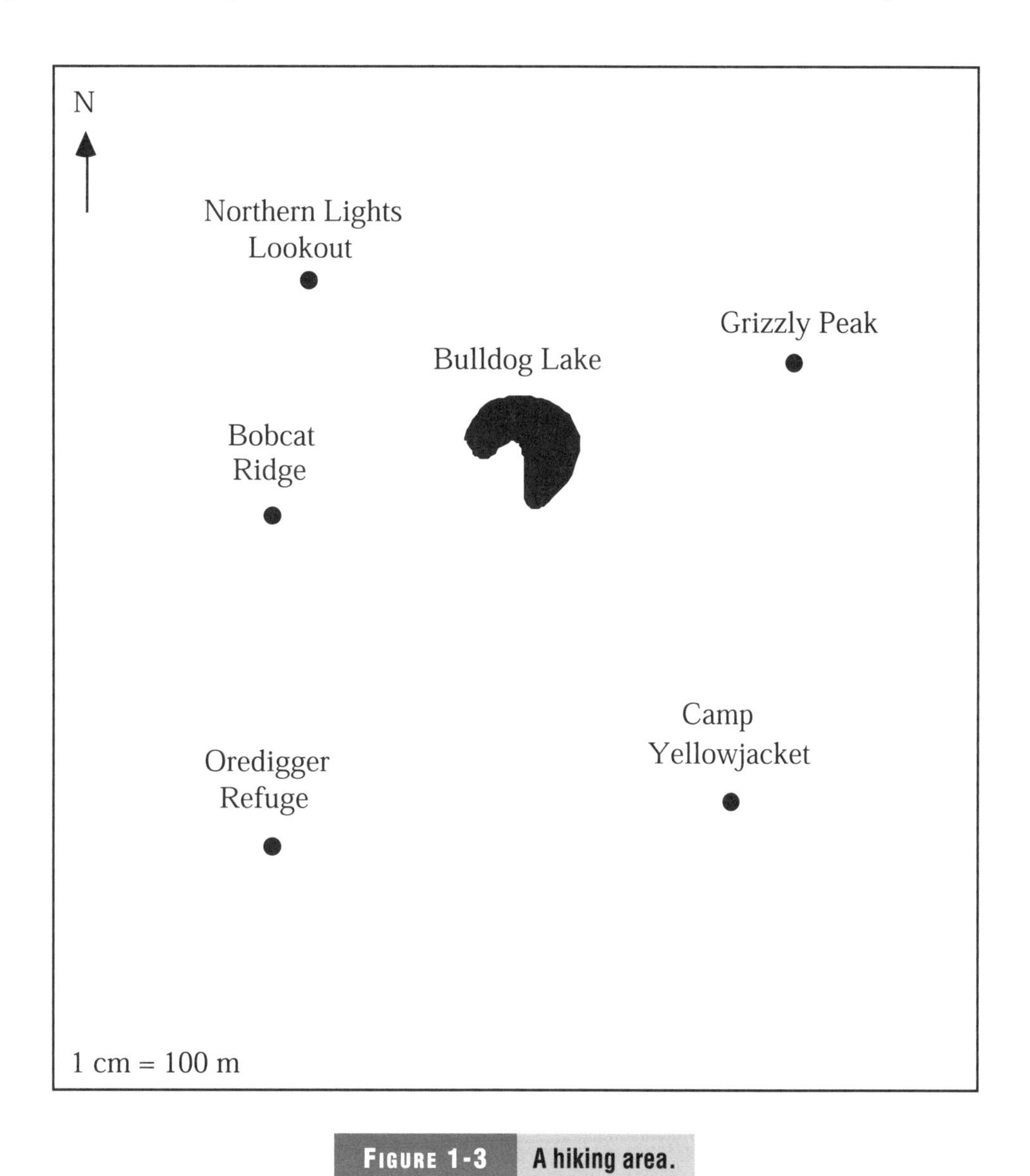

Figure 1-3 A hiking area.

a. Using a copy of Figure **1-3,** create a polar coordinate system with the pole at Oredigger Refuge and the polar axis extending due east.

b. Use polar coordinates to describe the locations of Grizzly Peak and Camp Yellowjacket.

c. 1. A polar angle describes an amount of rotation about the pole. This allows the coordinates of a single point to be represented by more than one positive value of θ.

   Find two different polar representations for the locations of Grizzly Peak and Camp Yellowjacket, using positive values of θ different from those in Part **b.**

   2. Because the polar angle is a directed angle, θ also can have negative values. (A positive value of θ represents an angle measured counterclockwise from the polar axis, a negative value of θ represents an angle measured clockwise from the polar axis.)

   Find two different polar representations for the locations of Grizzly Peak and Camp Yellowjacket using negative values of θ.

d. Many hikers use Northern Lights Lookout as a base camp for day trips in the region. To help these hikers plan their trips, create another polar coordinate system with the pole located at Northern Lights Lookout and the polar axis extending due west.

   Repeat Parts **b** and **c** using this polar coordinate system.

e. Repeat Part **d** on a polar coordinate system with the pole at Northern Lights Lookout and the polar axis extending due east.

f. Compare the polar coordinates you found for Grizzly Peak and Camp Yellowjacket in Parts **b–e** with those of your classmates.

Discussion 1

a. Describe how to locate the point (r, θ) on a polar coordinate system when θ is positive.

b. How many different ordered pairs of the form (r, θ) can be used to represent a given point on a specific polar coordinate system? Explain your response.

c. 1. How do the locations of the pole and the polar axis affect the coordinates of a point?

   2. Why might it be desirable for all users of a map to agree on the same locations of the pole and polar axis?

Exploration 2

Because of the dramatic changes in elevation between destinations, many hikers purchase a topographic map of the region you examined in Exploration **1.** A topographic map is a two-dimensional representation of a three-dimensional surface. On such maps, **contour lines** are used to depict points of equal elevation. In the map in Figure **1-4,** for example, each labeled contour line indicates points at the corresponding elevation (in meters) above sea level.

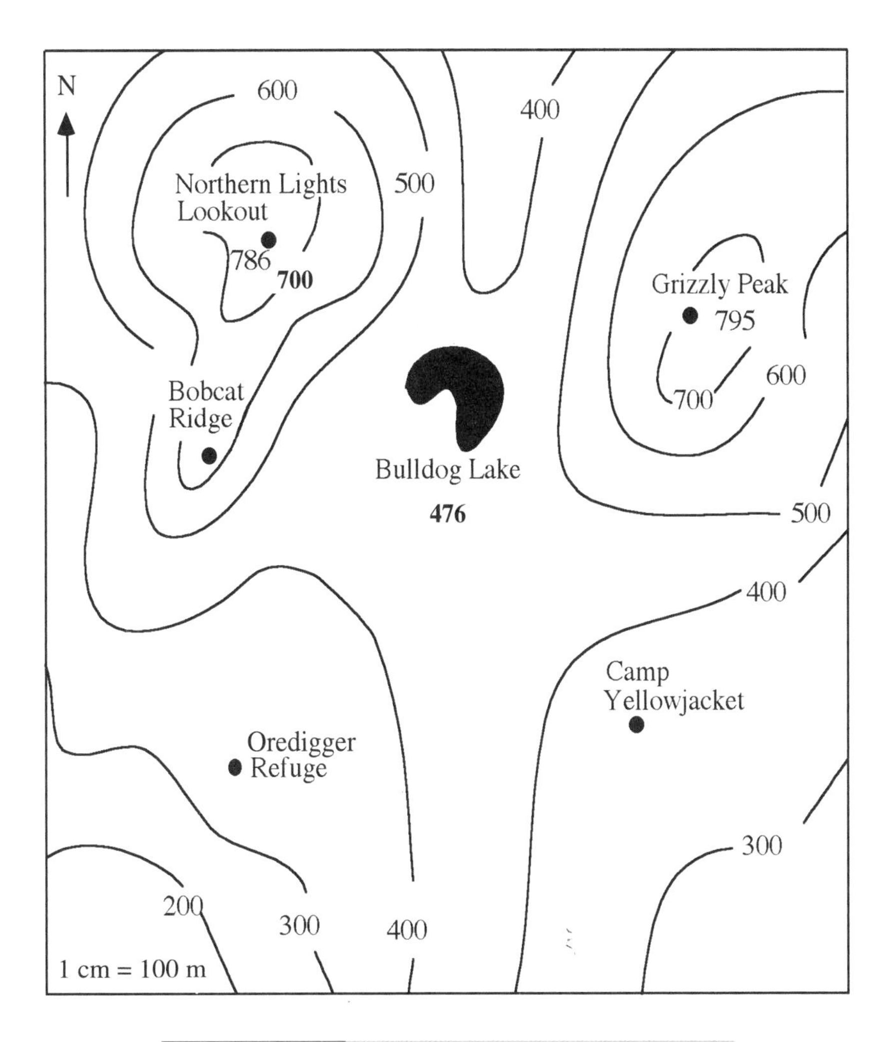

FIGURE 1-4 Topographic map of a hiking area.

mathematics note

Like a rectangular coordinate system, a polar coordinate system can be extended to three dimensions by adding a third dimension z.

In a **cylindrical coordinate system,** a point in space is represented by an ordered triple of the form (r, θ, z). The values of r and θ are measurements in the polar plane. The value of z is the directed distance between the point and the polar plane (the plane containing the polar axis). A positive value for z represents a distance above the polar plane. When a cylindrical coordinate system is used to describe locations on earth, the polar plane is typically located at sea level.

For example, Figure **1-5** shows the locations of three points on a cylindrical coordinate system. The coordinates of point A are $(5, \pi/3, 1)$, the coordinates of point B are $(4, 5\pi/6, -3)$, and the coordinates of point C are $(2, -\pi/6, 2)$.

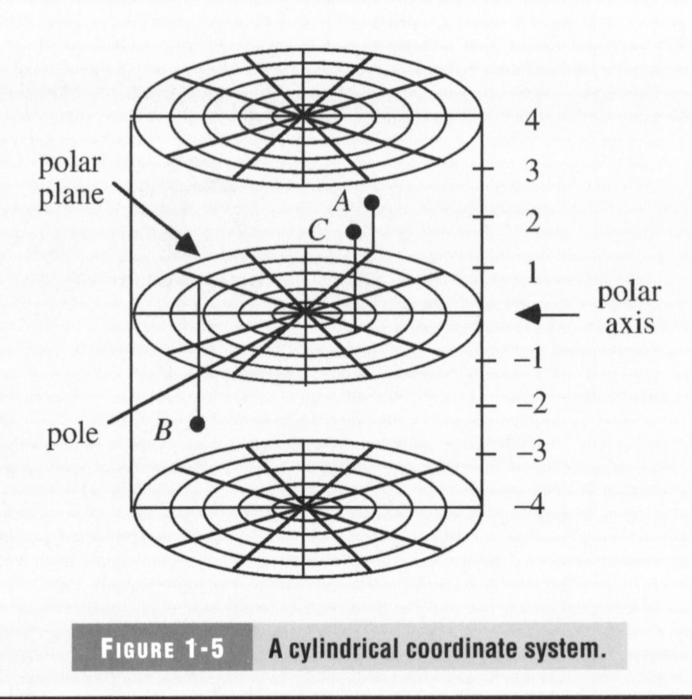

FIGURE 1-5 A cylindrical coordinate system.

a. On a copy of Figure **1-4,** create a cylindrical coordinate system with the pole located at the southwest corner of the map, the polar axis extending due east, and the polar plane at sea level.

b. Using your coordinate system from Part **a,** determine cylindrical coordinates for Oredigger Refuge in which:

   1. r, θ, and z are all positive

   2. r is positive, θ is negative, and z is positive.

Discussion 2

a. How can hikers use the contour lines on a topographic map to help them determine the character of the terrain?

b. Considering the map in Figure **1-4,** which point do you think would provide the best location for the pole of a cylindrical coordinate system?

c. In a cylindrical coordinate system, describe the geometric figure formed by all points that have the same value for each of the following:

1. r 2. θ 3. z

d. In Part **b** of Exploration **2,** you expressed the location of Oredigger Refuge using both positive and negative values for θ. Are there any points on a cylindrical coordinate system that could not be represented using only non-negative coordinates? Explain your response.

Warm-Up

1. Re-express the coordinates for each point in Parts **a** and **b** using only positive values.

   a. $C(7,-\pi/2)$ **b.** $D(5,-19\pi/6)$

2. Graph and label each of the following points on the same cylindrical coordinate system.

   a. $A(5,\pi/4,4)$ **b.** $B(5,7\pi/4,-2)$

   c. $C(3,\pi/4,3)$ **d.** $D(2,\pi/2,-2)$

   e. $E(5,3\pi/4,-4)$ **f.** $F(1,\pi/4,1)$

   g. $G(4,3\pi/4,0)$

3. **a.** Which of the points in Problem **2** lie on the same cylinder centered about the z-axis? Explain your response.

   b. Which two points in Problem **2** lie in a plane parallel to the polar plane? Explain your response.

   c. Which three points in Problem **2** determine a plane that contains the pole and is perpendicular to the polar plane? Explain your response.

Assignment

1.1 Obtain a copy of the map in Figure **1-4.** Locate the pole of a cylindrical coordinate system at Northern Lights Lookout with the polar axis extending due east. Using this system, find cylindrical coordinates to describe the locations of Grizzly Peak and Camp Yellowjacket. Describe the process that you used in each case.

1.2 Imagine that you are camped at Bobcat Ridge on the map in Figure **1-4.**

a. Using your camp as the pole and a polar axis extending due east, find polar coordinates for each of the other landmarks on the map: Northern Lights Lookout, Grizzly Peak, Camp Yellowjacket, Oredigger Refuge, and the center of Bulldog Lake.

b. Assume Bobcat Ridge is 625 m above sea level. Find cylindrical coordinates for each of the five landmarks named in Part **a.**

1.3 There are four other points of interest near your camp from Problem **1.2:** Argonaut Alley, Bear Crossing, Saint's Cave, and Devil's Den.

a. Using a copy of Figure **1-4** and the following polar coordinates, find and label each of these points: Argonaut Alley $(250, \pi/3)$, Bear Crossing $(400, 5\pi/3)$, Saint's Cave $(150, 7\pi/6)$, and Devil's Den $(125, 3\pi/4)$.

b. Write the approximate cylindrical coordinates for each of the four points of interest named in Part **a.**

* * * * *

1.4 The diagram below shows a cube with a volume of s^3. The lower left-hand vertex of the cube's rear face is located at the pole of a cylindrical coordinate system.

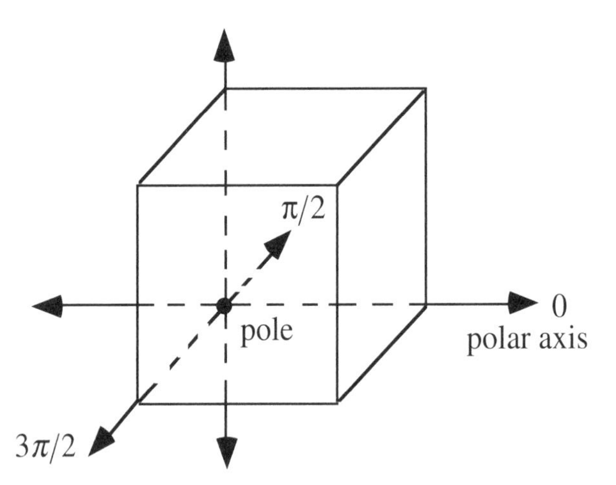

a. Determine cylindrical coordinates for each vertex of the cube.

b. Determine cylindrical coordinates for the center of the cube.

1.5 Suppose that the pole in Problem **1.4** were moved to the cube's center.

a. Describe how this would affect the r-coordinates of the cube's vertices.

b. Describe how this would affect the z-coordinates of the cube's vertices.

ACTIVITY 2

There are many methods for creating a flat map of a spherical surface—all of which involve mapping points with coordinates in three dimensions to points with coordinates in two dimensions. As you saw in the introduction to this module, flat maps of three-dimensional surfaces might contain distortions in shape, area, and distance. The distortions produced by a particular type of projection depend on several factors. In this activity, you investigate the distortion caused by a stereographic projection of points on a sphere to a flat map.

mathematics note

A **stereographic projection** is a projection of the points on a sphere onto a plane perpendicular to a given diameter of the sphere. The plane is the **plane of projection.** The endpoints of the diameter are the **poles** of the sphere.

The image of a point on the sphere is the point of intersection of a ray and the plane perpendicular to the diameter that contains the poles. The ray contains one of the poles, designated as the **center of projection,** and the point being projected. In any stereographic projection, there are points that have no image in the plane.

In Figure **1-6,** for example, point C' is a stereographic projection of point C, where point N is the center of projection and the plane of projection is perpendicular to the diameter $\overline{NS}$ at point S. In this projection, point N has no image on the plane, and the image of point S is itself.

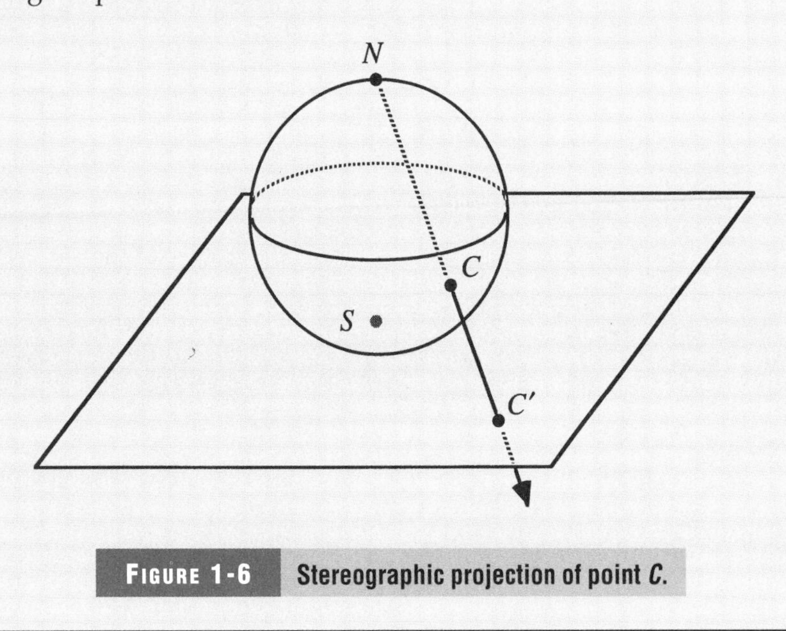

FIGURE 1-6 **Stereographic projection of point *C*.**

Exploration 1

Because a sphere is a closed surface and a plane is not, you should expect to observe some differences between a figure on a sphere and its projected image on a plane. In this exploration, you examine how a stereographic projection affects the image of a line on a sphere.

a. Label the two points at opposite ends of a diameter of a sphere *N* and *S*. Let these points represent the north and south poles, respectively. In this exploration, *N* will serve as the center of projection.

b. On a sphere, lines are defined as great circles. The great circles that contain the poles are lines of longitude. Complete the steps below to represent the projection of a line of longitude.

   1. Stretch a piece of string from *N* to *S* to represent part of a line of longitude. Mark the string where it touches these two points.

   2. Remove the string from the sphere. Mark three other points on the string so that the length determined in Step **1** is divided into four equal parts.

   3. Stretch the string from *N* to *S* again. Mark the three points from Step **2** on the sphere. Label these points *A*, *B*, and *C*.

c. As shown in Figure **1-7**, position the sphere so that a large sheet of paper is tangent to it at *S*. Insert three guides into the sphere and mark the points where the tips of the guides touch the paper. These marks will serve as reference points to maintain the same position of the sphere throughout the exploration.

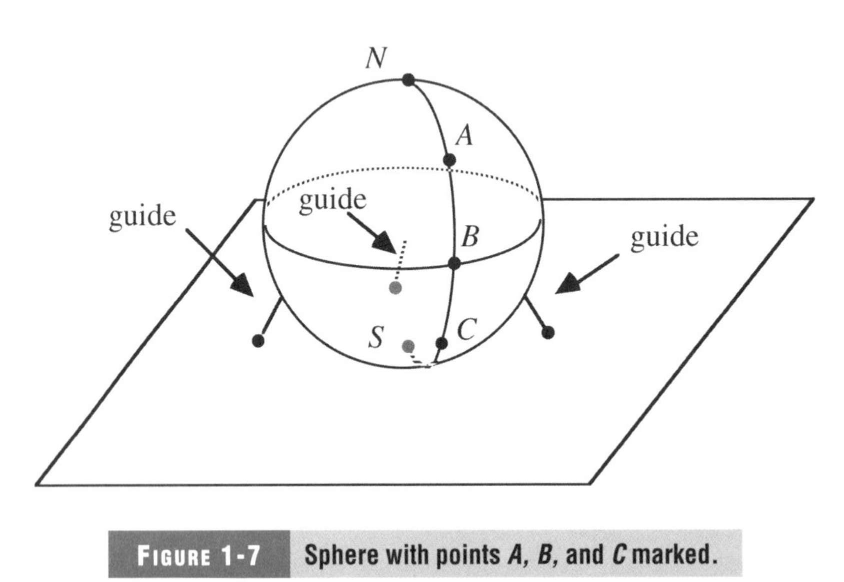

FIGURE 1-7 **Sphere with points *A*, *B*, and *C* marked.**

d. To find *C*′, the image of point *C* under a stereographic projection, use a skewer to model a ray. Carefully pass a skewer through the sphere from point *N* through point *C* until the tip of the skewer touches the paper. Mark the point of intersection of the skewer with the paper.

e. Repeat Part **d** for points A, B, and S.

f. Measure $\overline{C'S'}$, $\overline{B'C'}$, and $\overline{A'B'}$.

g. Because the equator is a great circle, it also represents a line on a sphere. Use the steps below to project an image of the equator on the same sheet of paper used above.

   1. Stretch a piece of string around the sphere to represent the equator.

   2. Remove the string from the sphere. Mark five points on the string so that the distance along the equator is divided into six equal parts.

   3. Stretch the string around the equator again. Mark the five points and the point where the endpoints of the string meet. Label these points D, E, F, G, H, and I.

   4. Use skewers to determine the image of each point under a stereographic projection where N is the center of projection and the plane is tangent to the sphere at S. **Note:** Save your work for use in the assignment.

Discussion 1

a. In Part **e** of Exploration **1,** what is the relationship between the south pole S and its image S'?

b. Consider a flat map of a globe created using a stereographic projection like the one in Exploration **1.**

   1. Describe how the images of the lines of longitude and the equator would appear on the flat map.

   2. What appears to be the relationship between the size of the equator and the size of its image?

   3. Why must the image of a line of longitude be a line in the plane?

c. 1. Recall that in a one-to-one correspondence, each element in the domain is paired with exactly one element in the range, and each element in the range is paired with exactly one element in the domain.

   Does the mapping of the points of a sphere to a plane as described in Exploration **1** represent a one-to-one correspondence? Defend your answer.

   2. A stereographic projection can be considered a function. Explain why this is true.

d. 1. Are lines preserved under a stereographic projection? In other words, are the projected images of lines on a sphere also lines in the plane? Explain your response. (Remember that a line on a sphere is defined as a great circle.)

   2. Is collinearity preserved under a stereographic projection? In other words, if the preimage points lie on the same great circle, do the image points lie on the same line in the plane? Explain your response.

e. 1. On a sphere, lines of longitude are perpendicular to the equator. Is perpendicularity preserved under a stereographic projection? Justify your response.

   2. Two lines of longitude can be perpendicular to each other at the poles. Would their images under a stereographic projection also be perpendicular? Explain your response.

f. Consider three points on a sphere—A, B, and C—where A and B are equidistant from C. Under a stereographic projection, would A' and B' be equidistant from C'? In other words, is distance preserved in a stereographic projection? Justify your response.

g. 1. Considering your results in Exploration **1**, which regions on a sphere appear to be most distorted in a stereographic projection?

   2. What does this imply about a map of Greenland created using this type of projection?

   3. Which regions on a sphere appear to be least distorted in a stereographic projection?

   4. In general, where would you place the point of tangency of the plane to obtain the least distortion of a preimage?

h. Consider a stereographic projection in which the globe's south pole is the center of projection and the plane is located tangent to the globe at the north pole. How would the amount of distortion in the image of Iceland compare with the amount of distortion in the image of Florida?

i. Describe the map created by a stereographic projection in which the globe's north pole is the center of projection and the plane contains the equator.

j. On a sphere, there are an infinite number of lines (great circles) that do not contain the poles. Describe the images of these lines under a stereographic projection like the one in Exploration **1**.

Exploration 2

In Exploration **1**, you discovered that the distance between points on a sphere generally is not preserved when those points are projected onto a plane. In this exploration, you create a mathematical model of a stereographic projection and use it to investigate these distortions.

a. Figure **1-8** shows a cross section of a sphere, where $\overline{NS}$ is a diameter of the sphere, and $\overrightarrow{NP}$ intersects the sphere in the plane of the cross section.

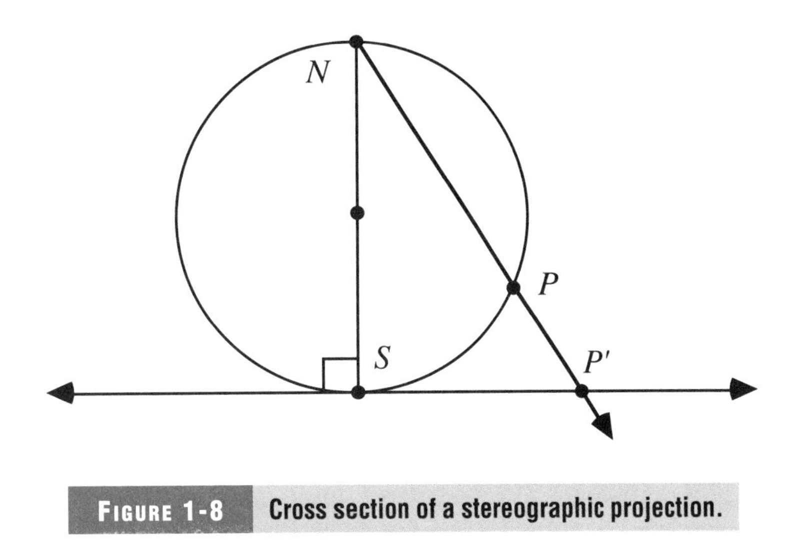

FIGURE 1-8 Cross section of a stereographic projection.

Reproduce this diagram using a geometry utility. Anchor $\overrightarrow{NP}$ at N, allowing point P to move around the circle. Make sure that the position of point P' changes as P moves around the circle.

b. Describe what happens to P' as you move P around the circle.

c. Construct the three points that correspond with A, B, and C in Part **b** of Exploration **1.** Make sure that $\overset{\frown}{NA} \cong \overset{\frown}{AB} \cong \overset{\frown}{BC} \cong \overset{\frown}{CS}$.

d. 1. Move point P so that it is concurrent with point C.

   2. Record the length of $\overline{P'S}$.

   3. Repeat Steps **1** and **2** for points A, B, S, and N.

e. Construct $\overline{PZ}$ perpendicular to $\overline{NS}$ as shown in Figure **1-9.** Make sure that $\overline{PZ}$ changes length as point P moves around the circle.

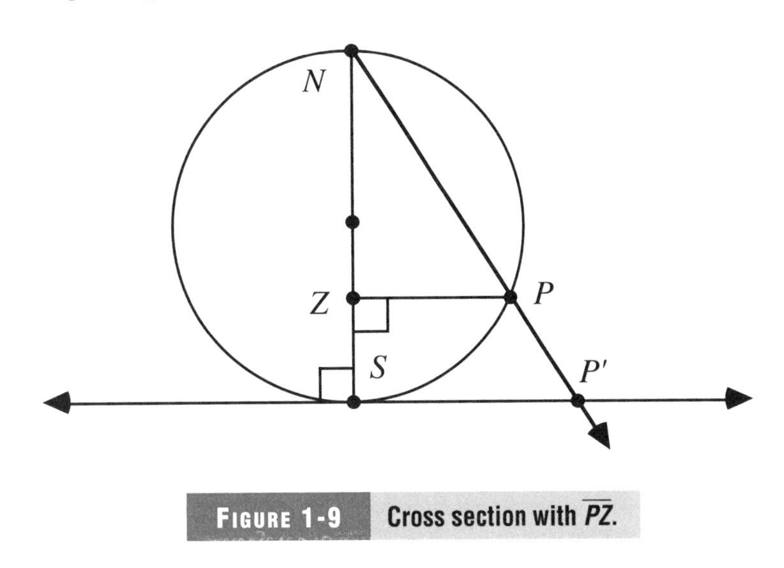

FIGURE 1-9 Cross section with $\overline{PZ}$.

f. Express the length of $\overline{P'S}$ in terms of the lengths of $\overline{NZ}$, $\overline{NS}$, and $\overline{PZ}$.

Discussion 2

a. What do the results found in Part **d** of Exploration **2** tell you about distances on a map made using a stereographic projection?

b. Describe what happens to the length of $\overline{P'S}$ as the length of $\overline{SZ}$ gets close to the length of $\overline{NS}$.

c. Triangles NPZ and $NP'S$ in Figure **1-9** are similar triangles. Explain how you know this is true.

d. In Exploration **1,** you observed that the image of the equator under a stereographic projection with the plane tangent to the sphere at the south pole appeared to be twice the diameter of the preimage. Use similar triangles to explain why this is true.

e. The image of a point P on a sphere under a stereographic projection like the one in Exploration **2** can be described using polar coordinates.

   Describe how the distance from point S to point P' can be used to help find the polar coordinates of P', where the pole of the graph is at S and the polar axis is opposite of $\overrightarrow{SP'}$.

Warm-Up

1. Describe the domain and range for a function defined by a stereographic projection.

2. Is distance preserved in a stereographic projection? Explain your response.

3. On your sheet of paper from Exploration **1,** mark a polar axis $\overrightarrow{S'A'}$.
   Using this polar axis, find the polar coordinates of points A', B', C', D', E', and F'.

Assignment

2.1 Is perimeter preserved in a stereographic projection? Describe how your response affects the use of flat maps to compare boundaries of countries and continents.

2.2 Virtually every map includes a scale to help users find the distance from one point to another. Describe the dangers in using this scale to determine precise distances.

2.3 Lines of latitude on a globe are not considered lines on a sphere. Using a stereographic projection like the ones in the explorations, what do the images of lines of latitude look like?

2.4 An angle whose vertex is a point on a circle and whose sides contain chords of a circle is an **inscribed angle.** In the diagram below, for example, $\angle LGH$ is an inscribed angle.

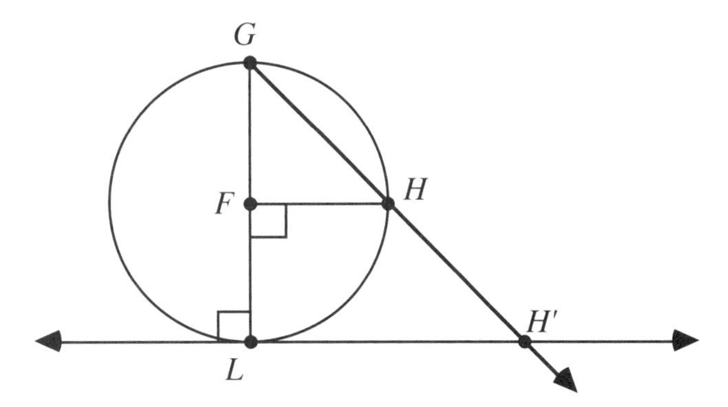

a. Given that circle F in the diagram above has a radius of 3 cm, determine the length of $\overline{LH'}$.

b. Determine the relationship between the measure of $\angle LGH$ and its intercepted arc HL.

c. The relationship you found in Part **b** is true for any inscribed angle and its intercepted arc. Use the diagram above to help prove why this is so.

2.5 The following diagram shows a cross section of a sphere like the one in Exploration **1**, where A, B, and C divide the length of $\overset{\frown}{NS}$ into four equal parts. Use this diagram to find the lengths of $\overline{SA'}$, $\overline{SB'}$, and $\overline{SC'}$. *Hint:* Use a technique similar to that described in Exploration **2.**

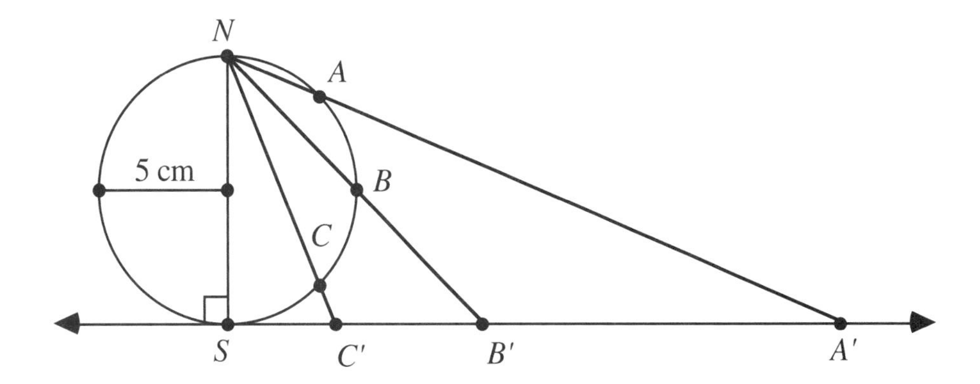

2.6 In the following diagram, S is the pole and $\overrightarrow{SX}$ is the polar axis of a polar coordinate system. Suppose point P represents a city on the globe with coordinates (r, θ, z) and P' is the stereographic projection of P. The diameter d of the sphere equals the length of $\overline{NS}$.

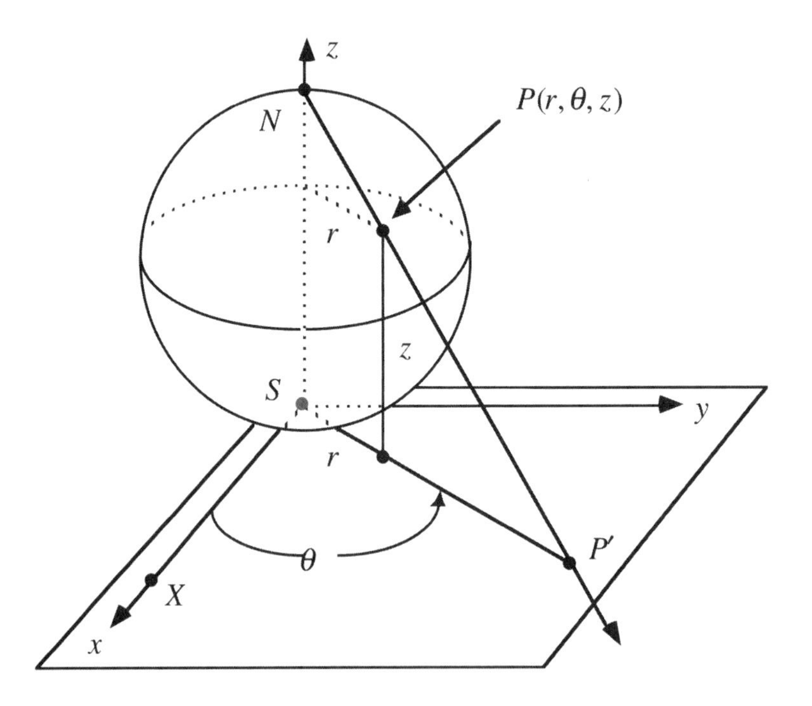

a. Describe how to find the polar coordinates of P' on the plane.

b. Determine the polar coordinates of P' in terms of d, r, z, and θ.

* * * * *

2.7 Consider a stereographic projection in which a globe's north pole is the center of projection and the plane contains the equator. In this case, is the image of a line of longitude also a line on the plane? Explain your response.

2.8 Points A, B, and C lie on a sphere of radius 10 cm. The pole of a cylindrical coordinate system is located at the south pole of the sphere. The approximate cylindrical coordinates of the three points are: A (8.66,1.13,15.00), B (10.00,1.13, 10.00), and C (8.66,1.13,5.00).

a. Describe the arrangement and position of A, B, and C on the sphere.

b. Determine the distance along the line of longitude from A to B and from B to C.

c. Find the polar coordinates of the images of A, B, and C under a stereographic projection in which the center of projection is at the north pole and the plane is tangent to the sphere at the south pole. Assume that the same pole and polar axis are used for both the cylindrical and the polar coordinate systems.

d. Describe the arrangement and position of the images A', B', and C' on the plane.

e. Find the distance from A' to B' and from B' to C'. Is distance preserved under this mapping?

ACTIVITY 3

Over the history of mapmaking, satellite imagery and supercomputers have replaced captain's logs and quill pens as the tools of choice. However, many centuries-old techniques are still useful and relevant to modern cartography.

For example, one common type of flat map is based on the work of the 16th-century Flemish cartographer Gerardus Mercator. A Mercator projection maps the surface of a sphere to a cylinder tangent to the sphere along a great circle (often the equator).

mathematics note

A **cylindrical projection** is a projection of the points of the sphere onto a tangent right circular cylinder. The image of a point on the sphere is the intersection of a ray and the cylinder. The ray contains the center of the sphere, designated as the **center of projection,** and the point being projected. In any cylindrical projection of a sphere, there are points that have no images on the cylinder.

For example, Figure **1-10** illustrates the cylindrical projection of point C on a sphere. Note that $\overrightarrow{OC}$ intersects the cylinder in at most one point.

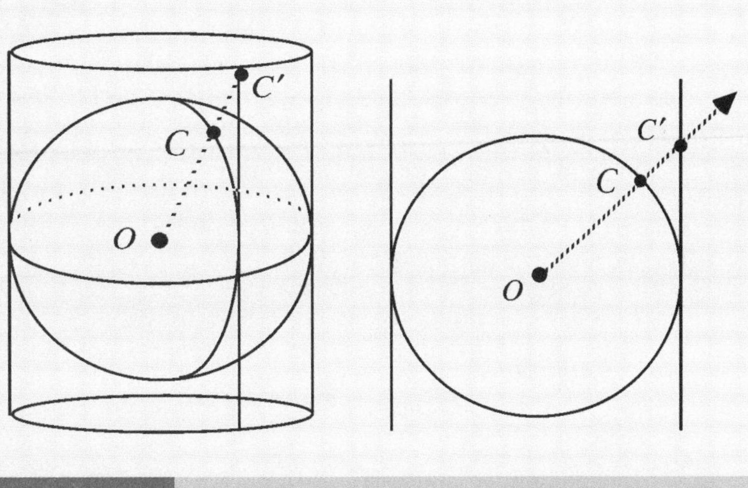

FIGURE 1-10 A cylindrical projection and its cross-sectional view.

Exploration 1

In this exploration, you investigate cylindrical projections of lines of longitude and of the equator. To simplify locating the sphere's center, you work with a hemisphere, as shown in Figure **1-11.**

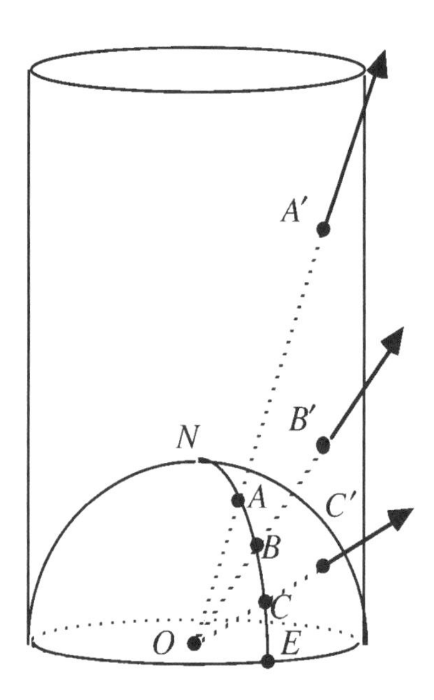

FIGURE 1-11 **Cylindrical projections of points on a hemisphere.**

a. Cut a sphere in half along a great circle. **Note:** Save the other half of the sphere for use in the assignment.

b. Label the center of the flat face of the hemisphere O. The outer edge of the hemisphere represents the equator.

c. Label the north pole N. Label a point on the equator E.

d. Label three equally spaced points—A, B, and C—along the line of longitude from point N to point E, as shown in Figure **1-11.**

e. Wrap a sheet of paper around the hemisphere to make a right circular cylinder that fits over the hemisphere tangent to the equator. Place a mark on the bottom edge of the cylinder at point E and label it E'. Keep points E and E' aligned throughout the exploration.

f. Pass a skewer from O through point C on the hemisphere to model the corresponding ray. Mark and label the intersection of the skewer with the cylinder on the cylinder's outside surface.

g. Repeat Part **f** for points A and B.

h. Repeat the mapping process for at least two other lines of longitude and for the equator.

i. Open the cylinder and lay it flat with the outside surface facing up. This is the map produced by a cylindrical projection.

Discussion 1

a. Describe the map you produced using a cylindrical projection.

b. 1. What would happen if you used the process described in the exploration to project a point close to N onto the cylinder?

   2. Where is the image of point N using this projection? Explain your response.

c. Suppose that all the points on a sphere that have an image under a cylindrical projection were mapped onto one cylinder.

   1. Describe the surface that would result when the cylinder was "unrolled" to produce a flat map.

   2. How would the image of a line of longitude appear on the map?

d. On a sphere, any pair of distinct lines (great circles) intersect in exactly two points. In other words, there are no parallel lines on a sphere.

   1. Under a stereographic projection, can the images of great circles form parallel lines on the flat map?

   2. Under a cylindrical projection, can the images of great circles form parallel lines on the flat map?

e. Is perpendicularity preserved under a cylindrical projection? Justify your response.

f. Describe a map of the lines of longitude and lines of latitude in the northern hemisphere created under a cylindrical projection.

g. Consider a cylindrical coordinate system in which the polar plane contains the equator of a sphere.

   1. What points on the sphere would have negative z-coordinates?

   2. Using a cylindrical projection, where would points with negative z-coordinates be projected on the flat map?

Exploration 2

In this exploration, you use a geometry utility to continue your investigation of cylindrical projections. Figure **1-12** shows a cross section of a sphere and a tangent right circular cylinder. Lines l and m represent parallel lines in the surface of the cylinder and $\overline{NS}$ is a diameter of the sphere.

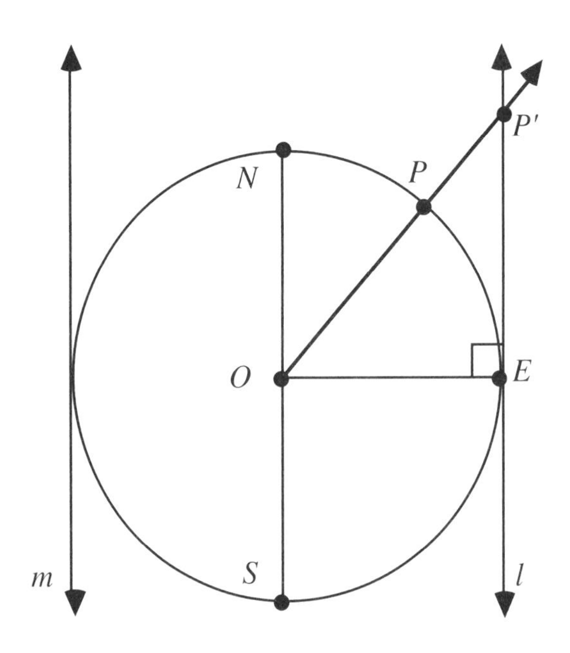

FIGURE 1-12 **Cross section of cylindrical projection.**

a. Use a geometry utility to reproduce the diagram in Figure **1-12.** Anchor $\overrightarrow{OP}$ at O, allowing point P to move around the circle. Make sure that the position of P' changes as P moves around the circle.

b. Describe what happens to P' as you move P from E to N.

c. Construct points A, B, and C so that $\overset{\frown}{NA} \cong \overset{\frown}{AB} \cong \overset{\frown}{BC} \cong \overset{\frown}{CE}$.

d. 1. Move point P so it is concurrent with point C.

   2. Record the length of $\overline{EP'}$.

   3. Repeat Steps **1** and **2** for points A, B, E, and N.

e. Construct $\overline{PZ}$ as shown in Figure **1-13** below. Make sure that $\overline{PZ}$ changes length as P moves around the circle.

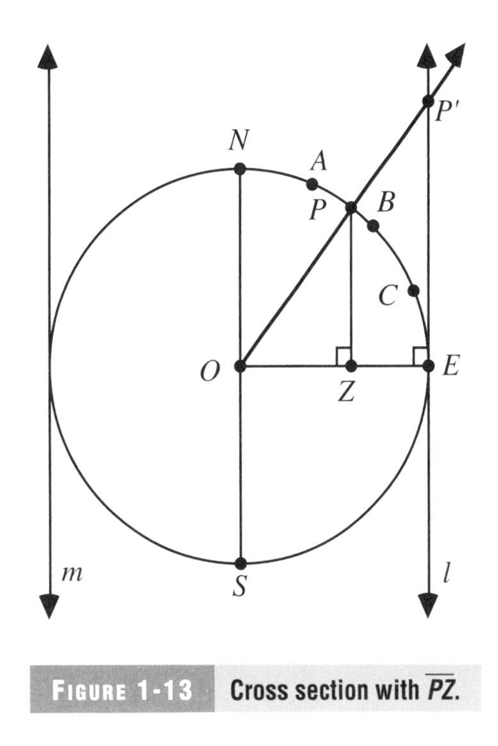

FIGURE 1-13 Cross section with $\overline{PZ}$.

f. Express the length of $\overline{EP'}$ in terms of the lengths of $\overline{OZ}$, $\overline{PZ}$, and $\overline{OE}$, the radius of the sphere.

Discussion 2

a. Describe what happens to the length of $\overline{EP'}$ as P gets closer and closer to N.

b. In Figure **1-13,** triangles POZ and $P'OE$ are similar triangles. Explain how you know this is true.

c. A point P on a sphere can be described by cylindrical coordinates of the form (r,θ,z), with the pole located at the sphere's center. Its image on a flat map under a cylindrical projection can be described by rectangular coordinates of the form (x,y).

   Suppose that the image of the intersection of the polar axis and the equator has the coordinates $(0,0)$.

   1. What is the image of the equator on the flat map?
   2. Describe how the value of θ in the cylindrical coordinates of P is related to the x-coordinate of P'.
   3. Describe how the distance EP' in Figure **1-13** can be used to find the y-coordinate of P'.

Warm-Up

1. Assuming that the polar axis is the positive x-axis, convert each pair of polar coordinates below to Cartesian coordinates.

   a. $(7,\pi/2)$

   b. $(12,\pi/3)$

2. In a cylindrical projection of a sphere, which point(s) on the sphere do not have an image? Explain your response.

3. Are distance, area, or perimeter preserved under a cylindrical projection? Explain your response.

Assignment

3.1 **a.** Using a cylindrical projection with the cylinder tangent to the equator, would the image of Venezuela be more or less distorted than the image of Greenland? Explain your response.

b. Which would produce a greater distortion of Greenland—a stereographic projection through the south pole or a cylindrical projection? Explain your response.

3.2 Lines of longitude and latitude are important aids for navigation. When navigators use flat maps, what type of projection would you expect them to prefer—stereographic or cylindrical? Justify your response.

3.3 Consider a figure on a sphere whose image, under a cylindrical projection, is a rectangle. One of the sides of this figure lies along the equator. Describe a possible shape for the preimage.

3.4 Consider a sphere with a paper cylinder wrapped around it, tangent to the equator. Any point on the sphere can be represented by cylindrical coordinates of the form (r,θ,z), with the pole located at the sphere's center.

When points on the sphere are projected onto the cylinder, and the cylinder is cut and unwrapped, a flat map is produced. The position of each point on the map can be described by rectangular coordinates of the form (x,y).

As shown in the following diagram on the left, a line drawn on the outside of the cylinder along the equator can represent the positive x-axis. The origin O can be located at the point where the polar axis ($\overrightarrow{PO}$) of the cylindrical coordinate system intersects the equator.

When the paper cylinder is cut through the origin perpendicular to the x-axis, then unwrapped and laid flat with its outside surface facing up, it resembles the diagram on the right.

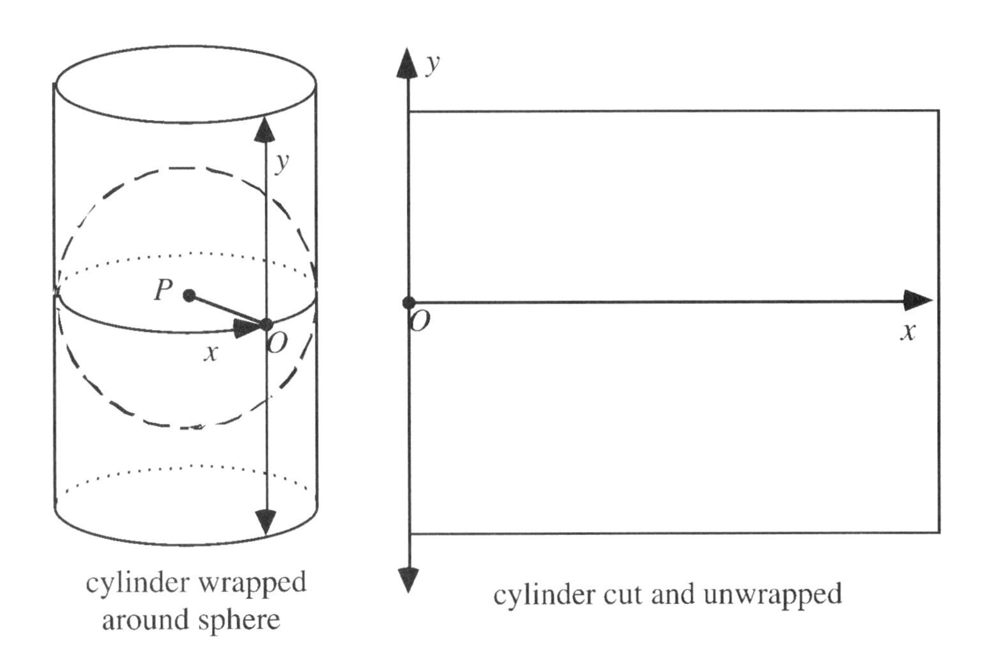

cylinder wrapped around sphere

cylinder cut and unwrapped

a. If the sphere's radius is 10 cm, what is the length of the portion of the x-axis on the unwrapped cylinder?

b. Point A on the sphere has cylindrical coordinates $(10.00, \pi/6, 0.00)$. What is the x-coordinate of A', the image of A under a cylindrical projection?

c. Point B on the sphere has coordinates $(2.59, 5.40, -9.66)$. What is the x-coordinate of B', the image of B under a cylindrical projection?

d. Let P represent any point on a sphere with radius w. If P has cylindrical coordinates (r, θ, z), find the x-coordinate of P', the image of P under a cylindrical projection.

e. Describe how to determine the value of the y-coordinate for the image point in a cylindrical projection.

3.5 **a.** Point A lies on a sphere of radius 20 cm. Using a cylindrical coordinate system with the pole at the sphere's center, the coordinates of A are $(7.32, \pi/2, 10)$.

Using a cylindrical projection as described in Problem **3.4,** what are the rectangular coordinates of A'?

b. Point B lies on a sphere of radius 20 cm. Using a cylindrical coordinate system with the pole at the sphere's center, the coordinates of B are $(1.74, 4.96, -19.92)$.

1. In what region is B located on the sphere?
2. Using a cylindrical projection as described in Problem **3.4,** what are the rectangular coordinates of B'?

* * * * *

3.6 Points D, E, and F lie on a sphere of radius 25 cm. Using a cylindrical coordinate system with the pole at the sphere's center, their coordinates are: $D\,(19.15, 0.25, -16.07)$, $E\,(19.15, 2.01, -16.07)$, and $F\,(19.15, 3.77, -16.07)$.

a. Describe the arrangement and position of D, E, and F on the sphere.

b. Find the arc lengths along the line of latitude from D to E and from E to F.

c. Using a cylindrical projection as described in Problem **3.4,** find the rectangular coordinates of D', E', and F'.

d. Describe the arrangement and position of D', E', and F' on the flat map.

e. Find the distance from D' to E' and from E' to F'. Is distance preserved under this mapping?

Research Project

Mapmakers use many different types of projections. Write a report that describes three projections not presented in this module. Your report should include the following information:

- how each projection is used to make a map
- how lines of latitude and longitude appear on the resulting map
- the geometric properties that are preserved in each projection
- the types of situations in which each projection is most useful
- the historical background of each projection.

Summary Assessment

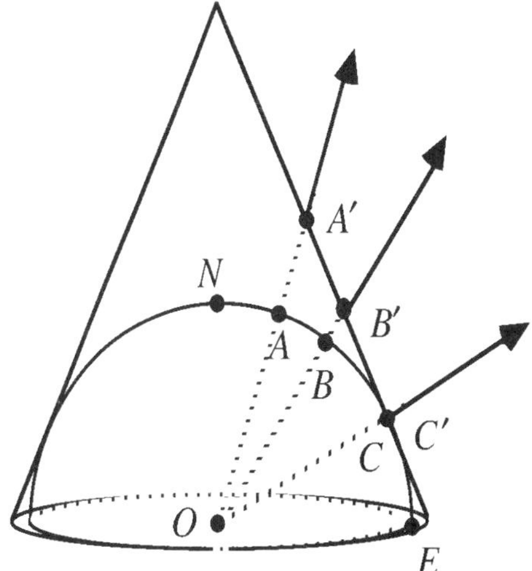

Maps made using a conic projection are similar to those made with a cylindrical projection. In a conic projection, however, points are projected onto a tangent right circular cone, instead of a tangent right cylinder, as shown in the diagram.

1. a. What figure is formed by the intersection of the sphere and the cone?

   b. How would the images of lines of latitude and longitude appear in a conical mapping?

   c. What geometric properties appear to be preserved under a conic projection? Justify your response.

2. The diagram below shows part of a cross section of a sphere and a tangent cone. The cone's vertex angle is the angle formed by the intersection of the cone and a plane perpendicular to the cone's base and passing through the apex.

   Suppose the vertex angle of the cone measures $\pi/2 \approx 1.57$ radians and A is a point on the sphere with cylindrical coordinates $(13.62, 5.43, 20.97)$. The radius of the sphere is 25 cm.

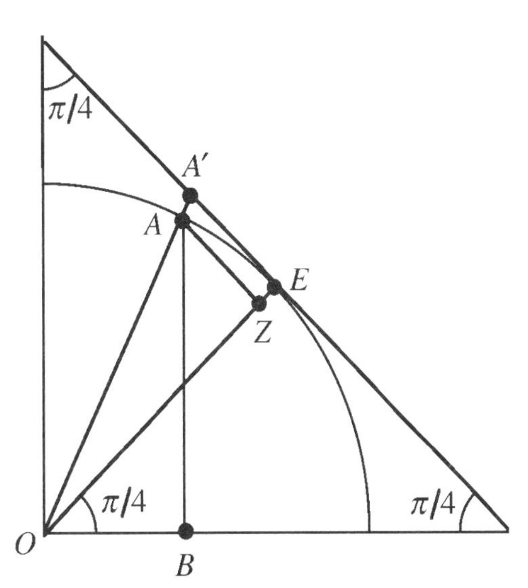

   If A' is the image of A under a conical projection, determine the ratio of the length of $\overline{A'E}$ to the length of $\overset{\frown}{AE}$.

3. Does the measure of the vertex angle of the cone affect the amount of distortion in a conic mapping? If so, how? *Hint:* Use a geometry utility to investigate this situation.

Module Summary

* A **polar coordinate system** describes the location of a point P in a plane using an ordered pair consisting of a **radius** r and a **polar angle** θ.

  The plane containing a polar coordinate system is the **polar plane.** The polar angle is an angle measured from a fixed ray, called the **polar axis.** The endpoint of the polar axis is the **pole.** The distance from the pole to point P, measured in the polar plane, is r.

* In a **cylindrical coordinate system,** a point in space is represented by an ordered triple of the form (r, θ, z). The values of r and θ are measurements in the polar plane. The value of z is the directed distance between the point and the polar plane (the plane containing the polar axis). A positive value for z represents a distance above the polar plane.

* A **stereographic projection** is a projection of the points on a sphere onto a plane perpendicular to a given diameter of the sphere. The plane is the **plane of projection.** The endpoints of the diameter are the **poles** of the sphere.

  The image of a point on the sphere is the point of intersection of a ray and the plane perpendicular to the diameter that contains the poles. The ray contains one of the poles, designated as the **center of projection,** and the point being projected. In any stereographic projection, there are points that have no image in the plane.

* A **cylindrical projection** is a projection of the points of the sphere onto a tangent right circular cylinder. The image of a point on the sphere is the intersection of a ray and the cylinder. The ray contains the center of the sphere, designated as the **center of projection,** and the point being projected. In any cylindrical projection of a sphere, there are points that have no images on the cylinder.

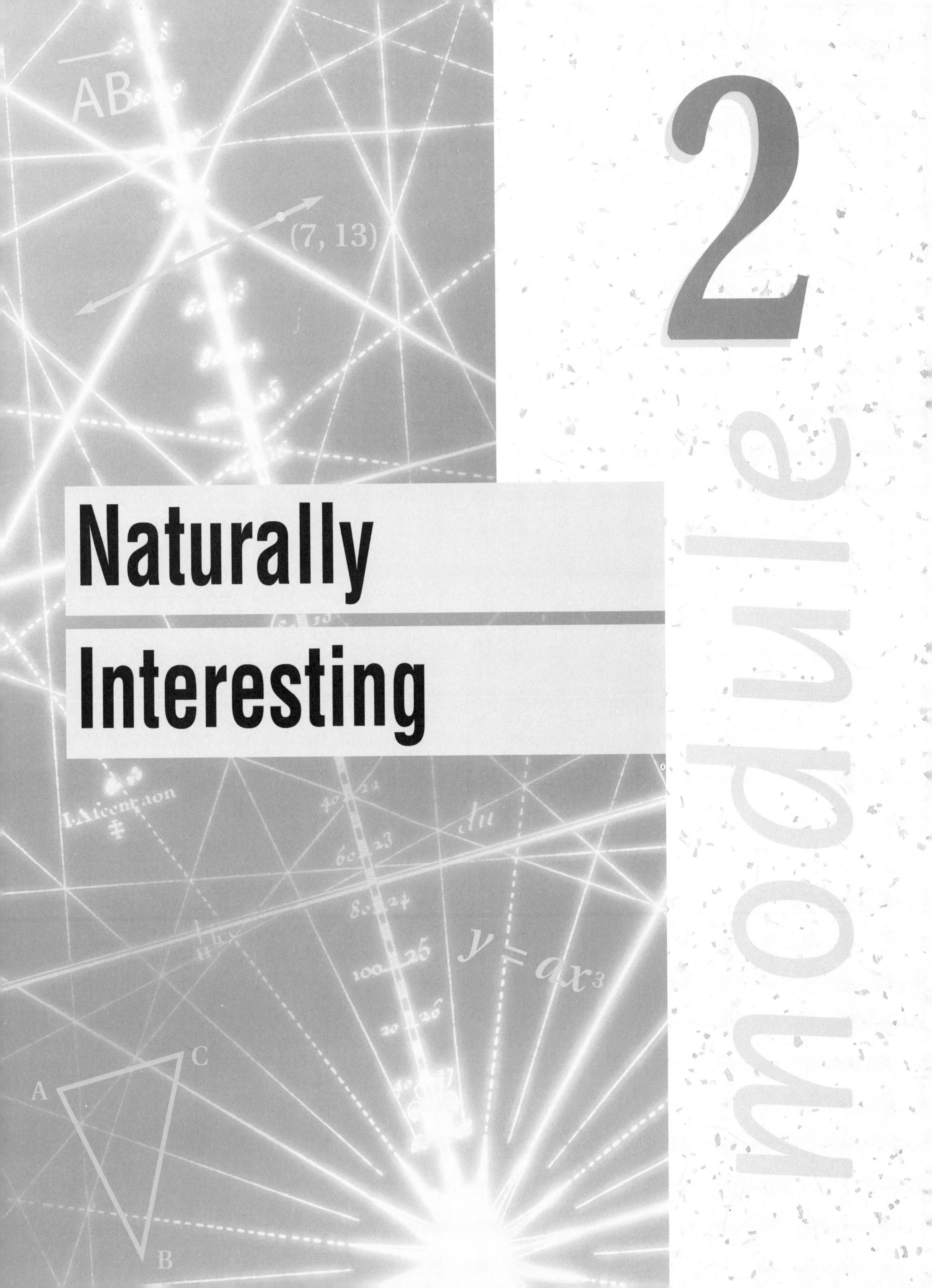

module 2

Naturally Interesting

Introduction

Banks and investment companies offer a variety of accounts to help customers reach their financial goals. These accounts may offer different rates of interest, based on the initial amount invested. How much money would a person need to invest today to be a millionaire at age 65? How long will it take an investment to double in value? These are questions financial advisers must be able to answer for their clients.

In banking, **principal** refers to the amount of money invested or loaned. **Interest** is the amount earned on invested money, or the fee charged for loaned money. The amount of interest received or paid depends on three quantities: principal, interest rate, and time. Interest also varies according to the method used to calculate it. In the following activities, you investigate how savings accounts earn money.

mathematics note

One method for determining the amount of interest earned or owed involves **simple interest.** In this case, interest is paid or charged only on the original principal. The formula for calculating simple interest, where I represents interest, P represents principal, r represents the interest rate per time period, and t represents the number of time periods, is shown below:

$$I = Prt$$

To use this formula, t must be expressed in the same units as time in the interest rate, r. For example, if the interest rate is 5% per year, then t must be expressed in years. If \$1000 is invested at an annual interest rate of 5% for 3 yr, the interest earned can be calculated as follows:

$$I = 1000(0.05)(3) = \$150$$

Discussion

a. What types of loans are available in your community? What are the current interest rates and terms for these loans?

b. Describe the opportunities available for investing or saving money in your community. What are the current interest rates and terms?

c. Consider an investment account that offers an annual interest rate of 10%. If you invest $1000 in this account, the interest earned after 1 yr is $100. If you reinvest the **account balance** (the original principal plus the $100 interest earned) at the same rate, how much interest will you earn in the second year?

ACTIVITY 1

Most savings accounts pay interest not only on the original principal, but also on the interest earned and deposited in any previous time periods. This is an example of **compound interest.** Each time compound interest is calculated, the interest earned is added to the principal. This sum (the account balance) becomes the new principal for the next interest calculation.

Exploration 1

In this exploration, you develop a method for determining the balance of an account that earns compound interest.

a. Imagine that you have invested $500 at a simple interest rate of 6% per year and plan to make no withdrawals for the next 20 yr.

   Use the formula for simple interest to determine the account balance after 20 yr.

b. When interest is compounded annually, the interest earned each year is added to the account at the end of that year. Predict the account balance after 20 yr if interest is compounded annually.

c. To determine the actual balance of the account after 20 yr when interest is compounded annually, you must examine what happens to the account balance at the end of each year.

   1. Determine the account balance at the end of the first year by adding the interest earned for 1 yr to the principal.

   2. Using the account balance at the end of the first year as the new principal, determine the account balance at the end of the second year.

d. Use a spreadsheet to repeat the process described in Part **c** for each of the next 18 yr. Record your data in a table similar to Table **2-1** below.

Table 2-1 ■ *$500 Invested at 6% for 20 yr, Compounded Annually*

Years (t)	Principal at Beginning of Year ($)	Account Balance at End of Year ($)
1	500	
2		
3		
⋮		
20		

e. Use the spreadsheet to investigate how account balances are affected by changes in the interest rate. Record your observations.

f. Let P_t represent the principal at the end of t years in an investment with an interest rate of 6% per year, compounded annually. Write an expression that describes P_t in terms of the principal for the previous year. (In other words, write a recursive formula for the account balance after t years.)

mathematics note

The principal at the end of each time period in an investment or savings account can be thought of as a sequence.

For example, consider an initial principal of $1000 invested at an interest rate of 8% per year, compounded annually. Assuming that no withdrawals are made and any interest earned is deposited in the account, the following geometric sequence is formed, where P_0 represents the initial principal, P_1 represents the principal after 1 yr, and so on:

$$P_0 = 1000$$
$$P_1 = 1080$$
$$P_2 = 1166.40$$
$$\vdots$$
$$P_{10} \approx 2158.92$$

In this case, the account balance at the end of 10 yr is approximately $2158.92.

Such a sequence can be defined recursively by the following formula:

$$P_t = P_{t-1} + r \bullet P_{t-1} = P_{t-1}(1 + r)$$

where P_t is the principal at the end of t years, r is the annual interest rate, and P_{t-1} is the principal for the previous year.

For example, given an initial principal $P_0 = \$345$ and an annual interest rate of 8%, the account balance at the end of 1 yr (P_1) can be determined as shown below (assuming that no withdrawals are made and any interest earned is deposited in the account):

$$P_1 = P_0 \bullet (1 + 0.08) = (345) \bullet (1 + 0.08) = \$372.60$$

g. To use the recursive formula given in the mathematics note, you must know the account balance in the previous year. An explicit formula, however, would allow you to find P_t without having to determine P_{t-1}.

   1. Write P_1 in terms of P_0 (the original principal) and r (the annual interest rate).

   2. Using substitution and the recursive formula, $P_t = P_{t-1}(1 + r)$, determine an explicit formula for P_2, the principal at the end of 2 yr, in terms of P_0 and r.

   3. Repeat Step **2** for P_3, the principal at the end of 3 yr.

h. Determine an explicit formula that could be used to find the account balance after t years (P_t) for an initial investment of P_0 at an annual interest rate of r, compounded annually.

i. Use your explicit formula to calculate the account balance, after 20 yr, of an investment of $500 at an annual interest rate of 6%, compounded annually. Compare this value to the one you determined using the spreadsheet.

Discussion 1

a. What advantages are there to using an explicit formula for account balance rather than a recursive formula?

mathematics note

When interest is compounded annually, the yearly account balances that result can be thought of as a sequence defined explicitly by the following formula (assuming that no withdrawals are made and any interest earned is deposited in the account):

$$P_t = P_0(1 + r)^t$$

where P_t is the account balance after t years, P_0 is the initial principal, r is the annual interest rate, and t is the time in years.

For example, given an initial principal of $2000 and an annual interest rate of 4%, compounded annually, the account balance after 12 yr can be determined as follows:

$$\begin{aligned} P_{12} &= 2000(1 + 0.04)^{12} \\ &\approx 3202.06 \end{aligned}$$

b. 1. How do the terms in the formula $P_t = P_0(1 + r)^t$ correspond with the terms of the following general formula for a geometric sequence?

$$g_n = g_1 r^{n-1}$$

2. How does $P_t = P_0(1 + r)^t$ compare with the formula you wrote in Part **h** of Exploration **1**?

c. How will doubling the initial investment affect the account balance after 20 yr?

d. Describe two ways to determine the time required for a $500 investment to double at an annual interest rate of 6%, compounded annually.

e. In previous modules, you modeled population growth with the equation $P_n = P_0(1 + r)^n$, where P_n is the population after n time periods, P_0 is the initial population, and r is the growth rate per time period.

1. Compare the equation for population growth with the explicit formula for account balance.
2. What does the expression $(1 + r)$ represent in each equation?

Exploration 2

In this exploration, you examine how the number of compoundings per year affects the amount of interest earned in an account.

a. Imagine that the \$500 invested in Exploration **1** is deposited in an account in which interest is compounded semiannually, or twice a year. The annual interest rate is 6%, so the rate for each half year is 0.06/2 or 3%.

   1. What is the account balance after 2 compounding periods, or 1 yr?
   2. Write an expression that describes the balance after 1 yr in terms of the original investment of \$500.
   3. Repeat Steps **1** and **2** for the balance after 2 yr (4 compounding periods) and the balance after 3 yr (6 compounding periods).

b. Using an annual interest rate r and an initial principal of P_0, write a formula for P_n, the account balance after n compounding periods, when interest is compounded semiannually for t years.

c. Repeat Parts **a** and **b** for an account in which interest is compounded quarterly, or four times a year.

d. Using an annual interest rate r and an initial principal of P_0, write a general formula for the account balance after n time periods, when interest is compounded c times a year for t years.

e. The number of compounding periods per year affects the account balance at the end of the year. Investigate this effect by using a spreadsheet and your formula from Part **d** to complete Table **2-2** below.

TABLE 2-2 ■ *\$500 Invested at 6%, with Different Compoundings*

Initial Principal: \$500

Annual Interest Rate: 6%

Type of Compounding	No. of Compoundings per Year	Account Balance (P_n)
annually	1	\$530.00
semiannually		
quarterly		
monthly		
daily		
hourly		
by the minute		
by the second		

f. Predict the account balance in Table **2-2** after 1 yr if interest is compounded continuously.

g. Change the initial principal and the interest rate in your spreadsheet. For each change in principal or interest rate, observe how the balance is affected as the number of compoundings increases.

mathematics note

When compounding interest c times per year for t years, the formula for the account balance after n compounding periods is:

$$P_n = P_0\left(1 + \frac{r}{c}\right)^n = P_0\left(1 + \frac{r}{c}\right)^{ct}$$

where P_n represents the principal after n compounding periods, P_0 represents the initial principal, and r is the annual interest rate. Note that, in this formula, $n = ct$.

For example, consider an initial investment of $1000 at an annual interest rate of 5%, compounded quarterly. Assuming that no withdrawals are made and any interest earned is deposited in the account, the principal after 3 yr (or $4 \bullet 3 = 12$ compounding periods) can be calculated as follows:

$$P_{12} = 1000\left(1 + \frac{0.05}{4}\right)^{12} = \$1160.75$$

Discussion 2

a. To find the account balance after t years when interest is compounded annually, you used the formula $P_t = P_0(1 + r)^t$. How does this formula differ from the one you wrote in Part **b** of Exploration **2**, when interest is compounded semiannually?

b. Describe what happens to the account balance in Table **2-2** as the number of compoundings per year increases.

c. How does increasing the number of compoundings per year appear to affect the total amount of interest earned after 1 yr?

d. As the number of compoundings increases, do you think that the sequence of account balances approaches a limit? Explain your response.

Warm-Up

1. Describe reasonable domains for r and c in the formula for account balance using compound interest (shown below).

$$P_n = P_0\left(1 + \frac{r}{c}\right)^{ct}, \quad n = ct$$

2. Choose values for P_0, c, and r and substitute these values into the formula above. To what family of functions does the resulting equation belong?

3. **a.** Graph your equation from Problem **2** as a function of t for 3 different values of r. Use the set of real numbers as the domain for t.

   b. What effect does the magnitude of r have on the graphs?

Assignment

1.1 Consider an initial investment of \$700 at an annual interest rate of 7.5% for 1 yr. Assuming that no withdrawals are made and any interest earned is deposited in the account, determine the account balance when interest is compounded:

   a. annually

   b. quarterly

   c. monthly

   d. daily.

1.2 **a.** On his 18th birthday, a student invests \$112.50 in an account with an annual interest rate of 9%, compounded annually. Assuming that he makes no withdrawals and any interest earned is deposited in the account, determine the account balance on his 65th birthday.

   b. Repeat Part **a** for an account in which interest is compounded monthly.

1.3 **a.** Imagine that, on the day you were born, someone deposited \$5000 in an account with an annual interest rate of 4.8%, compounded monthly. Determine how old you would be when the balance of the account reaches \$20,000.

   b. If the interest is compounded monthly, what annual interest rate would be required for the account to have a value of at least \$30,000 on your 18th birthday?

1.4 Most durable goods, such as cars and computers, decrease in value over time. This is known as **depreciation.**

Consider a car that cost $17,000 new and loses 15% of its value each year.

a. Write both recursive and explicit formulas to represent the depreciation of this car.

b. What is the car's value after 5 yr?

* * * * *

1.5 a. In 2004, China's estimated population was 1,300,000,000. The annual growth rate at the time was 0.57%. Assuming that this growth rate remains constant, write an equation that models China's population since 2004.

b. Use your model to estimate China's current population.

c. In 2004, India's estimated population was 1,065,000,000 with an annual growth rate of 1.44%. If this growth rate remains constant, predict the year in which India's population will surpass that of China.

1.6 As a financial advisor, you offer investment advice to your clients. One of your clients must decide whether to invest $1500 at an annual interest rate of 15%, compounded quarterly, or $1600 at an annual interest rate of 15.5%, compounded annually. Both investments have a 10-year term. Which one would you recommend? Explain your response.

ACTIVITY 2

With the development of calculators and computers, the determination of compound interest has become quick and easy. This allows banks to compound interest on an account balance up to the instant in which it is withdrawn. This method of calculating interest, known as **compounding continuously,** means that the number of compoundings per year approaches **infinity,** denoted by ∞. Written as $+\infty$ or $-\infty$, this symbol also may be used to depict boundlessness in either a positive or a negative direction.

Exploration

As you saw in Activity **1,** the number of compoundings per year can affect the balance of a savings account. What happens to this balance when the number of compoundings increases without bound? In this exploration, you investigate what happens as c, the number of compoundings, changes for specific values of P_0, r, and t.

a. Consider an investment of $1.00 at an annual interest rate of 100%, compounded continuously, for 1 yr. Predict the account balance at the end of the year.

b. Create a spreadsheet with columns similar to those in Table **2-3.** Use the formula for account balance when interest is compounded c times a year to complete the spreadsheet for an investment of $1.00 at an annual interest rate of 100%.

TABLE 2-3 ■ *Account Balances for Different Compoundings*

No. of Compoundings per Year (c)	Account Balance at End of Year ($)
1	
10	
100	
1000	
10,000	
100,000	
1,000,000	
10,000,000	
100,000,000	

c. As the number of compoundings per year increases, what happens to the sequence of account balances?

d. Because $P_0 = 1$, $r = 1$, and $t = 1$ in this situation, an explicit formula for the sequence of balances found in Table **2-3** is:

$$P_1 = 1\left(1 + \frac{1}{c}\right)^{c \bullet 1} = \left(1 + \frac{1}{c}\right)^{c}$$

In the context of this problem, c is a non-negative integer. However, this formula can be represented more generally as the function below:

$$y = \left(1 + \frac{1}{x}\right)^{x}$$

What are the domain and range of this function?

e. Graph the function from Part **d.** As x increases without bound, what limiting value does the graph appear to approach?

mathematics note

The limit of the following expression, as n approaches infinity, is an irrational number approximately equal to 2.71828:

$$\left(1+\frac{1}{n}\right)^n$$

This irrational number, represented as e, is sometimes called Euler's number in honor of Swiss mathematician Leonhard Euler. The value of e can be represented mathematically as shown below:

$$\lim_{n\to\infty}\left(1+\frac{1}{n}\right)^n = e$$

Another way to describe e is as the infinite series below:

$$1+\frac{1}{1!}+\frac{1}{2!}+\frac{1}{3!}+\cdots$$

The value of e can also be derived from continued fractions as follows:

$$e = 2+\cfrac{1}{1+\cfrac{1}{2+\cfrac{2}{3+\cfrac{3}{4+\cfrac{4}{\vdots}}}}}$$

f. In the formula for account balance after n compounding periods, $n = c \bullet t$, where c represents the number of compoundings per year and t represents time in years. Considering a period of 1 yr, therefore, $n = c \bullet 1 = c$. Given an initial principal of $1.00, the formula for account balance can be written as follows:

$$P_n = \left(1+\frac{r}{n}\right)^n$$

To investigate how a change in the value of r affects the limit of this expression, create and complete a spreadsheet with columns like those in Table **2-4** below.

TABLE 2-4 ■ *Balance in Dollars for Different Interest Rates*

n	$P_n = \left(1 + \frac{1}{n}\right)^n$	$P_n = \left(1 + \frac{2}{n}\right)^n$	$P_n = \left(1 + \frac{3}{n}\right)^n$
1			
10			
100			
1000			
10,000			
100,000			
1,000,000			
10,000,000			
100,000,000			

g. 1. Calculate e^2 and compare it to the values in the spreadsheet in Part **f.**

2. Calculate e^3 and compare it to the values in the spreadsheet in Part **f.**

Discussion

a. 1. Describe the relationship between e^2 and the following expression:

$$\lim_{n\to\infty}\left(1 + \frac{2}{n}\right)^n$$

2. Describe the relationship between e^3 and the expression below:

$$\lim_{n\to\infty}\left(1 + \frac{3}{n}\right)^n$$

3. What conjecture can you make about the value of this expression?

$$\lim_{n\to\infty}\left(1 + \frac{r}{n}\right)^n$$

b. The value of n has no effect on the value of the constant 25 in the product below:

$$25\left(1+\frac{1}{n}\right)^n$$

In fact, the following equation is true:

$$\lim_{n\to\infty} 25\left(1+\frac{1}{n}\right)^n = 25\left[\lim_{n\to\infty}\left(1+\frac{1}{n}\right)^n\right] = 25e$$

Use this fact to evaluate each of the expressions below:

1. $\lim_{n\to\infty} 10\left(1+\frac{2}{n}\right)^n$
2. $\lim_{n\to\infty} 20\left(1+\frac{3}{n}\right)^n$
3. $\lim_{n\to\infty} 8\left(1+\frac{r}{n}\right)^n$
4. $\lim_{n\to\infty} P_0\left(1+\frac{r}{n}\right)^n$

mathematics note

When compounding interest c times per year for t years, the formula for the account balance after n compounding periods, where $n = ct$, P_0 represents the initial principal, and r is the annual interest rate, is:

$$P_n = P_0\left(1+\frac{r}{c}\right)^{ct}$$

When the number of compoundings per year approaches infinity, then the interest is **compounded continuously.** In this case, the formula for account balance P can be written as follows:

$$P = \lim_{c\to\infty} P_0\left(1+\frac{r}{c}\right)^{ct} = P_0\left[\lim_{c\to\infty}\left(1+\frac{r}{c}\right)^{c}\right]^t = P_0e^{rt}$$

where P_0 represents the initial principal, r represents the annual interest rate, c represents the number of compoundings per year, and t represents number of years.

For example, consider an initial investment of $500 at an annual interest rate of 6%, compounded continuously. Assuming that no withdrawals are made and any interest earned is deposited in the account, the account balance after 5 yr can be calculated as follows:

$$P = 500e^{0.06\bullet 5} = \$674.93$$

c. What can you conclude about an investment whose account balance is calculated by the equation below?

$$P = 750e^{0.01t}$$

Warm-Up

1. Determine the value of a $1000 investment at the end of 1 yr if the annual interest rate is 9% and interest is compounded:

   a. annually
   b. quarterly
   c. monthly
   d. daily
   e. continuously.

2. Using your responses to Problem **1,** find an annual interest rate that, when compounded annually, will produce the same balance after 1 yr as an annual interest rate of 9% compounded:

   a. monthly
   b. daily
   c. continuously.

3. Describe how you determined your responses to Problem **2.**

business note

To help consumers compare interest rates, banks often report **annual percentage yield (APY)** for savings accounts and **annual percentage rate (APR)** for loans. The APY or APR is the interest rate that, when compounded annually, will produce the same account balance as the advertised interest rate, which is typically compounded more often.

For example, the annual percentage yield of an initial investment of P_0 at an annual interest rate of 9%, compounded quarterly, can be found as follows:

$$P_0\left(1+\frac{r_{\text{APY}}}{1}\right)^1 = P_0\left(1+\frac{0.09}{4}\right)^4$$

$$\left(1+r_{\text{APY}}\right) \approx 1.09308$$

$$r_{\text{APY}} \approx 0.09308 = 9.308\%$$

This means that, for any given initial investment, an annual interest rate of 9%, compounded quarterly, produces the same account balance as an annual interest rate of 9.308%, compounded annually.

Assignment

2.1 **a.** Consider an investment of \$1000 at an annual interest rate of 7.7%. Determine the annual percentage yield (APY) if interest is compounded:

  1. quarterly
  2. daily
  3. hourly.

  b. The APY reaches its maximum when interest is compounded continuously. Determine the maximum APY for an investment with an annual interest rate of 7.7%.

  c. Write a formula for determining maximum APY.

2.2 In the previous business note, the annual percentage yield (APY) is determined for a specific annual interest rate (r) and a given number of compoundings per year (c).

  a. To determine the general relationship among APY, r, and c, solve the equation below for r_{APY}.

$$P_0\left(1+\frac{r}{c}\right)^c = P_0\left(1+\frac{r_{\text{APY}}}{1}\right)^1$$

  b. As the number of compoundings per year increases without bound, what would you expect to find as a formula for r_{APY}?

  c. How does the initial principal affect the relationship among APY, r, and c?

2.3 Imagine that you have deposited \$5000 in a savings account at an annual interest rate of 3%, compounded continuously. Assuming that you make no withdrawals and any interest earned is deposited in the account, how old will you be when the account balance is \$20,000?

2.4 **a.** Over an interval of one year, will an account balance increase by a significant amount if interest is compounded every hour rather than every day? Use an example to support your response.

  b. In general, what effect does increasing the number of compoundings per year have on account balance?

* * * * *

2.5 One general equation used to model the growth or decay in a quantity is $N_t = N_0 e^{nt}$, where N_t represents the final amount, N_0 represents the initial amount, n represents some constant, and t represents time. When $n > 0$, the equation can be used to model growth; when $n < 0$, the equation can be used to model decay.

A population of bacteria has a constant n of 0.538 when t is measured in days. How many days will it take an initial population of 8 bacteria to increase to 320?

2.6 As mentioned in a previous mathematics note, e also can be described using the infinite series shown below:

$$1 + \frac{1}{1!} + \frac{1}{2!} + \frac{1}{3!} + \cdots$$

or by using continued fractions as follows:

$$e = 2 + \cfrac{1}{1 + \cfrac{1}{2 + \cfrac{2}{3 + \cfrac{3}{\vdots}}}}$$

Use both of these expressions to approximate the value of e to six decimal places.

2.7 In the Level 3 module "Nearly Normal," you learned that a normal probability distribution is symmetric about the mean and tapers to the left and right like a bell. A normal curve is defined by the following equation:

$$y = \frac{1}{\sigma\sqrt{2\pi}} e^{-0.5\left(\frac{x-\mu}{\sigma}\right)^2}$$

where μ and σ are the mean and standard deviation, respectively, of a normal distribution.

a. Select a value for μ, then choose several different values for σ and graph the resulting equations.

b. Select a value for σ, then choose several different values for μ and graph the resulting equations.

c. Use your graphs from Parts **a** and **b** to discuss the effects of μ and σ on a normal curve.

Research Project

In his studies of infinite sets of numbers, Georg Cantor (1845–1918) developed **transfinite numbers.** A transfinite number is the cardinal number of an infinite set. Cantor also described a method for determining when one infinite set of numbers was larger than another by comparing their cardinal numbers. Write a report on transfinite numbers and their relationship to infinite sets.

In Activity **2,** you wrote equations for determining account balances and annual percentage yields in which a value for time was used as an exponent. In this activity, you use logarithms to determine the amount of time required for an investment to reach a particular amount.

Exploration 1

In the Level 3 module "Log Jam," you investigated **common logarithms,** base-10 logarithms which can be written either as $\log_{10} x$ or $\log x$. In this exploration, you examine logarithms that have bases other than 10.

a. Complete Table **2-5** below, which relates corresponding exponential and logarithmic equations.

Table 2-5 ■ *Logarithmic and Exponential Equations*

Logarithmic Equation	Related Exponential Equation
$\log_2 8 = 3$	$2^3 = 8$
$\log_4 16 = 2$	
	$6^4 = 1296$
$\log_{1.5} 3.375 = 3$	
	$0.8^2 = 0.64$
$\log_{0.81} 0.9 = 0.5$	

b. Recall that $y = \log_a x$ is equivalent to $a^y = x$. Knowing the relationship between a (the base) and x for various values of y can help you determine an unknown base of a logarithm.

1. Select a value for x greater than 1.
2. Using the value for x from Step **1,** determine the value of a in the equation $a^y = x$ when $y = 1$.

3. Compare the value of a to the value of x.
4. Repeat Steps **2** and **3** for several values of y greater than 1.
5. Repeat Steps **2** and **3** for several values of y less than 1.

c. Table **2-6** shows the logarithms, using two unknown rational bases a and b, for various values of x. Use your results from Part **b** to help determine the approximate value of each base.

TABLE 2-6 ■ *Two Logarithms of x*

x	$\log_a x$	$\log_b x$
2	0.431	0.333
3		0.528
4	0.861	
5		0.774
6	1.113	0.862
7		0.936
8	1.292	
9		
10		
11	1.490	1.153
12	1.544	1.195

d. Given the logarithmic equation $\log_{10} 10 = 1$, the related exponential equation is $10^1 = 10$. Write similar equations for $\log_a x$ and $\log_b x$ in Table **2-6.**

e. Most calculators and computers offer a feature for determining the **natural logarithm** of a number, denoted as **ln*x*.**

Determine the natural logarithm of various values of x. Use your results to approximate the value of the base of the natural logarithm to five decimal places.

Discussion 1

a. In Part **a** of Exploration **1,** you found that $x < a$ when $\log_a x < 1$ and $x > a$ when $\log_a x > 1$. Explain why this must be true.

b. What value did you determine for the approximate base of the natural logarithm?

mathematics note

Logarithms with base e are referred to as **natural logarithms.** The natural log of x is denoted by $\ln x$, where $x > 0$. The equation $\ln x = y$ is true if $e^y = x$.

For example, $\ln 7 \approx 1.9$. The related exponential equation is $e^{1.9} \approx 7$.

c. Describe how you might estimate each of the following:

1. $\log_7 52$
2. $\log_{19.7} 18$
3. $\ln 2$
4. $\ln 20$ (*Hint:* $e^3 \approx 20$.)

d. Why does the definition of natural logarithms given in the previous mathematics note restrict x to values greater than 0?

Exploration 2

In this exploration, you use natural logarithms to determine the time required for an account to reach a desired balance when interest is compounded continuously.

a. Consider an initial investment of \$500 at an annual interest rate of 6%, compounded continuously. Write a function that describes the account balance after t years.

b. In the module "Log Jam," you used the properties of logarithms to solve equations such as the one below for x.

$$y = 3 \bullet 10^x$$

$$y/3 = 10^x$$

$$\log(y/3) = \log 10^x$$

$$\log(y/3) = x$$

Use natural logarithms and the properties of logarithms to solve the equation in Part **a** for t.

mathematics note

The properties that are true for $\log_b x$ also are true for $\ln x$. Therefore, for $b > 0$, $b \neq 1$, $x > 0$, and $y > 0$:

- $\log_b b = 1$ and $\ln e = 1$
- $\log_b b^x = x$ and $\ln e^x = x$
- $\log_b x^y = y \log_b x$ and $\ln x^y = y \ln x$
- $\log_b (xy) = \log_b x + \log_b y$ and $\ln(xy) = \ln x + \ln y$
- $\log_b (x/y) = \log_b x - \log_b y$ and $\ln(x/y) = \ln x - \ln y$
- $b^{\log_b x} = x$ and $e^{\ln x} = x$

c. Use your response to Part **b** to determine the approximate number of years required for the account balance to reach each of the following amounts:

1. $1660.10
2. $3024.80

Discussion 2

a. In the example given in Part **b** of Exploration **2**, the equation $y = 3 \bullet 10^x$ is solved for x. Describe how the properties of logarithms were used to solve this equation.

b. Explain how you used the properties of logarithms to solve the equation in Part **a** of Exploration **2** for t.

c. In Part **c** of Exploration **2**, you used natural logarithms to determine that an initial investment of $500 at an annual interest rate of 6%, compounded continuously, would require approximately 20 yr to reach a balance of $1660.10.

It also is possible to determine this solution using common logs, as shown below.

$$1660.10 = 500e^{0.06t}$$

$$1660.10/500 = e^{0.06t}$$

$$\log(1660.10/500) = \log e^{0.06t}$$

$$\log(1660.10/500) = 0.06t \log e$$

$$\frac{\log(1660.10/500)}{0.06 \log e} = t$$

1. What advantages are there to using natural logs to solve this equation for t?
2. Consider another equation in which the variable to be solved for is an exponent. Do you think it would be possible to solve this equation using logarithms of any base?

Warm-Up

1. Using natural logarithms, convert each of the following equations from exponential form to logarithmic form.

   a. $e^5 = x$ **b.** $e^0 = 1$ **c.** $e^{0.06x} = 3$

2. Solve $e^{0.06x} = 3$ for x.

3. Convert each of the following equations from logarithmic to exponential form.

   a. $\ln x = 2$ **b.** $\ln e = 1$ **c.** $\ln(y/750) = 0.05x$

Assignment

3.1 Imagine that a young child invests 100 pennies in an account which compounds interest continuously. Using the equation $P_0e^{rt} = 2P_0$, determine how long it will take the child's initial investment to double at each of the following annual interest rates.

a. 6%

b. 8%

c. 10%

3.2 **a.** To help pay for their newborn child's future education, two parents decide to open a savings account. They make an initial deposit of \$1275 at an annual interest rate of 7%, compounded quarterly.

1. How long will it take for the initial deposit to double?
2. How long will it take for the initial deposit to triple?
3. If the parents make no further deposits or withdrawals, what will the account balance be when the child is ready to enter college?

b. Repeat Part **a** for an initial deposit of \$1275 at an annual interest rate of 7%, compounded continuously.

c. Compare your responses to Part **b** with your responses to Part **a.** Describe any differences you observe.

3.3 Consider an initial investment of P_0 at an annual interest rate of r, compounded continuously.

a. Write an equation that describes the value of the investment after t years.

b. Solve the equation in Part **a** for t.

3.4 LaSasha wants to purchase a new stereo system. The one she has selected costs \$715. At the moment, however, she has only \$500 available to spend. While exploring her options, LaSasha examines an investment account that offers an annual interest rate of 8%, compounded continuously. Use natural logarithms to complete Parts **a–c** below.

a. If LaSasha decides to invest in this account, how long will it take for the account balance to reach \$715?

b. LaSasha would like to buy the stereo system within 6 months. What annual interest rate would she have to earn to make this possible?

c. Is it reasonable to expect an interest rate of this size?

* * * * *

3.5 At last count, the population of Central City was 410,000. City planners expect the population to increase at a rate of 4.25% each year.

a. Write a function to model the number of years t it will take for the city to grow to a given population p.

b. The city prefers to employ one law enforcement officer for every 1000 people. If its growth rate remains constant, determine when the city will need to employ each of the following numbers of officers:

1. 500
2. 1000

3.6 a. Describe how different values of k affect the graphs of the following equations:

1. $y = \ln x + k$
2. $y = \ln x + \ln e^k$

b. Repeat Part **a** for the equations below.

1. $y = k \ln x$
2. $y = \ln x^k$

c. 1. Describe a relationship between the pair of equations in Part **a**.

2. Describe a relationship between the pair of equations in Part **b**.

d. Use laws of exponents to support your responses to Part **c**.

Summary Assessment

1. As part of his savings plan, Vonzel invested $5000 in a one-year certificate of deposit (CD) at an annual interest rate of 7%, compounded daily. When Vonzel told his Aunt Theresa about his investment, she advised him to withdraw the money. Another bank in town, she said, advertises the same interest rate, compounded continuously.
   a. Because Vonzel's bank charges a $150 penalty for early withdrawal, he decided not to move the money. Did Vonzel make the right decision? Explain your response.
   b. How long will it take Vonzel's CD to earn $150 (the cost of the penalty) in interest?
   c. The total value of the certificates of deposit at each bank is $5 million. In this situation, how much more does it cost a bank to pay interest compounded continuously rather than daily?

2. Shortly after buying the $5000 certificate of deposit, Vonzel purchases a $1400 stereo system with his credit card. His credit card company charges interest at an annual rate of 13%, compounded daily. Another company has offered him a credit card with the same annual interest rate, compounded monthly. The annual fee for the new card is $55; the annual fee for his current card fee is $50. Should Vonzel change credit cards? Explain your response.

3. Vonzel's credit card company offers a no-minimum payment option to some customers with excellent credit ratings. Using this option, customers may carry any balance due until the end of the next month. The interest charged on the balance, however, continues to be compounded daily.

   Due to some unforeseen expenses, Vonzel can't afford to pay his $1400 credit bill. Should he withdraw his $5000 certificate of deposit, pay the $150 penalty, then use some of the remaining cash to pay his credit card bill? Explain your response.

Module Summary

- **Principal** is the amount of money invested or loaned.
- **Interest** is the amount earned on invested money, or the fee charged for loaned money.
- The formula for calculating **simple interest,** where I represents interest, P represents principal, r represents the interest rate per time period, and t represents the number of time periods is shown below:

$$I = Prt$$

- The principal at the end of each time period in an investment or savings account can be thought of as a sequence. Assuming that no withdrawals are made and any interest earned is deposited in the account, such a sequence can be defined recursively by the following formula:

$$P_t = P_{t-1} + r \bullet P_{t-1} = P_{t-1}(1 + r)$$

where P_t is the principal at the end of t years, r is the annual interest rate, and P_{t-1} is the principal for the previous year.

- When interest is compounded annually, the yearly account balances that result can be thought of as a sequence defined explicitly by the following formula (assuming that no withdrawals are made and any interest earned is deposited in the account):

$$P_t = P_0(1 + r)^t$$

where P_t is the account balance after t years, P_0 is the initial principal, r is the annual interest rate, and t is the time in years.

- When compounding interest c times per year for t years, the formula for the account balance after n compounding periods is:

$$P_n = P_0\left(1 + \frac{r}{c}\right)^n = P_0\left(1 + \frac{r}{c}\right)^{ct}$$

where P_n represents the principal after n compounding periods, P_0 represents the initial principal, and r is the annual interest rate. Note that, in this formula, $n = ct$.

- **Infinity,** represented by the symbol ∞, depicts an unlimited quantity or an amount larger than any fixed value. Written as $+\infty$ or $-\infty$, it also may be used to depict quantities that extend without bound in either a positive or a negative direction.

* The value of e can be represented mathematically as shown below:

$$\lim_{n\to\infty}\left(1+\frac{1}{n}\right)^n = e$$

* When the number of compoundings per year approaches infinity, then the interest is **compounded continuously.** In this case, the formula for account balance P can be written as follows:

$$P = \lim_{c\to\infty} P_0\left(1+\frac{r}{c}\right)^{ct} = P_0\left[\lim_{c\to\infty}\left(1+\frac{r}{c}\right)^c\right]^t = P_0e^{rt}$$

  where P_0 represents the initial principal, r represents the annual interest rate, c represents the number of compoundings per year, and t represents number of years.

* To help consumers compare interest rates, banks often report **annual percentage yield (APY)** for savings accounts and **annual percentage rate (APR)** for loans. The APY or APR is the interest rate that, when compounded annually, will produce the same account balance as the advertised interest rate, which is typically compounded more often.

* Logarithms with base e are referred to as **natural logarithms.** The natural log of x is denoted by $\ln x$ where $x > 0$. The equation $\ln x = y$ is true if $e^y = x$.

* The properties that are true for $\log_b x$ also are true for $\ln x$. Therefore, for $b > 0$, $b \neq 1$, $x > 0$, and $y > 0$:

  - $\log_b b = 1$ and $\ln e = 1$
  - $\log_b b^x = x$ and $\ln e^x = x$
  - $\log_b x^y = y \log_b x$ and $\ln x^y = y \ln x$
  - $\log_b (xy) = \log_b x + \log_b y$ and $\ln(xy) = \ln x + \ln y$
  - $\log_b (x/y) = \log_b x - \log_b y$ and $\ln(x/y) = \ln x - \ln y$
  - $b^{\log_b x} = x$ and $e^{\ln x} = x$

module 3

Building Confidence

Introduction

As you might recall from previous modules, a **parameter** is a numerical characteristic of a population, and a **statistic** is a numerical characteristic of a sample. To obtain reliable information on populations, researchers depend on sampling techniques.

The statistics obtained from samples typically are used to estimate the parameters of a population. For example, political parties and government officials use the results of polls to help them gauge public opinion. Manufacturers rely on sampling to monitor the quality of their products. And economists use business statistics to study market trends.

Using a sample to obtain accurate information about a population can be a complicated process. Before collecting any data, researchers must consider several questions. How large must the sample be to produce a dependable estimate? Is the sampling method biased in any way? How much confidence can be placed in the accuracy of the estimate?

In this module, you investigate how sample size affects accuracy, and determine the confidence that you should place in the results of the sampling.

Discussion

a. Describe the differences between a statistic and a parameter.

b. Describe some populations in your school and in your community.

c. What parameters might be of interest for each population described in Part **b**?

d. 1. Describe some different ways in which samples could be taken from the populations in Part **b.**

   2. Recall that a **simple random sample** is selected so that each member of the population has the same chance of being included in the sample. Which of these sampling methods generate simple random samples?

ACTIVITY 1

To make reasonable predictions about a population, you must decide how large a sample you need. First, you must understand how the information that is gained from samples of different sizes can vary.

Exploration 1

In this exploration, you draw samples from an unknown population and use the means and standard deviations of these samples to estimate parameters.

mathematics note

The mean value for a population, or **population mean,** is a parameter denoted by the Greek letter μ (mu).

The **population standard deviation** is a parameter denoted by the Greek letter σ (sigma). It can be calculated using the following formula:

$$\sigma = \sqrt{\frac{(x_1 - \mu)^2 + (x_2 - \mu)^2 + \cdots + (x_N - \mu)^2}{N}}$$

where the population has N members represented by $x_1, x_2, \ldots, x_n$.

The mean value for a sample, or **sample mean,** is a statistic denoted by $\bar{x}$ (read "x-bar").

The **sample standard deviation,** a statistic denoted by s, can be calculated as follows:

$$s = \sqrt{\frac{(x_1 - \bar{x})^2 + (x_2 - \bar{x})^2 + \cdots + (x_n - \bar{x})^2}{n - 1}}$$

where the sample has data from n members of the population represented by $x_1, x_2, \ldots, x_n$.

Notice that the denominator used to calculate the sample standard deviation is slightly different from the denominator used to calculate the population standard deviation. When calculating sample standard deviation, the denominator $n - 1$ provides a better estimate of the population standard deviation.

For example, consider a population of the digits from 0 to 9. The population mean μ is 4.5. The population standard deviation σ is approximately 2.87. For the following sample of 5 digits taken from this population—{4, 6, 8, 7, 9}—the sample mean $\bar{x}$ is 6.8. The sample standard deviation s is approximately 1.9.

a. Obtain a population of pennies from your teacher and place them in a container. To obtain the age data from a sample of size 5 from this population, complete the following steps:

   1. Draw five members of the population at random from the container.
   2. Record their ages. (A penny of the current year has an age of 0.)
   3. Return them to the container and mix the population thoroughly.

b. Determine the sample mean $\bar{x}$ and sample standard deviation s for the ages of the pennies. Record these values in a table with headings like those in Table **3-1.**

TABLE 3-1 ■ *Statistics for Samples of Five Pennies*

Sample Number	$\bar{x}$	s
1		
2		
3		
⋮		
10		

c. Repeat Parts **a** and **b** nine more times. **Note:** Save a copy of Table **3-1** for use in Activities **2** and **3.**

d. Create a frequency histogram of the means of your 10 samples.

e. Collect all of the sample means from each group in your class. Create a frequency histogram of these sample means. **Note:** Save the class data for use in Exploration **2.**

Discussion 1

a. In Part **b** of Exploration **1,** why were you instructed to use s for the standard deviation rather than σ?

b. Compare the frequency histogram of your 10 sample means with the one for the class data.

c. Describe how you could use a frequency histogram to estimate the mean age of the population in Exploration **1.**

d. Which histogram should provide a better estimate of the population mean: your histogram for 10 sample means or the one for the class data?

Exploration 2

In this exploration, you use a simulation to investigate how sample size can affect the results of a sampling.

a. With the help of technology, you can examine many samples from the population in Exploration **1** in a relatively short time.

   1. Use the simulation provided by your teacher to obtain 10 samples of size 20 from the population.
   2. Determine the mean age and standard deviation of each sample and record these values in a table with headings like those in Table **3-1. Note:** Save this data for use in Activities **2** and **3.**
   3. Create a frequency histogram of the means of your 10 samples.
   4. Collect all of the sample means from each group in your class. Create a frequency histogram of these sample means.

b. Repeat Part **a** for samples of size 40.

c. Using the class data for samples of size 5 from Exploration **1,** determine the mean and standard deviation for the sample means ($\bar{x}$). Record these values in a table with headings like those in Table **3-2.**

Table 3-2 ■ *Statistics for Samples of Different Sizes*

Sample Size (n)	Mean of Sample Means	Standard Deviation of Sample Means
5		
20		
40		

d. Repeat Part **c** for sample sizes of 20 and 40. **Note:** Save Table **3-2** and the histograms of the class data for use in the exploration in Activity **2.**

e. Estimate the mean age of the population of pennies.

Discussion 2

a. Describe how the frequency histograms in Exploration **2** change as the sample size increases.

b. Describe how the means and standard deviations recorded in Table **3-2** change as the sample size increases.

c. 1. How did you estimate the mean age μ for the population of pennies?
   2. How accurate do you think your estimate is? Explain your response.

mathematics note

The **sampling distribution of sample means** contains the means ($\bar{x}$) of *all* possible samples of size n from a population. Two important facts about this distribution are used to make estimates about population parameters.

1. The mean of the sampling distribution of sample means, denoted by $\mu_{\bar{x}}$, equals the population mean μ.
2. The standard deviation of the sampling distribution of sample means, denoted by $\sigma_{\bar{x}}$, equals $\sigma/\sqrt{n}$, where σ is the population standard deviation and n is the sample size. When σ is unknown, the standard deviation of the sample (s) may be used as an estimate of σ if the population is normally distributed and $n \geq 30$.

For example, consider a jar containing five pennies—A, B, C, D, and E—with ages in years of 2, 6, 6, 8, and 10, respectively. Table **3-3** shows the means of all possible samples of size 2 that can be drawn from this population.

TABLE 3-3 ■ *A Sampling Distribution of Sample Means*

Sample	AB	AC	AD	AE	BC	BD	BE	CD	CE	DE
$\bar{x}$	4	4	5	6	6	7	8	7	8	9

In this case,

$$\mu_{\bar{x}} = \frac{4+4+5+6+6+7+8+7+8+9}{10} = 6.4 \text{ yr}$$

The population mean μ can be calculated as follows:

$$\mu = \frac{2+6+6+8+10}{5} = 6.4 \text{ yr}$$

As noted above, $\mu_{\bar{x}} = \mu$.

Using the formula for the standard deviation of a population, the standard deviation of these sample means is approximately 1.88 yr. This also can be calculated as shown below:

$$\sigma_{\bar{x}} = \frac{\sigma}{\sqrt{n}} \approx \frac{2.65}{\sqrt{2}} \approx 1.88 \text{ yr}$$

d. Obtain the actual mean age and standard deviation for your population of pennies. Use the formulas $\mu_{\bar{x}} = \mu$ and $\sigma_{\bar{x}} = \sigma/\sqrt{n}$ to determine $\mu_{\bar{x}}$ and $\sigma_{\bar{x}}$ for sample sizes of 5, 20, and 40. Compare your results with the values you recorded in Table **3-2.**

e. How does sample size affect the spread of all the possible sample means about the population mean?

mathematics note

The **law of large numbers** states that the mean of a large number n of independent measurements of a random quantity tends, as n increases, toward the theoretical mean of that quantity.

This law guarantees that for very large sample sizes, there is a high probability that the sample mean is close to the population mean.

For example, suppose that you want to estimate the mean number of hours spent on homework in a population of 150 students. If you plan to sample this population, a sample of 50 students is likely to provide a better estimate of the population mean than a sample of 5 students.

f. 1. What sample size guarantees the best possible estimate of a population mean? Explain your response.

   2. Why might it be impractical to obtain a sample of this size?

g. Why would you expect an increase in sample size to produce a decrease in the standard deviation of the sample means?

h. 1. Why should the mean of one large sample from a population be approximately the same as the mean of a large number of sample means from the same population?

   2. Why should the standard deviation s of one large sample from a population be approximately the same as the standard deviation σ of the entire population?

Warm-Up

1. Each set of numbers in Parts **a–d** below represents a population. Without calculation, estimate the mean and standard deviation of each population. Then determine the actual mean and standard deviation and compare those values with your estimates.

   a. {32, 32, 32, 32, 32, 32, 32, 32, 32, 32}

   b. {2, 2, 2, 4, 4, 4}

   c. {2, 4, 6, 8, 10, 12, 14}

   d. {–18, –15, –12, –9, –6, –3, 0, 3, 6, 9, 12, 15, 18}

2. Each set of numbers in Parts **a–c** below represents a sample of a population. Calculate the mean and standard deviation for each sample and write your answers using correct mathematical notation.

   a. {2, 4, 5, 6, 7, 5, 3, 2, 4, 8, 2, 1}

   b. {145, 92, 91, 125, 100, 82, 96}

   c. {18, 13, 15, 16, 17, 15, 12, 15, 16, 18, 19}

3. Consider a population represented by the following set: {3, 4, 5, 6, 7}. Using this population, determine the sampling distribution of sample means for each sample size below. Calculate the mean and standard deviation of each sampling distribution.

   a. $n = 2$

   b. $n = 3$

   c. $n = 4$

4. Use your responses in Problem **3** to describe what happens to the mean and standard deviation of a sampling distribution of sample means for a given population as the sample size increases.

Assignment

1.1 The following table shows the ages, in years, of a simple random sample of 50 pennies taken from a piggy bank filled with pennies:

28	8	6	5	1	1	3	4	2	2
14	1	2	3	6	6	12	7	5	1
12	7	1	6	1	2	1	8	1	8
16	10	5	2	3	10	16	3	4	7
3	5	2	4	8	3	4	1	4	5

a. Determine the mean age $\overline{x}$ of these pennies.

b. Determine the sample standard deviation s.

c. Estimate the mean age μ for the population of pennies in the piggy bank.

1.2 **a.** Consider the whole numbers from 1 to 99 as a population. Using appropriate technology, generate three random samples from this population: one sample of 10 numbers, one of 20 numbers, and one of 80 numbers. Find the mean of each sample.

b. Repeat Part **a** at least three more times.

c. Compare the three sample means for each sample size to the population mean, $\mu = 50$. In a paragraph, describe how the results of this experiment relate to the law of large numbers.

1.3 The following table shows the summer earnings of a population of students.

\$1872	\$1341	\$1792	\$1650	\$1422
\$1413	\$1900	\$2143	\$786	\$451
\$2432	\$0	\$243	\$1381	\$187
\$0	\$2443	\$1408	\$187	\$0
\$1228	\$1119	\$748	\$949	\$2011
\$896	\$1740	\$0	\$483	\$846
\$556	\$780	\$314	\$768	\$635

a. Calculate the mean and standard deviation of the data.

b. 1. Select a random sample of five values from this population.

2. Calculate the mean and standard deviation of the sample.

c. 1. Is your sample mean a good estimate of the population mean?

2. How could you select a sample that would provide a better estimate?

1.4 To determine the mean annual income in a large city, a research group analyzed 1000 random samples of 40 adults from this population. The results of the study are shown in the following table.

Sample Mean (to nearest $1000)	Frequency
18,000	1
19,000	11
20,000	45
21,000	111
22,000	184
23,000	220
24,000	197
25,000	131
26,000	66
27,000	24
28,000	6
29,000	2
30,000	1
31,000	1

a. Use the mean of these sample means to estimate the mean $\mu_{\bar{x}}$ of all possible sample means (to the nearest thousand dollars) using samples of size 40.

b. Use the standard deviation of the sample means to estimate the standard deviation $\sigma_{\bar{x}}$ of all possible sample means using samples of size 40.

c. Estimate the mean μ and standard deviation σ for the population from which these samples came.

d. How accurate do you think your estimate is for μ? Explain your response.

1.5 When trying to estimate the average income of high school graduates in your state, Andreas claims that using a sample size of 240 instead of 120 would reduce the standard deviation of all possible sample means by half. Likewise, using a sample size of 480 instead of 240 would reduce $\sigma_{\bar{x}}$ again by half. Defend or refute Andreas' claim.

* * * * *

1.6 At Lincoln High School, many students take the Scholastic Aptitude Test (SAT). The following table shows the scores on the mathematics portion of the SAT for the students in one classroom.

410	770	430	420	400	780	440	420
610	630	400	440	430	500	430	450
680	500	720	450	520	470	440	740
440	580	550	590	770	400	500	610

a. Determine the mean score $\overline{x}$ (to the nearest whole number).

b. Determine the sample standard deviation s.

c. Estimate the mean score μ for the entire population of Lincoln High School students who took the exam.

d. Why might you hesitate to use the results of this sample to estimate the mean for the entire population?

1.7 The table below shows the ages, in years, of a sample of high school students in a community.

Age	Frequency
13	100
14	150
15	120
16	93
17	157
18	82
19	51

a. Determine the mean age, to the nearest year, of students in this sample.

b. Determine the standard deviation of this sample.

c. Estimate the mean μ for the population from which this sample came.

d. How confident are you that the estimates made from this sample are accurate? Explain your response.

1.8 The following table shows the numbers of persons per household for a sample of households taken in a large city:

Number in Household	Frequency
1	15
2	20
3	37
4	23
5	14
6	4
7	2

a. Determine the mean number of persons per household for this sample.

b. Determine the standard deviation of this sample.

c. Estimate the mean number of persons per household for the city from which this sample came.

d. How confident are you that the estimates made from this sample are accurate? Explain your response.

How well do you think a sample mean estimates the population mean? Your response is likely to depend both on the size of the population and the size of the sample. Because finding exact parameters for a large population is usually difficult (if not impossible), researchers must decide how much information is enough to provide an accurate estimate.

In Activity **1**, you found that a larger sample size typically can provide a more accurate estimate. But what are the mathematical reasons for this effect? And how large is large enough? In this activity, you begin to answer these questions.

Exploration

In previous explorations, you used sample sizes of 5, 20, and 40 to estimate the mean age of a population of pennies. In this exploration, you continue your investigations on the effects of sample size.

a. 1. Use technology to simulate 10 samples of size 50 from the population of pennies.

2. Determine the mean and standard deviation of each sample. **Note:** Save this data for use in Activity **3.**

b. 1. Collect the sample means from each group in your class and create a frequency histogram of the class data.

2. Determine the mean and standard deviation of the sample means. Add this information to Table **3-2** from Activity **1.**

c. Repeat Parts **a** and **b** for samples of size 75.

d. Estimate the mean age of the population of pennies.

Discussion

a. How do the mean and standard deviation of the sample means change as the sample size continues to increase?

b. Which sample size appears to give the best estimate of the actual mean age of the penny population? Why do you believe this is true?

c. Recall that a **normal distribution** is symmetric about the mean and tapers to the left and right like a bell. The curve that describes the shape of the graph is the **normal curve.** As in all continuous probability distributions, the total area between the x-axis and a normal curve is 1.

1. Figure **3-1** shows two normal curves with the same mean. What differences do you observe between the two curves?

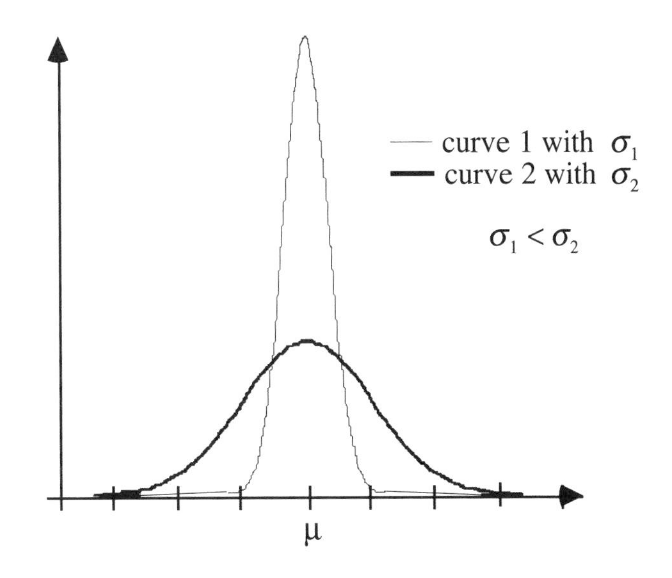

FIGURE 3-1 **Two normal curves with the same mean.**

2. Figure **3-2** shows two normal curves with the same standard deviation. What differences do you observe between these two curves?

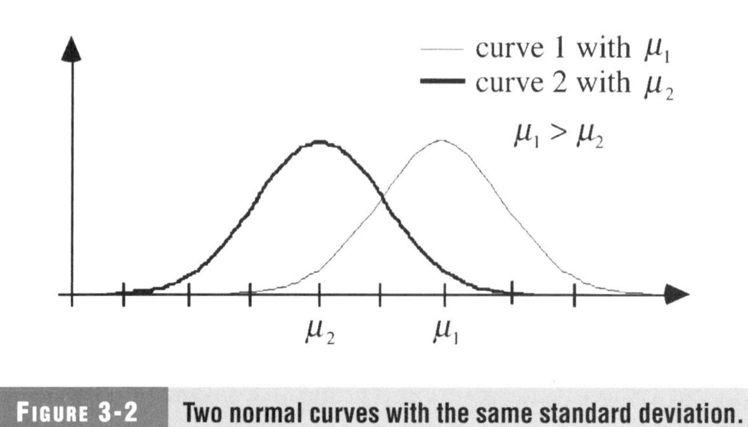

FIGURE 3-2 **Two normal curves with the same standard deviation.**

3. Describe how the value of σ affects the shape of a normal curve.
4. Describe how the value of μ affects the position of a normal curve.

d. Figure **3-3** shows a histogram of the ages of a penny population. Do the ages of these pennies appear to be normally distributed? Explain your response.

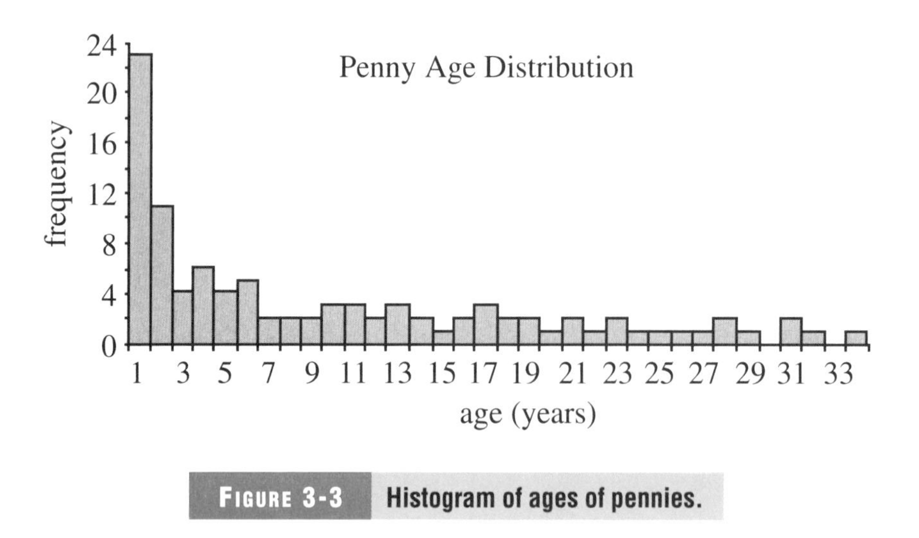

FIGURE 3-3 **Histogram of ages of pennies.**

e. Describe the shapes of the histograms of sample means from Part **b** of the exploration.

mathematics note

The **central limit theorem** states that even if the population from which samples are taken is not normally distributed, the distribution of the means of all possible samples of the same size will be approximately normal. In other words, if you collect many samples of size n and create a relative frequency histogram and polygon of the sample means, the graph will tend to assume the bell shape of a normal curve. Figure **3-4** shows an example of such a distribution.

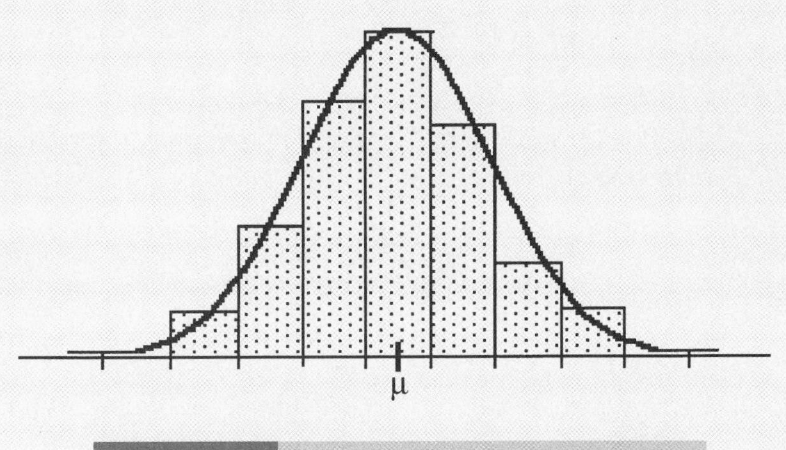

FIGURE 3-4 Normal distribution of sample means.

This approximation becomes more accurate as the sample size n increases. Statisticians generally agree that for $n \geq 30$, the distribution of sample means can be modeled reasonably well by a normal curve. This requirement is not necessary if the population itself is normally distributed.

f. 1. Obtain the standard deviation (σ) for the population of pennies in the exploration. Use this to determine the standard deviation of all sample means ($\sigma_{\bar{x}}$) for the following sample sizes: 5, 20, 40, 50, and 75.

2. Compare the values for $\sigma_{\bar{x}}$ with the standard deviations you recorded in Table **3-2.** Why might these values differ?

g. How does the sample size n affect the shape of the distribution of all possible sample means? Explain why this occurs.

h. When sampling a population, how can a researcher be reasonably confident that the sample mean is a good estimate of the population mean?

Warm-Up

1. The normal curve in the graph below represents a probability distribution with a mean of μ and a standard deviation of σ.

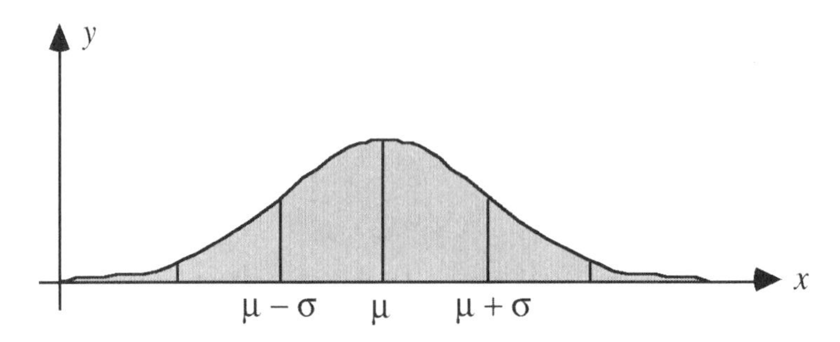

Use this information to describe the graphs of normal distributions with the following characteristics:

a. a mean greater than μ and a standard deviation equal to σ

b. a standard deviation less than σ and a mean equal to μ

c. a mean less than μ and a standard deviation greater than σ.

2. Each of Parts **a–d** describes a different set of data. Which of these sets would you expect to be normally distributed? Defend your responses.

a. The set of numbers in the table below:

1	2.5	3	3	4	5	5	5	5.5	5.5
5.5	6	6	6	6	6	6	6	6	6.5
6.5	6.5	6.5	7	7	7	7.5	7.5	8	8
8.5	9	9.5	11						

b. The set of even numbers between –20 and 20.

c. The means of 50 samples of size 50 drawn from the whole numbers 1 to 99.

d. The means of 50 samples of size 5 drawn from the whole numbers 1 to 99.

3. Consider an experiment in which simple random samples of size 40 are drawn from the set of whole numbers 1 to 50, inclusive.

a. Is the set of whole numbers from 1 to 50 normally distributed? Explain your response.

b. Would you expect the means of 20 of these samples to be normally distributed? Explain your response.

c. In a frequency histogram of the 20 means in Part **b,** where would you expect the histogram's axis of symmetry to intersect the x-axis?

d. For a sample size of 40, what are the mean and standard deviation for all possible sample means from this population?

Assignment

2.1 The figure below shows two normal curves. One curve represents the distribution of a characteristic in a population. The other represents the distribution of sample means for that characteristic in the same population, using a sample size of 16.

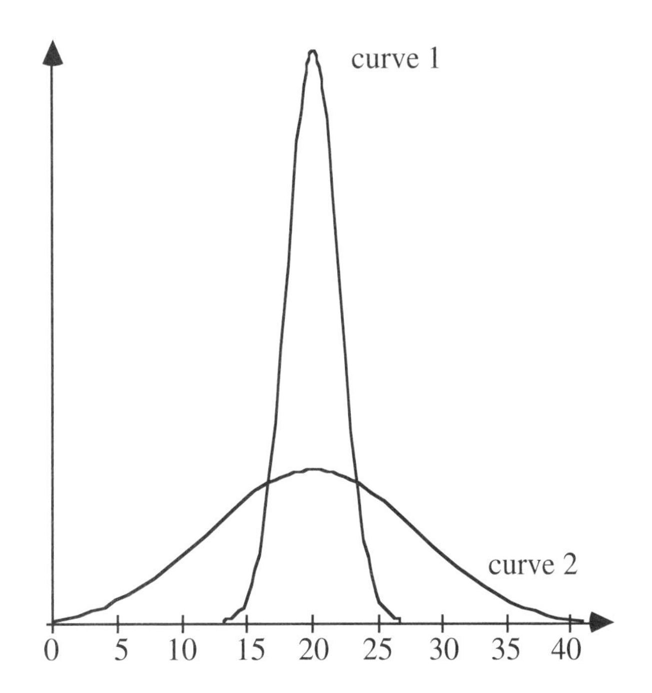

a. Which curve represents the distribution of sample means? Defend your choice, including an explanation for the difference in the shapes of the two curves.

b. Use the appropriate curve to estimate the mean and standard deviation of the population.

c. Use your responses from Part **b** to estimate the mean and standard deviation of the sample means.

2.2 A family of six has the following heights (in centimeters): 145, 156, 163, 170, 174, and 188.

a. Find μ for this population.

b. Use combinations to determine the number of samples of two heights that can be taken from this population.

c. List all the possible samples of two heights from the population.

d. Find the mean of each sample in Part **c.**

e. Find the mean of five randomly chosen sample means from Part **d.**

f. Find the mean of all the sample means from Part **d.**

g. Compare the values obtained in Parts **a, e,** and **f** and write a summary of your findings.

2.3 **a.** Randomly generate 10 whole numbers from 1 to 9. Calculate the mean of these numbers.

b. Repeat Part **a** 19 more times, creating a population of 200 numbers from 1 to 9, and a group of 20 sample means.

c. Create a relative frequency histogram of the population of 200 numbers and describe the shape of the graph.

d. Create a relative frequency histogram of the 20 sample means and describe the shape of the graph.

e. How does the distribution of sample means compare to the distribution of the population from which the samples were taken? Use the central limit theorem to explain why the difference occurs.

2.4 A bottling plant fills bottles with soda. The volumes of the population of filled bottles are normally distributed, with a mean of 355 mL and a standard deviation of 2 mL. As part of the quality control process, a sample of four bottles is selected every hour. A technician records the mean volume of each sample. What are the mean and standard deviation of these sample means?

* * * * *

2.5 Consider a population consisting of the whole numbers from 1 to 99.

a. Determine the standard deviation of this population (σ).

b. Determine the standard deviation of the sample means ($\sigma_{\bar{x}}$) for samples of size 30 taken from this population.

c. How does the standard deviation of the population differ from the standard deviation of the sample means? Explain why you would expect this difference to occur.

2.6 The Sure Grip Tire Company manufactures motorcycle tires. The life spans of a population of its tires are normally distributed with a mean of 85,000 km and a standard deviation of 3750 km.

a. What is the standard deviation of the sample means for samples of size 100 taken from this population?

b. How could the company decrease the size of the standard deviation of the sample means?

According to the central limit theorem, even if a population is not normally distributed, the distribution of sample means often can be approximated reasonably well by a normal curve. This is one of the most useful facts in statistics.

Quality-control engineers, for example, frequently measure quality in terms of a product's mean life span. Whenever possible, they model the results of their experiments with normal curves. When working with normal curves, they can express the proportion of the data located within a specific interval as a percentage. In Figure **3-5,** for example, the area under the curve that corresponds to the proportion of data in the interval $[a, b]$ is 55%. In this activity, you explore some of the properties that make normal curves so useful.

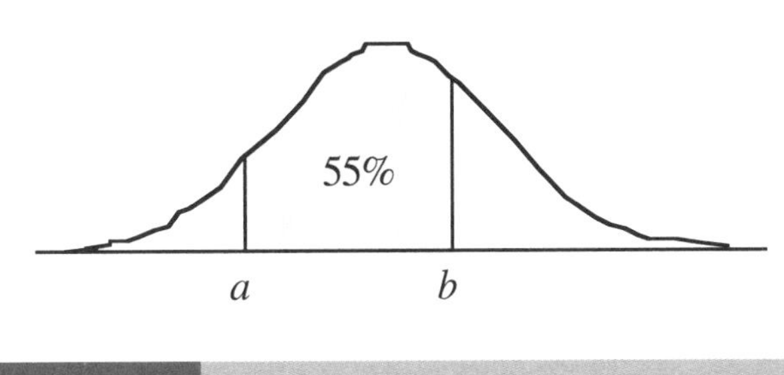

FIGURE 3-5 **Percentage of area corresponding to [*a*, *b*].**

Exploration

a. Use the data you compiled in Activity **1** for samples of size 5 to complete a table with headings like those in Table **3-4** below. To estimate $\sigma_{\bar{x}}$, use the value of s for each sample to approximate σ, then use the formula $\sigma_{\bar{x}} = \sigma / \sqrt{n}$.

Table 3-4 ■ *Statistics for Samples of Five Pennies*

Sample Number	$\bar{x}$	s	Estimate of $\sigma_{\bar{x}}$
1			
2			
3			
⋮			
10			

b. 1. For each sample in Table **3-4,** determine the interval $[\bar{x} - \sigma_{\bar{x}}, \bar{x} + \sigma_{\bar{x}}]$.

2. Graph each interval above a number line as a line segment with the midpoint $\bar{x}$ indicated as shown in Figure **3-6** below.

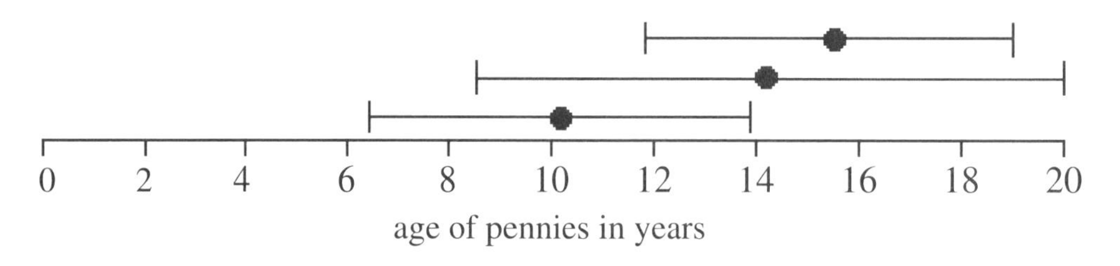

Figure 3-6 Intervals for three samples of pennies.

c. 1. Obtain the actual mean age of the population of pennies.

2. Draw a line on your graph to represent the population mean μ, as shown in Figure **3-7:**

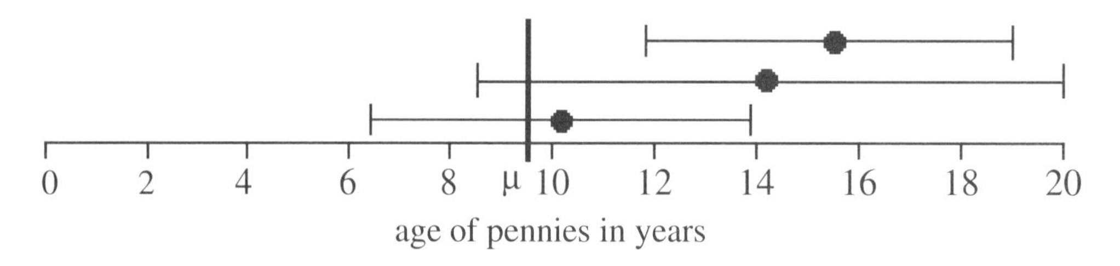

Figure 3-7 Graph of intervals with line at μ.

d. Determine the percentage of intervals that contain the population mean. In Figure **3-7,** for example, 2/3 or approximately 67% of the intervals contain the population mean. Record the result in a table with headings like those in Table **3-5.**

TABLE 3-5 ■ *Percentage of Intervals Containing μ*

Sample size (n)	Interval	Percentage Containing μ
5	$[\bar{x} - \sigma_{\bar{x}}, \bar{x} + \sigma_{\bar{x}}]$	
20	$[\bar{x} - \sigma_{\bar{x}}, \bar{x} + \sigma_{\bar{x}}]$	
40	$[\bar{x} - \sigma_{\bar{x}}, \bar{x} + \sigma_{\bar{x}}]$	
50	$[\bar{x} - \sigma_{\bar{x}}, \bar{x} + \sigma_{\bar{x}}]$	
75	$[\bar{x} - \sigma_{\bar{x}}, \bar{x} + \sigma_{\bar{x}}]$	
5	$[\bar{x} - 2\sigma_{\bar{x}}, \bar{x} + 2\sigma_{\bar{x}}]$	
20	$[\bar{x} - 2\sigma_{\bar{x}}, \bar{x} + 2\sigma_{\bar{x}}]$	
40	$[\bar{x} - 2\sigma_{\bar{x}}, \bar{x} + 2\sigma_{\bar{x}}]$	
50	$[\bar{x} - 2\sigma_{\bar{x}}, \bar{x} + 2\sigma_{\bar{x}}]$	
75	$[\bar{x} - 2\sigma_{\bar{x}}, \bar{x} + 2\sigma_{\bar{x}}]$	
5	$[\bar{x} - 3\sigma_{\bar{x}}, \bar{x} + 3\sigma_{\bar{x}}]$	
20	$[\bar{x} - 3\sigma_{\bar{x}}, \bar{x} + 3\sigma_{\bar{x}}]$	
40	$[\bar{x} - 3\sigma_{\bar{x}}, \bar{x} + 3\sigma_{\bar{x}}]$	
50	$[\bar{x} - 3\sigma_{\bar{x}}, \bar{x} + 3\sigma_{\bar{x}}]$	
75	$[\bar{x} - 3\sigma_{\bar{x}}, \bar{x} + 3\sigma_{\bar{x}}]$	

e. Determine the percentage of intervals of $[\bar{x} - 2\sigma_{\bar{x}}, \bar{x} + 2\sigma_{\bar{x}}]$ that contain the population mean. Record your results in your copy of Table **3-5.**

f. Determine the percentage of intervals of $[\bar{x} - 3\sigma_{\bar{x}}, \bar{x} + 3\sigma_{\bar{x}}]$ that contain the population mean. Record your results in your copy of Table **3-5.**

g. Using the data you saved in Activities **2** and **3,** repeat Parts **a–f** for sample sizes of 20, 40, 50, and 75.

h. Collect the data obtained by the entire class in this exploration. For each sample size, determine the percentages of the three intervals that contain the population mean.

Discussion

a. In Part **b** of the exploration, you used intervals to characterize sample data. Why does it make sense to designate $\bar{x}$ as the midpoint of each interval?

b. What appears to be the relationship between the number of standard deviations used to define the interval and the percentage of intervals that contain the population mean? Explain your response.

mathematics note

The **68–95–99.7 rule** states that approximately 68% of the total area between the normal curve and the x-axis lies within 1 standard deviation of the mean, 95% lies within 2 standard deviations of the mean, and 99.7% lies within 3 standard deviations of the mean. This rule is illustrated in Figure **3-8.**

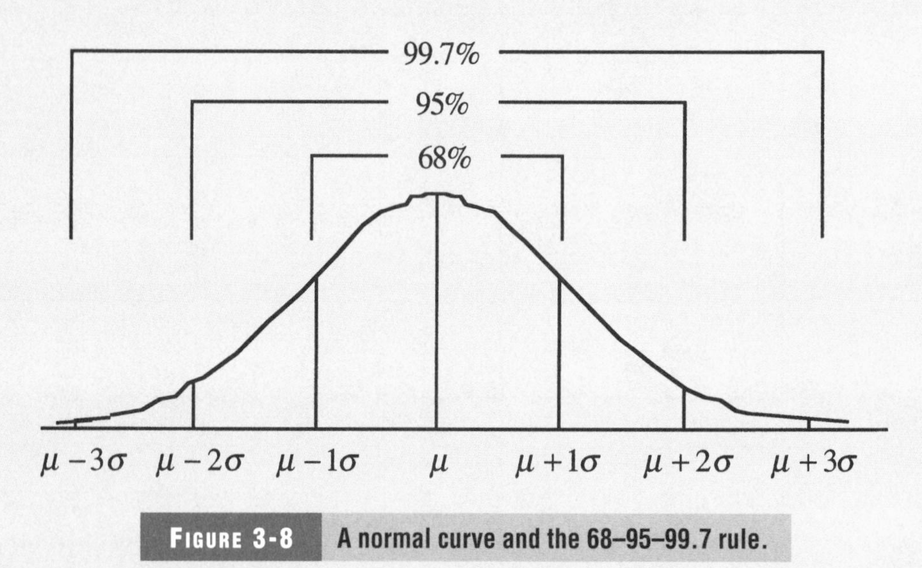

FIGURE 3-8 **A normal curve and the 68–95–99.7 rule.**

For example, consider a population for which the mean is 100 and the standard deviation is 10. Using a sample size of 50 to sample this population, the mean of the sampling distribution of sample means is 100 and the standard deviation of the sampling distribution of sample means is $10/\sqrt{50} = \sqrt{2}$. This implies that about 68% of the sample means lie within $\sqrt{2}$ of 100, 95% of the sample means lie within $2\sqrt{2}$ of 100, and 99.7% of the sample means lie within $3\sqrt{2}$ of 100.

c. How do your results in the exploration compare with the percentages predicted by the 68–95–99.7 rule?

d. Explain why you might expect some differences between the percentages obtained in the exploration and the percentages given in the mathematics note.

e. As the sample size changes, what happens to the widths of the corresponding intervals? Explain your response.

f. How would you modify the exploration to better approximate the 68–95–99.7 rule?

Warm-Up

1. Consider an experiment that involves collecting 50 samples of size 100 from a population with a mean of 20 and a standard deviation of 3. How many sample means would you expect to fall in each of the following intervals? Justify your responses.

   a. $[19.4, 20.6]$

   b. $[19.7, 20.3]$

   c. $[20, 20.9]$

   d. $[19.1, 19.4]$

   e. $[19.1, 20.6]$

2. Each of Parts **a–e** below lists an interval whose midpoint is the mean of a sampling distribution of sample means, along with the percentage of sample means contained in that interval for a sample size of 50. Use this information to identify the population mean, standard deviation of the sampling distribution of sample means, and population standard deviation for each case.

   a. $[10, 14]$; 68%

   b. $[1.35, 2.57]$; 95%

   c. $[-3, 19]$; 99.7%

   d. $[a, a + 2]$; 68%

   e. $[a, b]$; 95%

Assignment

3.1 While researching automobile tires, you find that the mean life for samples of one particular brand is 60,000 km with a standard deviation of 1200 km. Assume that the life spans of tires in this population are normally distributed.

   a. What percentage of the population would you expect to have life spans in the interval $[58{,}800, 61{,}200]$? Explain your response.

   b. What are the upper and lower bounds of the interval within which you would expect the life spans of 95% of these tires to be found? Describe how you determined this interval.

3.2 The life spans of a population of light bulbs are normally distributed, with a mean life span of 1015 hr and a standard deviation of 75 hr.

   a. What percentage of these bulbs would you expect to last longer than 1090 hr?

   b. If a company purchases 1000 of these bulbs for use in its manufacturing plant, how many of them would you expect to burn out after less than 865 hr of use?

3.3 A quality control engineer who tests automobile seat belts selects a random sample of 36 men, aged 18 to 74, and measures their masses in kilograms. These masses are shown in the following table.

67.7	81.0	50.6	74.4	94.8	65.8
79.7	93.8	56.2	72.8	89.6	89.3
63.6	76.3	85.2	88.4	69.6	77.6
64.9	69.1	55.2	80.7	63.4	59.4
53.6	59.2	96.4	57.4	103.4	90.2
103.8	81.4	65.6	101.2	87.5	65.6

a. The masses of the population from which the engineer selected the sample are normally distributed with a mean of 75 kg and a standard deviation of 14.9 kg. Determine an interval that the engineer could expect to contain 68% of the data.

b. Find the actual percentage of data that lies within the interval you determined in Part **a.**

c. Explain why the percentage calculated in Part **b** might differ from 68%.

3.4 The quality control engineer described in Problem **3.3** decides to collect data from 19 more random samples of men (20 in all). The means of the samples (in kilograms) are shown in the table below.

76.0	83.1	75.8	82.1	68.4
76.1	80.6	77.4	79.6	75.4
90.0	68.9	85.4	80.5	82.0
81.2	73.4	62.3	83.2	82.5

a. Find the percentage of sample means that lie within the interval calculated in Problem **3.3a.**

b. Compare the percentage of sample means that lie within the interval to the percentage of masses from the single sample in Problem **3.3.** Explain any differences you observe.

3.5 While analyzing the data collected from a sample of 1000 items, a researcher constructs the interval [1250, 1420] to represent values within 2 standard deviations of the mean of the sampling distribution of sample means. Considering her methods, she would expect 95% of the intervals created in this manner to contain the population mean. Use this information to identify the approximate values of $\bar{x}$, $\sigma_{\bar{x}}$, and s in this situation.

* * * * *

3.6 A test was given to 3,000,000 people. The scores on the test were normally distributed, with a mean of 900 and a standard deviation of 212.

a. Determine the interval that contains 99.7% of the scores.

b. What percentage of the population received scores less than or equal to 1324?

c. What percentage of the population received scores less than or equal to 688?

3.7 The supervisor of the waiters and waitresses at El Burrito restaurant noticed that the amount of tips reported per shift seemed to be normally distributed with a mean of $27.35 and a standard deviation of $10.17.

a. Find the interval that contains 95% of the reported tips.

b. Find the interval that contains 99.7% of the reported tips.

c. What percentage of the staff make more than $17.18 in tips per shift?

d. From your experience with restaurants, would you have expected the amount of tips reported per shift to be normally distributed? Explain your response.

When conducting statistical studies, researchers usually are concerned with large populations in which the mean value of a characteristic is unknown. In these situations, an estimate of the population mean is made using the statistics from a single sample. In this activity, you examine how confident researchers can be in the accuracy of their estimates.

Exploration

In this exploration, you use the whole numbers from 1 to 999 as a model population ($\mu = 500$ and $\sigma = 288$).

a. Select a random sample of 30 numbers from the population and calculate $\bar{x}$.

b. Determine s, the standard deviation of this sample.

c. 1. Use the value for s from Part **b** to estimate $\sigma_{\bar{x}}$.

2. Write the interval $[\bar{x} - 2\sigma_{\bar{x}}, \bar{x} + 2\sigma_{\bar{x}}]$.

d. Determine if the interval you created in Part **c** contains μ.

e. Repeat Parts **a–d** 49 more times (for a total of 50 samples). Record the number of times that the interval generated did *not* contain the population mean.

Discussion

a. What percentage of the time did the interval created in the exploration not contain the population mean?

b. The intervals you created in Part **c** of the exploration are known as **95% confidence intervals.** What would you expect to be true of these intervals?

c. Do your results in the exploration support the 95% figure?

mathematics note

A **confidence interval** for a parameter is an interval of numbers in which one would expect to find the value of that parameter. Every confidence interval has two aspects: an interval determined by the statistics collected from a random sample and a confidence level describing what percentage of the intervals created by that process would contain the parameter.

For example, a 95% confidence interval is generated by a process in which the parameter would fall in those intervals 95% of the time. In other words, you would expect 95% of the intervals produced by this process to contain the parameter, while 5% of the intervals would not.

The mean of all the sample means of a given sample size equals the mean of the population μ. For large sample sizes, the sampling distribution of sample means approximates a normal distribution, so the 68–95–99.7 rule can be applied. For example, the mean $\bar{x}$ of any one sample of size n will fall within 2 standard deviations of μ 95% of the time. This 95% confidence interval can be represented algebraically as shown below:

$$\bar{x} - 2\left(\frac{\sigma}{\sqrt{n}}\right) \leq \mu \leq \bar{x} + 2\left(\frac{\sigma}{\sqrt{n}}\right)$$

Because the population standard deviation usually is unknown, it is necessary to use the sample standard deviation s as an estimate of σ. To ensure that s properly approximates σ, the sample size n should be at least 30.

For example, imagine that a biologist selects a random sample of 100 fish from a lake. The mean length of the fish in the sample is 11 cm, with a standard deviation of 2.5 cm. To determine a 95% confidence interval, the biologist substitutes 11 for $\bar{x}$, 2.5 for s, and 100 for n as shown below:

$$11 - 2\left(\frac{2.5}{\sqrt{100}}\right) \leq \mu \leq 11 + 2\left(\frac{2.5}{\sqrt{100}}\right)$$

$$10.5 \leq \mu \leq 11.5$$

The biologist can then declare with 95% confidence that the mean length of fish in the population is in the interval [10.5,11.5].

d. How would you modify the process described in Part **c** of the exploration to obtain a 68% confidence interval?

e. How often would you expect 68% confidence intervals to not contain the population mean? Explain your response.

f. How would you modify the sampling procedure to obtain a narrower 95% confidence interval? Explain your response.

g. Suppose that a researcher surveys a random sample of 100 high school graduates and calculates their mean annual income. What other information is necessary to give a reasonable estimate of how close the sample mean is to the population mean?

h. Using the results of the survey, the researcher creates a 99.7% confidence interval. Is the probability that this interval contains the population mean 99.7%?

Warm-Up

1. Each of Parts **a–e** below lists a sample mean, sample size, and sample standard deviation. Use this information to determine the corresponding 68%, 95%, and 99.7% confidence intervals.

   a. $\bar{x} = 15;\ n = 100;\ s = 2$

   b. $\bar{x} = -6;\ n = 75;\ s = 9$

   c. $\bar{x} = 3.23;\ n = 56;\ s = 1.56$

   d. $\bar{x} = 10/3;\ n = 81;\ s = 3/2$

   e. $\bar{x} = 2a;\ n = 36;\ s = a$

2. Identify each of the following statements as true or false. Justify your responses.

   a. Approximately 0.3% of the intervals defined by $[\bar{x} - 3\sigma_{\bar{x}}, \bar{x} + 3\sigma_{\bar{x}}]$ would not contain the population mean.

   b. Approximately 68% of the intervals defined by $[\bar{x} - 2\sigma_{\bar{x}}, \bar{x} + 2\sigma_{\bar{x}}]$ would contain the population mean.

   c. For specific values of $\bar{x}$, s, and n, there is a 95% probability that the interval below will contain the population mean.

$$\left[\bar{x} - 2\frac{s}{\sqrt{n}}, \bar{x} + 2\frac{s}{\sqrt{n}}\right]$$

   d. For sample sizes greater than 30, the sample mean will fall within 1 standard deviation of the population mean approximately 68% of the time.

   e. It is possible to identify the population mean by collecting all possible samples of size 5, then finding the mean of those sample means.

   f. A cellular phone manufacturer claims that the mean life of its cell-phone batteries is 18 hr, with a standard deviation of 1.5 hr. When you test your battery, it lasts 17 hr. Because 17 falls within 2 standard deviations of the mean, you can be 95% confident that the manufacturer's claim is true.

Assignment

4.1 **a.** Imagine that you have selected two random samples of the same size from the same population. Using the statistics from the two samples, you then determine two 95% confidence intervals for the population mean. Would you expect the two confidence intervals to be the same? Explain your response.

b. If you took 20 samples of the same size from the same population and determined 20 corresponding 95% confidence intervals, how many of them would you expect to contain the population mean? Explain your response.

4.2 **a.** For a given sample, would a 99.7% confidence interval be wider or narrower than a 95% confidence interval? Explain your response.

b. Write an algebraic representation of a 99.7% confidence interval given the sample mean ($\bar{x}$), sample standard deviation (s), and sample size (n).

4.3 A fish food manufacturer is developing a product to increase first-year growth in trout. After a year on this experimental diet, a random sample of 100 trout revealed a mean gain in mass of 84 g with a standard deviation of 14 g.

a. Use s to approximate the standard deviation of all possible sample means for $n = 100$.

b. Determine a 95% confidence interval for the mean gain in mass of trout fed the experimental diet.

c. Describe the meaning of the confidence interval in Part **b.**

d. How might the standard deviation of sample means be affected if the sample size were increased to 400 trout?

e. Why might a smaller value for the standard deviation of sample means help the company market its fish diet?

4.4 A car manufacturer claims that the fuel efficiency of its new model is 14 km/L. To verify this claim, the quality control engineers at a competing company selected a sample of 16 cars. Their tests yielded a mean of 13.5 km/L and a standard deviation of 1.6 km/L.

a. Create a 68% confidence interval for the fuel efficiency and determine if it contains the figure claimed by the manufacturer.

b. Create a 95% confidence interval for the fuel efficiency and determine if it contains the figure claimed by the manufacturer.

c. Do you believe the manufacturer's claim? Write a paragraph explaining how you reached your conclusion.

4.5 An advertising agency is investigating the number of hours that the residents of a particular city spend watching television each day. As part of their study, they surveyed a random sample of city households. The results of the survey are shown in the frequency table below.

Number of Hours Watching Television Per Day	Frequency
1	4
2	5
3	10
4	6
5	4
6	2
7	1
8	1

a. Construct a 95% confidence interval for the mean number of hours that city households spend watching television per day.

b. What does your response to Part **a** indicate about television viewing?

4.6 A 95% confidence interval for the mean life (in hours) of a particular brand of batteries is $410 \le \mu \le 450$.

a. Determine a 99.7% confidence interval for the mean life of these batteries.

b. What does your response to Part **a** indicate about battery life?

4.7 What factors should investigators consider when deciding whether to use a 68%, a 95%, or a 99.7% confidence interval?

* * * * *

4.8 Ken sampled 20 bags of a certain brand of candy. He discovered that the mean mass was 52 g, with a standard deviation of 4 g.

a. Write a conclusion about the mean mass of all bags of this candy.

b. Considering the sample size, how sure should you be of your conclusion in Part **a**?

c. How could you make the results of this experiment more conclusive?

4.9 To determine the mean life expectancy of their tennis shoes, the Brand 10 company surveyed a random sample of 32 people. The results of the survey are shown in the table below.

Life of Tennis Shoes (in months)							
35	39	6	41	23	61	45	18
16	3	13	8	21	13	15	27
27	40	26	18	22	23	6	40
25	42	17	41	38	29	13	12

Assuming that the life expectancies of these tennis shoes are normally distributed, write a conclusion about the mean life of Brand 10 shoes, using:

a. a 68% confidence level

b. a 95% confidence level

c. a 99.7% confidence level.

4.10 A random sample of 500 savings account balances at Third National Bank resulted in $\bar{x} = \$720$ and $s = \$217$.

a. Estimate the standard deviation $\sigma_{\bar{x}}$ of all sample means for this sample size.

b. Construct the interval $[\bar{x} - 2\sigma_{\bar{x}}, \bar{x} + 2\sigma_{\bar{x}}]$.

c. How confident are you that the population mean falls in the interval from Part **b**?

4.11 A soft-drink company is monitoring the performance of its bottling equipment. According to the label, each bottle should contain 340 mL of soda. A quality-control specialist selects a random sample of 100 bottles each day for 5 days and measures their volumes. The table below displays the values for $\bar{x}$ and s for each day.

Day	$\bar{x}$ (mL)	s (mL)
1	340.8	2.6
2	340.2	2.1
3	340.9	1.7
4	340.4	2.3
5	340.1	0.9

a. Using the data for day 1, construct a 95% confidence interval for the mean volume of soda per bottle.

b. Using the data for day 2, construct a 95% confidence interval for the mean volume of soda per bottle.

c. **1.** Compare the two confidence intervals from Parts **a** and **b.**

2. How many different 95% confidence intervals would you get if you calculated one for each day of available data?

d. Is there any guarantee that any of the 95% confidence intervals obtained from the data will contain the actual mean volume per bottle? Explain your response.

e. Do you think that the company's labels accurately describe the milliliters of soda in a bottle? Write a paragraph to explain your conclusion.

Research Project

Select a population and choose one of its characteristics to study. For example, if you select the students at your school as a population, you might wish to examine the mean number of hours spent studying per week.

Develop a sampling method that will allow you to determine a reasonably good estimate of the mean of this characteristic. After conducting your study, write a report that includes the following:

- descriptions of the population you surveyed, the characteristic you examined, and your sampling method
- the data you collected and the statistics your data generated, including a confidence interval
- a statement summarizing the conclusions you drew from your analysis
- any suggestions or recommendations that you believe your study supports.

Summary Assessment

Imagine that you are a journalist for the local newspaper. Your editor has requested that you write an article that uses statistics to describe one characteristic of a population. Your article must include two parts.

The first part of your article should describe the population, the characteristic you measured, and the sampling method used. It also should include the sample data that you obtained.

To write this portion of your article, complete the following steps.

- Create a hypothetical population with some measurable characteristic.
- Design a method to sample this population.
- Create a simulation that models both your population and your sampling method.
- Use your simulation to generate some sample data.

The second part of your article should report on the results of your study. Include an estimate of the mean value of the characteristic for the population, and support your estimate with a discussion of confidence intervals and the normal distribution of sample means. To illustrate the mathematics involved in your analysis, you also should include the values for $\bar{x}$ and $\sigma_{\bar{x}}$ generated from your data, and a 95% confidence interval for μ.

Your article should conclude with any recommendations or suggestions that you feel your study supports.

Module Summary

- A **parameter** is a numerical characteristic of a population.
- A **statistic** is a numerical characteristic of a sample.
- A **simple random sample** is selected so that each member of the population has the same chance of being included in the sample.
- The mean value for a population, or **population mean,** is a parameter denoted by the Greek letter μ (mu).
- The **population standard deviation** is a parameter denoted by the Greek letter σ (sigma). It can be calculated using the following formula:

$$\sigma = \sqrt{\frac{(x_1 - \mu)^2 + (x_2 - \mu)^2 + \cdots + (x_N - \mu)^2}{N}}$$

where the population has N members represented by $x_1, x_2, \ldots, x_n$.

- The mean value for a sample, or **sample mean,** is a statistic denoted by $\bar{x}$ (read "x-bar").
- The **sample standard deviation,** a statistic denoted by s, can be calculated as follows:

$$s = \sqrt{\frac{(x_1 - \bar{x})^2 + (x_2 - \bar{x})^2 + \cdots + (x_n - \bar{x})^2}{n - 1}}$$

where the sample has data from n members of a population represented by $x_1, x_2, \ldots, x_n$.

- The **sampling distribution of sample means** contains the means ($\bar{x}$) of *all* possible samples of size n from a population. Two important facts about this distribution are used to make estimates about population parameters.
    1. The mean of the sampling distribution of sample means, denoted by $\mu_{\bar{x}}$, equals the population mean μ.
    2. The standard deviation of the sampling distribution of sample means, denoted by $\sigma_{\bar{x}}$, equals $\sigma/\sqrt{n}$, where σ is the population standard deviation and n is the sample size. When σ is unknown, the standard deviation of the sample (s) may be used as an estimate of σ.
- The **law of large numbers** states that the mean of a large number n of independent measurements of a random quantity tends, as n increases, toward the theoretical mean of that quantity.

  This law guarantees that for very large sample sizes, there is a high probability that the sample mean is close to the population mean.

* A **normal distribution** is a continuous probability distribution. The graph of a normal distribution is symmetric about the mean and tapers to the left and right like a bell. The curve that describes the shape of the graph is the **normal curve.** As in all continuous probability distributions, the total area between the x-axis and a normal curve is 1.

* Although all normal curves have the same general shape, the width of any particular curve depends on the standard deviation (σ) of the distribution that the curve models. Because the population mean (μ) is located at the point where the curve's axis of symmetry intersects the x-axis, the position of the curve along the x-axis depends on the value of μ.

* The **central limit theorem** states that, even if the population from which samples are taken is not normally distributed, the distribution of the means of all possible samples of the same size will be approximately normal.

  This approximation becomes more accurate as the sample size n increases. For $n \geq 30$, the distribution of sample means can be modeled reasonably well by a normal curve. This requirement is not necessary if the population from which samples are taken is normally distributed.

* The **68–95–99.7 rule** states that approximately 68% of the total area between the normal curve and the x-axis lies within 1 standard deviation of the mean, 95% lies within 2 standard deviations of the mean, and 99.7% lies within 3 standard deviations of the mean.

* A **confidence interval** for a parameter is an interval of numbers in which one would expect to find the value of that parameter. Every confidence interval has two aspects: an interval determined by the statistics collected from a random sample and a confidence level describing what percentage of the intervals created by that process would contain the parameter.

* A 95% confidence interval is generated by a process in which the parameter would fall in those intervals 95% of the time. In other words, you would expect 95% of the intervals produced by this process to contain the parameter, while 5% of the intervals would not.

Functioning on a Path

Introduction

In a mathematics video game called Gates, there are three different levels of play. In the first level, the object of the game is to determine the characteristics of a **continuous** function that passes through several "gates," represented by a pair of squares on the screen. For example, Figure **4-1** shows a first-level screen with a second-degree polynomial (or quadratic) function passing through five gates.

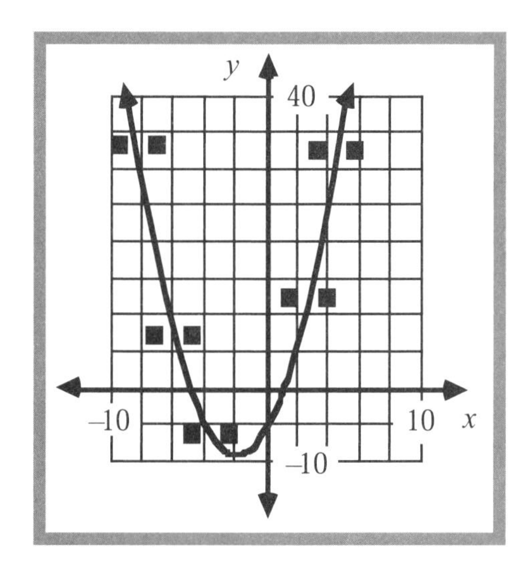

FIGURE 4-1 Quadratic function passing through gates.

mathematics note

A function is **continuous** at a point c in its domain if the following conditions are met:

- the function is defined at c, or $f(c)$ exists
- the limit of the function exists at c, or $\lim_{x \to c} f(x)$ exists
- the two values listed above are equal, or $f(c) = \lim_{x \to c} f(x)$

A function is continuous over its domain if it is continuous at each point in its domain.

A function is **discontinuous** at a point if it does not meet all the conditions for continuity at that point.

For example, a function is discontinuous at $x = c$ if the function is undefined at c, as shown in Figure **4-2.**

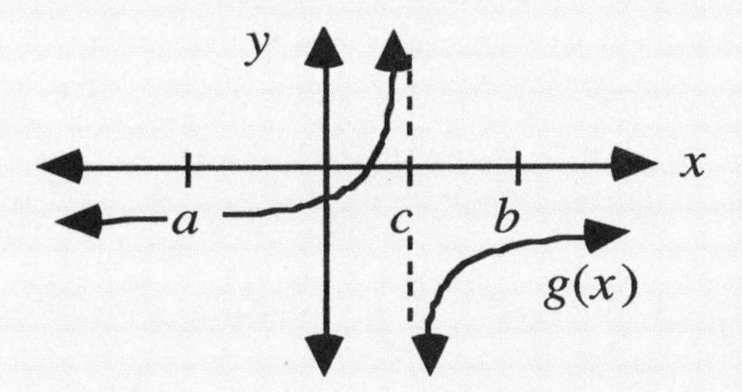

FIGURE 4-2 **Graph of the discontinuous function *g*(*x*).**

A function is also discontinuous at $x = c$ if the limit of the function does not exist at c, as shown in Figure **4-3.**

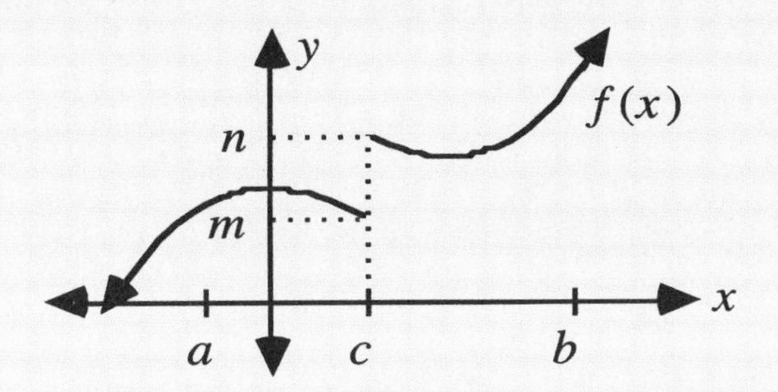

FIGURE 4-3 **Jump discontinuity in the function *f*(*x*).**

In this case, $f(x)$ approaches m as x approaches c from the left. As x approaches c from the right, $f(x)$ approaches n. Because $m \neq n$, the limit of $f(x)$ as x approaches c does not exist. This kind of discontinuity is referred to as a **jump discontinuity.**

A function is also discontinuous at $x = c$ if the value of the function at c does not equal the limit of the function as x approaches c, as shown in Figure **4-4.** In this case, the limit of $h(x)$ as x approaches c is m, while $h(c) = n$, and $m \neq n$.

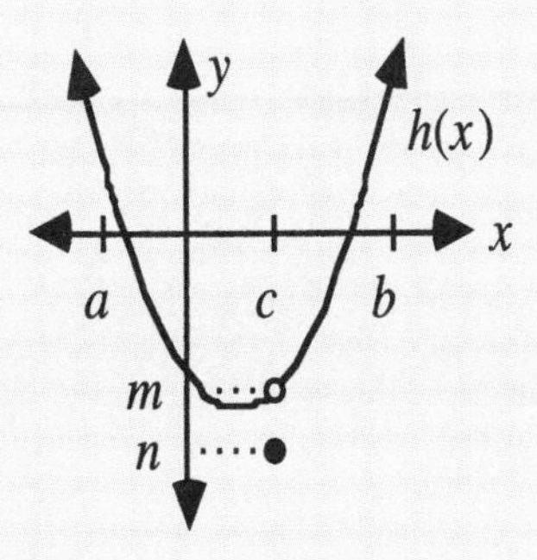

FIGURE 4-4 **Hole in the graph of the function *h*(*x*).**

Discussion

a. In the first level of Gates, players may use **polynomial functions.** Recall that a polynomial function can be written in the following general form:

$$f(x) = a_n x^n + a_{n-1}x^{n-1} + \cdots + a_1 x^1 + a_0$$

where $a_n, a_{n-1}, a_{n-2}, \ldots, a_0$ are real numbers and n is a non-negative integer.

Are the functions below polynomial functions? Explain your responses.

1. $f(x) = x^2 + \sqrt{3} \bullet x - 5$
2. $f(x) = x^2 + \dfrac{4}{x} - 5$

b. The **degree** of a polynomial is equal to the greatest exponent of the variable in the expression. The coefficient of that variable is the **leading coefficient.** For a polynomial written in the general form in Part **a,** the degree is n and the leading coefficient is a_n.

Identify the degree and leading coefficient of the polynomial below.

$$x^2 + 5x^4 - 5x^5$$

c. Do you think that all polynomial functions are continuous? Explain your response.

d. The graph in Figure **4-1** is a second-degree polynomial function. It is only one of many polynomial functions that could be drawn through the desired gates. Describe how you could use polynomial regressions to determine three other continuous functions that pass through these gates.

Figure **4-1** showed a screen from the first level of a game in which players must identify a polynomial function that passes through gates. One way to determine such an equation involves the relationship among the degree of a polynomial, its roots (or zeros), and the characteristics of its graph.

Exploration 1

A completed screen from a game of Gates is shown in Figure **4-5.** The degree of the polynomial function that produced this path can be predicted from the characteristics of the graph. In this exploration, you examine polynomial functions of several different degrees and attempt to identify the characteristics of their graphs.

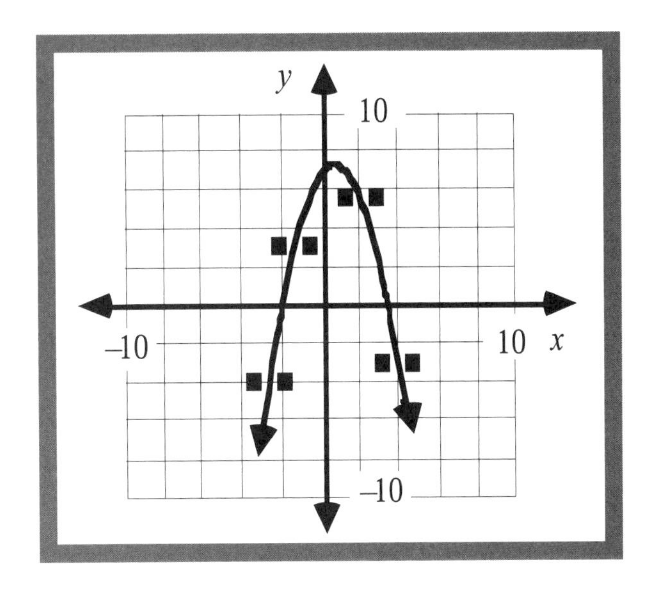

Figure 4-5 Screen in first level of Gates.

a. Make a conjecture about the least possible degree of a polynomial function that could pass through the gates in Figure **4-5.**

b. Choose the coordinates of any three noncollinear points on a two-dimensional coordinate system.

c. Use a quadratic regression to determine an equation for a polynomial function passing through those three points.

d. A quadratic function can be written in the following general form:

$$q(x) = a_2x^2 + a_1x + a_0$$

   1. Use the coordinates of the three points in Part **b** to write a system of equations involving a_2, a_1, and a_0.
   2. Use technology to solve the system for a_2, a_1, and a_0.
   3. Use the solutions to write a quadratic equation whose graph contains the original three points.

e. On the same coordinate system, plot the points selected in Part **b** and the function found in Part **d.**

Discussion 1

a. 1. If a quadratic function models the graph in Figure **4-5,** what do you know about its leading coefficient? Why?

   2. If any polynomial function with an even degree models the graph in Figure **4-5,** what do you know about its leading coefficient?

b. 1. Why should you expect the functions found in Parts **c** and **d** of Exploration **1** to be equal?

2. Why might the actual equations be slightly different?

c. Considering the class results to Part **d,** do you think that any three noncollinear points can be contained in the graph of a quadratic polynomial?

Exploration 2

a. Sketch the graph of a quadratic function whose leading coefficient is positive.

b. Use your sketch to predict the maximum number of times that a function of this degree can intersect the x-axis.

mathematics note

The **end behavior** of the graph of a polynomial function describes the characteristics of the graph as $|x|$ increases without bound.

For example, Figure **4-6** shows the graph of a fourth-degree polynomial function. As $|x|$ increases without bound, $f(x)$ also **increases** without bound.

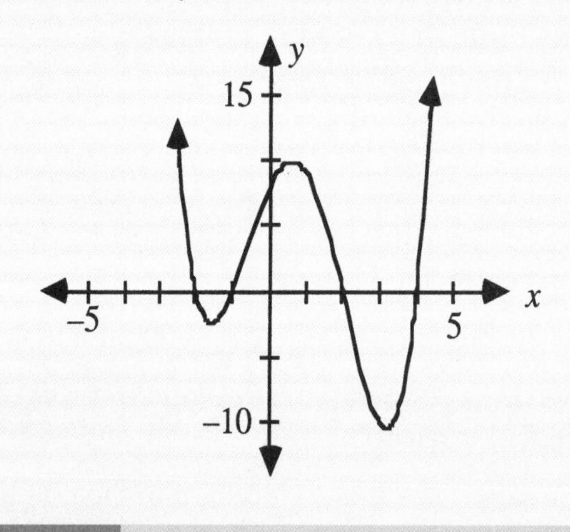

Figure 4-6 Graph of $f(x) = 0.5x^4 - 1.5x^3 - 4x^2 + 6x + 8$.

c. Describe the end behavior of the graph that you sketched in Part **a.**

d. Sketch graphs of quadratics that intersect the x-axis in 0, 1, . . . , n times, where n is the number you identified in Part **b.**

e. Using a graphing utility, repeat Parts **a–d** for each of the following:

1. a third-degree polynomial function with four different coefficients and a positive leading coefficient
2. a fourth-degree polynomial function with five different coefficients and a positive leading coefficient.

Discussion 2

a. Recall from the Level 3 module "Can It," that the **absolute maximum** of a function is the greatest value of the range, and the **absolute minimum** is the least value of the range.

1. Of the functions that you graphed in Exploration **2,** which ones had an absolute maximum?
2. Which functions had an absolute minimum?

b. If the leading coefficients of the equations in Exploration **2** had been negative, how would this have affected the absolute maximums or minimums of the functions identified in Part **a**?

c. 1. Describe a function that has both an absolute maximum and an absolute minimum.

2. Describe some functions that have neither an absolute maximum nor an absolute minimum.

d. The x-coordinate of each point where the graph of a polynomial intersects the x-axis is a **zero** or a **root** of the polynomial. What do you think is the maximum number of zeros a polynomial of degree n can have? Explain your response.

e. Consider a function $f(x)$. What is the value of $f(x)$ when x is a root of the function?

f. Given the graph of a polynomial function with three zeros, what do you think is the least possible degree for the polynomial?

g. Recall that a polynomial function also can be written as follows, where each expression of the form $(x - a_i)$ represents a factor of the polynomial:

$$f(x) = (x - a_n)(x - a_{n-1})(x - a_{n-2}) \cdots (x - a_0)$$

Consider a polynomial function with zeros of –6, 8, and 2. Write an equation for this function using the least possible degree.

h. How could you determine a polynomial of higher degree than the one in Part **g** that has exactly the same zeros?

Warm-Up

1. Write an equation of a polynomial function with the least possible degree whose graph contains each of the following sets of points.

   a. $(-8,-7)$ and $(5,10)$

   b. $(0,0)$, $(-1,1)$, and $(-8,64)$

2. **a.** Sketch the graph of a second-degree polynomial function with an absolute maximum of 7 when $x = 2$.

   b. Do you think every quadratic function has either an absolute maximum or minimum? Explain your response.

   c. What can you tell about a quadratic function if its graph has an absolute maximum? an absolute minimum?

3. **a.** Sketch the graph of a polynomial of degree greater than 2 that has an absolute maximum.

   b. Do you think that any polynomial of degree 3 has an absolute maximum or an absolute minimum? Explain your response.

Assignment

1.1 Consider a function that has exactly one zero. Identify the polynomial of least degree that could describe such a function. Justify your response with a graph and with a general equation for the polynomial.

1.2 **a.** Figure **4-6** shows a graph of $f(x) = 0.5x^4 - 1.5x^3 - 4x^2 + 6x + 8$. Do you think this function has an absolute maximum or an absolute minimum? Explain your response.

b. The "peaks" and "valleys" of the graph in Figure **4-6** might be used to identify "relative maximums" and "relative minimums." How would you define these terms?

1.3 Consider the polynomial $f(x) = 3(x - 2)^2 (x + 4)(x - \pi)$.

a. Describe how to determine the zeros of this function.

b. Identify the degree of this polynomial.

c. Determine whether the polynomial has an absolute minimum or absolute maximum.

d. Describe the end behavior of the polynomial.

1.4 **a.** Identify the general form of a polynomial function that has the least possible odd degree.

b. Describe the end behavior of this type of polynomial.

c. What do you think is true about the end behavior of any polynomial function with an odd degree? Explain your response.

1.5 Parts **a** and **b** below show two screens in the first level of Gates. Explain whether you think the degree of each polynomial shown is odd or even. Describe the characteristics that support your choice.

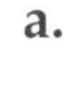

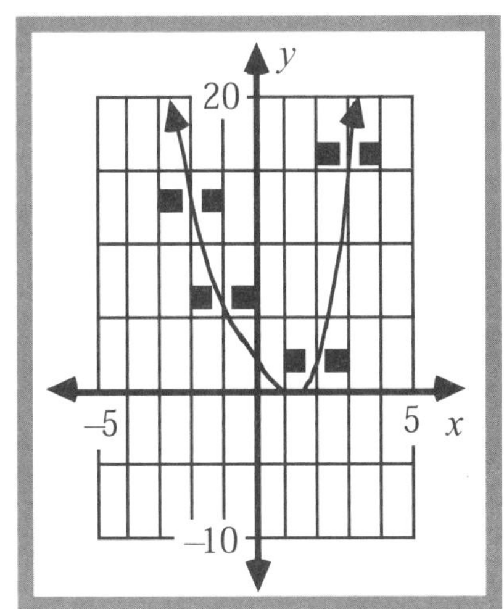

b.

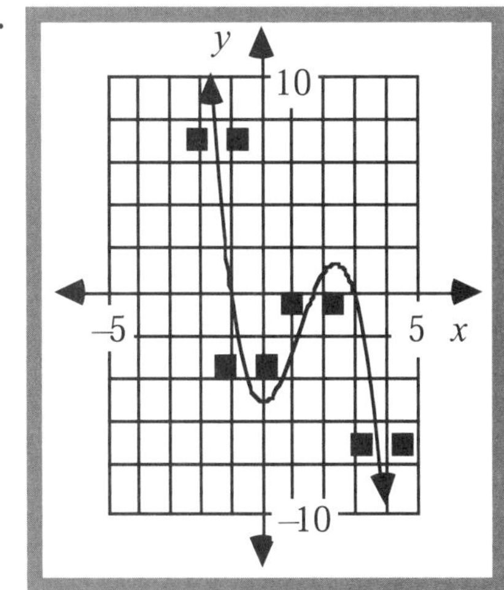

* * * * *

1.6 Given the second-degree polynomial $f(x) = x^2 + 5x + 6$, describe how you could find the exact values of its zeros.

1.7 The data in the following table was collected during the flight of a model rocket. The values for time represent the number of seconds after the engine burned out. The values for distance represent height in meters. Find an equation that closely models this data and describe how you identified your model.

Time (sec)	Distance (m)
2	90.4
3	85.9
4	71.6
5	47.5
6	13.6

ACTIVITY 2

In the second level of Gates, players use **piecewise functions** to describe graphs. Like any function, a piecewise function has a domain, a range, and a rule relating the two. In a piecewise function, however, different parts of the domain correspond with different rules.

For example, consider the absolute-value function, $f(x) = |x|$. In this function, the rule $f(x) = -x$ applies to the domain interval $(-\infty, 0)$, while the rule $f(x) = x$ applies to the domain interval $[0, \infty)$. This can be written as shown below:

$$f(x) = \begin{cases} -x \text{ if } x \in (-\infty, 0) \\ x \text{ if } x \in [0, \infty) \end{cases}$$

Exploration

In this exploration, you examine the use of piecewise functions to create successful functions for the game of Gates. For example, the screen in Figure **4-7** shows a piecewise function that passes through five gates.

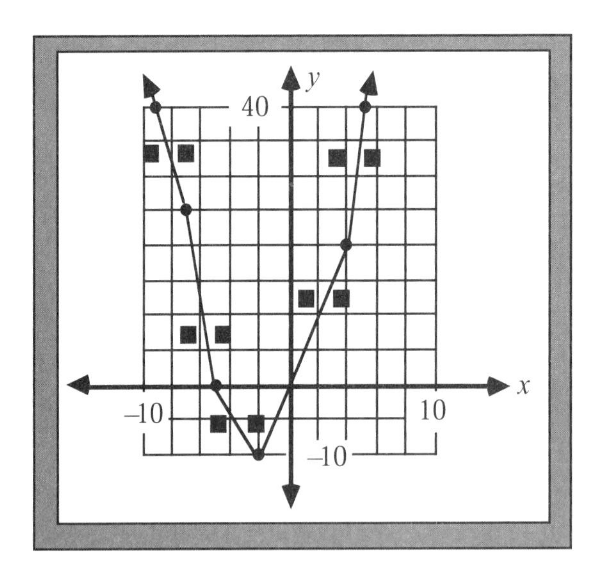

FIGURE 4-7 **Screen with piecewise function.**

The graph of this function consists of two rays and three segments. The ray in the upper left-hand portion of the screen has its endpoint at (–7,25) and contains the point (–9,40). The ray in the upper right-hand portion of the screen has its endpoint at (4,20) and contains the point (5,40).

The three segments have the following pairs of endpoints: (–7,25) and (–5,0); (–5,0) and (–2,–10); and (–2,–10) and (4,20).

a. The equation of a ray or a segment can be found by determining the equation of the line that contains it and restricting the domain to an appropriate interval.

   1. Write an equation for the ray that has its endpoint at (–7,25) and contains the point (–9,40). State the domain of the equation.

   2. Write an equation for the segment with endpoints at (–7,25) and (–5,0). State the domain of the equation.

   3. Write an equation for the segment with endpoints at (–5,0) and (–2,–10). State the domain of the equation.

   4. Write an equation for the segment with endpoints at (–2,–10) and (4,20). State the domain of the equation.

   5. Write an equation for the ray that has its endpoint at (4,20) and contains the point (5,40). State the domain of the equation.

b. Use the equations from Part **a** to write a piecewise function whose graph is the one shown in Figure **4-7.**

c. Use technology to graph the function defined in Part **b.**

Discussion

a. Describe how you used technology to graph the piecewise function in Part **c** of the exploration.

b. Because the endpoints of each segment in the graph are used twice (once in each consecutive part), the x-values of these points also are used twice. Considering this fact, why is this graph a function?

c. How could you show algebraically that two consecutive parts of a piecewise function contain a common point?

d. Explain why the function you wrote in Part **b** of the exploration is continuous.

e. Consider the following:

$$f(x) = \begin{cases} 1/x \text{ if } x \in (-\infty, 0) \cup (0, +\infty) \\ 0 \text{ if } x = 0 \end{cases}$$

   1. Is f a function? Explain your response.

   2. Is f a piecewise function? Explain your response.

   3. Is f continuous at 0? Explain your response.

f. Consider the piecewise relation below:

$$y = \begin{cases} x^2 \text{ if } x \geq 0 \\ 2x \text{ if } x = 0 \\ x - 5 \text{ if } x \leq 0 \end{cases}$$

Is this relation a function? Explain your response.

Warm-Up

1. The graphs of the functions $f(x) = x^2$ and $g(x) = 2x$ are shown below. Determine the coordinates of the intersections of these two functions.

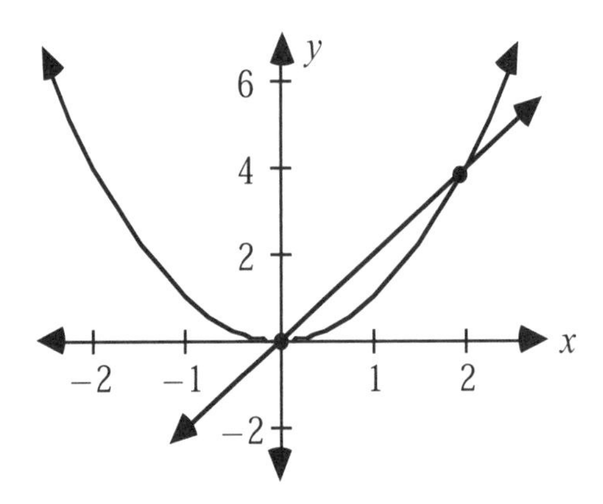

2. Each graph below shows a piecewise function that uses the rules for $f(x) = x^2$ and $g(x) = 2x$ over parts of its domain. Write a continuous piecewise function to describe each graph.

a.

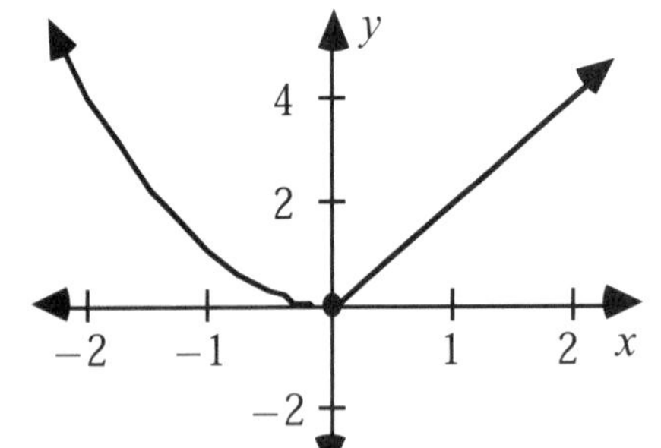

b.

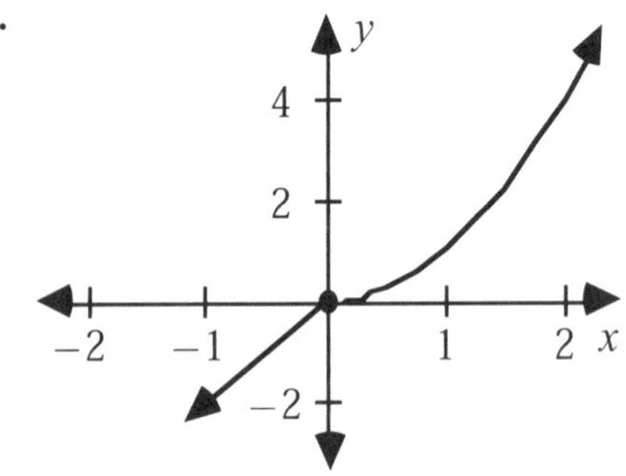

c.

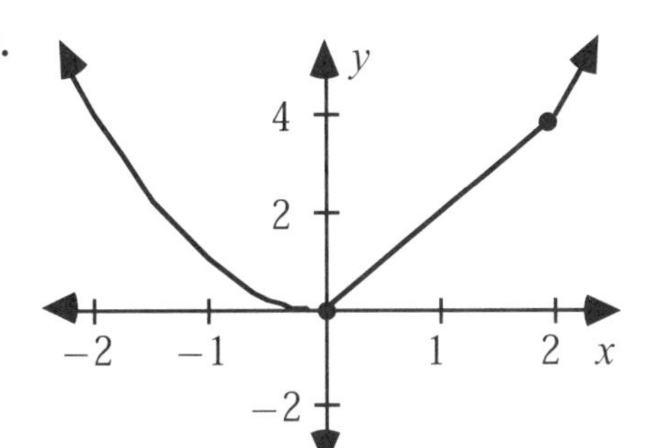

d.

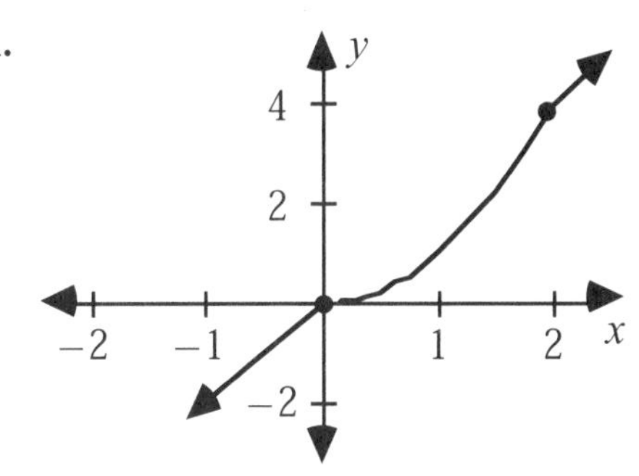

Assignment

2.1 For each screen shown in Parts **a–c** below, determine a continuous piecewise function that passes through all the gates.

a.

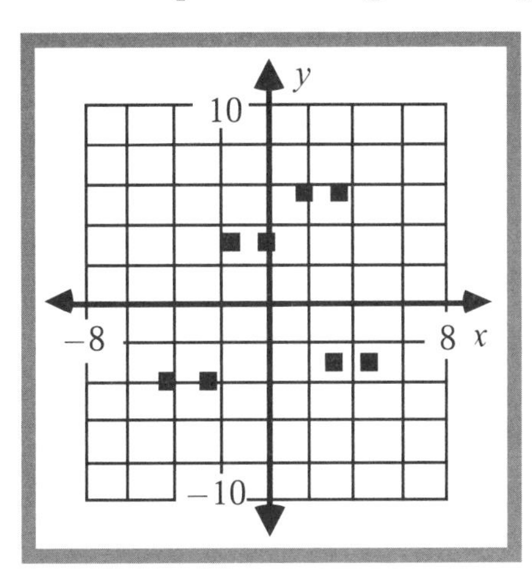

b.

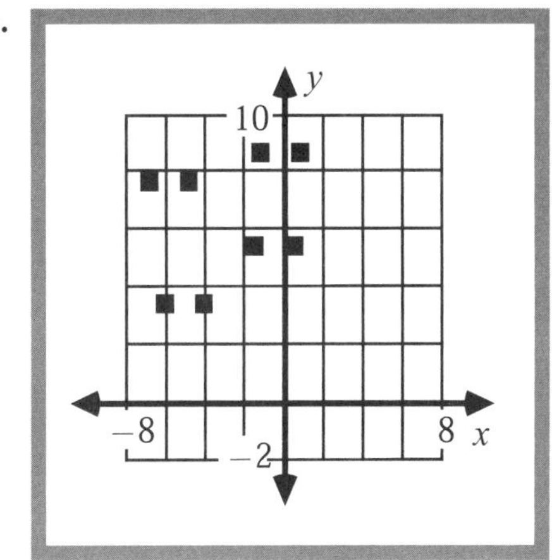

c.

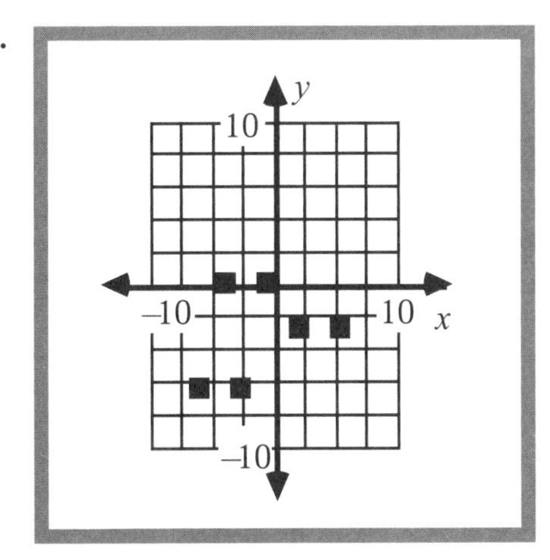

2.2 The greatest integer function, $f(x) = [x]$, pairs every element x in the domain with the greatest integer less than or equal to x. Explain why this function can be considered a piecewise function.

2.3 The graph below models the border to a flowerbed. Each piece of the border is made of a semicircular slab of concrete. Describe this curve using a piecewise function.

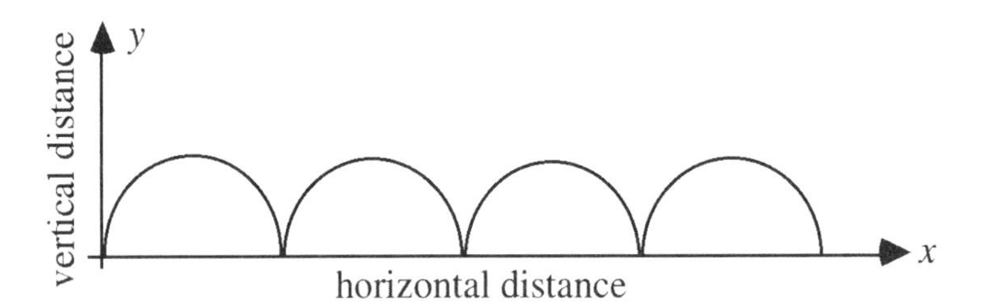

2.4 Use piecewise functions to describe a graph that passes through the gates in the following screen.

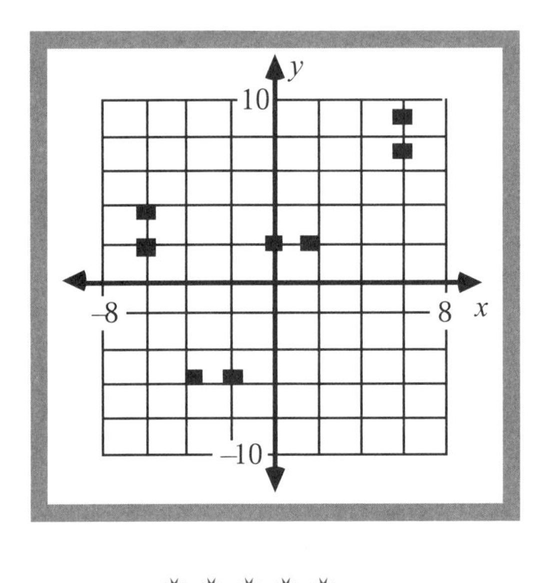

* * * * *

2.5 Recall that the height of a freely falling object can be described by the following function:

$$h(t) = -\frac{1}{2}gt^2 + v_0t + h_0$$

where g represents the acceleration due to gravity (9.8 m/sec^2), t is time in sec, v_0 is the object's initial velocity, and h_0 is its initial height.

a. Consider a ball dropped from a height of 1 m. On each successive bounce, it rises to two-thirds the height of the previous bounce. Describe the graph that you think would model the first three bounces of the ball. Justify your response.

b. The ball hits the ground at approximately 0.45 sec, 1.19 sec, 1.79 sec, and 2.29 sec. Determine a piecewise function that models the first three bounces of the ball.

c. Create a graph of your piecewise function.

In the previous activities, you investigated some characteristics of polynomial functions and piecewise functions while playing the first two levels of Gates. In this activity, you examine the graphs of yet another type of function. Your discoveries should help you develop a strategy for the next level of Gates.

Exploration 1

Figure **4-8** shows a screen from the third level of Gates. The line represents the graph of the polynomial function below:

$$f(x) = \frac{1}{3}x + 5$$

Your challenge is to alter the function so that its graph passes through all four gates.

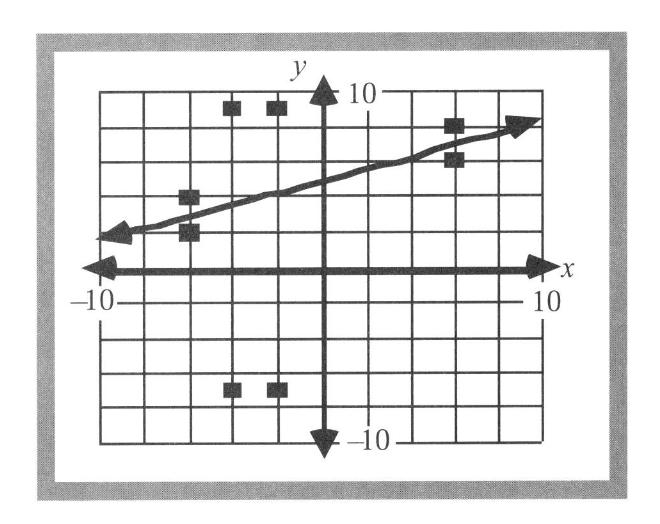

FIGURE 4-8 Screen in the third level of Gates.

One way to accomplish this task involves **rational functions.** In this exploration, you examine how the graph of a linear function is affected by the addition of a rational expression.

Recall from the Level 3 module "Big Business" that a **rational function** can be written in the following general form:

$$r(x) = \frac{f(x)}{g(x)}$$

where $f(x)$ and $g(x)$ are polynomial functions and $g(x) \neq 0$.

a. Any rational function also can be expressed in the form below, where $q(x)$ and $h(x)$ are polynomial functions such that $q(x)$ is the quotient and $h(x)$ is the remainder when $f(x)$ is divided by $g(x)$:

$$r(x) = q(x) + \frac{h(x)}{g(x)}$$

1. Choose a polynomial function $q(x)$ of degree 1.
2. Choose a polynomial function $g(x)$ of degree 1.

b. 1. Create a rational function $r(x)$ by adding the expression $1/g(x)$ to $q(x)$ as follows:

$$r(x) = q(x) + \frac{1}{g(x)}$$

2. Determine the domain of $r(x)$.
3. Recall that a discontinuity occurs in a rational function at any point where the value of the function is undefined. Predict the behavior of the graph of $r(x)$ near its point of discontinuity.

mathematics note

An **asymptote** to a curve is a line such that the distance from a point P on the curve to the line approaches zero as the distance from P to the origin increases without bound, where P is on a suitable part of the curve.

For example, Figure **4-9** shows a graph of the function $f(x) = \log x$. In this case, the suitable part of the curve lies below the x-axis. As a point P moves farther away from the origin on this part of the curve, the distance between P and the y-axis approaches 0. Therefore, the line $x = 0$ is an asymptote for the curve.

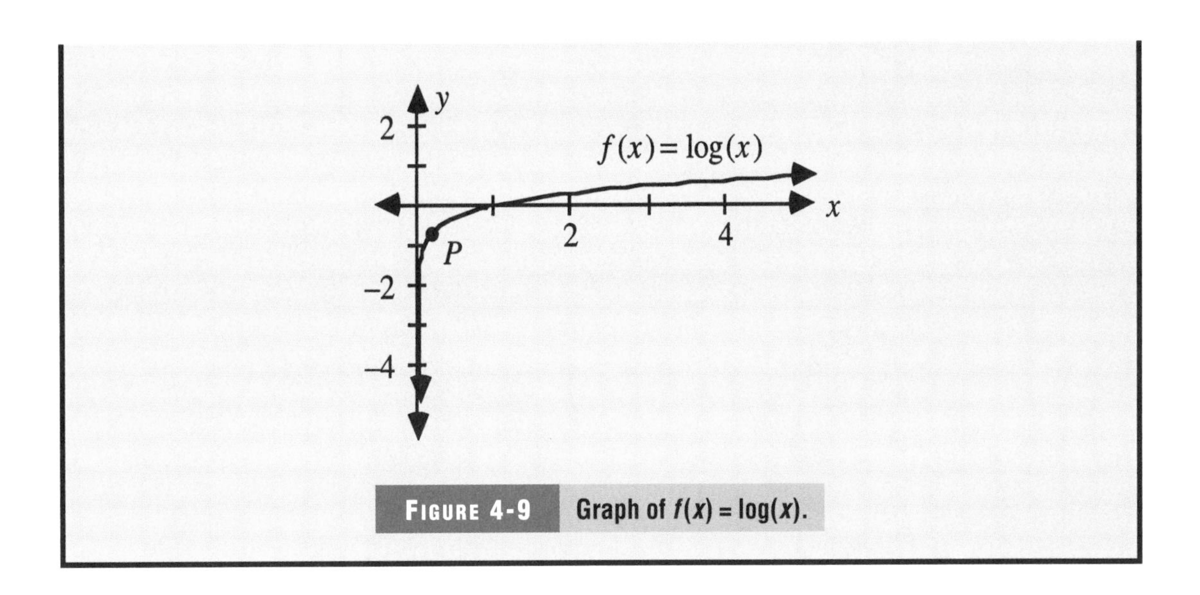

FIGURE 4-9 Graph of $f(x) = \log(x)$.

c. Graph $r(x)$ and $q(x)$ on the same coordinate system. Use an interval of the domain that includes the point where the graph is discontinuous.

d. Determine what happens to the values of the functions $q(x)$, $r(x)$, and $1/g(x)$ as each of the following occurs:

   1. x approaches the point of discontinuity
   2. $|x|$ increases without bound.

e. Select a new function $q(x)$ with degree 2 and a new function $g(x)$ with degree 1. Repeat Parts **b–d.**

f. Select a new function $q(x)$ with degree 3 and a new function $g(x)$ with degree 1. Repeat Parts **b–d.**

Discussion 1

a. Describe the graphs of $r(x)$ and $q(x)$ as x approaches the point of discontinuity. Why does this behavior occur?

b. How does the addition of the rational expression $1/g(x)$ affect the graph of a polynomial function $q(x)$?

c. Describe a rational function that has more than one vertical asymptote.

d. Suppose that, in Part **b** of Exploration **1,** you had added the additive inverse of $1/g(x)$ to $q(x)$. How would this have affected the graph of the resulting function $r(x)$?

e. What rational expression could you add to the following polynomial function to create a path that passes through all four gates in Figure **4-8**?

$$f(x) = \frac{1}{3}x + 5$$

f. Consider the rational function

$$r(x) = f(x) + \frac{1}{g(x)}$$

1. Describe the graph of $r(x)$ when $g(x)$ is a linear function.
2. How does the end behavior of $r(x)$ compare to that of $f(x)$?

g. Consider a rational function written in the following general form, where $q(x)$, $h(x)$, and $g(x)$ are all polynomial functions and $g(x) \neq 0$:

$$r(x) = q(x) + \frac{h(x)}{g(x)}$$

Describe how you could rewrite this function in the form below:

$$r(x) = \frac{f(x)}{g(x)}$$

Exploration 2

Figure **4-10** shows another screen in the third level of Gates. To complete this screen, you must alter the function $f(x) = 2$ so that its graph passes through all three gates without running into the brick wall.

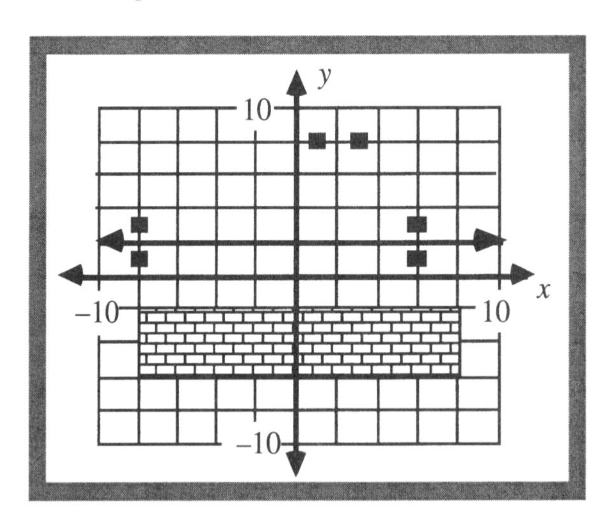

FIGURE 4-10 Screen in third level of Gates.

As you discovered in Exploration **1**, a rational function of the form below has the same end behavior as $f(x)$, when $g(x)$ is a first-degree polynomial.

$$r(x) = f(x) + \frac{1}{g(x)}$$

In this exploration, you experiment with other degrees for the denominator of the added rational expression.

a. Select a first-degree polynomial $k(x)$ and a constant function $h(x)$. Graph each of the following pairs of functions on a different set of axes. Note any similarities or differences between the two graphs, including their end behaviors.

1. $f(x) = h(x) + \dfrac{1}{k(x)}$ and $g(x) = h(x) + \dfrac{1}{(k(x))^2}$

2. $f(x) = h(x) + \dfrac{1}{(k(x))^3}$ and $g(x) = h(x) + \dfrac{1}{(k(x))^4}$

b. 1. Compare the graphs of the two functions below for a positive value of n, where n is an integer other than 1.

$$f(x) = h(x) + \frac{1}{(k(x))^2} \text{ and } g(x) = h(x) + \frac{n}{(k(x))^2}$$

2. Repeat Step **1** for several different positive values of n.

3. Repeat Step **1** for several different negative values of n.

Discussion 2

a. What similarities or differences did you observe in the graphs of the two functions below?

$$f(x) = h(x) + \frac{1}{k(x)} \text{ and } g(x) = h(x) + \frac{1}{(k(x))^2}$$

b. 1. How did the graphs of the following two functions compare when n was a positive integer?

$$f(x) = h(x) + \frac{1}{(k(x))^2} \text{ and } g(x) = h(x) + \frac{n}{(k(x))^2}$$

2. How did the graphs compare when n was a negative integer?

c. Consider the following two rational functions:

$$f(x) = 3 + \frac{1}{(x+6)^2} \text{ and } g(x) = 3 + \frac{-1}{(x+6)^2}$$

1. As $|x|$ increases without bound, the values of both $f(x)$ and $g(x)$ approach 3. Explain why this occurs.

2. As x approaches -6, however, $f(x)$ approaches $+\infty$ while $g(x)$ approaches $-\infty$. Explain why this occurs.

d. Consider a function of the form below, where c is a constant and d is a positive integer:

$$f(x) = h(x) + \frac{c}{(k(x))^d}$$

1. Describe how raising the denominator of the added rational expression from an odd power to an even power affects the graph of the resulting function.
2. Describe how changing the numerator of the added rational expression affects the graph of the resulting function.

e. 1. What rational expression could you add to $f(x) = 2$ to create a graph that passes through all the gates in Figure **4-10** but misses the brick wall?

2. Are there other rational expressions that would accomplish this task? Explain your response.

f. Consider a rational function written in the form below, where $g(x) \neq 0$:

$$r(x) = \frac{f(x)}{g(x)}$$

Describe how you could express this function in the following form, where $q(x)$ is a polynomial function and the degree of $h(x)$ is less than or equal to the degree of $g(x)$:

$$r(x) = q(x) + \frac{h(x)}{g(x)}$$

Warm-Up

1. Write each of the following rational functions as a polynomial expression plus a rational expression. Describe where asymptotic behavior might occur in the graph of each function.

   a. $h(x) = \dfrac{3x^2 + 29x - 39}{x + 11}$

   b. $g(x) = \dfrac{-16x^3 + 40x^2 - 8x + 18}{2x - 5}$

   c. $q(x) = \dfrac{x^5 - 7x^4 - x^3 + 4x^2 + 25x - 31}{x - 7}$

2. Rational functions generally are written as the quotient of two polynomials. In this activity, however, you wrote rational functions in a form that makes it easier to determine the locations of any vertical asymptotes. Use a symbolic manipulator to convert each of the following functions to the form $r(x) = f(x)/q(x)$. Test your answers by graphing both forms of each equation on the same coordinate system.

   a. $h(x) = 5x^2 + x - 10 + \dfrac{3}{x-7}$

   b. $g(x) = -11x + 4 + \dfrac{-11}{3x+2}$

   c. $q(x) = x^3 + x^2 + \dfrac{3}{x+1}$

Assignment

3.1 The figure below shows a screen in the third level of Gates. Add a rational expression to $f(x) = -2$ so that the graph of the resulting function passes through all four gates. Identify the domain and range of your function.

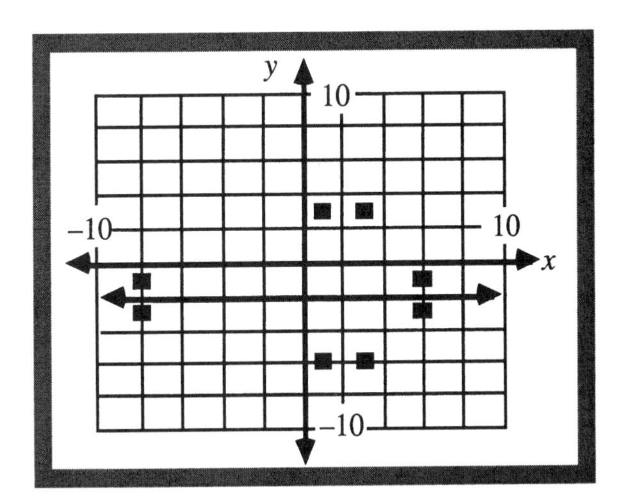

3.2 The following screen in the third level of Gates includes three gates and a brick wall. The curve shown on the screen represents a graph of the function

$$f(x) = \frac{1}{2}x^2 - 3x - \frac{7}{2}$$

Add a rational expression to $f(x)$ so that the graph of the resulting function passes through all three gates while avoiding the brick wall. Identify the domain and range of your function.

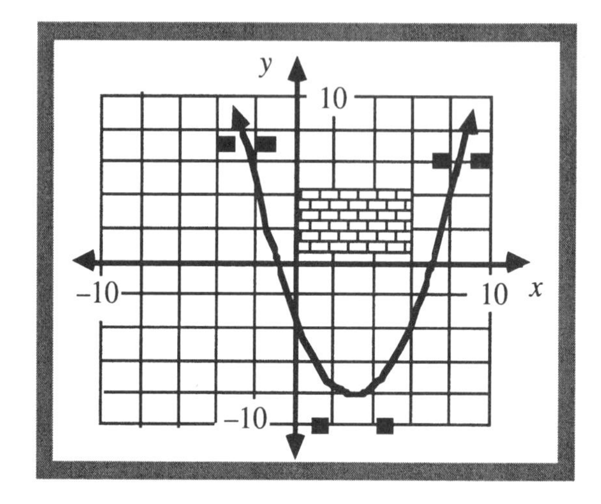

3.3 The figure below shows another screen in the third level of Gates. Determine a rational function that passes through all five gates without touching the brick walls.

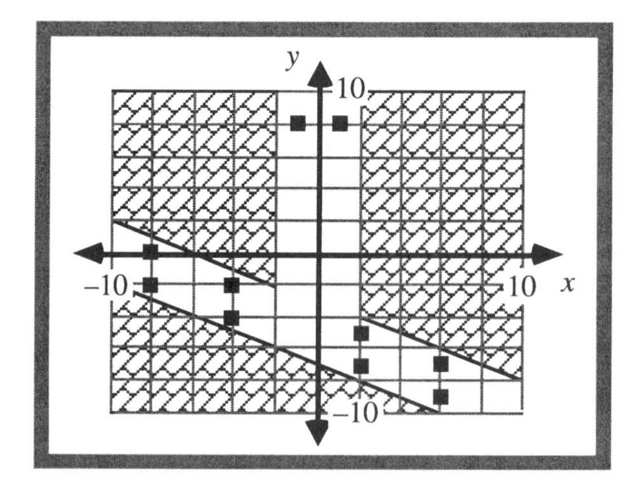

3.4 **a.** Create a rational function that passes through all the gates shown on the screen below.

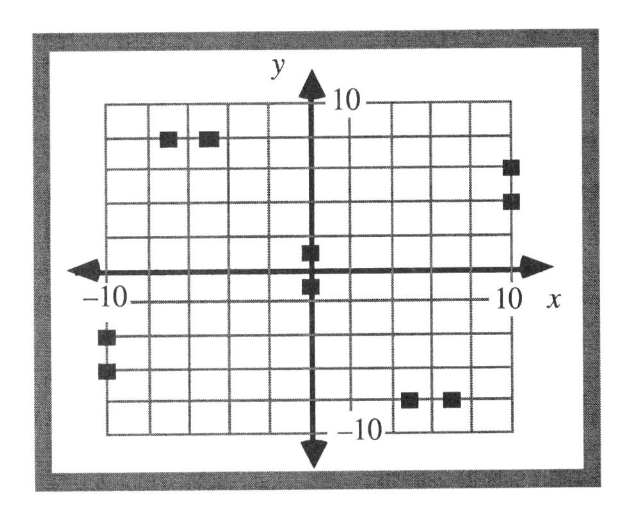

b. Create a continuous piecewise function that passes through all the gates shown on the screen in Part **a.**

c. Compare the domains and ranges of the two functions created in Parts **a** and **b.**

3.5 A screen in the third level of Gates has six gates and a brick wall. The locations of the gates are defined by the following pairs of points: (–7,–1) and (–5,–1); (–5,0) and (–3,0); (–3,1) and (–1,1); (1,–2) and (3,–2); (5,5) and (7,5); (7,6) and (9,6).

The region occupied by the brick wall is defined by the following constraints: $1 \le x \le 3$ and $4 \le y \le 6$.

a. Use a graphing utility to recreate this screen.

b. Find a rational function whose graph passes through all the gates without hitting the brick wall.

3.6 Create a screen for the third level of Gates that includes five gates and two brick walls. Find a rational function whose graph passes through all the gates without hitting the walls. Identify the domain and range of your function.

* * * * *

3.7 A cattle rancher would like to create a rectangular corral with an area of 150 m^2 using the least possible amount of fencing materials.

a. Let x represent the width of the rectangle. Write a rational function that describes the perimeter of the rectangle in terms of x.

b. Graph the function and determine the location of any asymptotes that occur. If an asymptote occurs, describe what its location represents in this situation.

c. Considering the context, identify a reasonable domain and range for the function.

d. What is the minimum value for the perimeter of the rectangular corral? What are the corresponding values for the width and length of the corral?

e. Describe the shape of the rectangle that minimizes the perimeter for an area of 150 m^2. Do you think that this shape will minimize the perimeter for any rectangular region of a given area? Use examples to support your response.

Summary Assessment

1. a. The figure below shows a screen in the third level of Gates. The line represents the graph of the polynomial function $f(x) = x$. Add a rational expression to $f(x) = x$ so that the graph of the resulting function passes through all four gates.

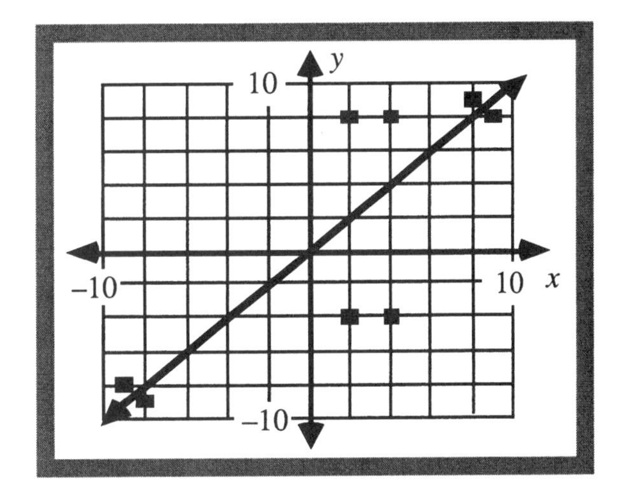

   b. Write your function from Part **a** in the general form of a rational function, shown below:

$$r(x) = \frac{f(x)}{g(x)}$$

   c. Use piecewise functions to create a graph that passes through the four gates shown in Part **a.**

2. The figure below shows another screen in the third level of Gates.

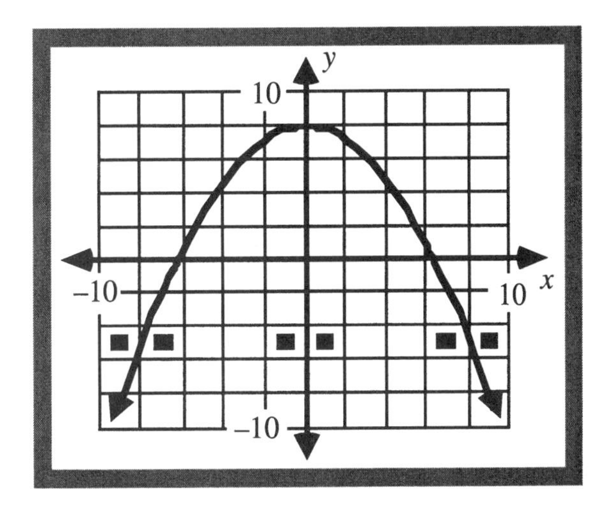

a. The curve shown represents the graph of the function below:

$$f(x) = -\frac{1}{5}x^2 + 8$$

Does this function have an absolute maximum or minimum? Justify your response.

b. Add a rational expression to $f(x)$ so that the graph of the resulting function passes through all the gates.

c. Write the new function in the general form of a rational function and identify its domain and range.

3. The figure below shows a screen in the third level of Gates. Determine a function whose graph passes through all four gates without touching the brick walls.

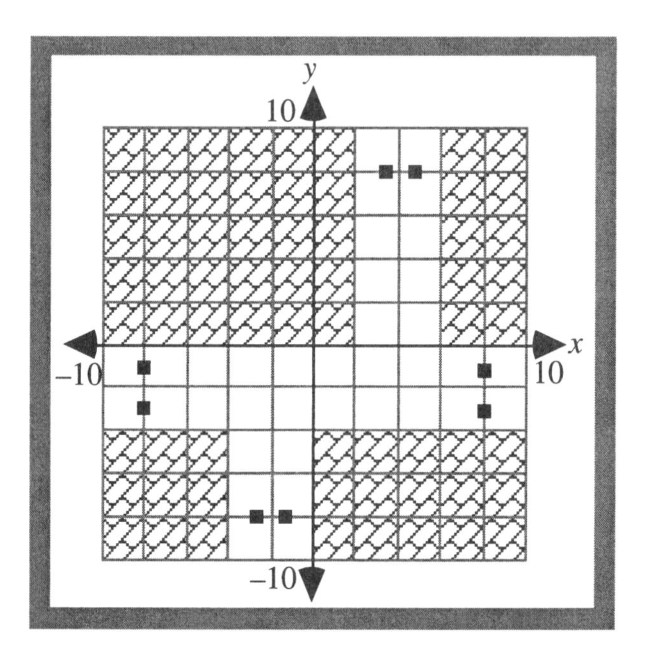

Module Summary

* A function is **continuous** at a point c in its domain if the following conditions are met:
  1. the function is defined at c, or $f(c)$ exists
  2. the limit of the function exists at c, or $\lim_{x \to c} f(x)$ exists
  3. the two values listed above are equal, or $f(c) = \lim_{x \to c} f(x)$.
* A function is continuous over its domain if it is continuous at each point in its domain.
* A function is **discontinuous** at a point if it does not meet all the conditions for continuity at that point.
* A **polynomial function** is a function of the form below, where $a_n, a_{n-1}, a_{n-2}, \ldots, a_0$ are real numbers and n is a non-negative integer.

$$f(x) = a_n x^n + a_{n-1} x^{n-1} + \cdots + a_1 x^1 + a_0$$

* The **degree** of a polynomial is equal to the greatest exponent of the variable in the expression. The coefficient of that variable in the expression is the **leading coefficient.**
* The **end behavior** of the graph of a polynomial function describes the characteristics of the graph as $|x|$ approaches infinity.
* The **absolute maximum** of a function is the greatest value of the range, and the **absolute minimum** is the least value of the range.
* The x-coordinate of each point where the graph of a polynomial intersects the x-axis is a **zero** or a **root** of the polynomial.
* As $|x|$ approaches infinity, the graph of a polynomial function of even degree has the same behavior at both ends. As $|x|$ approaches infinity, the graph of a polynomial function of odd degree has opposite behavior at each end.
* In a **piecewise function,** different parts of the domain correspond with different rules.
* A **rational function** is a function of the form

$$r(x) = \frac{f(x)}{g(x)}$$

  where $f(x)$ and $g(x)$ are polynomial functions and $g(x) \neq 0$.
* An **asymptote** to a curve is a line such that the distance from a point P on the curve to the line approaches zero as the distance from P to the origin increases without bound, where P is on a suitable part of the curve.

* The graph of a rational function of the form

$$r(x) = f(x) + \frac{g(x)}{h(x)}$$

where $h(x) \neq 0$ and the degree of $g(x)$ is less than the degree of $h(x)$, approaches the graph of $f(x)$ as $|x|$ increases without bound. This function also may be asymptotic to the vertical line $x = k$, where $h(k) = 0$, or it may have a point of discontinuity at $x = \text{k}$.

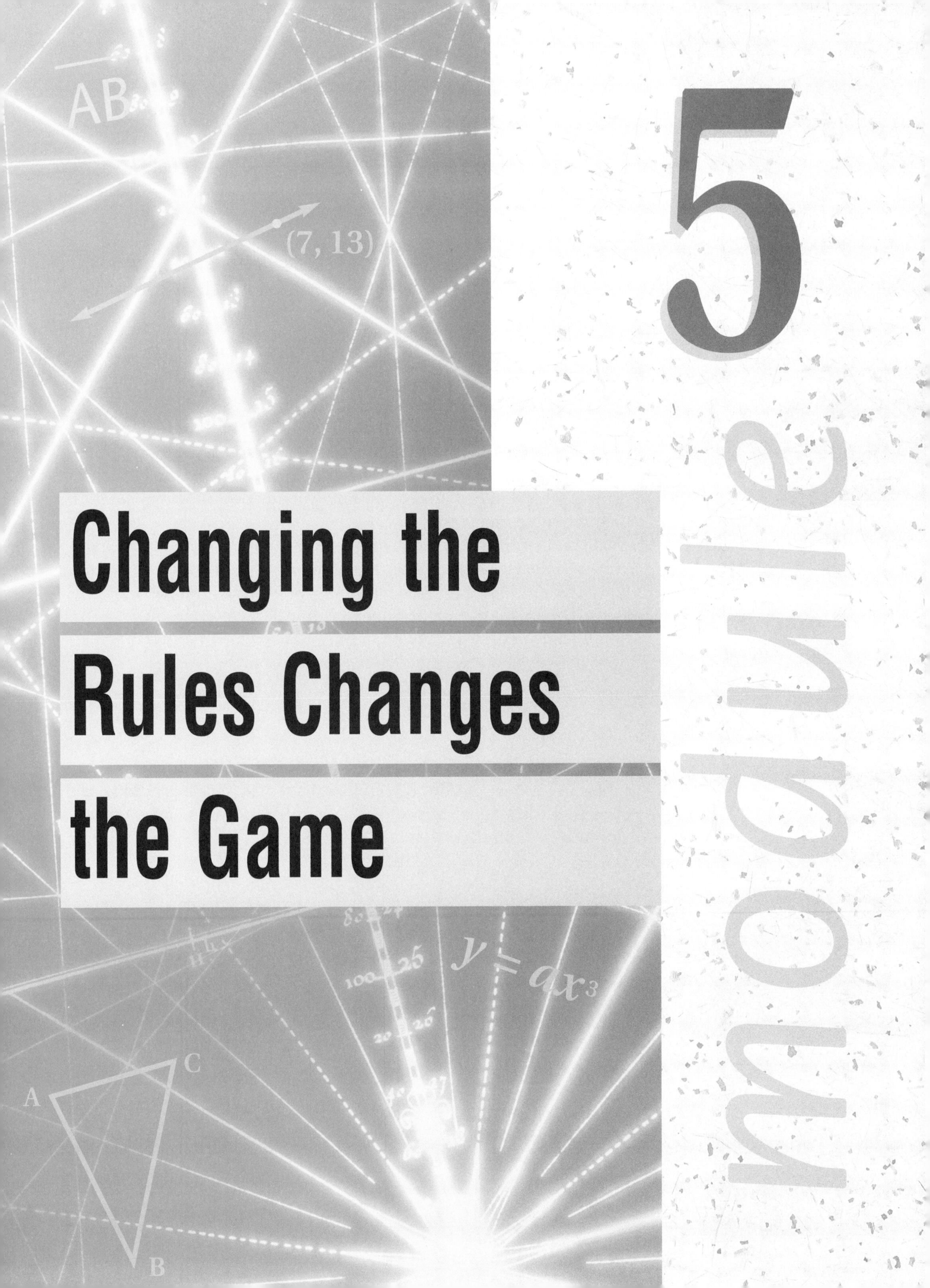

module 5

Changing the Rules Changes the Game

Introduction

In about 300 B.C., the Greek mathematician Euclid recorded a set of basic notions and **axioms** for geometry. Axioms are statements that are assumed to be true. Euclid's axioms described the properties of geometric figures and the relationships among them, including the concepts that a line is straight, that lines could be parallel, and that there is only one parallel line to a given line through a point not on the line (called the Parallel Postulate).

Since Euclid's era, his ideas about geometry have become a part of our everyday lives. But what would happen to a geometry if its basic notions were not those described by Euclid? For example, Euclid tacitly assumed that a line had infinitely many points. This is not the case in finite geometries.

To understand the coordinate system associated with a finite geometry, you must be able to perform arithmetic using a finite set of integers. One place to explore finite arithmetic systems is on the face of a clock. These arithmetic operations on a clock then can be linked to a non-Euclidean finite geometry. In this module, you investigate some properties of a finite geometry and a finite arithmetic.

Exploration

In **clock arithmetic,** an n-hour clock contains the digits $1, 2, 3, \ldots, n$. In such a system, addition is accomplished by moving clockwise around the dial, and subtraction is accomplished by moving counterclockwise around the dial.

a. Draw a 12-hour clock face.

b. 1. Describe a method for representing integers greater than 12 on a 12-hour clock.

   2. Describe a method for representing integers less than 1 on a 12-hour clock.

   3. Use your method to determine the 12-hour clock values for 15 and –5.

c. To distinguish the symbols for operations in clock arithmetic from those used in real-number arithmetic, they are often drawn with circles around them. The symbol $\oplus$, for instance, indicates clock addition. On a 12-hour clock, 11 hours after 4 o'clock can be symbolized as $4 \oplus 11$, or 3 o'clock. Similarly, 3 hours before 2 o'clock can be written as $2 \ominus 3$, or 11 o'clock.

1. Describe a method to represent addition of integers on a 12-hour clock.
2. Describe a method to represent subtraction of integers on a 12-hour clock.
3. Use your method to determine the sum $8 \oplus 7$ and the difference $5 \ominus 10$.

d. In real-number arithmetic, 0 is the additive identity because, for any real number a, $a + 0 = 0 + a = a$.

An additive identity also exists for 12-hour clock arithmetic. Determine its value.

e. In real-number arithmetic, multiplication can be thought of as "multiple additions." This is also the case in 12-hour arithmetic. For example, the multiplication $7 \otimes 3$ can be considered as shown below:

$$\begin{aligned} 7 \otimes 3 &= (7 \oplus 7) \oplus 7 \\ &= 2 \oplus 7 \\ &= 9 \end{aligned}$$

1. Determine the value of $4 \otimes 2$ in 12-hour arithmetic.
2. Determine the value of $4 \otimes 5$ in 12-hour arithmetic.

Discussion

a. Compare the method you described for representing positive and negative integers on a 12-hour clock with others in your class.

b. What number is the additive identity for 12-hour arithmetic? Justify your response.

c. 1. Two numbers are said to be additive inverses if their sum is the additive identity. Identify an additive inverse for each number in 12-hour arithmetic.

2. In real-number arithmetic, each number has exactly one additive inverse. Is the corresponding statement true in 12-hour arithmetic? Justify your answer.

d. In real-number arithmetic, 1 is the multiplicative identity because, for any real number a, $a \bullet 1 = 1 \bullet a = a$.

A multiplicative identity also exists for 12-hour arithmetic. What number do you think is this identity? Explain your response.

e. Two numbers are said to be multiplicative inverses if their product is the multiplicative identity. Do you think that each number in 12-hour arithmetic has a multiplicative inverse? If so, identify the multiplicative inverse for each number on a 12-hour clock. If not, describe a number that does not have a multiplicative inverse.

ACTIVITY 1

To explore other finite arithmetic systems, mathematicians developed **modular arithmetic.** Modular arithmetic can provide some basic tools for exploring finite geometries. In this activity, you examine modular arithmetic and determine some of its properties.

mathematics note

The modular arithmetic system of **modulo** n (or **mod** n) contains the digits $0, 1, 2, 3, \ldots, n-1$. For example, a modulo 8 (or mod 8) clock contains the numbers 0, 1, 2, 3, 4, 5, 6, and 7.

Like clock arithmetic, modular arithmetic can be thought of as taking place on a circular dial, as shown in Figure **5-1** below.

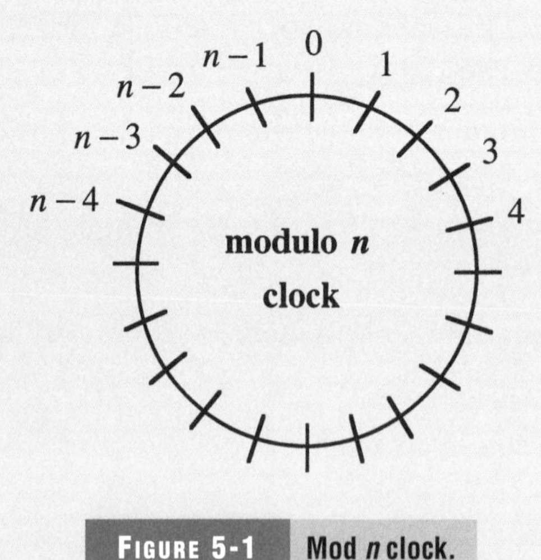

FIGURE 5-1 Mod n clock.

Exploration 1

One way to visualize a modular arithmetic system is to consider a number line of integers "wrapped" around a mod n clock. Using this analogy, you can determine which modulo n values correspond with each integer on the number line.

For example, the integer 0 on the number line corresponds with 0 on the modulo clock. Moving clockwise around the clock face corresponds to moving along the positive portion of a number line.

a. Sketch a circle on a sheet of paper. Mark and label the circle to form a modulo 5 clock.

b. 1. Use your mod 5 clock from Part **a** to complete Table **5-1** for the integers 0 through 12.

TABLE 5-1 ■ *Integers and Their Corresponding Mod 5 Values*

Integer on Number Line	Mod 5 Value
0	0
1	
2	
⋮	
12	

2. Moving counterclockwise around the modulo clock face corresponds to moving along the negative portion of a number line. Use this notion to complete Table **5-1** for the integers –1 through –12.

c. By examining the values in Table **5-1,** you should observe that the same mod 5 value corresponds with more than one integer.

1. To help visualize this relationship, create a scatterplot of the data in Table **5-1.** Represent the integers along the x-axis and the corresponding mod 5 values along the y-axis.

2. Use the scatterplot to identify all the integers from –12 to 12 that correspond with the same value in mod 5.

d. In Part **c**, you should have observed that 12 and –8 both correspond with 2 (mod 5). This fact can also be illustrated using the division algorithm. When using the division algorithm, the remainder must be a non-negative integer less than the divisor.

As shown below, for example, 12 and –8 both have a remainder of 2 when divided by 5.

$$\begin{array}{r} 2 \text{ R2} \\ 5\overline{)12} \\ \underline{-10} \\ 2 \end{array} \qquad \begin{array}{r} -2 \text{ R2} \\ 5\overline{)-8} \\ \underline{-(-10)} \\ 2 \end{array}$$

The division algorithm allows you to determine the mod 5 values that correspond with large integers.

Identify two integers with absolute values greater than 500, one positive and one negative, that correspond with the same mod 5 value.

mathematics note

In modulo n, two integers are **congruent** (symbolized by ≡) if they have the same remainder when divided by n.

In mod 5, for example, the integers 12 and 2 are congruent because 12 divided by 5 and 2 divided by 5 both have a remainder of 2. This can be written symbolically as $12 \equiv 2 \pmod 5$.

Discussion 1

a. How is congruence illustrated on the scatterplot you created in Part **c** of Exploration **1**?

b. Describe the process you would follow when using the division algorithm to determine the congruent mod n value of a negative number.

c. Wrapping a number line of integers around the mod 5 clock can be thought of as a function. What are the domain and range of this function?

Exploration 2

In real-number arithmetic, the numbers 1 and 0 play special roles. In this exploration, you create addition and multiplication tables and use them to identify numbers that play similar roles in mod n arithmetic. You then use these numbers to solve some mod n equations.

a. Complete Table **5-2,** a table of addition facts for mod 5.

TABLE 5-2 ■ *Addition Facts for Modulo 5*

+	0	1	2	3	4
0					
1		2			0
2					
3				1	
4					

b. Complete Table **5-3,** a table of multiplication facts for mod 5.

TABLE 5-3 ■ *Multiplication Facts for Modulo 5*

×	0	1	2	3	4
0					
1		1			
2					3
3				4	
4					

c. Create a table of subtraction facts for mod 5. Each entry in the table should represent the row value minus the column value.

d. Determine the additive identity for mod 5.

e. Identify the additive inverse for each element in mod 5.

f. Determine the multiplicative identity for mod 5.

g. The multiplicative inverse of x also is referred to as the reciprocal of x. For the set of real numbers, $1/x$ is the multiplicative inverse of x, for $x \neq 0$, because

$$x \bullet \frac{1}{x} = \frac{1}{x} \bullet x = 1$$

The multiplicative inverse of any element x (other than the additive identity) can be denoted by x^{-1}.

Identify the multiplicative inverse for each element in mod 5.

mathematics note

Many of the properties of congruence are comparable to properties of equality.

The **substitution property of congruence** states that if a, b, and c are any real numbers with $a \equiv b$ and $b \equiv c$, then $a \equiv c$.

The **addition property of congruence** states that if a, b, and c are any real numbers with $a \equiv b$, then $a + c \equiv b + c$.

The **multiplication property of congruence** states that if a, b, and c are any real numbers with $a \equiv b$, then $a \bullet c \equiv b \bullet c$.

h. Congruences in mod n can be solved using methods similar to those used to solve algebraic equations involving real numbers. For example, the solution to the congruence $5x - 6 \equiv 4 \pmod 7$ is shown below.

$5x - 6 \equiv 4 \pmod 7$	given
$5x \equiv 4 + 6 \pmod 7$	addition property of congruence
$5x \equiv 3 \pmod 7$	definition of congruence mod 7
$3(5x) \equiv 3(3) \pmod 7$	multiplication property of congruence
$1x \equiv 2 \pmod 7$	definition of congruence mod 7
$x \equiv 2 \pmod 7$	multiplicative identity

The solution can be checked by substituting 2 into $5x - 6 \equiv 4 \pmod 7$. Because $5(2) - 6 \equiv 3 - 6 \equiv 4 \pmod 7$, 2 is a solution to the equation.

Use the process described above to solve the equation $3x + 1 \equiv 2 \pmod 4$. Record the justification for each step in your solution.

Discussion 2

a. Which of the following modular operations are commutative?

1. addition
2. subtraction
3. multiplication

b. 1. How can you define division in mod 5 arithmetic?

2. Is division commutative in mod 5 arithmetic? Explain your answer.

c. Consider the following congruence equation: $16 \bullet 6 \equiv x \pmod 5$. One way to determine a solution that is a mod 5 value is to multiply the two factors, then convert the product to mod 5.

Is the solution affected by converting both factors to mod 5 before multiplying?

d. For real numbers, addition and multiplication are both associative. This means that for any real numbers a, b, and c:

$$(a + b) + c = a + (b + c)$$
and
$$(a \bullet b) \bullet c = a \bullet (b \bullet c)$$

Are addition and multiplication associative in modular arithmetic?

e. For real numbers, multiplication is distributive over addition. In other words, for any real numbers a, b, and c:

$$a(b + c) = ab + ac$$

Do you think that multiplication (mod 5) is distributive over addition (mod 5)? Use an example to illustrate your response.

f. 1. Why is there no multiplicative inverse for 2 (mod 6)?

2. Because there is no multiplicative inverse for 2 (mod 6), the equation $2x - 5 \equiv 4 \pmod 6$ has no solution. To verify that this is true, substitute each number in mod 6 into the equation.

g. 1. Why is there no multiplicative inverse for 3 (mod 6)?

2. Although there is no multiplicative inverse for 3 (mod 6), the equation $3x \equiv 3 \pmod 6$ has three solutions: 1 (mod 6), 3 (mod 6), and 5 (mod 6).

Describe how you might find these solutions.

h. Describe some situations in which you might expect to use a modular arithmetic.

Warm-Up

1. Describe how to determine the number in mod 5 that is congruent to 33.

2. Calculate each of the following in mod 5:

   a. $3 + 2$

   b. $12 \bullet 8$

   c. $13 - 20$

3. Evaluate each of the following expressions.

   a. $2 + 1 \pmod 3$

   b. $2 \bullet 2 \pmod 3$

   c. $16 + 9 \pmod 8$

   d. $11 \bullet 7 \pmod{10}$

4. Find each of the following inverses.

   a. the additive inverse of 3 (mod 5)

   b. the additive inverse of 2 (mod 3)

   c. the multiplicative inverse of 3 (mod 5)

   d. the multiplicative inverse of 0 (mod 5)

Assignment

1.1 Complete the following addition and multiplication tables for mod 3.

+	0	1	2
0			
1			
2			

×	0	1	2
0			
1			
2			

1.2 **a.** What is the additive identity in mod 3?

b. Find the additive inverse in mod 3 for each of the following: 0, 1, and 2.

c. Recall that **proof by exhaustion** is the process of examining all possibilities to prove a statement. Use proof by exhaustion to show that 1 is the multiplicative identity for mod 3.

d. Prove or disprove the statement: "Every element in mod 3 has a multiplicative inverse."

1.3 Division in modular arithmetic may be defined as follows: $a \div b \equiv c \pmod{n}$ if and only if $b \bullet c \equiv a \pmod{n}$. Use this definition to find each of the following:

a. $1 \div 2 \pmod{5}$

b. $3 \div 2 \pmod{5}$

c. $4 \div 0 \pmod{5}$

1.4 Prove that 2 does not have a multiplicative inverse in mod 4.

1.5 Solve for x in each of the following.

a. $x + 3 \equiv 1 \pmod{7}$

b. $4x \equiv 1 \pmod{7}$

c. $3x - 5 \equiv 4 \pmod{6}$

d. $2x + 1 \equiv 0 \pmod{3}$

e. $x^2 \equiv 1 \pmod{3}$

* * * * *

1.6 Solve each of the following equations:

a. $11x - 6 \equiv 8 \pmod{13}$

b. $3x + 4 \equiv 5 \pmod{11}$

1.7 A monitoring device uses 0.5 m of paper per hour. Each roll of paper is 200 m long. If a new roll is installed at 9:00 A.M., at what time will the device run out of paper?

Research Project

One common application of modular arithmetic is the Universal Product Code (UPC) found on nearly every consumer product. In January 2005, there were five versions of UPC, using from 8 to 14 digits.

Figure **5-2** shows a 12-digit UPC bar code and number. The first number on the left (0) identifies the product. The last number on the right (8) is the check digit. To make certain that each code is read correctly, bar-code readers (such as those at supermarket cash registers) use an algorithm to perform an internal check.

FIGURE 5-2 A 12-digit UPC bar code.

For this research project, find an algorithm that performs a check on a bar code. Write an explanation of the algorithm. Collect some samples of UPC bar codes and verify that the algorithm works. Then create one valid and one invalid UPC bar code of your own.

In Activity **1,** you examined some of the basic principles of modular arithmetic. In this activity, you investigate a finite geometry coordinatized with a modular arithmetic system.

mathematics note

Finite geometries are unlike traditional Euclidean geometry because they use only finite numbers of points.

For example, one finite geometry is based on a modulo 3 arithmetic system. In this system, each point of a lattice has coordinates (x,y) where x and y are elements of the set {0, 1, 2}. Figure **5-3** shows the nine-point lattice used to construct this finite geometry.

(0,2)	(1,2)	(2,2)
(0,1)	(1,1)	(2,1)
(0,0)	(1,0)	(2,0)

Figure 5-3 Coordinatized nine-point lattice.

In this geometry, a line is defined as the set of all points that satisfies a mod n equation of the form $Ax + By + C = 0$ (mod 3) where A, B, and C are elements of the set {0, 1, 2} with A and B not both 0. For example, one line is identified with the equation $x + y + 0 = 0$ (mod 3) or $x + y = 0$ (mod 3). This line contains only the points with coordinates (0,0), (2,1), and (1,2). A graph of this line is shown in Figure **5-4.**

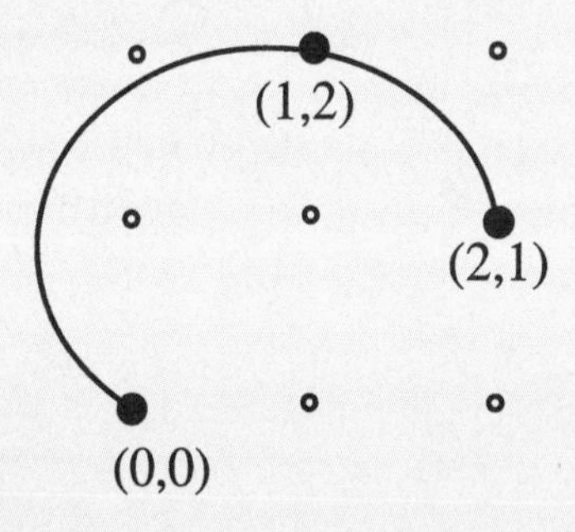

Figure 5-4 Graph of the line $x + y = 0$ (mod 3).

Although Figure **5-4** shows the three points on the line connected by an arc, the line contains only those three points. There are no other coordinates that satisfy the equation. **Note:** For the remainder of this module, mod n equations will be written with equals signs rather than congruence signs.

Discussion 1

a. Compare the characteristics of a line in Euclidean geometry with the characteristics of a line in the finite geometry described in the previous mathematics note.

b. How do these characteristics of a line compare with its characteristics in spherical geometry?

c. 1. How might a triangle be defined in this nine-point geometry?

   2. Give an example of a triangle that satisfies your definition.

   3. How does your definition compare with the definition of a triangle in Euclidean geometry?

Exploration

In this exploration, you continue to investigate the nine-point geometry described in the mathematics note.

a. Determine the number of possible equations of the form $Ax + By + C = 0$ (mod 3). List each of these equations.

b. Determine the coordinates of all the points in the nine-point geometry that satisfy each equation identified in Part **a.**

c. Graph each of the equations on a copy of the lattice template (available from your teacher). Connect each set of points in the solution with segments or arcs.

d. 1. It is possible for more than one equation to define the same line. Identify the equations of the unique lines in this nine-point system.

   2. Label the points in a nine-point lattice A through I, as shown in Figure **5-5** on the right.

   3. Record both the coordinates and the letters that correspond with the points which satisfy each unique line. **Note:** Save this information for use in the warm-up and assignment.

○	○	○
G	H	I
○	○	○
D	E	F
○	○	○
A	B	C

Figure 5-5

A nine-point lattice.

e. Determine if each of the following properties of lines in traditional Euclidean geometry is true in this nine-point geometry.

   1. Two points determine a unique line.

   2. If two distinct lines contain a common point, they contain exactly one common point.

f. Lines in a plane are **parallel** if they have either no points in common or all points in common. Are there parallel lines in this geometry? If so, identify them.

g. According to the Parallel Postulate (mentioned in the introduction), there is exactly one line parallel to a given line through a point not on that line.

1. Select a line in the nine-point geometry and a point not on the line. Determine if the parallel postulate is true for your selections.
2. Repeat Step **1** for each point not on the line until you have checked all appropriate points.
3. Select another line in the finite geometry and repeat Steps **1** and **2.**
4. Repeat Step **3** until all lines have been checked.

Discussion 2

a. What patterns do you observe among the values of A, B, and C in the equations of parallel lines?

mathematics note

In the nine-point geometry, a line given by $Ax + By + C = 0 \pmod 3$, where $B \neq 10$, may be expressed in the form $y = mx + b \pmod 3$ where m and b are elements of the set {0, 1, 2} and m represents the **slope** of the line.

For example, consider the line defined by the equation $1x + 2y + 1 = 0 \pmod 3$. This equation may be rewritten using mod 3 arithmetic as follows:

$$1x + 2y + 1 = 0 \pmod 3$$
$$2y = -1x + -1$$
$$2(2y) = 2(-1x + -1)$$
$$1y = -2x + -2$$

However, –2 may be rewritten as 1 in mod 3 because $-2 \equiv 1 \pmod 3$. Therefore,

$$1y = 1x + 1$$
$$y = x + 1$$

In this case, the slope of the line is 1.

b. When the equation for a line in the form $Ax + By + C = 0 \pmod 3$ is rewritten in slope-intercept form, it becomes:

$$y = -\frac{A}{B}x - \frac{C}{B} \pmod 3$$

1. Describe the slope of the line when $A = 0$.
2. Describe the slope of the line when $B = 0$.

c. In a real-number coordinate plane, the slope of a line can be found using the coordinates of two points on the line. Is it possible to determine the slope of a line in the nine-point geometry using the coordinates of two points on the line? Justify your response.

d. Compare the slope of a line in Euclidean geometry to the slope of a line in nine-point geometry.

Warm-Up

1. Write each of the distinct equations found in the exploration in the form $y = mx + b \pmod 3$ or $x = a \pmod 3$.

2. Use the equations from Problem **1** and the information you recorded in Part **d** of the exploration to complete the chart supplied by your teacher. The following diagram shows one completed cell in the chart. **Note:** Save this chart for use throughout the remainder of this module.

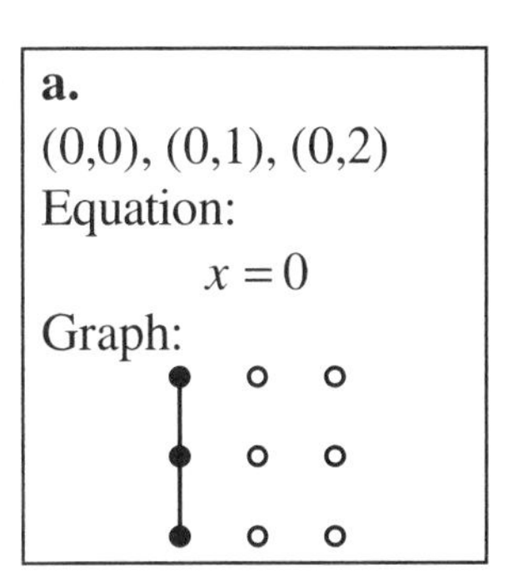

Assignment

2.1 Consider a line in the nine-point geometry that contains the point (0,1) and has a slope of 1.

a. Write an equation for the line.

b. Use the completed chart from the Warm-Up to verify your equation from Part **a** and identify the other points on the line.

2.2 How many triangles are there in the nine-point geometry? Explain your response.

2.3 Each row of your chart from the Warm-Up contains three lines. By considering them in pairs, prove that the lines in each row are parallel. Recall that in coordinate geometry, two lines are parallel if they either have the same slope or both have undefined slopes and are vertical.

2.4 In Euclidean geometry, two lines with non-zero slopes are perpendicular when the product of their slopes is –1. A line with an undefined slope is perpendicular to a line with a slope of 0.

a. Consider two perpendicular lines with non-zero slopes in the nine-point geometry. If a comparable definition of perpendicular lines is true, what must be the product of their slopes?

b. Identify all pairs of perpendicular lines in the nine-point geometry.

c. In Euclidean geometry, the following properties involving perpendicular lines in a plane are true.

1. At a point on a line, there is exactly one line perpendicular to the given line.

2. From a point not on a line, there is exactly one line perpendicular to the given line.

3. Two lines perpendicular to the same line are parallel.

Determine if these properties are true in the nine-point geometry by considering every possible case.

2.5 Consider the lines defined by the following mod 3 equations:

$$y = 2$$
$$y = 2x$$

a. Find the intersection, if any, of these two lines.

b. Repeat Part **a** for the mod 3 equations below:

$$y = x$$
$$y = 2x$$

2.6 Is every pair of intersecting lines in the nine-point geometry perpendicular? Explain your response using a proof.

* * * * *

2.7 Consider a geometry based on a modulo 4 number system in which each point of a lattice has coordinates (x,y) where x and y are elements of the set $\{0, 1, 2, 3\}$. In this geometry, a line is defined as the set of all points on the lattice that satisfies a mod 4 equation of the form $Ax + By + C = 0$.

a. Construct a lattice and graph the equation $y = 2x + 3$ (mod 4).

b. Write the equation (in mod 4) of a line parallel to the line given in Part **a** and containing point (0,0).

c. Find the equation (in mod 4) of a line perpendicular to the line given in Part **a** and containing point (0,0).

2.8 Does every pair of perpendicular lines in the nine-point geometry intersect? Verify your response using proof by exhaustion.

Research Project

A triangle with two sides perpendicular is a **right triangle.** By this definition, the points with coordinates (0,0), (0,2), and (2,1) in the nine-point geometry determine a right triangle. This fact can be proven as described below.

The slope of the line through the points with coordinates (0,0) and (2,1) can be calculated as follows:

$$\frac{1-0}{2-0} = \frac{1}{2}$$

Because $1 \div 2 \equiv 2 \pmod 3$, the slope of the line is 2. Similarly, the slope of the line through (0,2) and (2,1) is 1. The product of the two slopes is 2.

As mentioned in Problem **2.4,** two lines with non-zero slopes are perpendicular when the product of their slopes is –1. Because –1 is congruent to 2 (mod 3), the lines are perpendicular. Therefore, the triangle is a right triangle.

A picture of the triangle formed by (0,0), (0,2), and (2,1) is shown in Figure **5-6.**

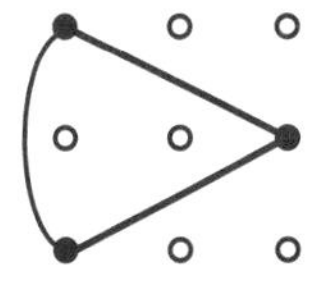

FIGURE 5-6 A right triangle in the nine-point geometry.

How many other right triangles can be formed in the nine-point geometry?

ACTIVITY 3

In Activity **2,** you investigated a finite geometry using algebra and the coordinates of points. In this activity, you explore a finite geometry as an **axiomatic system.** In other words, you use undefined terms, definitions, axioms, and proven theorems to describe the system.

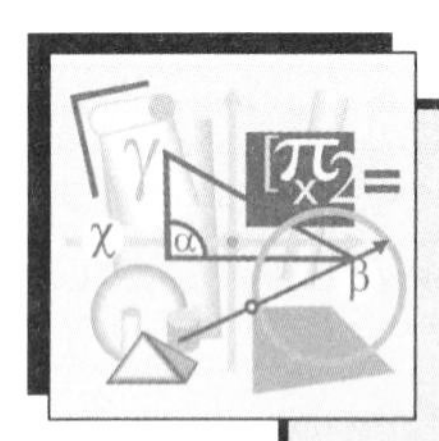

mathematics note

An **axiomatic system** is a mathematical system that contains:

- **undefined terms** (terms assumed without definition)
- **definitions** (terms defined using undefined terms and other definitions)
- **axioms** (rules assumed to be true that describe relationships among terms)
- **theorems** (statements proven true using logic)

In Euclidean geometry, for example, both *line* and *point* are undefined terms. The statement, "A line extends indefinitely in two directions" is an axiom, because it is assumed to be true. The statement, "The square of the length of the hypotenuse of a right triangle is equal to the sum of the squares of the lengths of the legs" is a theorem because it can be proven.

Exploration

Gino Fano was one of the first mathematicians to study a finite geometry. In 1892, he built a geometry to satisfy the following five axioms, leaving the terms *point, line,* and *on* undefined. (In these axioms, the words *contains* and *has* also are undefined terms.)

1. There exists at least one line.
2. Every line has exactly three points.
3. Not all points are on the same line.
4. For any two points, there exists exactly one line that contains both of them.

5*f*. Every two different lines have at least one point in common. (The *f* in 5*f* stands for Fano.)

In this exploration, you use Fano's axioms to deduce the properties of his geometry.

a. Considering only Axioms **1** and **2,** determine the minimum number of points in this geometry. *Hint:* Start listing points by designating each one in order with the letters *A, B, C,* and so on.

b. Considering only Axioms **1–3,** determine the minimum number of points in this geometry.

c. Now consider all five of Fano's axioms. Determine the number of points and the number of lines in this geometry.

d. Draw a model of Fano's geometry using the number of points and lines from Part **c.**

e. By changing Fano's fifth axiom, John Wesley Young developed another finite geometry (referred to as "Young's geometry" in this module). Young's fifth axiom reads as follows:

   5*y*. For each line *l* and each point *B* not on line *l,* point *B* is on one line that does not contain any other points from line *l.* (The *y* in 5*y* stands for Young.)

   Young's geometry has nine points. Use a lattice similar to the one shown in Figure **5-7** to draw a model of Young's geometry.

G *H* *I*

D *E* *F*

A *B* *C*

FIGURE 5-7 **A nine-point lattice.**

Discussion

a. In Fano's geometry, does Axiom **1** tell you that there are any points on a line? Does it give any hint about how a line might look?

b. What does it mean to say that Fano's five statements are axioms?

c. In either Fano's or Young's geometry, is it possible for two distinct lines to contain the same two points? Explain your response.

d. How does Young's geometry compare to Fano's geometry?

mathematics note

The process of **deductive reasoning** begins with a hypothesis, then uses a logical sequence of valid arguments to reach a conclusion.

In mathematical proofs by deductive reasoning, each argument typically is supported by an axiom, definition, or previously proven theorem. A **direct proof** makes direct use of the hypothesis to arrive at the conclusion.

For example, consider the following statement: "In Fano's geometry, each point on a line is a member of at least three lines." To prove this statement using a direct proof, it first should be restated in if-then form: "If a point is on a line, then it is a member of at least three lines."

Assuming that the hypothesis, "If a point is on a line," is true, it can be symbolized as follows: Point B is on one line, l_1.

By Axiom **2,** l_1 must contain two other points: A and C.

By Axiom **3,** there must exist a point D not on l_1.

By Axiom **4,** there must be a line through points B and D: l_2.

From Part **c** of Discussion **1,** both A and B cannot be on l_2. Similarly, both A and C cannot be on l_2. By Axiom **2,** however, l_2 must contain one other point: E.

By Axiom **4,** there exists a line, l_3, that contains A and D.

To satisfy Axiom **2,** l_3 also must contain a third point, F.

According to Axiom **4,** another line, l_4, must contain B and F.

Lines l_1, l_2, and l_4 all contain B. Therefore, point B is contained in at least three lines.

In conclusion, the following statement is true in Fano's geometry. "If a point is on a line, then it is a member of at least three lines."

e. How does a theorem differ from an axiom?

f. The points and lines used to prove the statement in the mathematics note were given arbitrary names. Describe how this helps prove that the theorem is true for all points and lines in Fano's geometry.

Warm-Up

1. Consider the following theorem in Young's geometry: "For any point, there is a line not containing it."

   a. Rewrite this theorem as an if-then statement.

   b. Identify the hypothesis.

   c. Identify the conclusion.

2. When considering the theorem in Problem **1** for any point D and a line m, there are two possible cases. If D is not on line m, then there is nothing to prove. If D is on line m, then the theorem can be proved using the steps described below. Give a reason for each step in this proof.

   a. Point D is on line m.

   b. There exists a point E not on line m.

   c. Through E there is a line l not containing any points of line m.

   d. In conclusion, given any point, there is a line not containing it.

Assignment

3.1 For two different lines to be parallel, they must not intersect. In other words, the two lines must have no points in common.

Prove that there are no parallel lines in Fano's geometry. Begin your proof with the hypothesis "Lines l_1 and l_2 are different lines in Fano's geometry." Conclude your proof with the statement, "Line l_1 is not parallel to l_2."

3.2 In Young's geometry, prove that every point is contained in at least four lines. Draw a sketch to support your proof.

3.3 In Young's geometry, prove that given any line, there is a different line parallel to it.

3.4 How would your model of Young's geometry change if a line contained four points?

3.5 Consider the points in Young's geometry with coordinates (0,0) and (1,1). Do you think that the Pythagorean theorem could be used to find the distance between these two points? Explain your response. If so, can the distance be expressed in mod 3?

* * * * *

3.6 Use a direct proof to prove the following statement: "If n is an even number, then n^2 is an even number."

3.7 Use a direct proof to prove the following statement: "If n is an integer, then $n^3 - n$ is even." *Hint:* you will need to prove two cases, one in which n is even and one in which n is odd.

In Activity **3,** you examined some properties of Fano's and Young's geometries using proofs by exhaustion and direct proofs. In this activity, you use **indirect proofs** to continue your investigations of these two geometries.

Exploration

Indirect proofs are based on the notion of *reductio ad absurdum,* or "reduction to the absurd." In an indirect proof, the property to be proven true is assumed to be false. From this assumption, statements are argued logically with supporting reasons (axioms, definitions, and proven theorems) until a contradiction to either a known fact or an assumption is reached. If a contradiction can be reached, then the assumption must be false. Therefore, the original statement is true.

For example, consider a number n that is an even perfect square. In the following exploration, you prove that the square root of n also is even using an indirect proof.

a. Suppose that m is the square root in question—in other words, that $m^2 = n$. Assume that m is not even. Use an algebraic equation to express m in terms of a, another natural number. Your equation should show that m is indeed odd.

b. Square both sides of the equation from Part **a.** Is the result an even or an odd natural number?

c. 1. Can the statement that n is an even perfect square and the result in Part **b** both be true?

   2. Do you believe that the following statement is true: "The square root of an even perfect square also is even"? Explain your response.

Discussion

a. What is the negation of the statement: "The square root of 2 is an irrational number"?

b. In general, the negation of a statement "if p, then q" is "p and not q." How do truth tables verify this relationship?

mathematics note

In an **indirect proof,** a statement is proven true by proving that its negation cannot be true.

For example, consider this statement in Young's nine-point geometry: "If a line intersects one of two parallel lines, then it intersects the other." This statement may be rewritten as follows: "If line l_1 is parallel to l_2, and lines l_2 and l_3 each contain point B, then lines l_1 and l_3 intersect."

To prove this statement using an indirect proof, assume that line l_1 is parallel to l_2, that lines l_2 and l_3 each contain point B, and that lines l_3 and l_1 do not intersect. A sketch of this situation is shown in Figure **5-8.** (The three points in each line are connected for organizational purposes.)

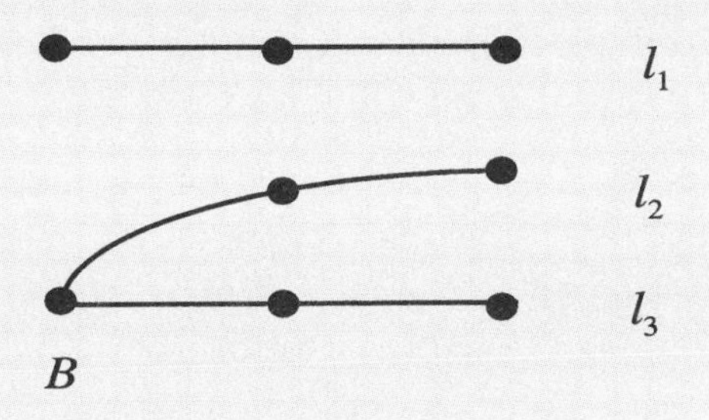

FIGURE 5-8 **Sketch created using an assumption.**

If l_3 and l_1 do not intersect, then l_3 and l_1 have no points in common because of the meaning of non-intersecting.

Line l_1 is parallel to l_2, by the hypothesis.

Point B is on l_3 and l_2, by the hypothesis.

Now there are two lines, l_3 and l_2, that both contain point B and both are parallel to l_1. This contradicts Axiom **5y,** which states that through a point B not on a line l, there is exactly one line that has no points in common with the given line.

Therefore, the assumption that lines l_3 and l_1 do not intersect must be false because this would mean there could be more than one line that has no point in common with the given line. Consequently, lines l_3 and l_1 intersect.

In conclusion, the following statement is true: "If a line intersects one of two parallel lines, then it intersects the other."

Warm-Up

1. Identify a counterexample for each of the following statements.

   a. If an odd number is multiplied by an even number, the product is always odd.

   b. If a triangle has two congruent sides, then it is an equilateral triangle.

2. Write the negation of each statement below.

   a. There are at least 6 elements in this set.

   b. This set has no more than 9 elements.

   c. The number of elements in this set is exactly 7.

3. Identify each of the following statements as true or false. Justify your responses.

   a. In Fano's geometry, line m contains four points.

   b. In Fano's geometry, lines l and k are parallel.

   c. In Young's geometry, there are no lines.

   d. In Young's geometry, if a point is not contained in a given line, then there exists exactly one line through that point that does not intersect the given line.

Assignment

4.1 Consider the following theorem in Young's nine-point geometry: "If two lines intersect, then they intersect in exactly one point."

   a. Identify the hypothesis and the conclusion in this statement.

   b. To prove this statement using an indirect proof, what must you assume to be true?

   c. Sketch a picture of the situation that includes your assumption.

   d. Which axiom does your assumption contradict?

   e. What does this contradiction indicate about your assumption?

   f. What can you now conclude about the theorem to be proved? Explain your response.

4.2 Prove indirectly the following statement in Young's geometry: "If two lines are parallel to the same line, then they are parallel to each other." *Hint:* Use the theorem proven in the mathematics note.

4.3 Prove that every two different lines in Fano's seven-point geometry have exactly one point in common. Begin your proof with the hypothesis that l_1 and l_2 are different lines. Conclude your proof with the statement that lines l_1 and l_2 have exactly one point in common.

* * * * *

4.4 The following paragraph provides an indirect proof of the statement, "The $\sqrt{2}$ is an irrational number." Describe the contradiction which shows that the assumption must be false.

Assume $\sqrt{2}$ is a rational number. This means that $\sqrt{2} = p/q$ where p and q are whole numbers and p/q is in lowest terms. Square both sides of the equation, as shown below:

$$\left(\sqrt{2}\right)^2 = (p/q)^2$$
$$2q^2 = p^2$$

Because p^2 is even, p must be even. Because p is even, it can be written in the form $p = 2r$, where r is a whole number. By substitution,

$$(2r)^2 = 2q^2$$
$$4r^2 = 2q^2$$
$$2r^2 = q^2$$

Because q^2 is even, q also must be even. Therefore, the square root of 2 must be irrational.

4.5 Use an indirect proof to prove the following: "If a cash register contains \$1.45 in nickels and dimes, there must be an odd number of nickels."

Summary Assessment

1. a. Construct addition and multiplication tables for mod 4.

   b. Use these tables to describe the existence of additive inverses, an additive identity, multiplicative inverses, and a multiplicative identity in mod 4. Use specific examples in your response.

2. Consider a four-point geometry that has the following three axioms.

   - There are exactly four points.
   - Through any two points there is exactly one line.
   - Given two points there is exactly one line containing them.

   In this geometry, the terms *point, line,* and *contains* are undefined.

   a. Draw a model to represent this geometry.

   b. Create a coordinate system in mod 2 for this geometry.

   c. Construct addition and multiplication tables for mod 2.

   d. Find the equations for all distinct lines in this geometry.

   e. If parallel lines are defined as having no points in common, prove that this system has at least three pairs of parallel lines.

   f. Use a direct proof to prove that any point in the system is contained in at least three lines.

3. Use an indirect proof to show that if n is an integer and n^2 is odd, then n is odd.

Module Summary

* In **clock arithmetic,** an n-hour clock contains the digits 1, 2, 3, . . . , n. In such a system, addition is accomplished by moving clockwise around the dial, and subtraction is accomplished by moving counterclockwise around the dial.
* To distinguish the symbols for operations in clock arithmetic from those used in real-number arithmetic, they are often drawn with circles around them. The symbol $\oplus$, for instance, indicates addition.
* A modular arithmetic system of **modulo n** (or **mod n**) contains the digits 0, 1, 2, 3, . . . , $n - 1$. In such a system, addition and subtraction are accomplished in a manner similar to clock arithmetic.
* In modulo n, two numbers are **congruent** if they have the same remainder when divided by n. The symbol $\equiv$ denotes congruence.
* Given a set and the operation of addition defined on that set, an **additive identity** is the unique element a of the set such that when a is added to any element x, the result is that element x. In other words, $x + a = a + x = x$.
* Two elements whose sum is the additive identity are **additive inverses.** In other words, b is an additive inverse of x if $x + b = b + x = a$. The additive inverse of x is denoted by $-x$.
* Given a set and the operation of multiplication defined on the set, a **multiplicative identity** is the unique element c of the set such that when any element x is multiplied by c, the result is that element x. In other words, $x \bullet c = c \bullet x = x$.
* Two elements whose product is the multiplicative identity are **multiplicative inverses.** In other words, d is the multiplicative inverse of x if $x \bullet d = d \bullet x = c$. The multiplicative inverse of any element x (other than the additive identity) can be denoted by x^{-1}. The multiplicative inverse of x also is referred to as the reciprocal of x.
* The **substitution property of congruence** states that if a, b, and c are any real numbers with $a \equiv b$ and $b \equiv c$, then $a \equiv c$.
* The **addition property of congruence** states that if a, b, and c are any real numbers with $a \equiv b$, then $a + c \equiv b + c$.
* The **multiplication property of congruence** states that if a, b, and c are any real numbers with $a \equiv b$, then $a \bullet c \equiv b \bullet c$.
* An **axiomatic system** is a mathematical system that contains:
  - **undefined terms** (terms assumed without definition)
  - **definitions** (terms defined using undefined terms and other definitions)
  - **axioms** (rules assumed to be true that describe relationships among terms)
  - **theorems** (statements proven true using logic).

* A **finite geometry** is an axiomatic system which, unlike traditional Euclidean geometry, uses a finite number of points.

* The process of **deductive reasoning** begins with a hypothesis, then uses a logical sequence of valid arguments to reach a conclusion.

  In mathematical proofs by deductive reasoning, each argument typically is supported by an axiom, definition, or previously proven theorem. A **direct proof** makes direct use of the hypothesis to arrive at the conclusion.

* In an **indirect proof,** the property to be proven true is assumed to be false. From this assumption, statements are argued logically with supporting reasons (axioms, definitions, and proven theorems) until a contradiction to either a known fact or an assumption is reached. If a contradiction can be reached, then the assumption must be false. Therefore, the original statement is true.

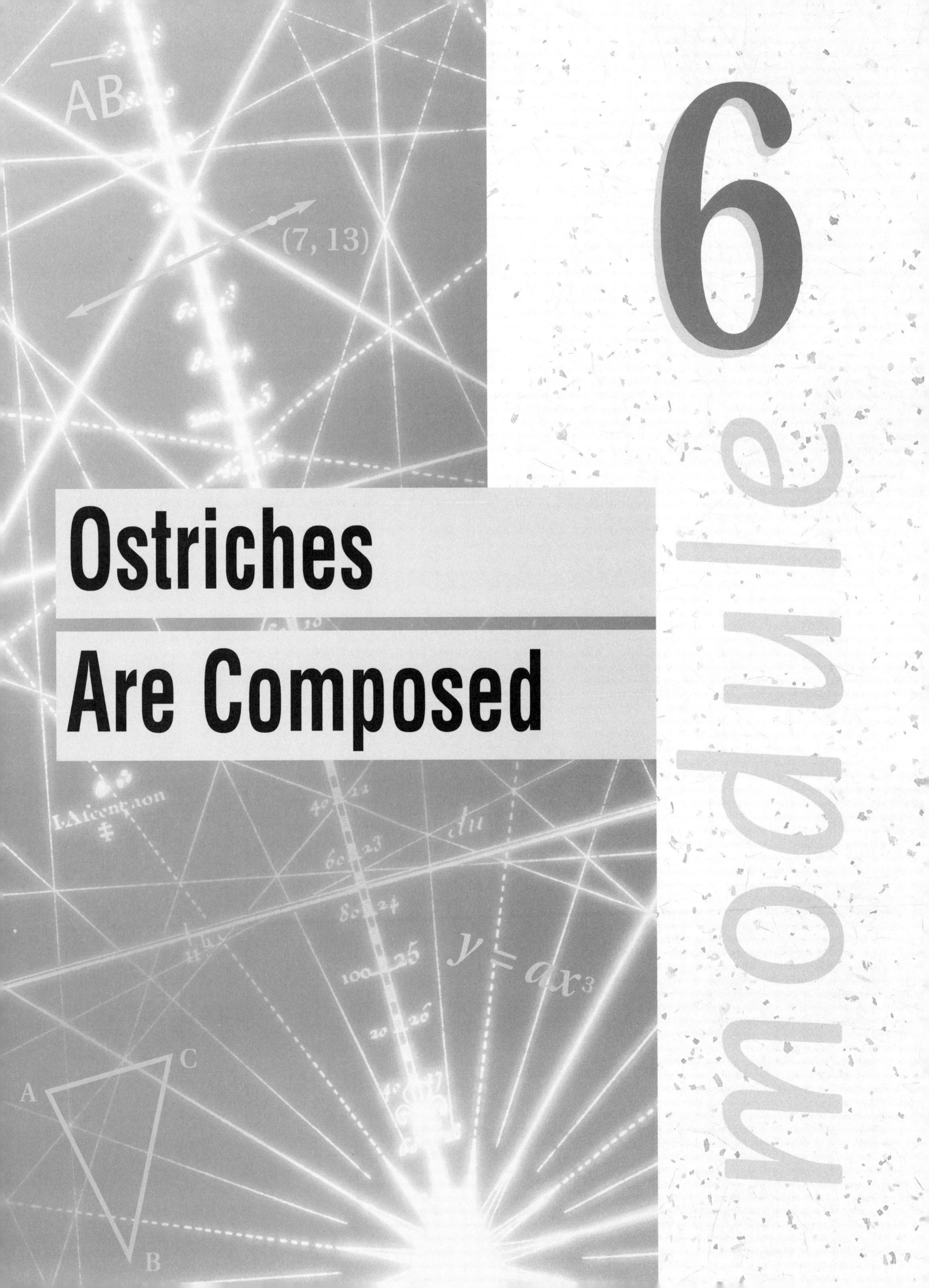

Module 6

Ostriches Are Composed

Introduction

Sal and Guinn are partners in a new venture: an ostrich ranch. Although ostrich ranching has flourished in South Africa for over a century, it only recently has become popular in North America.

After months of research, Sal and Guinn buy several pairs of breeding ostriches. Shortly thereafter, the first chicks hatch. The two partners plan to market both unhatched eggs and adult birds. To help attract customers, they decide to come up with a catchy phrase for their new toll-free number—something like 1-800-OSTRICH or 1-800-BIG-BIRD. Unfortunately, both of these numbers are already in use. The telephone company assigns them the number 1-800-825-2445. With a little bit of creative thought, Sal and Guinn plan to use this number to remind their customers of ostriches.

Discussion

a. Using the keypad in Figure **6-1** for reference, what telephone numbers correspond to OSTRICH and BIG BIRD?

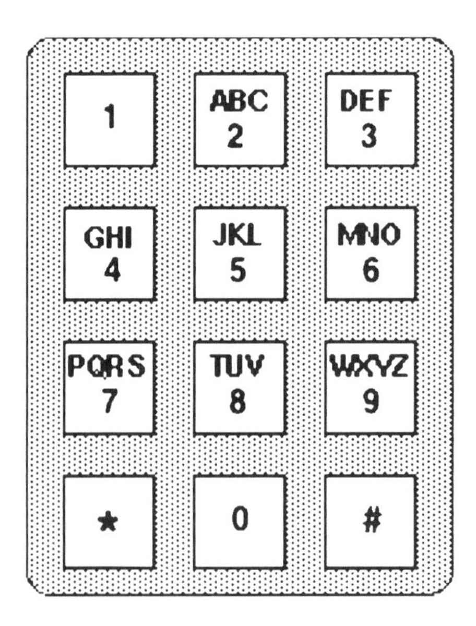

FIGURE 6-1 A telephone keypad.

b. What catchy phrase might Sal and Guinn use for their assigned number, 1-800-825-2445?

c. Compare the processes you used to respond to Parts **a** and **b.**

d. Use ordered pairs to define the pairing of letters of the alphabet to numbers on the telephone keypad in Figure **6-1.**

e. Use ordered pairs to define the pairings of numbers to letters on the keypad.

f. Describe the differences between the pairings in Parts **d** and **e.**

Sal and Guinn are excited about the potential for profit in their new business. Ostriches are valued for beautiful feathers, leathery hides, and flavorful meat. Sal and Guinn plan to sell both unhatched eggs and adult birds, so their income will depend on the number of breeding pairs in their flock. In turn, the number of birds they can keep will depend on the availability of such resources as fenced pasture and fresh water.

In applications such as ostrich ranching, it is often important to know how two quantities—such as profit and flock size—are related.

Exploration

Recall that a **relation** is a set of ordered pairs in which the **domain** is the set of first elements and the **range** is the set of second elements. A **function** is a relation from a domain to a range in which each element of the domain occurs in exactly one ordered pair. Both relations and functions sometimes are specified by a rule relating the domain and range.

Functions often are written without listing a domain. In such cases, the domain is considered to contain all elements for which the function is mathematically meaningful. If the function is composed of numerical ordered pairs, the domain is typically either the set of real numbers or one of its subsets. For example, given the function $f(x) = \sqrt[4]{x}$, the understood domain is all real numbers for which the function is defined. Because this function is not defined when x is negative, the domain for $f(x) = \sqrt[4]{x}$ is the real-number interval $[0,\infty)$.

Determine a possible domain and range for each of the following functions. Record your responses using interval notation. Use a graphing utility to check your results.

a. $f(x) = \sqrt{x-1}$

b. $g(x) = -|x|$

c. $h(x) = \sqrt{4-x^2}$

d. $k(x) = \dfrac{\sin x}{x-5}$

Discussion

a. Explain why the domains of some of the relations in the exploration are restricted.

b. How did your graphing utility indicate limitations in the domain for these relations?

c. Which of the relations in the exploration are functions?

d. Consider graphs in which domain values are represented on the horizontal axis and range values are represented on the vertical axis.

   Describe how a vertical line can be used to show that the graph of a relation does not represent a function.

e. Define a relation from a subset of the set of digits on a telephone keypad to the letters on a telephone keypad.

   1. What is the domain of the relation?
   2. What is the range of the relation?
   3. Is this relation a function? Explain your response.

f. Consider the relation of the set of letters on the telephone keypad in Figure **6-1** to the set of digits $\{0, 1, 2, \ldots, 9\}$.

   1. What is the domain of the relation?
   2. What is the range of the relation?
   3. Is this relation a function? Explain your response.

g. Describe a reasonable domain and range for a function that Sal and Guinn might use to calculate their profit, if profit is a function of the number of ostriches in their flock. Justify your response.

h. As you noted in Part **a** of this discussion, a domain may be restricted because of the operations involved in the function. Other restrictions might be necessary because of the problem setting.

   For example, when using a linear function $d(t)$ to model distance traveled with respect to time, you might restrict the domain of t to values greater than or equal to 0.

   1. Describe two functions in which the domain is restricted because of the operations used.
   2. Describe two problem settings in which a function might require a restricted domain.

Warm-Up

1. Each of Parts **a–e** below describes a relation from x to y. Identify the domain and range for each relation.

   a. $t = \{(3,4), (5,3), (-2,3), (-5,1)\}$

   b.

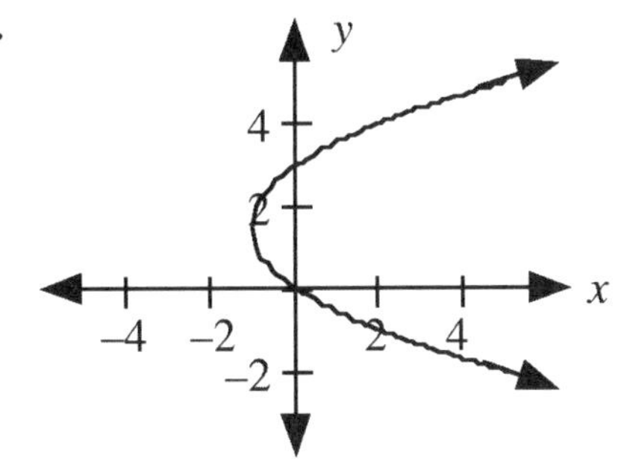

   c. $y = 3/x$

   d. $y = \sqrt{x^3 + 8}$

   e. $y = 3\sin x$

2. Which of the relations in Problem **1** also are functions? Explain your response.

3. Describe the domain and range of a function used to model each of the following.

   a. the number of unhatched eggs as a function of breeding pairs

   b. the air temperature as a function of elevation above sea level

   c. the measure of the angle formed by the minute hand and the hour hand of a clock as a function of the time

Assignment

1.1 **a.** Identify the domain, range, and a possible rule for each of the following relations.

   1. $h = \{(1,1), (1,-1), (4,2), (4,-2), (9,3), (9,-3), (16,4), (16,-4)\}$

   2. $r = \{(1,1), (-2,-8), (3,27), (-4,-64)\}$

   3.

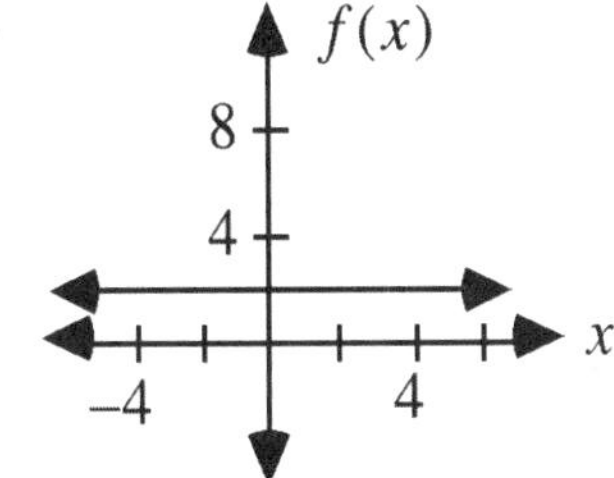

   b. Which of the relations in Part **a** are functions? Explain your response.

mathematics note

One way to represent a function is with a **set diagram,** using an arrow to represent the rule. The set diagram in Figure **6-2** illustrates the domain and range of the function f for $f(x) = x^2$. The domain is the set of real numbers; the range is the set of real numbers greater than or equal to 0.

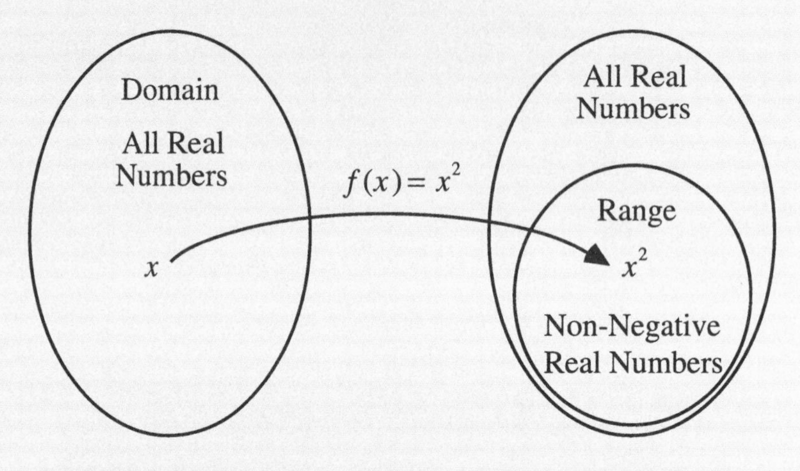

FIGURE 6-2 Set diagram illustrating the function $f(x) = x^2$.

Another way to represent a function between two sets is a **mapping diagram.** Figure **6-3** shows a mapping diagram for the function $h(x) = x + 2$. Both the domain and range are the set of real numbers. The arrows indicate pairings of some elements in the domain with the corresponding elements in the range.

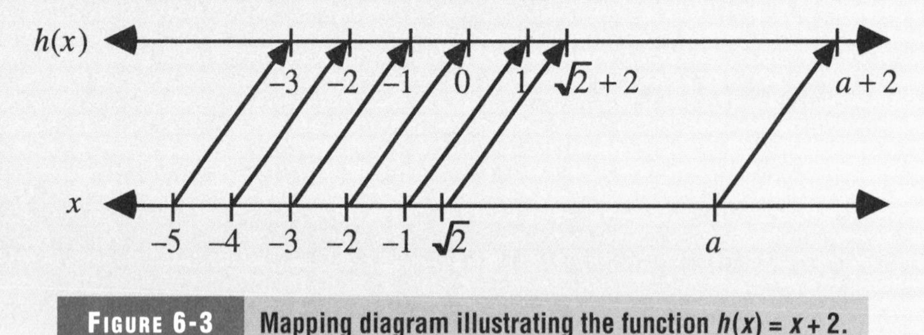

FIGURE 6-3 Mapping diagram illustrating the function $h(x) = x + 2$.

1.2 Consider the telephone keypad shown in Figure **6-1.** Select a key that displays both letters and a number.

a. Consider the relationship between the number and the letters.

1. Draw a set diagram of this relationship.

2. Draw a mapping diagram of this relationship.

3. Write a description of the relationship.

b. Consider the relationship between the letters and the corresponding number. Repeat the steps in Part **a** for this relationship.

c. Which relationship(s) in Parts **a** and **b** are functions? Justify your response.

1.3 Although ostriches cannot fly, they can run exceptionally well. An ostrich can maintain a speed of about 50 km/hr.

a. Using function notation, write an equation for the distance an ostrich can run in terms of time measured in minutes.

b. Determine a possible domain and range for the function.

c. Create a graph that could be used to estimate the distance an ostrich can run in a given time.

1.4 The domain of a function f is the set of real numbers. The function is defined by the rule $f(x) = 3x$.

a. What is the range of this function? Justify your response algebraically.

b. Given the restricted domain $[-1,1]$, find the corresponding range for this function.

c. Find the domain for which $f(x) = 3x$ results in the range $[-1,1]$.

1.5 Consider the function defined by the rule $f(x) = 3x - 2$, with domain $[-5,10]$, where x is a real number. Find the range of this function.

1.6 When cold air blows on exposed skin, our bodies lose heat more quickly. This effect is known as "wind chill."

One formula for calculating wind chill at 0°C is shown below, where v is the wind speed in kilometers per hour:

$$t(v) = 0.4158v - 7.82595\sqrt{v} + 17.48175$$

a. Considering the setting, should the domain for this relation be restricted? Justify your response.

b. Graph this relation and determine if it is a function. Justify your response.

c. Do you think this relation is a good model for determining the wind chill? Justify your response.

1.7 For each of Parts **a–c** below, suggest a rule for a function with the given domain and range. Illustrate each rule graphically.

a. domain: (∞,∞); range: $(-\infty,4]$

b. domain: $(-\infty,0)\cup(0,\infty)$; range: $(-\infty,0)\cup(0,\infty)$

c. domain: $[3,\infty)$; range: $[0,\infty)$

* * * * *

1.8 Write a function, giving its domain and range, in which each element of the range is paired with two elements of the domain.

1.9 At standard temperature and pressure, water boils at 100°C or 212°F. Likewise, water freezes at 0°C or 32°F. The relationship between temperatures measured in degrees Fahrenheit and Celsius is linear.

a. Write a function, $f(c)$, that can be used to convert any given temperature in degrees Celsius to its corresponding temperature in degrees Fahrenheit.

b. Describe the domain and range of the function.

1.10 The Greek mathematician Diophantus (ca. 250 A.D.) has sometimes been called the "father of algebra." A set of special equations bears his name. The solutions to a Diophantine equation consist of ordered pairs, each of whose elements are integers. For example, the solutions to the linear Diophantine equation $x - y = 0$ are the ordered pairs in the set below:

$$\{\ldots,(-3,-3),(-2,-2),(-1,-1),(0,0),(1,1),\ldots\}$$

Find the solutions, if any, to the following Diophantine equations:

a. $x + 5y = 11$

b. $3x + 6y = 71$

1.11 Identify an appropriate domain and range for each function described below.

a. The cost in dollars of producing x number of shirts by a clothing company is modeled by the function:

$$c(x) = 23 + 2x$$

b. The distance in meters that an object falls in t seconds can be modeled by the function:

$$d(t) = 4.9t^2$$

c. The quantity of radioactive carbon-14 remaining after t years is modeled by the following function, where $q_\circ$ is the initial quantity:

$$q(t) = q_\circ e^{-0.000121t}$$

ACTIVITY 2

Sal and Guinn's ranch receives income from two sources: selling unhatched eggs and selling adult breeding pairs. Although the partners could determine a separate profit function for each of these income sources, they would like to simplify the process of projecting potential profits. In this activity, you examine how two functions can be combined into a single function.

Exploration 1

Sal and Guinn hope to sell eggs for $500 each. The number of eggs that they sell each year depends on the number of adult breeding pairs in their flock. Each breeding pair produces an average of 40 viable eggs per year. Not all of the eggs are sold, however. Four of every 40 eggs are kept for hatching on the ranch. Annually, the ranch spends about $60,000 in overhead related to egg production.

In the past, mature breeding pairs have sold for $10,000 per pair. Like the number of eggs sold, the number of breeding pairs sold is a function of the number of breeding pairs in the flock. Each breeding pair annually produces 4 eggs that are hatched on the ranch and raised to maturity. (Assume that 50% of the hatched chicks are male and 50% are female.) The ranch spends about $80,000 per year to maintain its adult ostrich flock.

a. 1. Using the information given above, determine a function $e(x)$ that describes the projected annual profit on the sale of eggs, where x is the number of breeding pairs in the flock.

   2. Determine another function $p(x)$ that describes the projected annual profit on the sale of breeding pairs, where x is the number of breeding pairs in the flock.

b. 1. The size of Sal and Guinn's flock varies from 5 to 15 breeding pairs a year. Use appropriate technology to create a table that evaluates $e(x)$ for each element of this domain.

   2. In the same table, evaluate $p(x)$ for each element of the domain described in Step **1.**

c. To find a function for the ranch's total profit, add the two functions in Part **a** to obtain $(e + p)$. Determine a rule for this new function.

d. Assuming the flock varies from 5 to 15 breeding pairs, determine the domain and range for $(e + p)$.

Discussion 1

a. Compare the profit functions e and p you obtained in Part **a** of Exploration **1** with those of others in the class.

b. Compare the rule you determined for $(e + p)$ with those of others in the class.

c. Describe the domains for the functions e, p, and $(e + p)$.

d. Describe how the range of the function $(e + p)$ was derived from the ranges of e and p.

e. Using the function $(e + p)$ as a model, can the total profit for any one year on Sal's and Guinn's ranch ever be exactly \$200? Explain your response.

f. When adding functions, the distributive property of multiplication over addition allows like terms to be combined. For example, consider the sum of the functions $f(x) = 32x$ and $g(x) = 16x$. Because $32x$ and $16x$ have the common factor of x, the sum can be rewritten as a product as follows:

$$\begin{aligned} f(x) + g(x) &= 32x + 16x \\ &= (32 + 16)x \\ &= 48x \end{aligned}$$

Using the distributive property, which of the following sums can be rewritten as products?

1. $16x^2 + 16x^3$
2. $12\sqrt{x} + 3\sqrt{x}$
3. $\cos x + 5\cos x$
4. $2\sin x + \sin(2x)$

Exploration 2

In Exploration **1**, you added two functions together. In this exploration, you examine the results of some other operations on functions.

a. Consider the following functions:

$$\begin{aligned} f(x) &= \sqrt{x} \\ g(x) &= \sqrt{-x + 5} \end{aligned}$$

1. Graph the two functions on the same coordinate system.
2. Determine the domain and range of each function.
3. Find the intersection of the domains of $f(x)$ and $g(x)$.

mathematics note

The function $(f+g)$ is defined by $(f+g)(x) = f(x) + g(x)$. Likewise, $(f-g)(x) = f(x) - g(x)$, and $(f \bullet g)(x) = f(x) \bullet g(x)$.

When adding, subtracting, or multiplying two or more functions, the operations are defined only for those values common to the domains of all the functions involved.

For example, consider the function $f(x) = 2/x$, with a domain of $(-\infty, 0) \cup (0, \infty)$, and the function $g(x) = 5$, with a domain of $(-\infty, \infty)$. The domains have common values of $(-\infty, 0) \cup (0, \infty)$. Because addition, subtraction, or multiplication of the two functions is defined only for those common values of x, the domain of $(f+g)(x)$ is $(-\infty, 0) \cup (0, \infty)$.

b. Using the functions from Part **a,** graph each of the following on a separate coordinate system and determine its domain and range:

1. $(f+g)(x)$
2. $(f-g)(x)$
3. $(f \bullet g)(x)$

c. Functions also may be divided. When $f(x)$ is divided by $g(x)$, it can be represented as

$$\frac{f(x)}{g(x)}$$

or $(f/g)(x)$, where $g(x) \neq 0$.

1. Graph the function $(f/g)(x)$. Determine the domain and range.
2. Graph the function $(g/f)(x)$. Determine its domain and range.

d. Repeat Parts **a–c** for the functions $f(x) = 2$ and $g(x) = \sin x$.

Discussion 2

a. Consider two functions: f and g. The domain of f is $\{1, 2, \ldots, 10\}$, while the domain of g is $\{-3, -2, \ldots, 5\}$. The range of each is a subset of the real numbers. In this case, what is the domain of $(f+g)$? Explain your response.

b. Figure **6-4** below shows a graph of the functions $h(x)$ and $j(x)$.

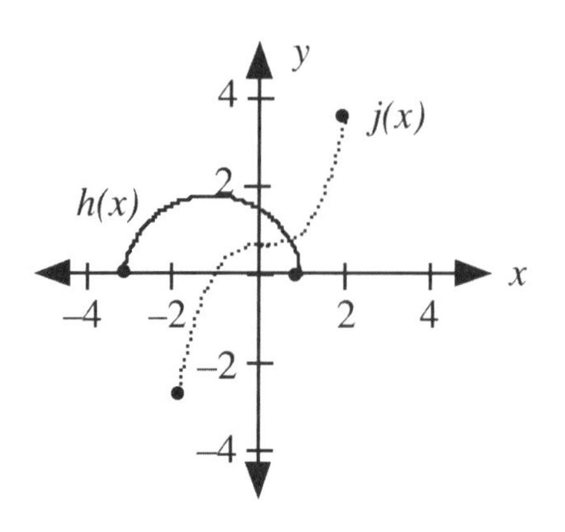

FIGURE 6-4 Graphs of $h(x)$ and $j(x)$.

1. Describe how you could create a graph of the sum of these two functions.
2. Identify the approximate domain of the sum.
3. Identify the approximate range of the sum.

c. In the function defined by f/g, why is it important that $g(x) \neq 0$?

d. Compare the domain and range of $(f/g)(x)$ and $(g/f)(x)$ when $f(x) = \sqrt{x}$ and $g(x) = \sqrt{-x+5}$.

Warm-Up

1. In each of Parts **a–c** below, determine the domains for which the functions $(f+g)(x)$, $(f-g)(x)$, $(f \bullet g)(x)$, $(f/g)(x)$, and $(g/f)(x)$ are defined.

a.

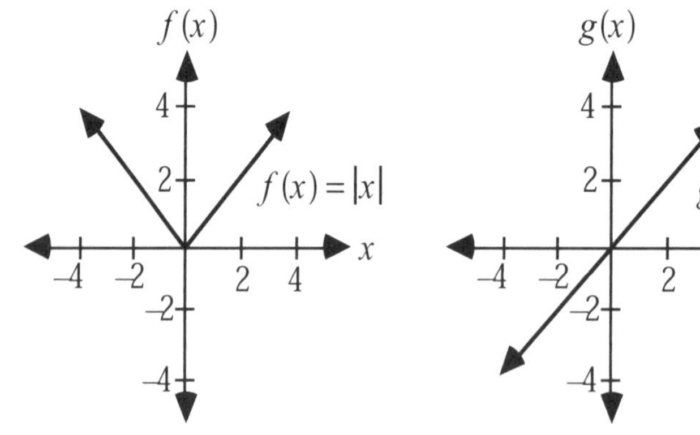

b.

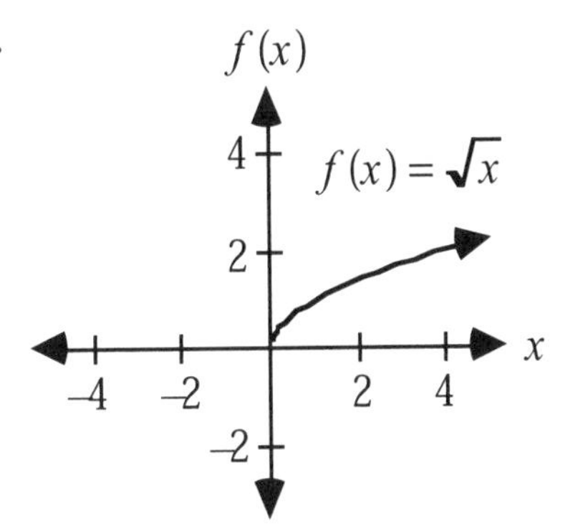

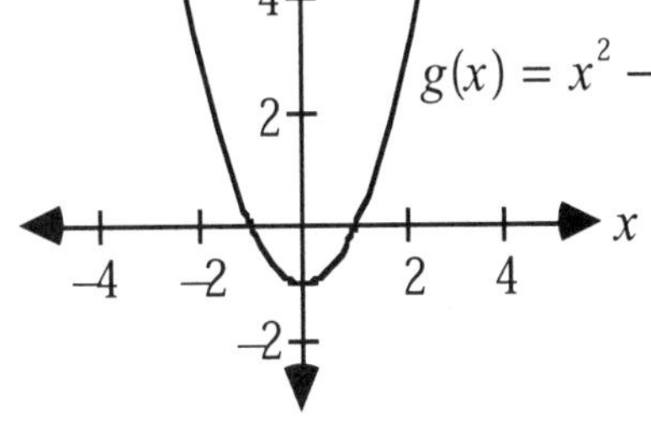

c.

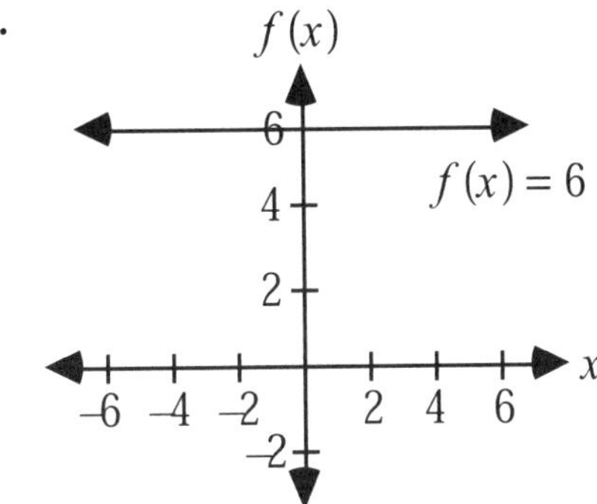

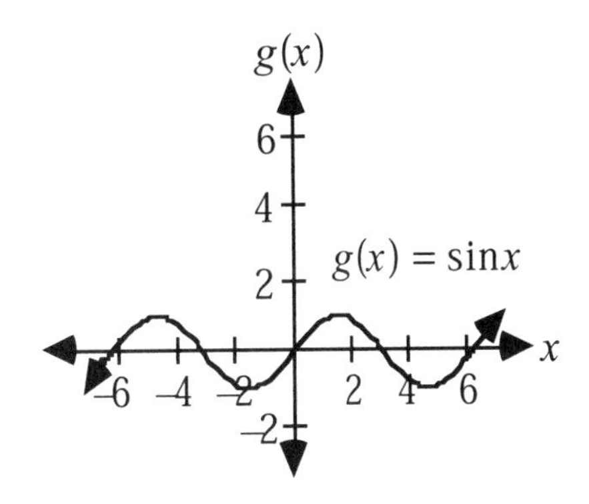

2. Use the following graph of $h(x)$ and $j(x)$ to sketch the graphs of $(h + j)(x)$ and $(h - j)(x)$. Identify the approximate domain and range for both.

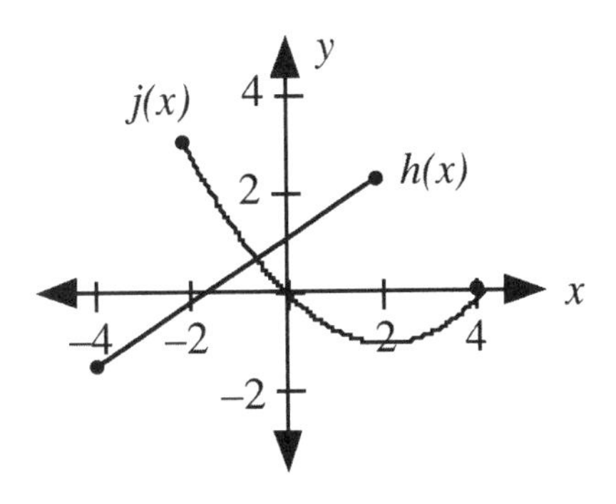

3. For each pair of functions below, determine the rules for $(f + h)(x)$, $(f - h)(x)$, $(f \bullet h)(x)$, and $(f/h)(x)$. Graph each new function and identify its approximate domain and range.

   a. $f(x) = x + 5$ and $h(x) = -2x - 3$

   b. $f(x) = x^2 + 3x$ and $h(x) = x - 2$

Assignment

2.1 **a.** If $f(x) = \sin x$ and $g(x) = \cos x$, graph $(f(x))^2$ and $(g(x))^2$ on the same coordinate system. Determine the domain and range for $(f(x))^2$ and $(g(x))^2$.

b. Assume that $(f(x))^2 = (\sin x)^2$ and $(g(x))^2 = (\cos x)^2$. Write an expression for $(f^2 + g^2)(x)$ and graph this new function. Determine the domain and range of this function.

c. Use the graph from Part **b** to write a simplified expression for $(f^2 + g^2)(x)$.

d. An equation involving trigonometric functions that is true for all real numbers in its domain is a **trigonometric identity.** Does the expression that you wrote in Part **c** form a trigonometric identity? Explain your response.

e. Recall that the division of $\sin x$ by $\cos x$ results in $\tan x$. Using a graph, determine the domain and range of the tangent function.

f. Is the following expression a trigonometric identity? Explain your response.

$$\tan x = \frac{\sin x}{\cos x}$$

2.2 At another ostrich ranch, the owners sell either newly hatched chicks or breeding pairs. They charge $700 for each chick and have a total of $36,000 in annual overhead expenses related to the hatching operation. The ranch sells breeding pairs for $10,000 per pair and spends a total of $40,000 per year to maintain the adult ostrich flock.

a. **1.** Determine a function $c(x)$ to model the profit on the sale of ostrich chicks, where x represents the number of chicks sold.

2. Describe the domain and range for $c(x)$.

3. Determine a function $p(y)$ to model the profit from selling breeding pairs, where y is the number of breeding pairs sold.

4. Describe the domain and range for $p(y)$.

b. What do $c(5)$ and $p(5)$ represent?

c. Explain why it is not reasonable to add the two profit functions in this setting to form a new profit function, $(c + p)(x)$.

d. Consider the profit function $r(x,y) = c(x) + p(y)$ where x is the number of chicks sold and y is the number of breeding pairs sold.

1. What does $r(10,8)$ represent?

2. Describe a possible domain for r. What is the corresponding range?

3. Is r a reasonable function to use for determining the ranch's total profit from the sale of chicks and breeding pairs? Explain your response.

2.3 Consider the functions $f(x) = 3x$, $g(x) = 1/(3x)$, and $h(x) = x - 3$ with their appropriate domains and ranges. Given these functions, find the simplest possible rule for each of the following and describe its domain.

a. $(f + g)(x)$

b. $(f - h)(x)$

c. $(f \bullet g)(x)$

d. $(h/g)(x)$

e. $(f/h)(x)$

* * * * *

2.4 Since its fifth month in business, Bea's Beauty Salon has earned a profit in every month from at least one of two areas: product sales or customer services. The profit from customer services can be described by the function $c(x)$, where x represents time in months. The total profit can be described by the function $f(x)$. The following diagram shows graphs of these two functions.

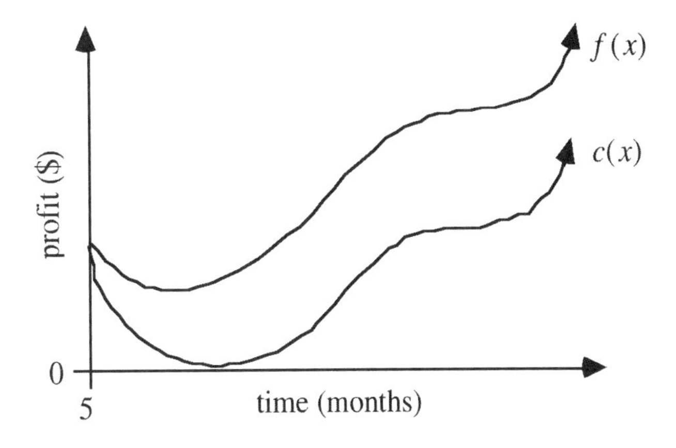

Sketch a graph of the function $p(x)$ that describes the profit from product sales only.

2.5 The function $h(t) = 2 + 15t - 4.9t^2$ models the height (in meters) after t sec of an object thrown straight up in the air at 15 m/sec from a distance of 2 m above the ground. This function can be thought of as the sum of three other functions: $s(t) = 2$, $p(t) = 15t$, and $g(t) = -4.9t^2$.

The function $s(t)$ describes the object's initial height (in meters). The function $p(t)$ describes the effect produced by the object's initial velocity. The function $g(t)$ describes the effect produced by the acceleration due to gravity.

a. Determine a function that models the height (in meters) after t sec of an object thrown straight down from a height of 50 m with an initial velocity of 10 m/sec.

b. How long will it take the object described in Part **a** to hit the ground?

ACTIVITY 3

During their first year of operation, Sal and Guinn found that the size of their flock could be represented as a function of time. They also observed that the number of births at the ranch depended on the number of breeding pairs—more adult ostriches meant that more chicks were hatched. In this respect, the number of births could be thought of as a function of the number of adult ostriches.

The number of births is a function of the number of adult ostriches, and the number of adults is a function of time, so it is also possible to consider the number of births as a function of time. The diagram in Figure **6-5** shows how this can be done by forming a **composite function** $f(g(x))$.

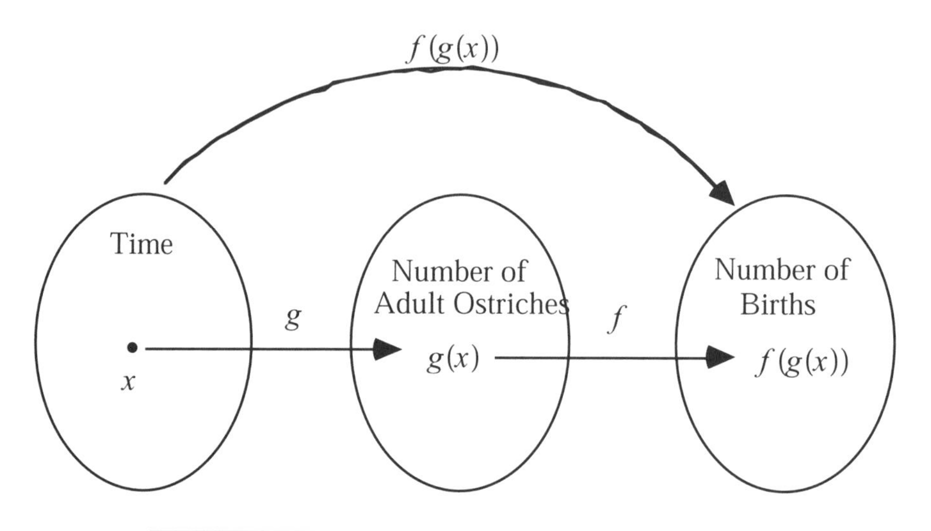

FIGURE 6-5 Diagram of a composition of functions.

mathematics note

Given two functions f and g, the **composite function** $f \circ g$, read as "f composed with g" is defined as

$$(f \circ g)(x) = f(g(x))$$

The domain of $f \circ g$ is the set of all values of x in the domain of g such that $g(x)$ is in the domain of f.

For example, if g is the set of ordered pairs {(1,3), (2,4), (5,11)}, its domain is {1,2,5}. If f is the set of ordered pairs {(3,8), (4,12), (7,13)}, then its domain is {3,4,7}. The domain of $f \circ g$ is {1,2}. This is because {1,2} is part of the domain of g and $g(1) = 3$ and $g(2) = 4$ are values in the domain of f. Figure **6-6** illustrates these relationships using a mapping diagram.

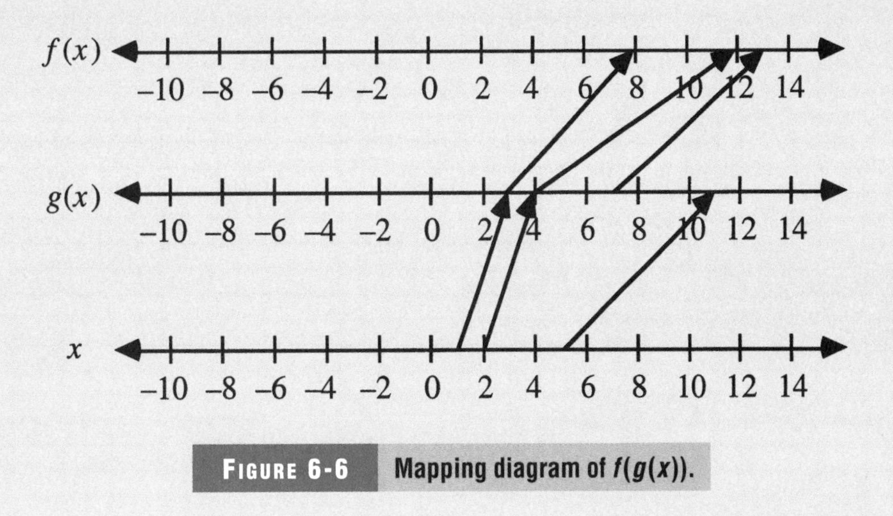

FIGURE 6-6 **Mapping diagram of $f(g(x))$.**

Notice in the mapping diagram in Figure **6-6** that $g(5) = 11$. However, 11 is not in the domain of f, therefore 5 is not in the domain of $f \circ g$. Figure **6-7** shows a simplified version of the mapping diagram for $f \circ g$.

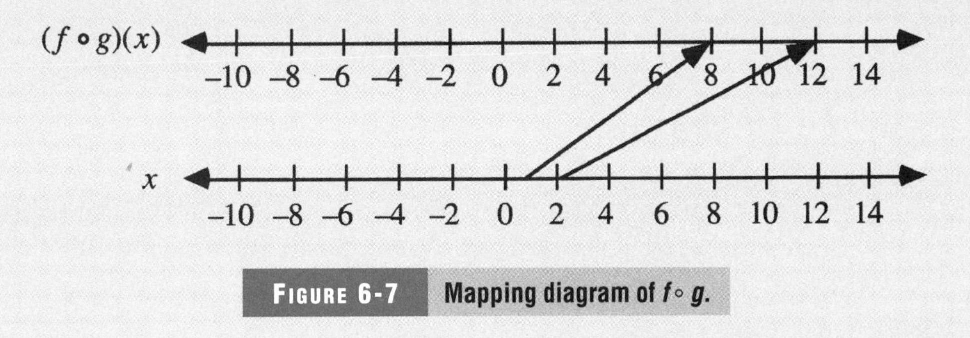

FIGURE 6-7 **Mapping diagram of $f \circ g$.**

From Figure **6-7,** the domain of $f \circ g$ is {1,2} and the range is {8,12}.

Exploration

In this exploration, you investigate the composition of functions using $f(x) = 3x$ and $g(x) = x^2$ and the domain $\{-5, -4, -3, \ldots, 5\}$.

a. Determine the range for $g(x)$.

b. 1. Find the range for $f(g(x))$ by completing a mapping diagram like the one shown in Figure **6-8.**

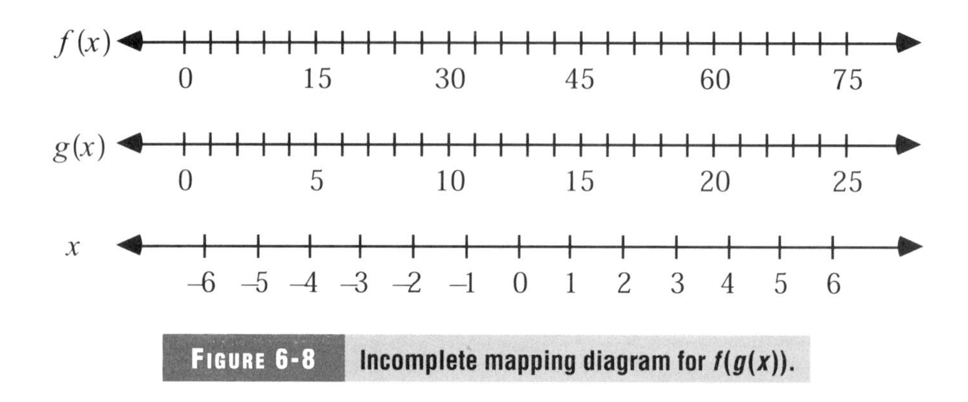

FIGURE 6-8 **Incomplete mapping diagram for *f*(*g*(*x*)).**

2. Determine a rule for $f(g(x))$. State the domain and range for $f(g(x))$.

c. 1. Determine the range for $f(x)$.

2. Find the range for $g(f(x))$ by completing a mapping diagram.

3. Determine a rule for $g(f(x))$. State the domain and range for $g(f(x))$.

Discussion

a. The diagram in Figure **6-6** shows an arrow representing $f(7) = 13$. Why is 13 not included in the range of the composite function $f(g(x))$?

b. Consider the two functions $q(x) = 3x + 2$ and $p(x) = x^2$.

1. Describe what $q(a)$ indicates.

2. Describe what $p(q(a))$ indicates.

c. How do the ranges of $f(g(x))$ and $g(f(x))$ from the exploration compare?

d. Does composition of functions appear to be commutative? Explain your response.

e. If m is the set of ordered pairs $\{(3,5), (4,6), (7,13)\}$ and n is the set $\{(5,10), (6,14), (9,15)\}$, what ordered pairs would be in $n(m(x))$? Explain your response.

f. 1. Describe two functions for which the domain of their composition would be restricted.

   2. Describe a problem setting that would require a restricted domain for a composition of functions.

g. Consider the functions $h(x) = \sqrt{x + 5}$ and $j(x) = x^3 + 3$.

   1. Describe the domain and range for $h(j(x))$.

   2. How does the process of finding $h(j(2))$ differ from the process of finding $j(h(2))$?

   3. Does the domain of $h \circ j$ include all the values in the domain of $j(x)$? Explain your response.

   4. Does the domain of $j \circ h$ include all the values in the domain of $h(x)$? Explain your response.

h. Figure **6-9** below shows graphs of two functions, $y = s(x)$ and $y = t(x)$.

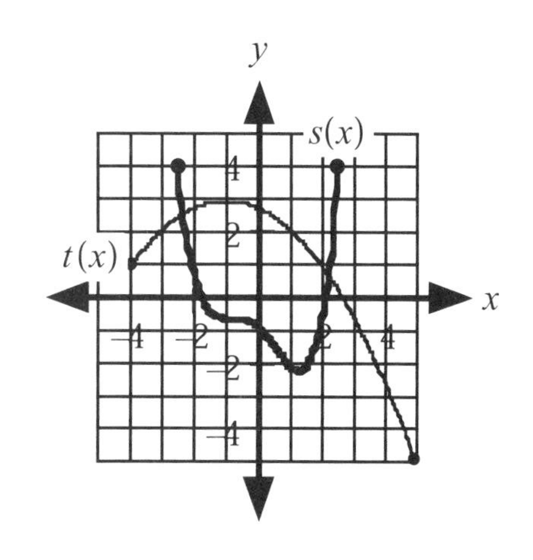

FIGURE 6-9 **Graphs of $s(x)$ and $t(x)$.**

   1. Describe how to find $s(t(-3))$.

   2. Describe how to find $t(s(1))$.

   3. When asked to identify domain values of $t(x)$ for which $s(t(x))$ does not exist, a classmate makes the following argument:

      "The least and greatest values of x for which $s(x)$ is defined are –2.5 and 2.5, respectively. If you draw the horizontal lines $y = -2.5$ and $y = 2.5$, they intersect $t(x)$ at the points with approximate x-coordinates of –2.5, 0, and 4. For the interval (–2.5,0), the graph of $t(x)$ is above the line $y = 2.5$. For the interval (4,5), the graph of $t(x)$ is below the line $y = -2.5$. Therefore, the composite function $s(t(x))$ does not exist over the intervals (–2.5,0) and (4,5)."

      Do you agree with this argument? Explain your response.

   4. For what values of x does $t(s(x))$ not exist? Explain your response.

i. When a pebble is thrown into a pond, a ring of concentric circles is formed. Suppose the radius of the ring increases at a rate of 5.4 cm per second.

   1. Describe a function, $r(t)$, that models the change in the radius over time.
   2. Describe a function, $A(r)$, that models the area of the ring given the radius.
   3. Determine a composite function to model the area of the ring over time.
   4. What are the domain and range of your composite function? Explain your response.

Warm-Up

1. Using the domain $D = \{-3, -2, -1, 0, 1, 2, 3\}$, draw a mapping diagram for each composition below.

   a. $g(f(x))$, where $f(x) = x + 3$ and $g(x) = x^2 - 2$

   b. $(f \circ g)(x)$, where $f(x) = x^2 - 3$ and $g(x) = \sqrt{x + 2}$

   c. $f(g(x))$, where $f(x) = x^2$ and $g(x) = x - 2$

2. Use the following graph to evaluate each composition below.

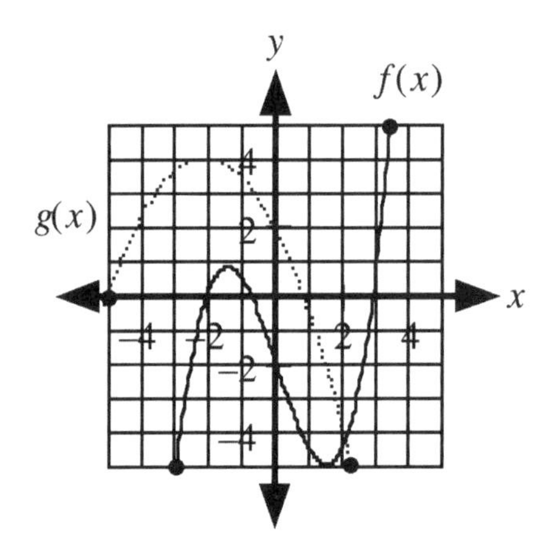

   a. $f(g(0))$

   b. $(g \circ f)(3)$

   c. $f(g(-4))$

   d. $g(f(0))$

   e. $(f \circ g)(2)$

3. For each pair of functions below, determine a rule that describes the composition $f(g(x))$. Indicate the domain and range of the composition.

   a. $f(x) = 2x + 3$ and $g(x) = 3x/5$

   b. $f(x) = 2/x$ and $g(x) = x + 5$

   c. $f(x) = 3x^2$ and $g(x) = \sin x$

   d. $f(x) = 2\sqrt{x}$ and $g(x) = x - 7$

   e. $f(x) = \sqrt{x} + 3$ and $g(x) = \cos x$

Assignment

3.1 Suppose an ostrich ranch keeps 4 eggs for hatching each year and sells the rest. The number of eggs for sale can be modeled by the function $h(x) = x - 4$, where x represents the total egg production that year.

About 20% of each year's eggs are lost to breakage. Because 100% – 20% = 80% = 0.8, the number of unbroken eggs can be modeled by $g(x) = 0.8x$.

a. Suggest an appropriate domain and range for both $h(x)$ and $g(x)$.

b. If there are 40 eggs in a given year, which of the following correctly describes the number of unbroken eggs that are not kept by the ranch for hatching: $h(g(40))$ or $g(h(40))$?

c. Use your answer from Part **b** to help show that composition of functions is not commutative.

3.2 Given the functions $f(x) = x^2$ and $g(x) = \sin x$, what are the domain and range of the composite function $(f \circ g)(x)$?

3.3 Consider the functions $h(x) = x^2$ and $k(x) = \sqrt{x}$.

a. Find the domain and range of each of the following compositions:

1. $(h \circ k)(x)$
2. $(k \circ h)(x)$

b. Write each of the composite functions below in simplified form:

1. $(h \circ k)(x)$
2. $(k \circ h)(x)$

c. Explain why the compositions in Part **b** result in different equations.

3.4 Given the functions $g(x) = x + 4$ and $f(x) = 4x$, simplify the following:

$$c(x) = \frac{f(g(x)) - f(x)}{4}$$

3.5 Sal and Guinn have agreed to invest 20% of the profit from their ostrich operation in a retirement fund. The remaining amount will be divided evenly between them as salary.

a. Determine a function $s(x)$, where x represents annual profit, that can be used to determine the salary for each partner. Suggest an appropriate domain for this function.

b. In the exploration in Activity **2,** you predicted Sal and Guinn's annual profit using the function $n(x) = (e + p)(x) = 38{,}000x - 140{,}000$, where x represents the number of breeding pairs in the flock. Use composition of functions to predict the annual salary for each partner if the ranch maintains a flock of 7 breeding pairs.

c. Determine a function that could be used to calculate the partners' annual salaries given the number of breeding pairs. Suggest an appropriate domain and range for this function.

3.6 Sal and Guinn employ high-school students to clean the ostrich barn. The amount that each student earns depends on the number of hours worked. The amount that each saves for college depends on the total earnings.

a. Choose an appropriate wage for a student. Express earnings as a function of the number of hours worked.

b. Select a realistic proportion of earnings for a student to save for college. Express the amount saved as a function of earnings.

c. Use composition of functions to describe the amount saved for college as a function of the number of hours worked.

* * * * *

3.7 Consider the functions $g(x) = \sqrt{16 - x^2}$ and $h(x) = 5x - 1$.

a. Identify the domain and range of each function.

b. Write each of the composite functions below in simplified form:

1. $(g \circ h)(x)$
2. $(h \circ g)(x)$

c. Find the domain and range of each of the following compositions:

1. $(g \circ h)(x)$
2. $(h \circ g)(x)$

3.8 To complete Parts **a** and **b** below, consider the functions, $f(x) = x - 9$, $g(x) = \sqrt{x} + 5$, and $h(x) = x^2$.

a. Find $g(f(h(7)))$, $f(h(g(7)))$, and $g(h(f(7)))$.

b. Determine a rule for $g(f(h(x)))$ and identify the domain.

3.9 Sal and Guinn store water in a rectangular tank 1 m wide, 3 m long, and 2 m deep. Water flows from the tank into a trough for the ostriches. The water level in the tank drops at a rate of approximately 2.4 cm/hr.

a. Write a function to model the water level in the tank over time.

b. Write a composite function to model the volume of water in the tank over time.

c. If no water is added, how long will it take for the tank to empty? Justify your response.

d. To maintain the water level in the tank, Sal and Guinn decide to use a hose. The hose delivers water at a rate of 60 L/hr. How long will it take for the tank to empty using this system? Explain your response.

Although ostriches can survive for days without water, they prefer to drink and bathe frequently. On Sal and Guinn's ranch, each ostrich consumes about 8 L of water per day. The ranch faces a possible drought this summer. Should Sal and Guinn reduce the size of their flock or should they start looking for more water?

The way in which the partners approach this problem depends on their plans for the business. If they would like to maintain a certain number of birds, they can determine the total amount of water required to sustain a flock of that size. Once that amount is known, they can estimate the volume of water the ranch can provide during a drought, then acquire any additional water needed.

On the other hand, if Sal and Guinn want to use only the available water, they can determine the number of ostriches this supply will maintain and reduce their flock accordingly. The functions involved in analyzing these two different approaches are **inverses** of each other.

mathematics note

The **inverse** of a relation results when the elements in each ordered pair of the relation are interchanged.

For example, the relation {(0,2), (1,3), (4,–2), (–3,–2)} has an inverse relation {(2,0), (3,1), (–2,4), (–2,–3)}. The domain of the original relation becomes the range of the inverse, and the range of the original relation becomes the domain of the inverse.

If a relation is a function, and its inverse is also a function, then the inverse is an **inverse function.** The inverse function of $f(x)$ is denoted by $f^{-1}(x)$, often shortened to f^{-1}.

For example, consider the function $f = \{(1,5), (2,4), (-1,0)\}$. Its inverse is the function $f^{-1} = \{(5,1), (4,2), (0,-1)\}$.

Exploration 1

a. Use technology to create a scatterplot of the relation f and its inverse using the domains and ranges given in Table **6-1.** To simplify comparisons, make the length of 1 unit on the x-axis the same as the length of 1 unit on the y-axis.

Table 6-1 ■ *Relation f and the Inverse of f*

Relation	Domain	Range
$f(x) = 2x - 5$	{–2, –1, 0, . . . , 10}	{–9,–7,–5, . . . ,15}
Inverse of f	range of f	domain of f

b. Determine the point of intersection of the graph of f and the graph of its inverse.

c. Determine the equation of the line containing the origin and the point identified in Part **b.** Plot this line on the same graph as in Part **a.**

d. Describe any special relationships you observe among the graphs of f, its inverse, and the line graphed in Part **c.**

e. Create another linear function $g(x)$ and repeat Parts **a–d.** You may choose a different domain for $g(x)$.

f. Repeat Part **a** using the quadratic function $h(x) = x^2 + 2$. You may choose a different domain for $h(x)$.

g. Plot the line that you found in Part **c** on the graph from Part **f.** Describe any special relationships you observe among the graphs of h, its inverse, and this line.

Discussion 1

a. Describe the relationship between the domain and range of a function and those of its inverse.

b. Describe the graphs of the inverses of f, g, and h.

c. Is each inverse also a function? Explain your responses.

d. What relationships are there among the graphs of each function, its inverse, and the graph of the line $y = x$? Explain your response.

Exploration 2

Each morning when Guinn turns the ostrich chicks into the fenced pasture, she opens the pasture gate, then drives the chicks out of the barn. In the evening, she drives the chicks back into the barn, then closes the gate. In one sense, her chores in the evening represent the "inverse" of her chores in the morning. In the evening, Guinn undoes her actions of the morning and the chicks are returned to the barn.

a. A similar process can be used to determine the equation that represents the inverse of a function, such as $f(x) = 2x + 8$. In this case, the function multiplies a domain value by 2, then adds 8 to the product. The equation that represents the inverse of $f(x)$ undoes these actions, first by subtracting 8, then by dividing the result by 2:

$$y = \frac{x - 8}{2}$$

This equation defines a function, so it can be denoted as follows:

$$f^{-1}(x) = \frac{x - 8}{2}$$

Use this method to determine an equation that represents the inverse of each of the following relations. Describe any restrictions on the domain of each inverse, and determine whether or not each is a function.

1. $f(x) = 3x - 1$
2. $g(x) = \sqrt{x + 7}$
3. $h(x) = 9x^2$
4. $k(x) = x^3 - 8$

Note: The inverse of a set of ordered pairs (x,y), where y represents the function values of x, is a set of ordered pairs (y,x). To obtain the rule for the inverse, x and y should be interchanged in the original equation. This new equation should then be solved for y, subject to any necessary restrictions.

b. When two functions f and g are inverses of each other, $(f \circ g)(x) = (g \circ f)(x) = x$. For example, considering $f(x) = 2x + 8$ and its inverse f^{-1}, the following equations are true:

$$
\begin{aligned}
(f \circ f^{-1})(x) &= 2\left(\frac{x-8}{2}\right) + 8 \\
&= (x - 8) + 8 \\
&= x - 8 + 8 \\
&= x + 0 \\
&= x
\end{aligned}
\qquad
\begin{aligned}
(f^{-1} \circ f)(x) &= \frac{(2x + 8) - 8}{2} \\
&= \frac{2x + 8 - 8}{2} \\
&= \frac{2x + 0}{2} \\
&= \frac{2x}{2} \\
&= x
\end{aligned}
$$

Use this definition to verify that each inverse you obtained in Part **a** is correct.

Discussion 2

a. Which of the relations in Part **a** of Exploration **2** have inverses that are not functions? Explain your response.

b. The graphs in Figure **6-10** below show two relations and their inverses. In each case, the graph of the relation is indicated by a solid curve, and the graph of the inverse is indicated by a dotted curve.

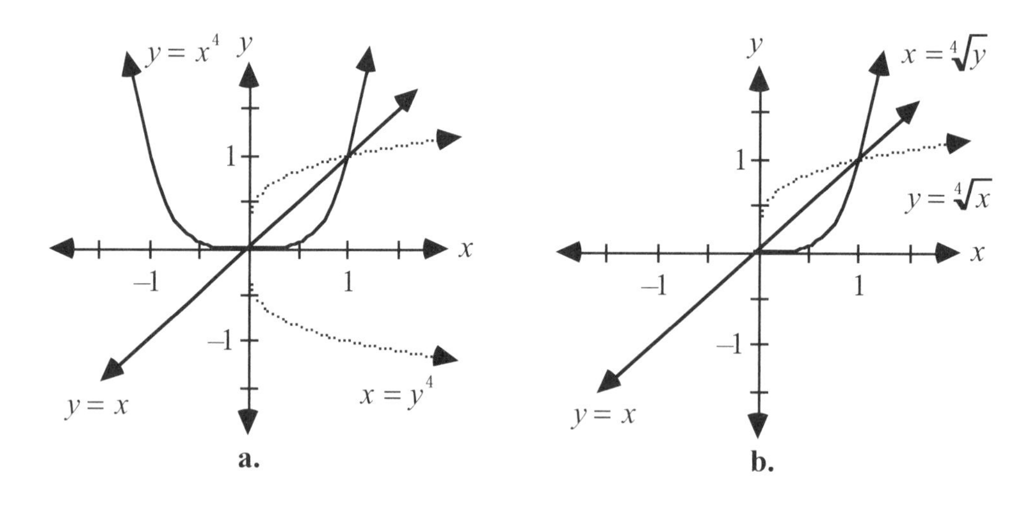

FIGURE 6-10 Two relations and their inverses.

1. Describe the relationship between the line $y = x$ and the graphs in Figure **6-10.**
2. Explain why the graphs in Figures **6-10a** and **b** are identical in the first quadrant but not in the second and fourth quadrants.
3. If a horizontal line intersects the graph of a function in more than one point, then its inverse is not a function. Use this notion to explain whether or not the inverse of each relation in Figure **6-10** is a function.

c. 1. Given the graph of a relation, describe how you could create the graph of its inverse using the line $y = x$.

2. Use the definition of an inverse to explain why your method works.

mathematics note

A **one-to-one function** is a function such that each element in the range corresponds to a unique element of the domain. In other words, if $f(x_1) = f(x_2)$, then $x_1 = x_2$. One-to-one functions are important because they are the only functions whose inverses also are functions.

For example, the one-to-one function $f = \{(-3,-13), (-1,-7), (1,-1), (3,5), (5,11)\}$ has the inverse function $f^{-1} = \{(-13,-3), (-7,-1), (-1,1), (5,3), (11,5)\}$. The function $g = \{(-2,4), (-1,1), (1,1), (2,4)\}$, however, is not a one-to-one function. Its inverse is $\{(4,-2), (1,-1), (1,1), (4,2)\}$, which is not a function.

d. Use ordered pairs to illustrate why the function $h(x) = 9x^2$ is not one-to-one.

e. Explain why a horizontal line test can be used to determine when a graph is not a one-to-one function.

f. Explain why the trigonometric functions sine, cosine, and tangent do not have inverse functions.

Exploration 3

As you discovered in Exploration **2,** only one-to-one functions have inverses that are also functions. In some cases, however, it might be desirable to allow an inverse function to exist by placing restrictions on a function's domain. In other words, it is sometimes helpful to restrict the domain of a function that is not one-to-one in order to create a one-to-one function.

a. **1.** Create a graph of $f(x) = \cos x$.

  2. Determine the domain and range of $f(x)$.

b. Identify the domain and range of the inverse of $f(x)$.

c. Many calculators feature a button labeled "$\cos^{-1}$," "$\cos^{-1}(x)$, or "arccos." All of these labels indicate the inverse of cosine. When two functions f and g are inverses of each other, $f(g(x)) = x$ and $g(f(x)) = x$.

  1. Using various values of x from the domain in Part **b,** test the composition $\cos(\cos^{-1}(x))$. Record your findings.

  2. Repeat Step **1** for $\cos^{-1}(\cos(x)) = x$ using various values of x from the domain in Part **a.**

d. Describe the restrictions necessary for $f(x) = \cos x$ to have an inverse function in which every unique value of the range of $f(x)$ is included in the domain of $f^{-1}(x)$.

e. On the same coordinate system, sketch a graph of the function and its inverse over this restricted domain.

f. Repeat Parts **a–e** for $f(x) = x^2$ and its inverse $\sqrt{x}$.

Discussion 3

a. **1.** Describe the restrictions you placed on the domain of $f(x) = \cos x$ to create a function that has an inverse function.

  2. Would any other restricted domains also produce a range that contains every unique value of the range of $f(x) = \cos x$?

b. From the Level 3 model "Can It," you might recall that a unit circle is a circle with center at the origin and a radius of 1 unit. The coordinates of points on the unit circle are of the form $(\cos\theta, \sin\theta)$, where θ is the measure of an angle formed by a radius that contains the point and the positive x-axis.

Figure **6-11** below shows a graph of a unit circle. Use this graph to justify the restricted domain you described in Part **a**.

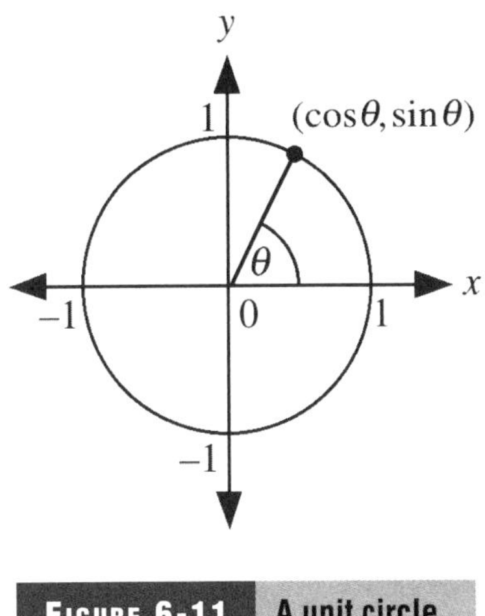

FIGURE 6-11 A unit circle.

c. 1. Describe the restrictions that you placed on the domain of $f(x) = x^2$ to create a function that has an inverse function.

2. Use a graph of the function to explain why the restrictions you placed on the domain make sense.

d. In addition to an inverse cosine function, most calculators also feature an inverse sine and an inverse tangent.

1. Describe the restrictions that you would expect to place on the domain of the sine function.

2. Describe the restrictions that you would expect to place on the domain of the tangent function.

e. What other types of functions might require restricted domains in order to have inverse functions?

f. Describe the restrictions on x necessary to solve each equation below.

$$\cos(x) = -0.36$$
$$\cos^{-1}(\cos(x)) = \cos^{-1}(-0.36)$$
$$x \approx 1.939$$

$$\cos^{-1}(x) = 0.23$$
$$\cos\left(\cos^{-1}(x)\right) = \cos(0.23)$$
$$x \approx 0.974$$

g. Are the solutions shown in Part **f** above the only possible ones for these equations? Explain your response.

Warm-Up

1. Each of Parts **a–c** below shows a function and its graph. Identify the functions that have an inverse function. Justify your responses.

   a. $j(x) = \frac{x^4}{2} - 3x^2 - \frac{1}{2}$

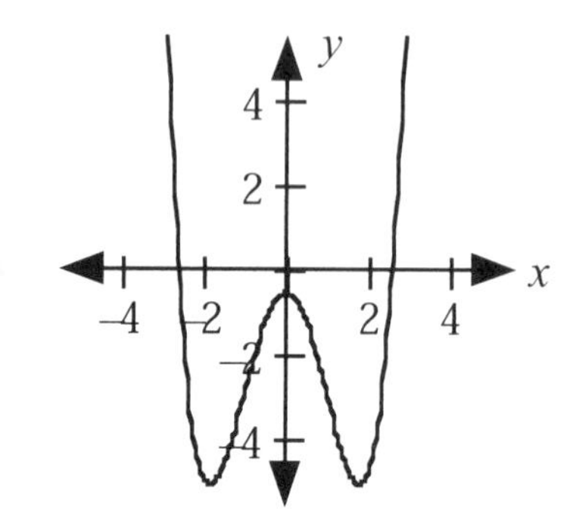

   b. $h(x) = x^3 + x^2 - 4.75x - 2$

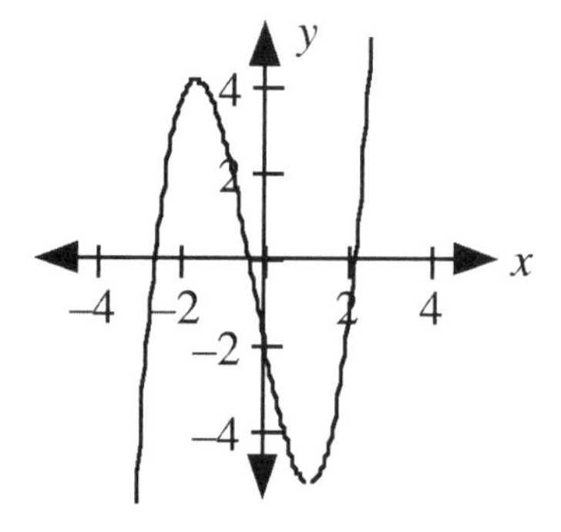

   c. $g(x) = \frac{3}{4}x^3 + \frac{9}{4}x^2 + \frac{9}{4}x + \frac{7}{4}$

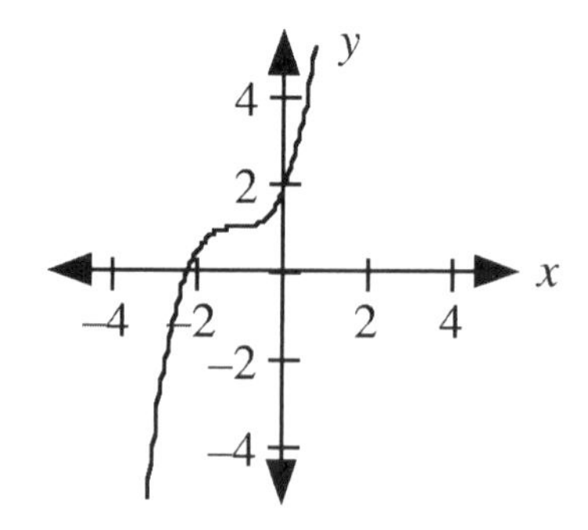

2. Sketch a graph of the inverse relation for each function in Problem **1.**

3. Determine the inverse function, $f^{-1}(x)$, for each of the one-to-one functions below. Demonstrate that your response is correct by showing that $f^{-1}(f(x)) = f(f^{-1}(x)) = x$.

   a. $t(x) = 3x - 5$

   b. $s(x) = 4x^3 + 8$

   c. $r(x) = \frac{1}{2}\sqrt[3]{(x-1)}$

4. Identify the restrictions necessary for each function below to have an inverse function. Find each inverse function and describe its domain and range.

   a. $q(x) = 3x^4 + 2$

   b. $v(x) = 0.25\cos(x) - 3$

   c. $t(x) = 2(x - 0.75)^2 + 3.875$ (*Hint:* This equation is written in vertex form.)

Assignment

4.1 To help themselves analyze the effects of a potential drought on the ranch, Sal and Guinn decide to create two different sets of graphs.

   a. If they want to maintain their current flock, Sal and Guinn must examine the relationship between water consumption and time. Recall that each ostrich uses about 8 L of water per day. The following graph shows the average amount of water needed by one ostrich versus time in days.

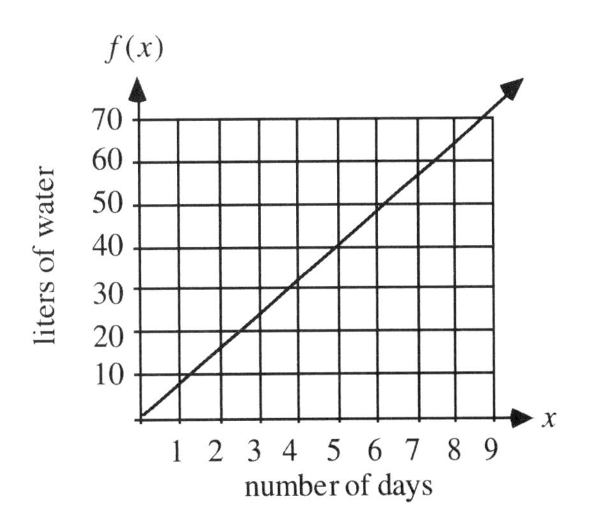

      1. What assumptions were made in the creation of this model?

      2. Use the graph in Part **a** to estimate the amount of water that an ostrich will use over 5 days.

3. Estimate the time it will take for one ostrich to use 20 L of water.
4. Write an equation that describes the liters of water used per ostrich as a function of time in days.
5. Suppose that Sal and Guinn want to maintain a flock of 40 birds. If the drought lasts for 60 days, how much water will they need?

b. If Sal and Guinn want to use only the water they currently have available on the ranch, they must determine the number of birds their present resources will maintain during a drought. The following graph shows time in days versus liters of water needed per ostrich.

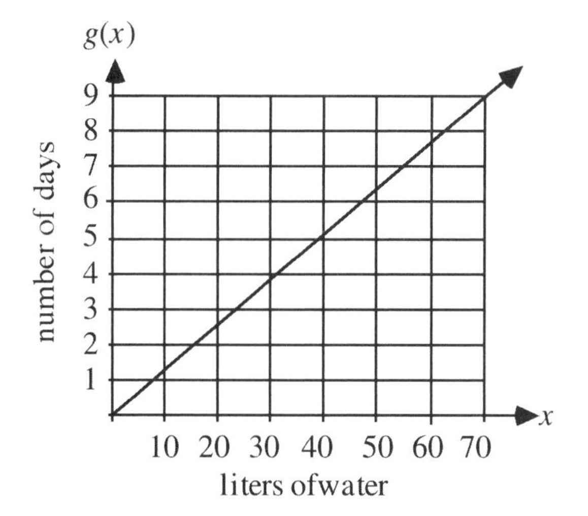

1. What assumptions were made in the creation of this model?
2. Use the graph above to estimate how many days it will take one ostrich to consume 70 L of water.
3. Estimate the liters of water that one ostrich will consume in 2 days.
4. Write an equation that describes time in days as a function of liters of water available per ostrich.
5. The water tank at the ranch holds 16,000 L. If the drought lasts for 60 days, determine the size of the flock that Sal and Guinn can maintain.

c. What relationship exists between the two equations you found in Parts **a** and **b**?

d. Graph the equations from Parts **a** and **b** on the same axes. How does this graph support your response to Part **c**?

4.2 **a.** Which of the following functions are one-to-one functions?

1. $f(x) = 2x + 3$
2. $f(x) = x^3$
3. $f(x) = (x - 4)/5$
4. $f(x) = x^4$

b. For each one-to-one function identified in Part **a,** write the equation of its inverse using $f^{-1}(x)$ notation.

c. For each one-to-one function identified in Part **a,** list the domain and range of $f(x)$ and $f^{-1}(x)$.

d. For each function that is not one-to-one, find a restricted domain for which an inverse function exists.

mathematics note

The inverse of the exponential function $f(x) = a^x$ where $a > 0$ is $f^{-1}(x) = \log_a x$, where $x > 0$ and read "log of x base a" or "log base a of x."

For example, if $f(x) = 12^x$, then $f^{-1}(x) = \log_{12} x$.

4.3 **a.** Describe the domain and range of $f(x) = 10^x$.

b. Write the inverse of $f(x) = 10^x$ using logarithmic notation.

c. Complete the table below without using technology.

$f(x) = 10^x$		inverse of $f(x)$	
x	10^x	x	$\log x$
−4		0.0001	
−2		0.01	
−1		0.1	
0		1	
1		10	
2		100	
4		10,000	

d. Compare the ordered pairs of $f(x) = 10^x$ to those of its inverse.

e. Graph $f(x)$ and the inverse of $f(x)$ on the same coordinate system.

f. Describe the domain and range of the inverse of $f(x) = 10^x$.

g. Is the inverse of $f(x)$ a function? Explain your response.

4.4 **a.** Create a scatterplot of the graph of $f(x) = \sin x$ over the domain $[-4\pi, 4\pi]$.

b. On the same coordinate system, create a scatterplot of the inverse of the function defined in Part **a.**

c. Explain why the inverse of $f(x) = \sin x$ over the domain $[-4\pi, 4\pi]$ is not a function.

d. Find a restricted domain of $f(x) = \sin x$ so that its inverse is also a function, and so that all possible values of the range of $f(x) = \sin x$ are values of the domain in the inverse.

e. Graph $f(x) = \sin x$ and its inverse over this restricted domain.

4.5 New industries, such as ostrich farming, often suffer rapid changes in the prices of their products.

The following table shows the average prices of three-month-old ostriches from 1993 to 1998.

Years after 1992	Average Price ($)
1	4085
2	2646
3	946
4	415
5	98
6	50

SOURCE: Gillespie and Schupp, 2002.

a. Create a scatterplot of this data.

b. Determine an appropriate function to model the data.

c. Is your model a one-to-one function? Explain your response.

d. Use logarithms to find the inverse of your model from Part **b.**

What information is represented by this inverse relation?

e. In Activity **2,** you estimated the profits for an ostrich ranch assuming that prices would remain constant. How does the information in the table above affect those estimates?

Research Project

As you discovered in Problem **4.5,** prices in the ostrich industry fell dramatically from 1993 to 1998. Sudden price drops have affected other markets as well. One famous example occurred during the Dutch "tulipmania" of the 17th century, in which speculators drove prices for flower bulbs to incredible heights, then were wiped out as the market crashed.

Conduct some research on one of these so-called market "bubbles." Obtain some data that shows changes in price over time. Determine a function that fits this data. Identify another model to estimate profit as a function of price. Then use a composition of functions to model the change in profit over time.

* * * * *

4.6 **Parametric equations** allow rectangular coordinates to be expressed in terms of another variable (the parameter). On an xy-plane, for example, both x and y can be expressed as functions of a third variable t.

a. Consider the relation $y = 5x^2$. Graph this relation parametrically using the equations $x = t$ and $y = 5t^2$. Graph its inverse using the equations $x = 5t^2$ and $y = t$.

b. How can you verify that the graphs in Part **a** represent inverses?

c. Why does the method described in Part **a** result in inverse relations?

4.7 **a.** Graph the function $f(x) = \tan x$.

b. Identify an interval in which $f(x) = \tan x$ is a one-to-one function.

c. What is the range of the function $f(x) = \tan x$ over the interval in Part **b**?

d. Find the domain and range of the inverse of $f(x)$ over the interval in Part **b.**

e. Graph $f^{-1}(x)$ over the restricted domain in Part **d.**

4.8 What is true about the composition of a function with its inverse function?

Summary Assessment

Sal and Guinn have just sold one pair of ostriches to their friend Terry. In approximately two years, this pair will become mature adults and produce approximately 40 eggs per year. Sal and Guinn have recommended that Terry increase the size of his flock by keeping two pairs of ostriches out of each year's eggs and selling the rest. It will take approximately three more years for each new pair of ostriches to mature and produce their own eggs. Function f models the approximate number of ostrich pairs Terry will have in x years:

$$f(x) = 10^{0.1618x}$$

1. Use this function to predict the total number of ostrich pairs Terry will have in 7 years.

2. Terry wants to know how many years it will take before he has a certain number of ostrich pairs. Use function f to determine a new function that will give the number of years it will take to produce x ostrich pairs.

3. a. Graph the functions in Problems **1** and **2** on the same set of axes.

   b. Describe the graphs in Part **a,** including their domains and ranges.

   c. Explain whether or not the functions in Problems **1** and **2** are one-to-one functions.

4. Terry would like to determine the cost of fencing a pasture for the ostriches. The cost per meter for chain-link fence is \$30 for materials and \$10 for labor. According to Sal and Guinn, each pair of ostriches should have 1400 m^2 of pasture.

   Assuming that Terry fences a single square pasture, determine functions for each of the following:

   a. the length of fence required for x pairs of ostriches

   b. the cost of materials for x meters of fence

   c. the cost of labor for x meters of fence.

5. Identify the domain and range of each function in Problem **4.**

6. Use the functions in Problems **4b** and **4c** to determine a new function that describes the total cost for x meters of fencing.

7. a. Compose two or more of the functions in the problems above to determine a function that describes the total cost of fencing sufficient to contain Terry's growing flock of ostriches for x years.

   b. Identify the domain and range of the function in Part **a.**

Module Summary

- A **relation** is a set of ordered pairs in which the **domain** is the set of first elements and the **range** is the set of second elements.
- A **function** is a relation from a domain to a range in which each element of the domain occurs in exactly one ordered pair.
- One way to represent a function between two sets is to use a **set diagram** with an arrow to represent the rule. A second way to represent a function between two sets is a **mapping diagram.**
- The function $(f+g)$ is defined by $(f+g)(x)=f(x)+g(x)$. Likewise, $(f-g)(x)=f(x)-g(x)$, $(f \bullet g)(x)=f(x) \bullet g(x)$, and $(f/g)(x)=f(x)/g(x)$ where $g(x) \neq 0$.
- When adding, subtracting or multiplying two or more functions, these operations are defined only for those values common to the domains of all the functions involved.
- Given two functions f and g, the **composite function** $f \circ g$, read as "f composed with g" is defined as

  $$(f \circ g)(x) = f(g(x))$$

  The domain of $f \circ g$ is the set of all values of x in the domain of g such that $g(x)$ is in the domain of f.
- The **inverse** of a relation results when the elements in each ordered pair of the relation are interchanged. The domain of the original relation becomes the range of the inverse, while the range of the original relation becomes the domain of the inverse.
- If a relation is a function, and its inverse is also a function, the inverse is an **inverse function.** The inverse function of f is denoted by f^{-1}.
- The graph of the inverse is a reflection of the graph of the function in the line $y=x$.
- A **one-to-one function** is a function such that each element in the range corresponds to a unique element of the domain. In other words, if $f(x_1)=f(x_2)$, then $x_1=x_2$. One-to-one functions are important because they are the only functions whose inverses also are functions.
- The inverse of the exponential function $f(x)=a^x$, where $a>0$, is $f^{-1}(x)=\log_a x$, where $x>0$ and read "log of x base a" or "log base a of x."

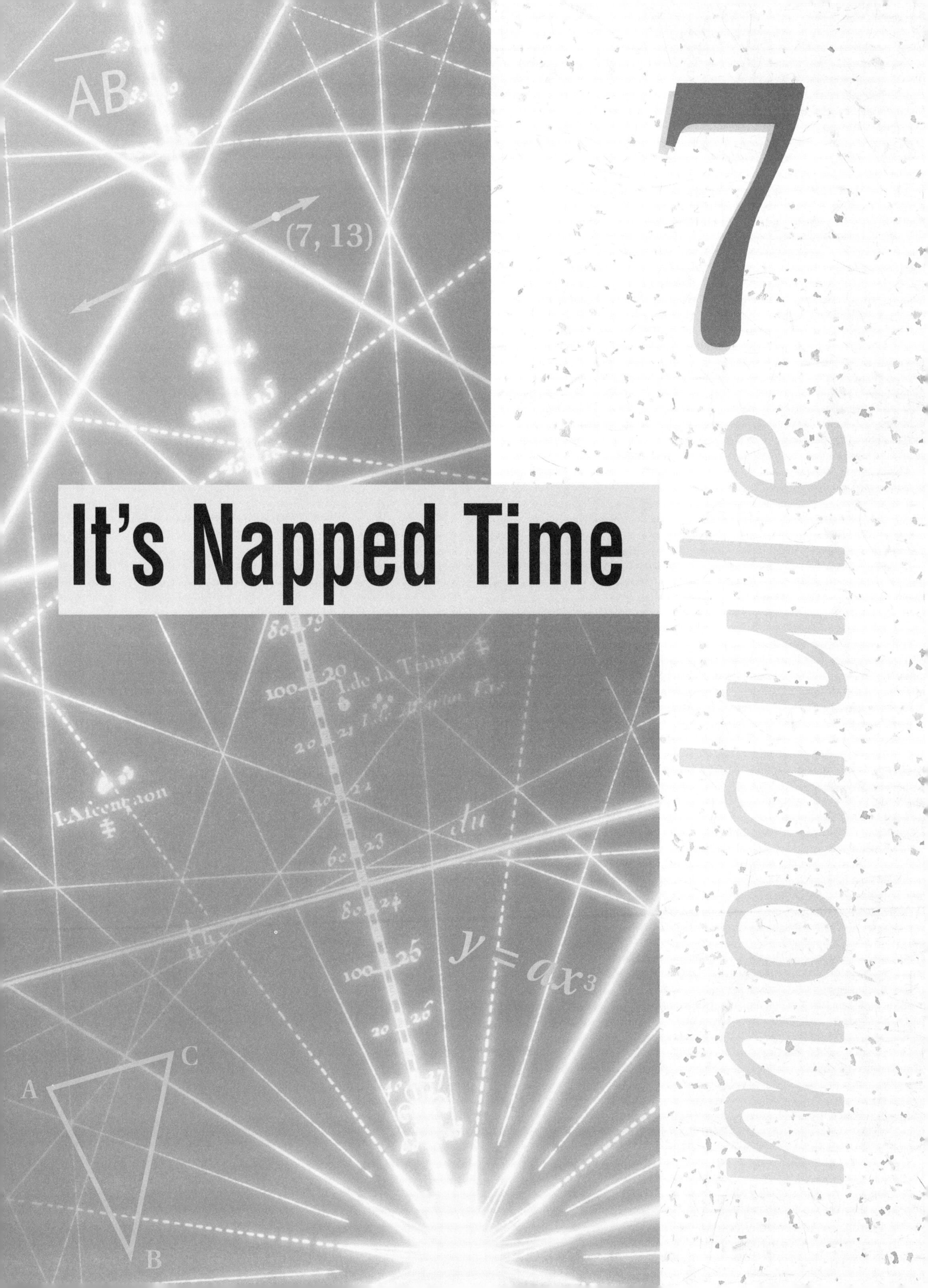

Module 7
It's Napped Time
AB
(7, 13)
$y = ax^3$
A
B
C

Introduction

At a stadium in Pasadena, California, two soccer teams stand ready. In Rome, Italy, fans anxiously await the beginning of the match. It's the World Cup final—the world's most watched sporting event! Millions of soccer fans expect to view every second of the game, live on television. But how can a television signal be received at countless locations, all over the globe, all at the same time?

The answer involves parabolic reflectors. First, a reflector whose cross-section is a parabola focuses a signal from a broadcasting station near the stadium, transmitting it to a satellite 36,000 km above the earth's surface. After receiving this signal, the satellite broadcasts it back towards earth. Parabolic dishes throughout the world receive and concentrate the signal. Local networks then transmit it to the television screens of eager fans.

In today's fast-paced world of telecommunications, satellite dishes have become common sights. They sprout from backyards and office buildings, roam the streets on mobile transmission trucks, and bring a world of information to schools and communities. How does the shape of a satellite dish affect how the dish works? You can answer this question by investigating **conic sections.**

Mathematicians have written about these shapes for well over 2000 years. In fact, the Greek geometer Appollonius of Perga wrote eight books on conic sections in the third century B.C. Since that time, mathematicians have continued to investigate and explore the special properties of these curves.

mathematics note

The set of all points that satisfy a given geometric condition is a **locus** (plural **loci**). For example, a circle is the locus of all points in a plane that are a given distance, the radius, from a fixed point, the center.

The equation defining a locus is determined by the coordinates of the points belonging to the locus and by no other points. In a coordinate plane, for example, the locus of the equation $y = 2x + 3$ is the set of all points on a line with a slope of 2 and a y-intercept of 3.

A locus of points also can be defined in three dimensions. To visualize one three-dimensional locus, hold a pencil at its midpoint between your thumb and finger, as illustrated in Figure **7-1.** While keeping the midpoint of the pencil stationary, move the pencil so that its tip draws a circle.

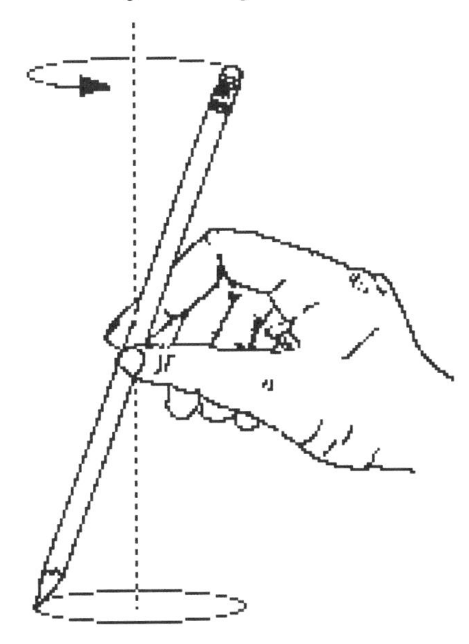

Figure 7-1 Pencil drawing a circle.

Now imagine the line that contains the pencil. The path of that line as you move the pencil describes the locus of points for a **double-napped cone.** The midpoint of the pencil represents the **apex** of the cone. As the name implies, each conic section is a portion of a double-napped cone.

mathematics note

A **conic section** can be formed by the intersection of a plane with a double-napped cone. In a right circular cone, the conic section formed depends on the slope of the intersecting plane. The intersection may be a **circle,** an **ellipse,** a **parabola,** or a **hyperbola,** depending on the placement of the plane. The four conic sections and the plane-cone intersections that produce them are shown in Figure **7-2.**

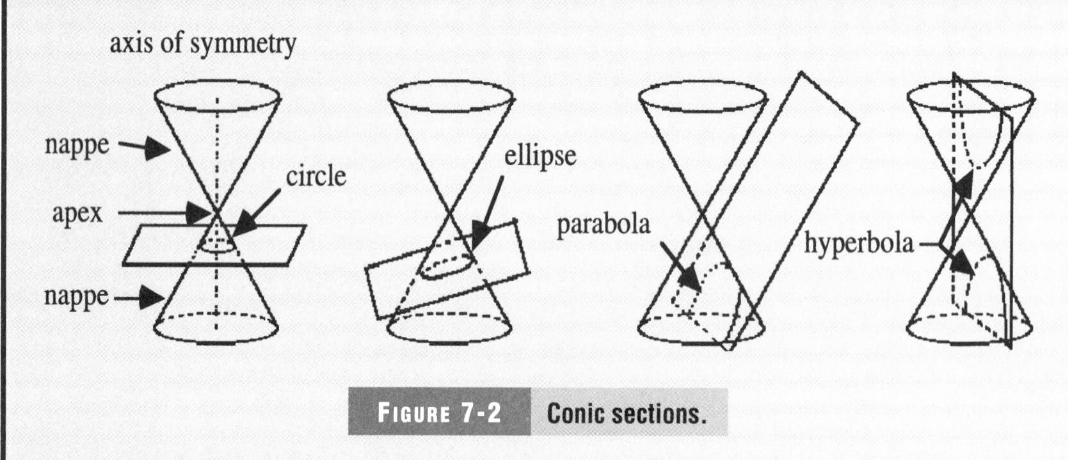

FIGURE 7-2 Conic sections.

When the plane is perpendicular to the cone's axis of symmetry and intersects the cone in more than one point, the intersection is a circle. As the slope of the plane gradually changes, the intersection is an ellipse. When the plane is parallel to a line generating the cone, a parabola is formed. When the plane intersects both nappes, a hyperbola is formed.

Figure **7-3** shows the four conic sections. Note that circles and ellipses are closed figures, while parabolas and hyperbolas are not closed. Notice also that a hyperbola has two parts or **branches.**

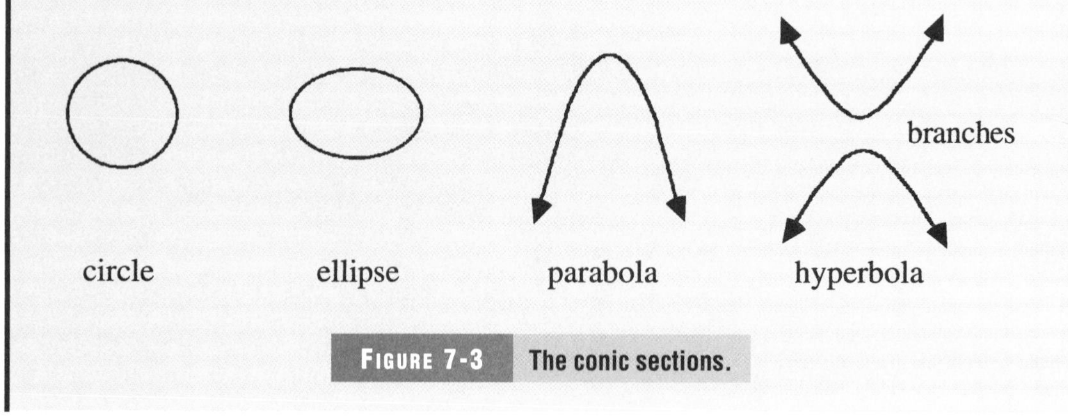

FIGURE 7-3 The conic sections.

Each conic separates a plane into three regions: the conic itself, an "interior," and an "exterior." In Figure **7-4** below, the interior of each conic is shaded. Note that the boundaries are not included in the interior, and that the interior of a hyperbola also has two branches.

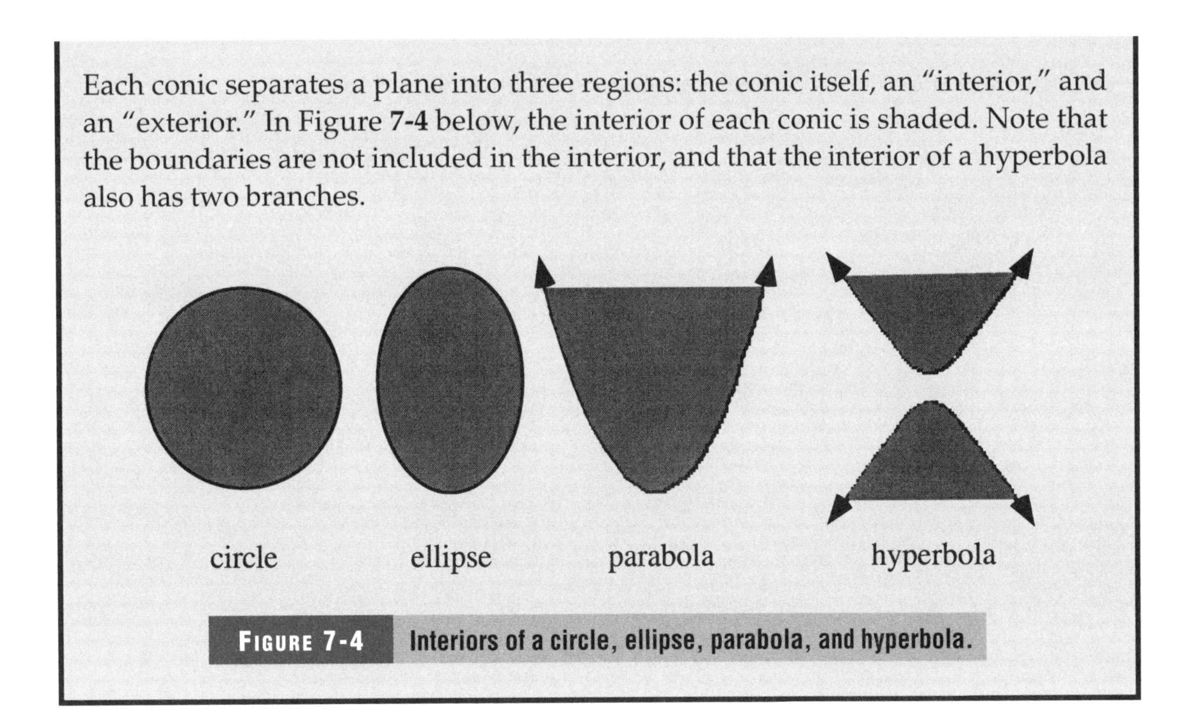

FIGURE 7-4 Interiors of a circle, ellipse, parabola, and hyperbola.

Exploration

A flashlight produces a partial cone of light. As shown in Figure **7-5,** the light defines a shape when it strikes a flat surface.

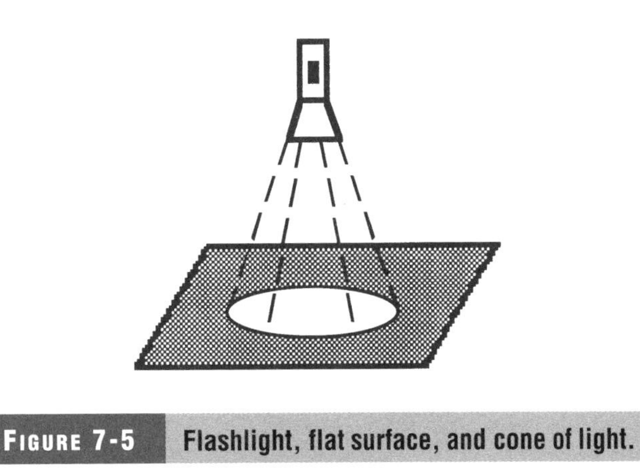

FIGURE 7-5 Flashlight, flat surface, and cone of light.

a. 1. Use a flashlight to create a partial cone of light. Holding the flashlight still, position a flat surface so that the light forms a circle.

   2. Record the relationship between the cone of light and the position of the flat surface.

b. Repeat Part **a** for an ellipse, a parabola, and one-half of a hyperbola.

Discussion

a. In the exploration, you used a partial cone of light to create models of the conic sections. Describe how you modeled each conic section below:

 1. a circle
 2. an ellipse
 3. a parabola
 4. one-half of a hyperbola.

b. Describe how each of the following are represented in your models:

 1. the interior of a conic section
 2. the exterior of a conic section
 3. the conic section itself.

c. Describe some familiar items that contain objects shaped liked conic sections.

d. How would you describe the shapes of the conic sections to someone who has never seen them before?

e. When the intersection of a plane and a cone contains the cone's apex, geometric figures other than a circle, an ellipse, a parabola, or a hyperbola are formed. These other intersections are **degenerate conic sections.**

 There are three degenerate conic sections. Describe the shape of each one and the location of the plane relative to the cone.

ACTIVITY 1

The shapes of conic sections are a part of our natural and physical world. From previous modules, you may recall that the path of a projectile traces a parabola, while the orbit of a moon or planet describes an ellipse. Circles, of course, can be found almost everywhere you look.

In this activity, you investigate the mathematical properties of that most familiar of the conic sections: the circle.

mathematics note

A **circle** is the locus of points in a plane that are a given distance, the **radius,** from a fixed point, the **center.** A circle is named for its center.

For example, circle O in Figure **7-6** has a radius of 5 cm. Points A and B, and all the other points on the circle, are 5 cm from point O.

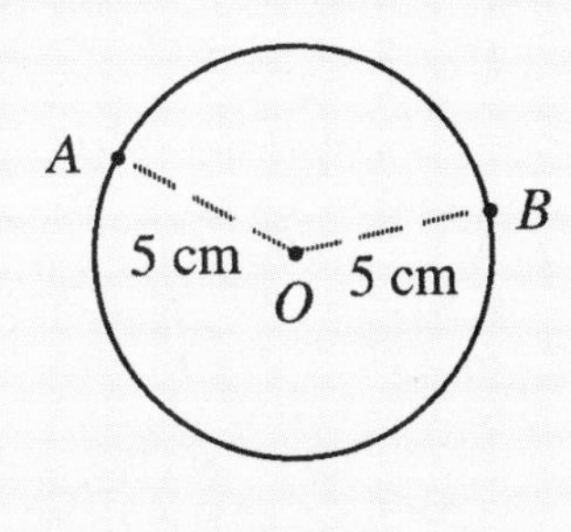

FIGURE 7-6 Circle *O*.

Exploration

In this exploration, you use the Pythagorean theorem to develop an equation that describes a circle.

a. 1. Create a rectangular coordinate system with the same scale on the x- and y-axes.

   2. On the coordinate plane, select a point at an intersection of grid lines as the center of the circle.

b. Select a distance for the radius, r. Draw the locus of points that lie this distance from the center of the circle.

c. As you might recall from previous modules, the distance d between two points (x_1,y_1) and (x_2,y_2) can be found using a formula derived from the Pythagorean theorem:

$$d = \sqrt{(x_2 - x_1)^2 + (y_2 - y_1)^2}$$

Use the distance formula to determine an equation for the circle you drew in Part **b.**

d. Repeat Parts **a–c** four more times, using a different radius for each circle and placing the center of each circle in a different quadrant.

Discussion

a. A type of compass used by architects and mapmakers has two rigid legs. One leg typically ends in a sharp tip, while the other holds a pencil. If you plant the sharp tip on the paper, then move the pencil, the pencil traces a geometric figure. Explain how you know this figure will be a circle.

b. Consider a circle with center at (h,k) and a radius of r. Given an arbitrary point (x,y) on the circle, how could you use the distance formula to write an equation for the radius?

c. To write an equation without a radical, you must isolate the radical on one side of the equation, then square both sides of the equation. For example,

$$\sqrt{(x^2 + y^2)} = 4$$

$$\left(\sqrt{(x^2 + y^2)}\right)^2 = 4^2$$

$$x^2 + y^2 = 16$$

Apply this technique to the equation you wrote in Part **b** of the discussion.

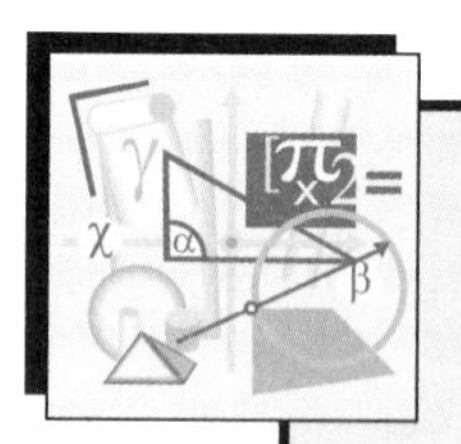

mathematics note

The **standard form** of the equation of a circle with center at (h,k) and radius r is:

$$(x - h)^2 + (y - k)^2 = r^2$$

For example, the standard form of the equation for a circle with center at $(-2,4)$ and a radius of 5 is $(x + 2)^2 + (y - 4)^2 = 25$.

d. How does the standard form of the equation of a circle compare to the equation you determined in Part **c** of the discussion?

e. How could you determine whether or not any point in the coordinate plane is a point on a given circle?

f. 1. If $x^2 = 16$, is it always true that $\sqrt{x^2} = 4$? Justify your response.

2. If $x^2 = 16$, is it always true that $x = 4$? Justify your response.

g. Some graphing utilities can graph only functions. Explain why a circle is not a function.

h. To represent a circle on a graphing utility that graphs only functions, you might have to use two functions—each of which represents half of the circle.

   1. How would you identify the appropriate two functions for the circle described by $x^2 + y^2 = 16$?
   2. What is the appropriate domain and range for each of these functions?
   3. Do you believe that a combined graph of these two functions includes all the points of the circle defined by $x^2 + y^2 = 16$?

Warm-Up

1. Write the equation in standard form of each of the following:

   a. a circle with center at the origin and a radius of 3

   b. a circle with center at (–1.3,8.9) and a radius of $\sqrt{21}$

   c. a circle with center at (a,b) and a radius of $\sqrt{c}$.

2. Identify the centers and radii of the circles described by the following equations:

   a. $(x - 30)^2 + (y - 120)^2 = 289$

   b. $(x + 21)^2 + (y - 73)^2 = 141$

   c. $x^2 + y^2 = 121$

3. Given the center of the circle and a point on the circle, find the equation of each circle in standard form.

   1. center at (–2,–8); point on the circle at (2,6)

   2. center at (3,5); point on the circle at (–2,3)

   3. center at (1,–4); point on the circle at (5,–7)

Assignment

1.1 **a.** Select a center for a circle that is in the third quadrant and whose radius is greater than 5 units. Write the equation for the circle in standard form.

   b. List the coordinates of each of the following:

   1. a point on the circle

   2. a point inside the circle

   3. a point outside the circle.

   c. When the coordinates of a point outside the circle are substituted into its equation in standard form, what must be true of the result?

   d. When the coordinates of a point inside the circle are substituted into its equation in standard form, what must be true of the result?

1.2 Radio signals may be thought of as concentric circles (circles with the same center) emitted from a transmitter. Write the equations of three concentric circles.

1.3 Zhang listens to radio station KIZY, 105.3 on the FM dial. Zhang's home is located 32 km north and 75 km east of the station's transmitter, on the edge of KIZY's maximum broadcast range.

a. Determine the distance traveled by the signal when it is received by Zhang's home radio and make a sketch of the station's listening area.

b. If the radio station has coordinates (0,0), find the equation that represents the locus of KIZY's maximum broadcast range.

c. Determine the approximate coordinates of four locations—other than Zhang's home—that lie on the locus of KIZY's maximum broadcast range.

* * * * *

1.4 A new radio station, KZME, is building a transmitter 23 km east and 57 km north of Zhang's house.

a. Determine the location of KZME relative to KIZY.

b. Zhang's home also happens to be on the edge of KZME's maximum broadcast range. Determine the distance traveled by the signal when it is received by Zhang's home radio.

c. Determine an equation that represents the locus of KZME's maximum broadcast range.

d. Find the approximate coordinates of two locations other than Zhang's home that lie on the locus of KZME's maximum broadcast range.

e. Make a sketch of the listening areas for both KZME and KIZY.

f. Estimate the coordinates of the points where the two maximum broadcast ranges intersect.

g. Describe the location of Zhang's home relative to the intersection points of the two maximum broadcast ranges.

h. What does the region formed by the intersection of the two listening areas represent?

1.5 By assigning coordinates to points on a screen, then manipulating those points using mathematical equations, video game designers can create realistic special effects.

a. Imagine that you are a game designer. You have been asked to create a radar screen within a game. The screen should show a two-dimensional region within 100 units of a specific location.

1. What is the shape of this region? Explain your response.
2. Select a point for the origin of your coordinate system, then write an equation that describes the outer edge of the region.

b. How would you adjust your equation from Part **a** to identify objects that are within 100 units of a specific location? Justify your response.

c. In a new version of the game, the radar will detect objects within 100 units of a specific location in three dimensions. What is the shape of this region? Justify your response.

ACTIVITY 2

In the Level 2 module, "Traditional Design," you examined lines that intersect a circle in exactly one point. Such **tangent lines** also exist for other conic sections.

mathematics note

A **tangent line** to a conic is a line in the plane of the conic that intersects the curve at exactly one point and contains no points in the interior. The point at which the conic and the tangent line intersect is the **point of tangency.**

For example, Figure **7-7** shows a line tangent to circle *O*. The point of tangency is *P*.

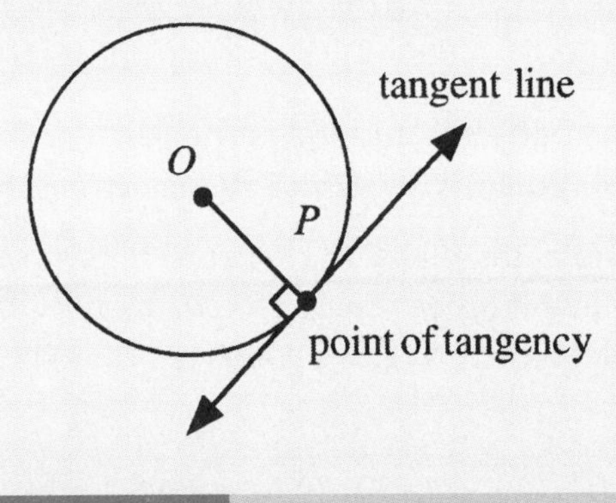

FIGURE 7-7 **A tangent line to circle *O*.**

In a circle, the radius containing the point of tangency is perpendicular to the tangent. For example, radius $\overleftrightarrow{OP}$ in Figure **7-7** is perpendicular to the tangent at point *P*.

Exploration 1

In this exploration, you use a circle—along with a geometry utility—to create another conic section. For this conic, the sum of the distances from a point on the conic to a pair of fixed interior points remains constant.

a. Construct a large circle and label its center O. Construct a point P_1 on the circle so that it moves freely around the circle without changing the circle's size.

b. Construct a point P in the interior of the circle, but not at the center.

c. Construct $\overline{PP_1}$.

d. Construct the perpendicular bisector of $\overline{PP_1}$.

e. Construct $\overleftrightarrow{OP_1}$.

f. Mark the intersection of the perpendicular bisector from Part **d** and $\overleftrightarrow{OP_1}$. Label this point X. Your construction should now resemble the one shown in Figure **7-8.**

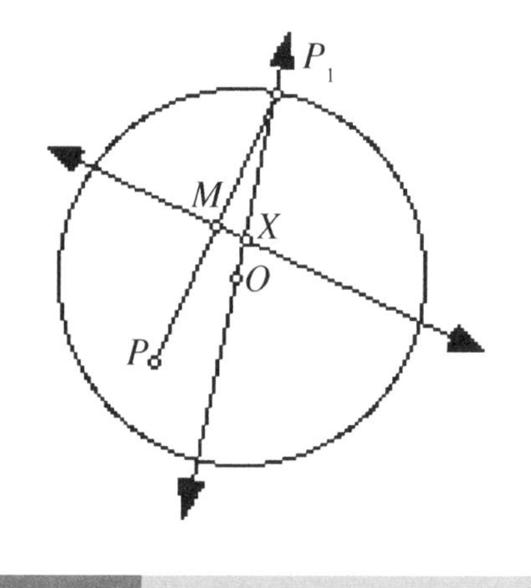

FIGURE 7-8 Beginning conic construction.

g. Trace the path of X and the perpendicular bisector of $\overline{PP_1}$ as P_1 is moved around the circle. Identify the conic that is formed by this path.

h. Erase the paths that you traced in Part **g.** Move P to a different location inside the circle and repeat Part **g.** Experiment with several other locations of P inside the circle. **Note:** Save this construction for use in Activity **3** and Activity **4.**

Discussion 1

a. Which conic section appears to result from the process described in Exploration **1**?

b. Would you expect everyone in the class to create exactly the same figure? Explain your response.

c. 1. What appears to define the locus of points for this conic section?

   2. Why is the perpendicular bisector that passes through point X a tangent line for the conic section?

d. What happens to the shape of the conic section when P is moved closer to the center of the circle?

e. How does the conic section you created compare to the ones shown in Figures **7-9** and **7-10**?

mathematics note

An **ellipse** is the locus of points in a plane such that the sum of the distances from two fixed points, the **foci,** is a constant.

For example, Figure **7-9** shows an ellipse with foci at F_1 and F_2. For any point P on the ellipse, $PF_1 + PF_2$ is a constant.

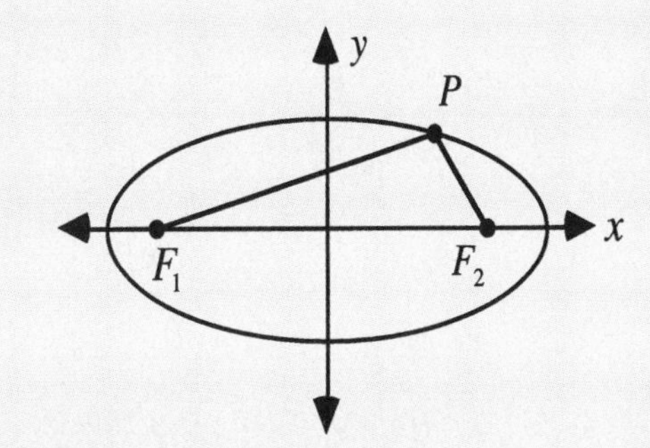

FIGURE 7-9 An ellipse with its foci on the *x*-axis.

The **major axis** of an ellipse is the segment, with endpoints on the ellipse, that contains the foci. The **minor axis** is the segment, with endpoints on the ellipse, contained in the perpendicular bisector of the major axis. The major and minor axes intersect at the **center** of the ellipse. The endpoints of the major and minor axes are the **vertices** of the ellipse.

For example, Figure **7-10** shows an ellipse with foci at F_1 and F_2. In this case, $\overline{MN}$ is the major axis and $\overline{TW}$ is the minor axis. The origin O is the center of the ellipse. Points M, N, W, and T are the vertices of the ellipse.

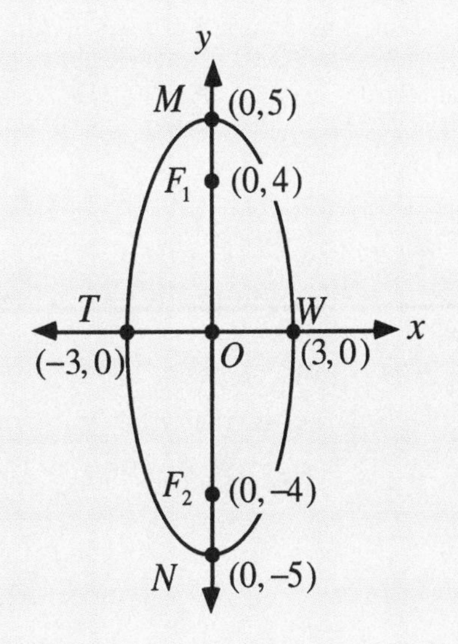

FIGURE 7-10 An ellipse with its foci on the *y*-axis.

f. Describe the symmetries found in an ellipse.

g. Using the construction described in Exploration **1,** the figure generated when P is located inside the circle appears to be an ellipse—but appearance alone is not enough to prove that it is one. For this to be true, the figure must satisfy the definition of an ellipse.

In Figure **7-11,** P is any point within the circle that is not the center. The point X is a point on the figure.

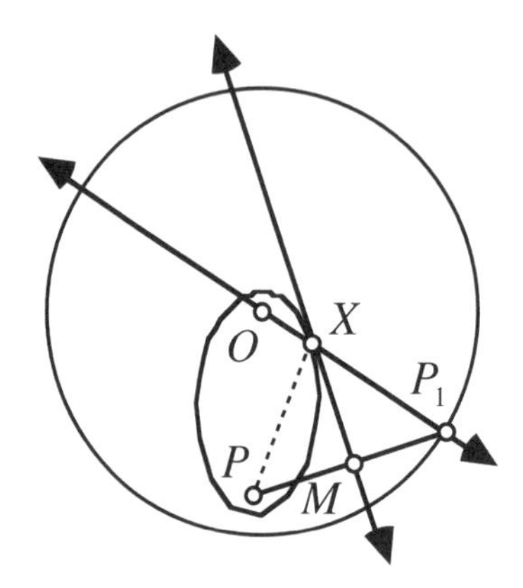

FIGURE 7-11 **Construction from Exploration 1.**

1. Which points appear to be the foci of the figure?
2. If the figure generated is an ellipse, what sum must remain constant?
3. Because $\overline{MX}$ is the perpendicular bisector of $\overline{PP_1}$, what is the relationship between P_1X and PX?
4. Why is the length of $\overline{OP_1}$ always the same, no matter where on the circle P_1 is located?
5. Why is the length of $\overline{OP_1}$ equal to $OX + XP$?
6. How does the fact that $OX + XP = OP_1$ prove that the generated figure is indeed an ellipse?

h. 1. What is the major axis of the ellipse in Figure **7-11**?

2. How could you identify the minor axis of this ellipse?

i. If you moved P to the center of the circle in Exploration **1,** what type of conic would be defined by the locus of points X? Explain your response.

Exploration 2

If you had located point P at the center of the circle in Exploration **1,** the path of X would have traced a circle. By moving P away from the center, you could argue that the circle has been "stretched" into an ellipse. In this exploration, you examine how this "stretching" transformation can be used to develop an algebraic equation for an ellipse.

a. Write an equation for a circle with its center at the origin.

b. In the Level 3 module "It's All in the Family," you observed that a function can be stretched horizontally by m if each point in the function is transformed from (x,y) to (mx,y), where $m \neq 0$. The equation that describes the result of this transformation can be found by replacing x with x/m in the original equation.

   Similarly, a function can be stretched vertically by n if each point in the function is transformed from (x,y) to (x,ny), where $n \neq 0$. The equation that describes the result of this transformation can be found by replacing y with y/n in the original equation.

   Write the equation that results when the equation for the circle in Part **a** is stretched horizontally by 3 and stretched vertically by 2.

c. 1. Rewrite the equation from Part **b** by multiplying both sides of the equation by $1/r^2$, where r represents the radius of the circle.

   2. Simplify this equation and write it in the form below:

$$\frac{x^2}{a^2} + \frac{y^2}{b^2} = 1$$

d. 1. Solve the equation from Part **c** for y and graph both parts of your solution.

   2. Identify the points where the graph intersects the x- and y-axes.

e. Repeat Parts **b–d** when the equation for the circle in Part **a** is stretched horizontally by 2 and stretched vertically by 3.

Discussion 2

a. Compare the ellipses you created in Parts **d** and **e** of Exploration **2.**

b. How do the intersections of each ellipse and the x- and y-axes relate to its equation in the form below?

$$\frac{x^2}{a^2} + \frac{y^2}{b^2} = 1$$

c. How could you use an equation in the form above to identify the lengths of the major and minor axes of the ellipse?

d. Figure **7-12** shows another method for drawing an ellipse. Two thumbtacks are inserted in a sheet of paper. A length of string is then tied to the tacks. The string is pulled taut with the tip of a pencil. By maintaining tension on the string, the pencil can be used to draw a conic.

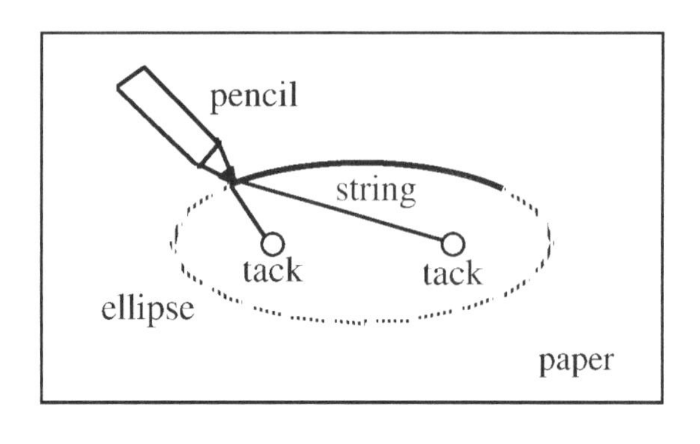

FIGURE 7-12 **Drawing an ellipse.**

1. How do you know that the resulting shape is an ellipse?
2. How is the length of the string related to the length of the major axis?
3. What is the length of the string in terms of a or b in the equation below?

$$\frac{x^2}{a^2} + \frac{y^2}{b^2} = 1$$

e. 1. In Figure **7-12,** the points represented by the two tacks and the tip of the pencil form a triangle. What type of triangle is formed when the pencil is located at an end of the minor axis? Explain your response.
2. How could you use this fact to locate the center of this ellipse?

f. How could you describe each of the following distances in terms of a or b?
1. the distance from each focus to an end of the minor axis
2. the distance from the center to an end of the minor axis

g. Let c represent the distance from the center of the ellipse to each focus. Describe an equation that relates the variables a, b, and c.

h. Given the endpoints of the major and minor axes, how could you find the foci of an ellipse?

mathematics note

The **standard form** of the equation of an ellipse with its center at the origin and foci on the x-axis is:

$$\frac{x^2}{a^2} + \frac{y^2}{b^2} = 1$$

where a is half the length of the major axis and b is half the length of the minor axis.

The **standard form** of the equation of an ellipse with its center at the origin and foci on the y-axis is:

$$\frac{x^2}{b^2} + \frac{y^2}{a^2} = 1$$

In both cases, $c^2 = a^2 - b^2$, where c represents the distance from the center to each focus.

For example, consider an ellipse with center at the origin and major axis contained in the y-axis. If the length of its major axis is 10 units, while the length of its minor axis is 6 units, the equation of this ellipse in standard form is:

$$\frac{x^2}{9} + \frac{y^2}{25} = 1$$

The distance from the center to each focus is $\sqrt{5^2 - 3^2} = \sqrt{16} = 4$ units.

i. Given the equation, in standard form, of an ellipse with center at the origin, describe how to identify the coordinates of the vertices and the foci.

j. In Activity **1**, you found that the equation for a circle with center at a point (h,k) is $(x - h)^2 + (y - k)^2 = r$. Suggest a general equation for an ellipse with center at the point (h,k). Justify your response.

k. Describe how to determine an equation for the ellipse in Figure **7-13** below.

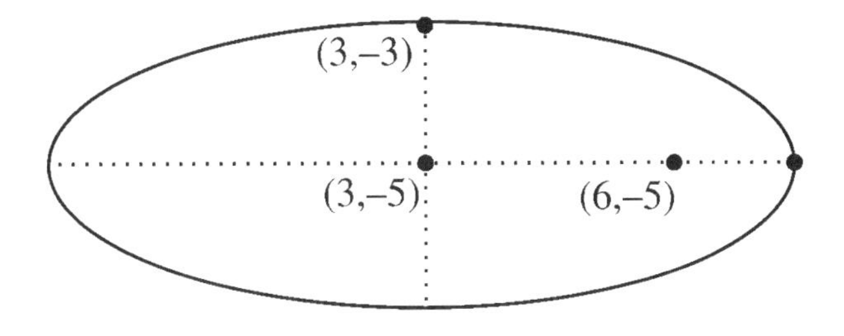

FIGURE 7-13 **Ellipse with center at (3,–5).**

1. Describe how you could find the lengths of the major and minor axes and the distance from the center to the foci of an ellipse with center at (h,k), a vertex on the major axis at (x_1,y_1), and a vertex on the minor axis at (x_2,y_2).

Warm-Up

1. Sketch a graph of the ellipse described by each of the following equations.

   a. $\frac{x^2}{36} + \frac{y^2}{25} = 1$

   b. $16x^2 + 9y^2 = 144$

   c. $\frac{(x-4)^2}{225} + \frac{(y+2)^2}{121} = 1$

2. Identify the coordinates of the vertices, foci, and center for each ellipse in Problem **1.**

3. In Parts **a** and **b,** use the given information to sketch a graph of each ellipse, including the coordinates of the vertices, the foci, and the center.

   a. This ellipse has foci at (3,0) and (–3,0). The sum of the distances from the foci to a point on the ellipse is 16 units.

   b. This ellipse has its center at (–4,–1) and one focus at (–4,12). The distance from the center to a vertex on the minor axis is 9 units.

4. Approximate the coordinates of the center and foci of each ellipse shown below and write its equation in standard form.

a.

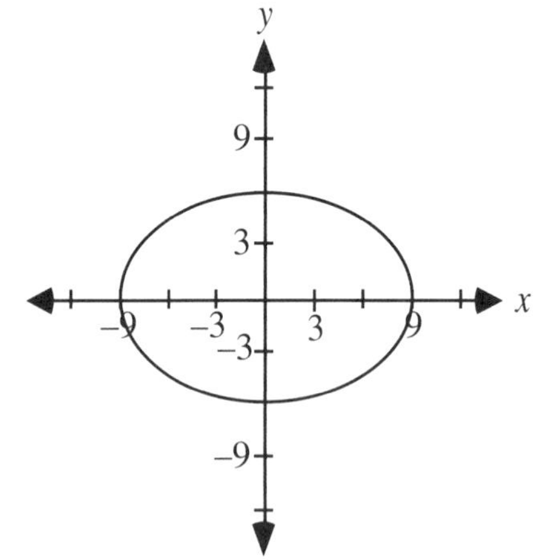

b.

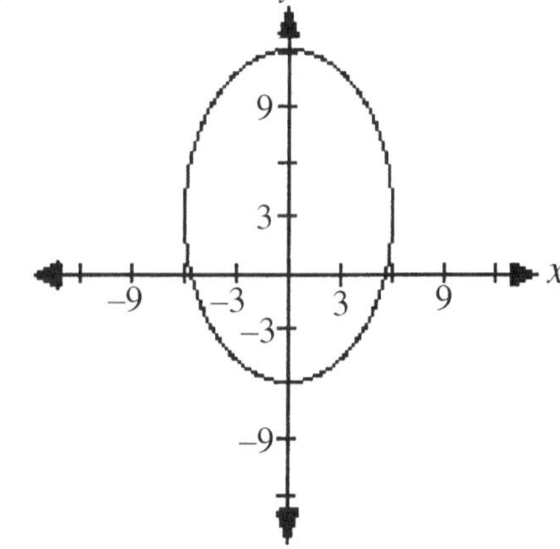

c.

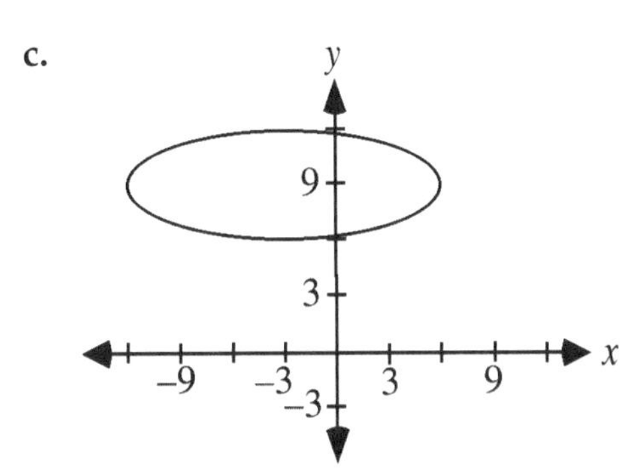

Assignment

2.1 Although tanker trucks often use tanks that are circular in cross section, some tanks have elliptical cross-sections. In other words, the tank is a cylinder with elliptical bases. The elliptical shape gives the truck a lower center of gravity, for better handling on the road, and a lower profile.

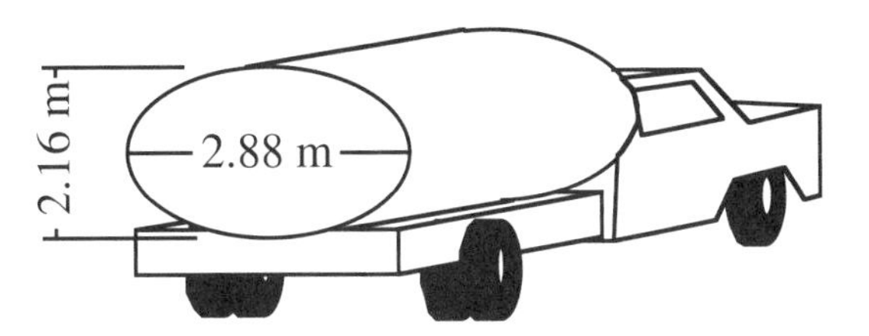

Imagine that you are a member of an engineering team. Your team has been asked to design a tank 2.16 m high and 2.88 m wide, with elliptical bases.

a. Your task is to specify the dimensions for the elliptical bases. Write an equation that describes an appropriate ellipse.

b. Determine the coordinates of the foci. Round your answers to the nearest 0.01 m.

c. The machinist who is building the prototype makes an error on one of the bases. On that ellipse, the foci are 5 cm closer to the center than you specified. What difference will this cause in the bases? Explain your response.

2.2 Earth's orbit around the sun is approximately an ellipse with the sun located at one focus. The sun is $2.99 \bullet 10^6$ km from the center of the ellipse. The length of the major axis is $2.99 \bullet 10^8$ km.

a. As the earth travels its elliptical path, what is the shortest distance between the earth and the sun?

b. What is the greatest distance between the earth and the sun?

2.3 Consider the ellipse described by the equation below:

$$\frac{x^2}{25} + \frac{y^2}{9} = 1$$

a. Write an equation that describes the image of this ellipse translated 8 units horizontally and 6 units vertically. List the coordinates of its center.

b. Use the equation of the translated ellipse from Part **a** to complete the following steps.

1. Determine the coordinates of the endpoints of the major axis.

2. Determine the coordinates of the endpoints of the minor axis.

c. What are the coordinates of the foci of the translated ellipse?

d. Write the equation in standard form of an ellipse with center at (h,k) and foci on the line $y = k$.

2.4 The diagram below shows the "K-drive," a bicycle design in which the pedals follow an elliptical path. In the early 1990s, a bicycle using the K-drive set a speed record in the United Kingdom.

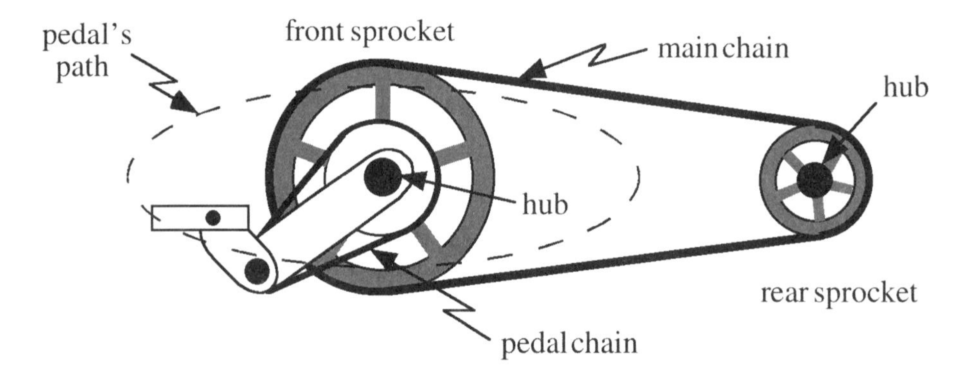

a. The hub of the front sprocket is the center of the pedal's path. The length of the major axis is 390 mm, and the length of the minor axis is 90 mm. Determine an equation for the path followed by the pedal, using the hub of the front sprocket as the origin.

b. The rear sprocket is a circle 120 mm in diameter. Its hub is 650 mm to the right of the front sprocket. Again, using the hub of the front sprocket as the origin, determine an equation that describes the rear sprocket.

c. If you relocate the origin to the hub of the rear sprocket, how will the equation for the path of the pedal change? Justify your response.

mathematics note

Given an equation containing two square roots, the following process may be used to eliminate them:

- Given: $$\sqrt{x} + \sqrt{y} = k$$
- Isolate one of the radicals. $$\sqrt{x} = k - \sqrt{y}$$
- Square both sides and simplify. $$\left(\sqrt{x}\right)^2 = \left(k - \sqrt{y}\right)^2$$ $$x = k^2 - 2k\sqrt{y} + \left(\sqrt{y}\right)^2$$ $$x = k^2 - 2k\sqrt{y} + y$$
- Isolate the next radical. $$\frac{x - k^2 - y}{-2k} = \sqrt{y}$$
- Square both sides and simplify. $$\left(\frac{x - k^2 - y}{-2k}\right)^2 = \left(\sqrt{y}\right)^2$$ $$\left(\frac{x - k^2 - y}{-2k}\right)^2 = y$$

For example, to remove the square roots from the equation $\sqrt{x} + \sqrt{y} = 10$, you could use the following steps:

$$\sqrt{x} + \sqrt{y} = 10$$
$$\sqrt{x} = 10 - \sqrt{y}$$
$$\left(\sqrt{x}\right)^2 = \left(10 - \sqrt{y}\right)^2$$
$$x = 100 - 20\sqrt{y} + y$$
$$\frac{x - 100 - y}{-20} = \sqrt{y}$$
$$\left(\frac{x - 100 - y}{-20}\right)^2 = \left(\sqrt{y}\right)^2$$
$$\left(\frac{x - 100 - y}{-20}\right)^2 = y$$

When using this process, it is possible to introduce an **extraneous root.** An extraneous root is an incorrect solution that may result from correct algebraic manipulation.

For example, consider the equation $3-\sqrt{x}=7$. This can be solved using the following steps:

$$\begin{aligned} 3-\sqrt{x} &= 7 \\ -\sqrt{x} &= 4 \\ \sqrt{x} &= -4 \\ \left(\sqrt{x}\right)^2 &= (-4)^2 \\ x &= 16 \end{aligned}$$

However, when 16 is substituted for x in the original equation, the result is false.

$$\begin{aligned} 3-\sqrt{x} &= 7 \\ 3-\sqrt{16} &= 7 \\ 3-4 &\neq 7 \end{aligned}$$

Because of this possibility, you should take extra care in verifying your solutions.

2.5 In the mathematics note above, $x = 16$ is an extraneous root for the equation $3-\sqrt{x}=7$.

a. One way to find the solution(s), if any, to this equation is to set each side equal to y, then graph the resulting two equations, $y=3-\sqrt{x}$ and $y=7$, on the same coordinate system.

Describe how to identify the solutions(s), if any, from this graph.

b. How does the graph in Part **a** show that 16 is an extraneous root for $3-\sqrt{x}=7$?

2.6 Consider the ellipse described by the following equation:

$$21x^2 + 25y^2 = 525$$

a. Rewrite the equation of the ellipse in standard form.

b. Determine the coordinates of the foci.

c. Identify the constant sum for the distances between any point on the ellipse and the foci.

d. Using the constant sum from Part **c**, determine an equation for the ellipse based on the distance formula.

e. Show that your equations in Parts **a** and **d** are equivalent by solving both for y.

2.7 Demonstrate that the following equation of an ellipse,

$$\sqrt{(x+2)^2+(y+1)^2}+\sqrt{(x+2)^2+(y-7)^2}=10$$

is equivalent to its equation in standard form:

$$\frac{(x+2)^2}{9}+\frac{(y-3)^2}{25}=1$$

2.8 As shown in the following diagram, the Tycho Brahe Planetarium in Copenhagen, Denmark, resembles a portion of a cylinder. Its base is a circle with a diameter of 38 m. The roof is shaped like an ellipse. The angle formed by the roof and the horizontal is 30°.

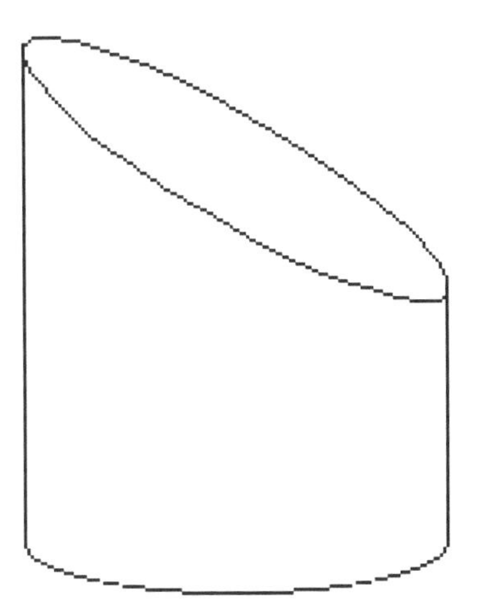

Determine an equation to describe the shape of the roof. Include the location of the origin in your response.

* * * * *

2.9 Demonstrate that the following equation of an ellipse,

$$\sqrt{(x+4)^2+(y-0)^2}+\sqrt{(x-4)^2+(y-0)^2}=34$$

is equivalent to its equation in standard form:

$$\frac{x^2}{289}+\frac{y^2}{273}=1$$

2.10 A communications satellite has been placed in an elliptical orbit around Earth. The satellite's orbital path is directly above the equator. One focus is at Earth's center, and each focus is 410 km from the center of the ellipse. The length of the major axis is 13,960 km.

a. Write an equation that describes the satellite's orbit.

b. How does the satellite's orbit compare to a circular orbit?

c. Earth's radius at the equator is about 6400 km. At its lowest point, how close is the satellite to Earth's surface?

d. At its highest point, how far is the satellite from Earth's surface?

2.11 The Ellipse in Washington, D.C., is the park directly south of the White House where the National Christmas Tree is erected each year. As its name implies, the park is elliptical in shape. The park measures about 212 m east to west and approximately 196 m north to south. The nearest edge of the park is approximately 261 m south of the White House.

a. Imagine that you are standing in front of the White House. Your best friend is standing on one focus of the Ellipse. How far apart are the two of you?

b. Using your location as the origin, write an equation that describes the park's boundary.

In the introduction, you read about the ability of parabolic reflectors to concentrate radio and television signals. Other applications of reflectors require the scattering of heat, light, or sound. For example, an effective wall heater disperses heat uniformly in a room, and a band shell reflects sound so that the entire audience can hear.

Exploration 1

In this exploration, you create the conic section whose reflective properties are well-suited for these applications. Like the circle and the ellipse, this conic can be defined as a locus of points that satisfies a common rule. In this case, the *difference* of the distances from a point on the conic to a pair of fixed interior points remains constant.

a. Figure **7-14** below shows your construction from Exploration **1** in Activity **2.**

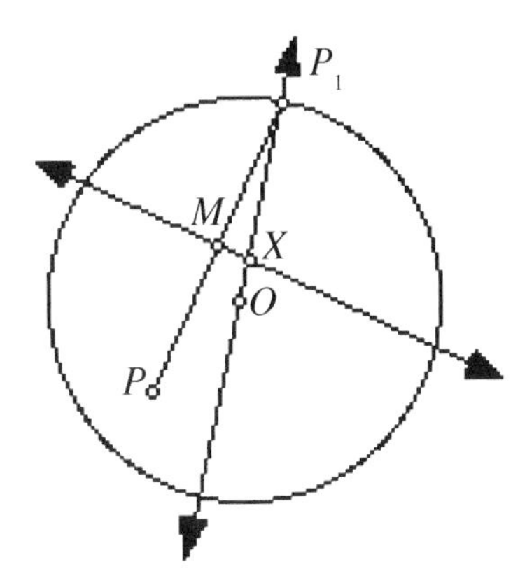

FIGURE 7-14 **Beginning conic construction.**

Using this construction, locate P outside the circle. Trace the path of point X and the perpendicular bisector of $\overline{PP_1}$ as P_1 moves around the circle. Describe the conic section that is formed.

b. 1. Hide points M and X, and $\overleftrightarrow{MX}$. Hide circle O, but not its center. Hide $\overline{PP_1}$ but not its endpoints. Hide $\overleftrightarrow{P_1O}$ but not the two named points.

2. Construct $\overline{OP}$ and its midpoint C.

3. Create point A and place it where the conic section and $\overline{CP}$ appear to intersect.

4. Create a circle with its center at C and a radius of $\overline{CP}$.

5. Create the perpendicular to $\overline{CP}$ through point A. Label the intersections of circle A and the perpendicular line as B_1 and B_2.

6. Construct lines $\overleftrightarrow{CB_1}$ and $\overleftrightarrow{CB_2}$.

c. Describe how the lines $\overleftrightarrow{CB_1}$ and $\overleftrightarrow{CB_2}$ are related to the conic section you created.

d. 1. Move P to a different location outside circle O. Generate another conic section by moving P_1 around the circle. (If the location is appropriate, the construction should generate the same type of conic as in Part **a.**)

2. Relocate point A so it is at the intersection of the conic section and $\overline{CP}$. Repeat Part **c.**

Discussion 1

a. Describe the figure traced by the path of point X when point P is located outside the circle.

b. Describe how the location of P affects the shape of the figure.

mathematics note

A **hyperbola** is the locus of points in a plane for which the positive difference of the distances from two designated foci is a constant.

In Figure **7-15,** for example, points F_1 and F_2 represent the foci. The hyperbola formed is the set of all points P in a plane for which the difference between PF_1 and PF_2 is a constant.

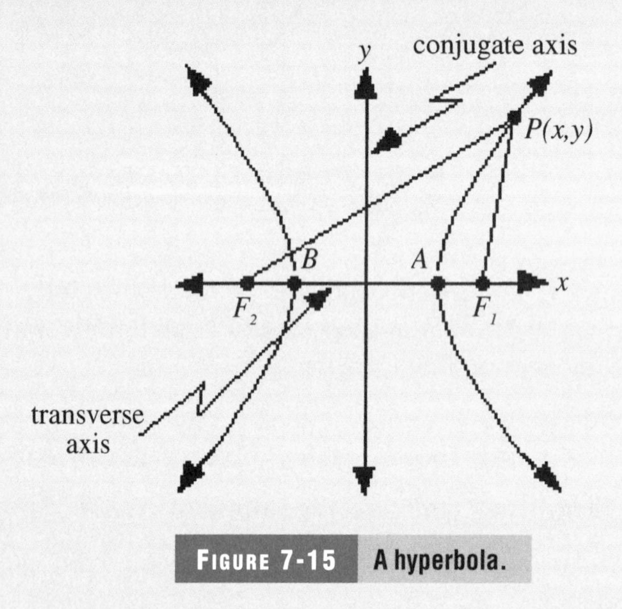

FIGURE 7-15 A hyperbola.

The midpoint of $\overline{F_1F_2}$ is the **center** of the hyperbola. The **vertices** of the hyperbola occur at the intersections of the **branches** and $\overline{F_1F_2}$. In the hyperbola in Figure **7-14,** the vertices occur at points A and B.

The line segment joining the vertices is the **transverse axis.** The perpendicular bisector of the transverse axis lies on the **conjugate axis.**

c. The figure you generated when P is located outside the circle appears to be a hyperbola, but as with the ellipse, appearance alone is not enough to prove this conjecture. In Figure **7-16,** P is any point outside the circle. The point X is a point on the figure.

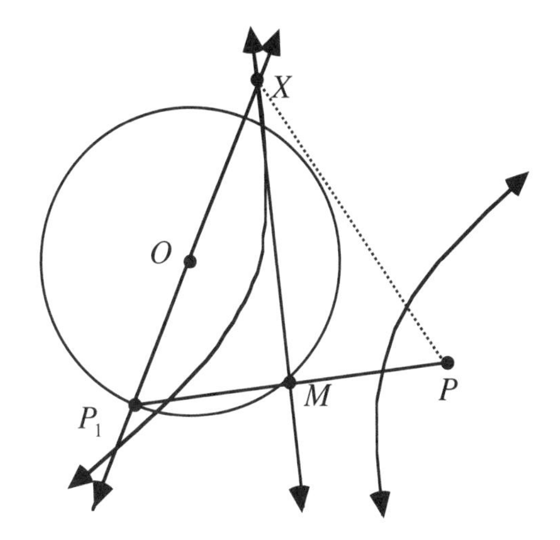

FIGURE 7-16 **Construction from Exploration 1.**

1. Which points appear to be the foci of the figure?
2. As P_1 moves along the circle, how is the length of $\overline{OP_1}$ affected? Explain why this occurs.
3. Because $\overline{MX}$ is the perpendicular bisecstor of $\overline{PP_1}$, what is the relationship between P_1X and PX?
4. Why is the length of $\overline{PX}$ equal to $OX + OP_1$?
5. Why does $PX - OX = OP_1$?
6. How does the fact that $PX - OX = OP_1$ prove that the generated figure is indeed a hyperbola?

d. Describe the symmetries that exist within a hyperbola.

e. 1. The hyperbola shown in Figure **7-14** has its center at the origin. If the coordinates of F_1 are $(c,0)$, what are the coordinates of F_2?
   2. If the coordinates of vertex A are $(a,0)$, what is the difference between AF_1 and AF_2?
   3. Is the difference between BF_1 and BF_2 the same as the difference between AF_1 and AF_2? Why or why not?
   4. What can you conclude about the constant difference for the hyperbola?

f. In the construction you created in Exploration **1,** $\overleftrightarrow{CB_1}$ and $\overleftrightarrow{CB_2}$ are **asymptotes** of the hyperbola. How would you describe such lines to someone who has not encountered them before?

g. In Figure **7-17** below, the distance from the center of the hyperbola to each vertex is a. The distance from the center of the hyperbola to each focus is c. If the distance from the vertex to B_1 is b, describe how a, b, and c are related.

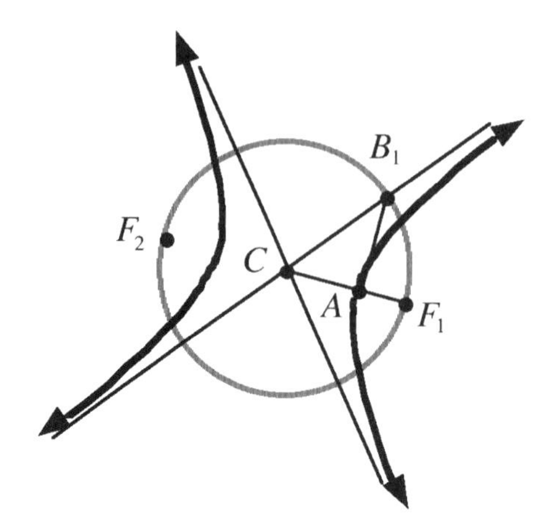

FIGURE 7-17 **Hyperbola with asymptotes.**

h. Consider a rectangle with side lengths of $2a$ and $2b$. The center of the rectangle coincides with the center of the hyperbola in Figure **7-17** and one side is tangent to the hyperbola at point A. Describe how the rectangle and the asymptotes are related.

mathematics note

The **standard form** of the equation of a hyperbola with center at the origin and foci on the x-axis is:

$$\frac{x^2}{a^2} - \frac{y^2}{b^2} = 1$$

The coordinates of the vertices are $(-a,0)$ and $(a,0)$. The coordinates of the foci are $(-c,0)$ and $(c,0)$, where $b^2 = c^2 - a^2$. As shown in Figure **7-18,** the transverse axis is the x-axis and the conjugate axis is the y-axis.

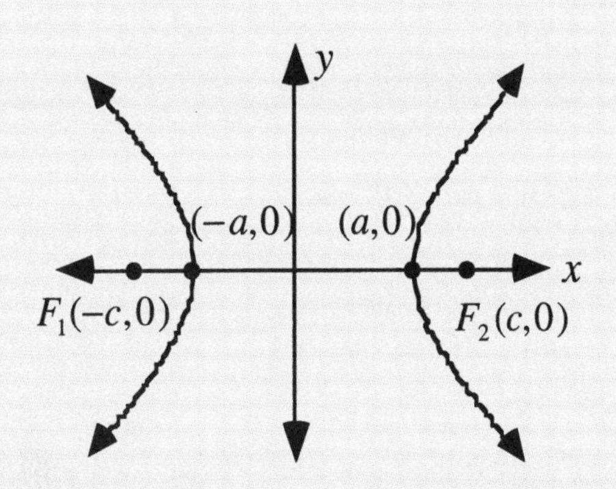

FIGURE 7-18 **A hyperbola with foci on the *x*-axis.**

For example, consider a hyperbola with foci at (−5,0) and (5,0) and vertices at (−3,0) and (3,0). In this case, $c = 5$, $a = 3$, and $b = \sqrt{25 - 9} = 4$. The equation of this hyperbola, in standard form, is:

$$\frac{x^2}{3^2} - \frac{y^2}{4^2} = 1$$

Exploration 2

In this exploration, you continue your investigation of a hyperbola and its asymptotes.

a. Select values for a and b in the following equation of a hyperbola:

$$\frac{x^2}{a^2} - \frac{y^2}{b^2} = 1$$

b. 1. Determine the coordinates of the vertices.

   2. Determine the coordinates of the foci.

   3. Determine the distance between each focus and the center.

c. Solve the equation in Part **a** for y and graph both parts of your solution.

d. 1. Select a point P on the hyperbola in the first quadrant. Find $|PF_1 - PF_2|$, where F_1 and F_2 are the foci.

   2. Select a point Q on the hyperbola in the second quadrant. Verify that $|QF_1 - QF_2|$ equals the constant difference found in Step **1**.

3. Determine the distance between the vertices of the hyperbola.

4. Describe the relationship between the constant difference and the distance between the vertices.

e. The hyperbola in Part **a** is not a function because each x-value in the domain, other than the vertices, has two corresponding y-values.

Complete Table **7-1** for points on the hyperbola, using the given x-values to find the two corresponding y-values. Describe any trends or patterns that you observe.

TABLE 7-1 ■ *Coordinates of Points on a Hyperbola*

x	10	10	100	100	1000	1000	10,000	10,000
y								
y/x								

f. Determine the values of b/a and $-b/a$ for the hyperbola. Compare these values with the ratios for y/x in Table **7-1.**

g. In Part **f,** you found that as the value of x increases, the ratio y/x appears to approach b/a or $-b/a$. If $b/a = y/x$, then $y = (b/a)x$.

1. Graph the lines $y = (b/a)x$ and $y = -(b/a)x$ on the same coordinate system as the hyperbola in Part **c.**

2. Compare the y-values for points on the hyperbola with those of the corresponding points on the lines.

h. On your graph from Part **g,** draw a rectangle with center at the origin, a horizontal length of $2a$, and a vertical length of $2b$. Draw the diagonals of the rectangle and note any relationships you observe between the rectangle and the hyperbola.

i. 1. Replot the graphs of $y = (b/a)x$, $y = -(b/a)x$, and the hyperbola using intervals for the domain and range that are 10 times those in Part **g.** Compare the y-values for points on the hyperbola with those of the corresponding points on the lines.

2. Repeat Step **1** using intervals for the domain and range that are 100 times those in Part **g.**

j. Using the values you chose for a and b in Part **a,** repeat Parts **b** and **c** for the following equation:

$$\frac{y^2}{b^2} - \frac{x^2}{a^2} = 1$$

mathematics note

An **asymptote** to a hyperbola is a line such that the distance from a point P on the hyperbola to the line approaches zero as the distance from P to a focus increases without bound.

Given the equation of a hyperbola in standard form,

$$\frac{x^2}{a^2} - \frac{y^2}{b^2} = 1 \text{ or } \frac{y^2}{b^2} - \frac{x^2}{a^2} = 1$$

the equations of its asymptotes are $y = (b/a)x$ and $y = -(b/a)x$.

For example, Figure **7-19** shows a graph of the hyperbola described by the equation:

$$\frac{y^2}{4^2} - \frac{x^2}{3^2} = 1$$

The equations of its asymptotes are $y = (4/3)x$ and $y = -(4/3)x$.

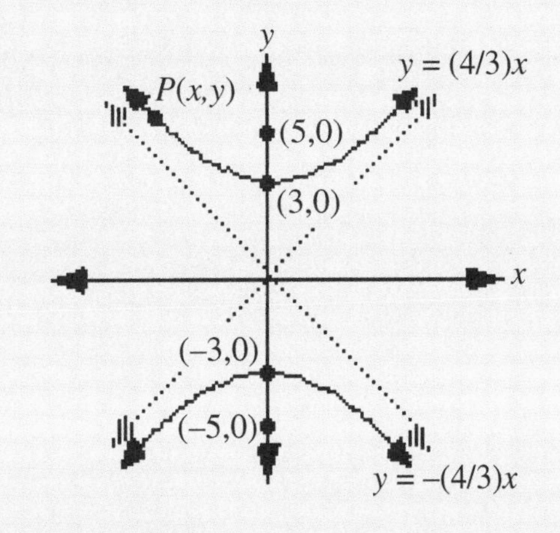

FIGURE 7-19 Hyperbola and its asymptotes.

Discussion 2

a. Compare the graph of your hyperbola in Part **c** of Exploration **2** with those of others in the class. What role do the values of a and b in the equation below have in determining the shape of the hyperbola?

$$\frac{x^2}{a^2} - \frac{y^2}{b^2} = 1$$

b. How are the values of a and b related to the distance between each focus and the center?

c. Given an equation, in standard form, of a hyperbola with center at the origin, how could you find the coordinates of the foci?

d. 1. If a graphing utility graphs only functions, it will not graph the equation of a hyperbola in standard form. Explain why this occurs.

   2. How could you create a graph of a hyperbola on such a graphing utility?

e. Given an equation of a hyperbola in standard form, how could you find the constant difference between the distances from the foci to a point on the hyperbola?

f. Compare the graphs of the hyperbolas in Parts **c** and **j** of Exploration **2.**

g. Describe the equation, in standard form, of a hyperbola with vertices located on the y-axis.

h. How could you determine the equations of the asymptotes for a hyperbola with its foci on the y-axis?

i. Suppose that you know the coordinates of a hyperbola's center and the equation of its transverse axis, along with the values of a and c.

   1. Explain why this is sufficient information to graph the hyperbola.

   2. Describe how you could create the graph without the use of technology.

   3. If you did not know the equation of the transverse axis, would you still be able to create the graph?

j. 1. Describe the equation of a hyperbola with center at (h,k) and a transverse axis parallel to the x-axis.

   2. How could you find the equations of the asymptotes for this hyperbola?

k. 1. Describe the equation of a hyperbola with center at (h,k) and a transverse axis parallel to the y-axis.

   2. How could you find the equations of the asymptotes for this hyperbola?

l. The equations of the asymptotes can be found by solving the equation of the hyperbola for y, then finding the **limit** of each solution as $|x|$ approaches ∞.

   1. Solving the equation of the hyperbola in Figure **7-19** for y results in the following:

$$y = \frac{4}{3}\sqrt{x^2 - 3} \text{ and } y = -\frac{4}{3}\sqrt{x^2 - 3}$$

   Why are there two solutions to the equation?

2. As x approaches ∞, the values of $y = (4/3)\sqrt{x^2 - 3}$ approach $y = (4/3)x$. In other words,

$$\lim_{x\to\infty}\left(\frac{4}{3}\sqrt{x^2 - 3}\right) = \frac{4}{3}x$$

Why is this true?

3. What is the following limit?

$$\lim_{x\to-\infty}\left(\frac{4}{3}\sqrt{x^2 - 3}\right)$$

Explain your response.

4. What are the two limits below?

$$\lim_{x\to\infty}\left(-\frac{4}{3}\sqrt{x^2 - 3}\right) \text{ and } \lim_{x\to-\infty}\left(-\frac{4}{3}\sqrt{x^2 - 3}\right)$$

Explain your response.

5. How are these limits related to the equations of the asymptotes?

Warm-Up

1. Sketch a graph of the hyperbola described by each of the following equations.

   a. $\frac{x^2}{36} - \frac{y^2}{25} = 1$

   b. $9y^2 - 16x^2 = 144$

   c. $\frac{(x-4)^2}{225} - \frac{(y+2)^2}{121} = 1$

2. Identify the coordinates of the vertices, foci, and center for each hyperbola in Problem **1.**

3. In Parts **a** and **b,** use the given information to sketch a graph of each hyperbola, including the coordinates of the vertices, the foci, and the center.

   a. This hyperbola has foci at (8,0) and (–8,0). The difference between the distances from the foci to a point on the hyperbola is 6 units.

   b. This hyperbola has its center at (–4,–1) and one focus at (–4,12). The slope of one of its asymptotes is 6/2.5.

4. Estimate the coordinates of the center, vertices, and foci of each hyperbola in Parts **a–c.** Use your estimates to write equations for each hyperbola and its asymptotes.

a.

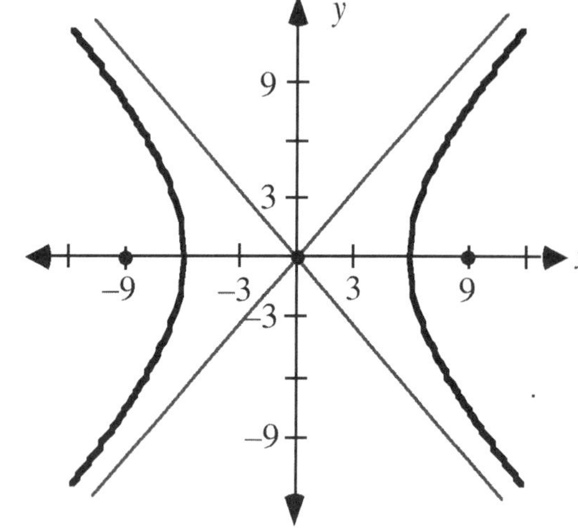

b.

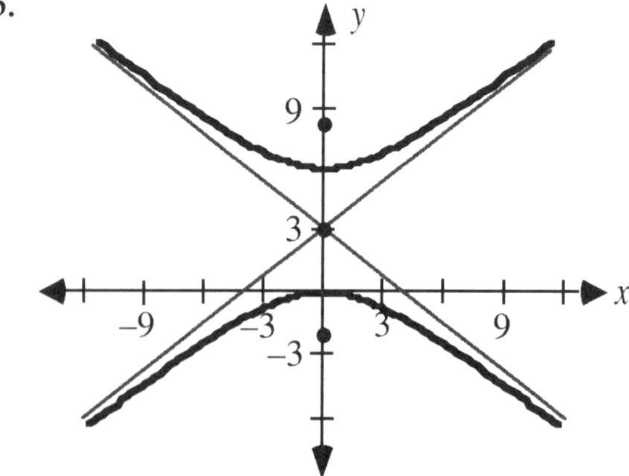

c.

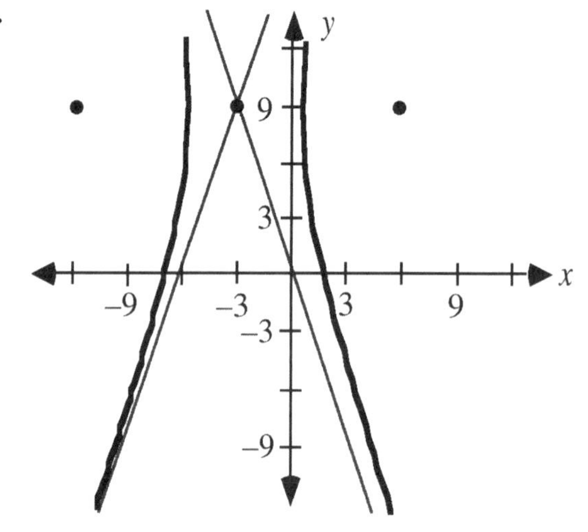

Assignment

3.1 **a.** How does the definition of a hyperbola compare to the definition of an ellipse?

b. Use appropriate technology to demonstrate that the following equation for a hyperbola,

$$\sqrt{(x-4)^2+(y-0)^2}-\sqrt{(x+4)^2+(y-0)^2}=6$$

is equivalent to the equation in standard form below:

$$\frac{x^2}{9}-\frac{y^2}{7}=1$$

3.2 Consider the hyperbola described by the equation below:

$$\frac{x^2}{4}-\frac{y^2}{9}=1$$

a. Identify the vertices of the hyperbola.

b. **1.** Use a symbolic manipulator to solve the equation for y.

2. Graph the solutions from Step **1.**

3. As $|x|$ increases, what does the value of $\sqrt{(x^2-4)}$ approach?

4. Rewrite the equations from Step **1** for large $|x|$. What kind of function is described by these equations?

5. Do the expressions that you wrote in Step **4** describe the actual values of y for the hyperbola?

c. Are the lines $y = (3/2)x$ and $y = -(3/2)x$ asymptotes of the hyperbola? Explain your response.

d. Describe how the denominators in the equation of the hyperbola can be used to find the equations of the asymptotes.

e. Identify the asymptotes for a hyperbola described by the equation:

$$\frac{x^2}{a^2}-\frac{y^2}{b^2}=1$$

3.3 Two hyperbolas are **conjugates** if they have the same asymptotes. The following hyperbolas are conjugates of each other.

$$\frac{y^2}{144} - \frac{x^2}{25} = 1 \text{ and } \frac{x^2}{25} - \frac{y^2}{144} = 1$$

a. Graph these hyperbolas on the same coordinate system.

b. Compare the coordinates of the foci of the conjugate hyperbolas.

3.4 The conductor of a community band is designing a band shell shaped like one branch of a hyperbola. In this application, the asymptotes of the hyperbola describe the area within which sound waves will scatter when reflected off the band shell.

Write an equation, in standard form, for the hyperbolic band shell shown in the diagram below.

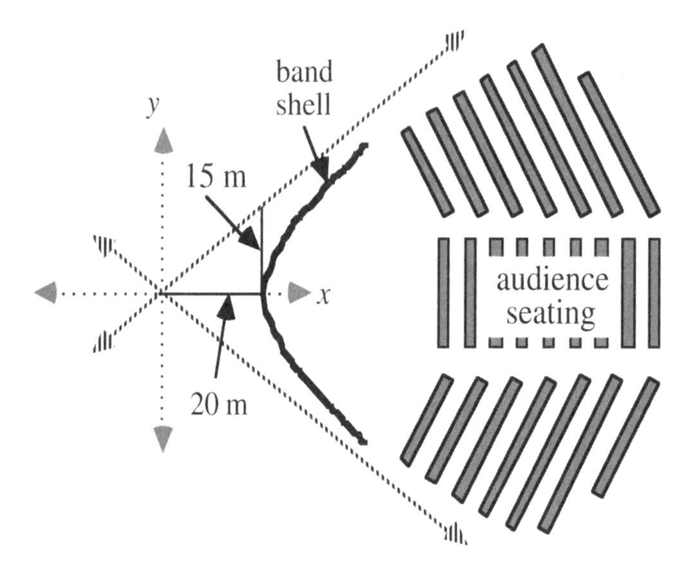

3.5 The path traced by a hyperbola revolving around its axis describes a surface called a **hyperboloid.** The 108-m high Port Tower in Kobe, Japan, is in the shape of hyperboloid. The center of the hyperbola is located about 2/3 of the way up the tower. At that point, the tower is approximately 11.5 m in diameter.

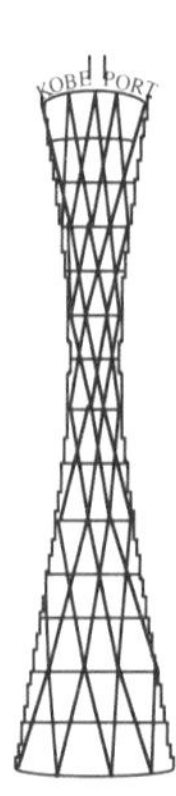

a. Kenji is making a scale drawing of the tower. To help determine the appropriate measurements, he places a coordinate grid over a photograph of the tower. In the photo, the tower measures 1 cm across at the center of the hyperbola. If Kenji wants the completed drawing to be 2 m high, by what scale factor should he multiply the dimensions in the photo?

b. When Kenji places the origin of his coordinate grid at the center of the hyperbola in the drawing, one point on the tower's outline has the coordinates (2.0,9.3). What equation should he use to draw the tower?

* * * * *

3.6 Graph the following hyperbola:

$$\frac{(x+1)^2}{4} - \frac{(y+3)^2}{1} = 1$$

On your graph, list the equations of the asymptotes and the coordinates of the foci, center, and vertices.

3.7 Demonstrate that the following equation for a hyperbola,

$$\sqrt{(x-5)^2 + (y-0)^2} - \sqrt{(x \quad 5)^2 \quad (y \quad 0)^2} \quad 8$$

is equivalent to the equation below:

$$\frac{x^2}{16} - \frac{y^2}{9} = 1$$

3.8 The light cast on the wall by the lamp in the diagram on the right forms a hyperbola.

Trace a copy of this hyperbola onto a sheet of graph paper. Assuming that the center is located at the origin, write an equation that approximately describes the hyperbola.

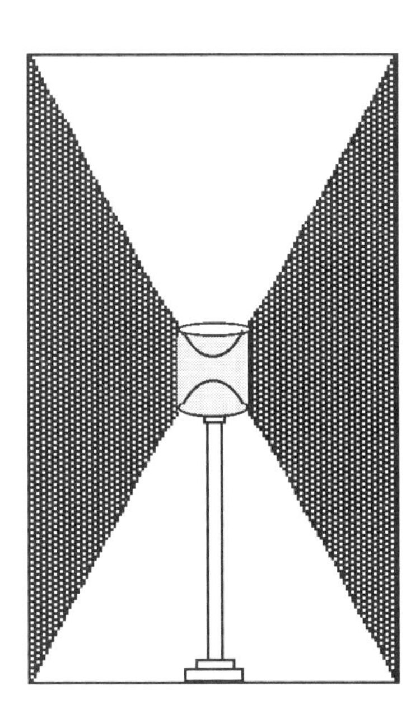

3.9 An engineer is designing a wall-mounted heater. To help disperse heat around the room, she wants to place a hyperbolic reflector behind the heat source. The diagram below shows a preliminary sketch of her design.

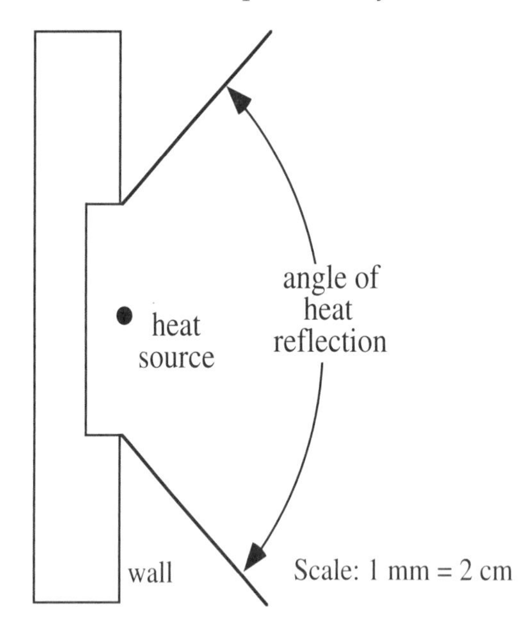

a. On a copy of this diagram, sketch the shape of a hyperbolic reflector with the heat source at its focus.

b. Use your sketch to determine the lengths of a and b in centimeters.

c. Write an equation, in standard form, for your hyperbolic reflector.

3.10 Like the Kobe Port Tower, the McDonnell Planetarium at the St. Louis Science Center has the shape of a hyperboloid. This means that a silhouette of the building forms a portion of a hyperbola, as shown in the diagram below.

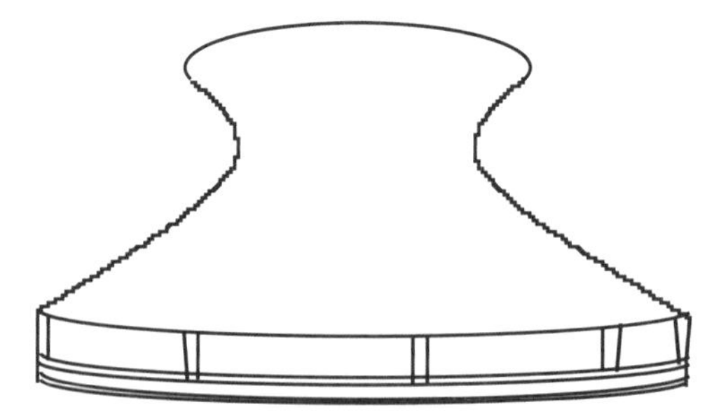

Determine an equation that could be used to model the curved silhouette in this diagram. Describe your method for finding the equation.

Research Project

Because of their reflective properties, conic sections have many scientific and industrial applications. In addition to their use in satellite dishes, parabolic shapes appear in automobile headlights, telescopic lenses, and microwave transmitters.

Hyperbolas also can be found in certain telescopes, in heat reflectors, and in performance halls.

For this research project, choose from one of the following options:

a. Write a report describing the reflective properties of ellipses, hyperbolas, and parabolas. In your report, cite at least one practical use for each and explain how the reflective properties are applied.

b. Create a demonstration that illustrates the reflective properties of ellipses, hyperbolas, and parabolas. Describe how these properties can be used in real-world applications.

ACTIVITY 4

As you observed in the previous activity, circles, ellipses, and hyperbolas can all be generated in a similar manner. The remaining conic section, however, has different restrictions than the others. In this activity, you examine the geometric properties of a **parabola.**

mathematics note

A **parabola** is a locus of points in a plane equidistant from a fixed line and a fixed point not on the line. The fixed line is the **directrix** of the parabola. The fixed point is the **focus** of the parabola.

In Figure **7-20,** for example, the directrix of the parabola is line l and the focus is point F. The distances from any point P on the parabola to F or l are equal.

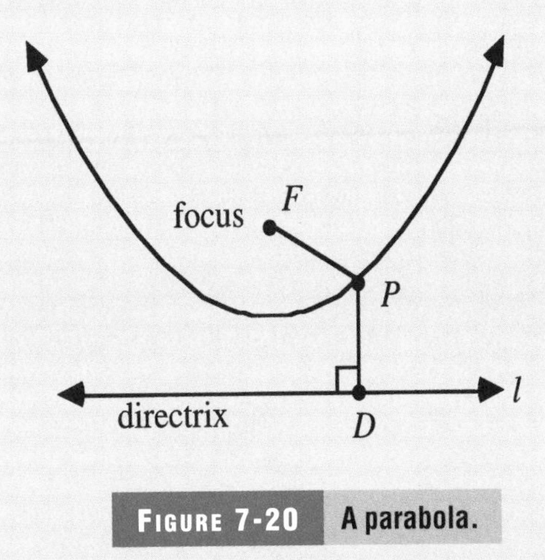

FIGURE 7-20 A parabola.

Exploration 1

In this exploration, you create a construction for generating a parabola and determine an equation that describes its locus of points.

a. Using a geometry utility, construct a horizontal line to represent the directrix of a parabola. Construct point D on the line.

b. Construct a point F not on the line. This point represents the focus of the parabola.

c. Construct $\overline{FD}$.

d. Construct the perpendicular bisector of $\overline{FD}$.

e. Construct a line perpendicular to the horizontal line through D.

f. Construct a point at the intersection of the line from Part **e** and the perpendicular bisector of $\overline{FD}$. Label this intersection P. This point represents a point on a parabola.

Your construction should now resemble the one shown in Figure **7-21.**

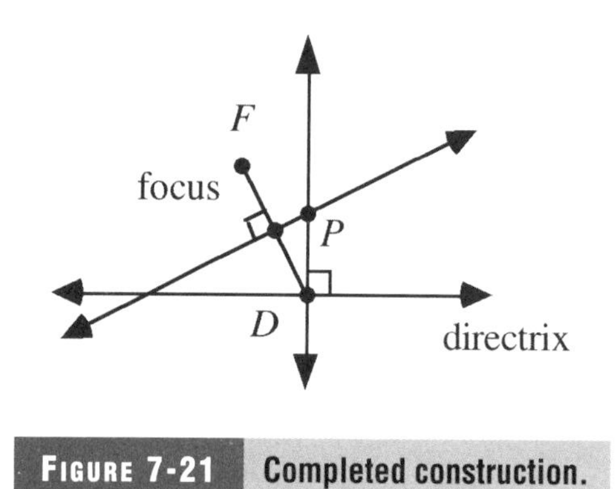

FIGURE 7-21 **Completed construction.**

g. Trace the path of P as D is moved along the horizontal line. As you trace the path of P, record its coordinates for at least 10 different locations.

h. 1. Graph the coordinates of each point you recorded in Part **g** in a scatterplot.

2. Determine an equation that models the scatterplot.

3. Graph the equation found in Step **2** on the same coordinate system as the scatterplot.

i. Move point F to at least two other locations and repeat Parts **g** and **h.** Locate point F below the line through D at least once.

Discussion 1

a. How could you prove that the construction in the exploration produces a parabola?

b. Describe any symmetries you observe in the parabola in Figure **7-20.**

c. The **vertex** of a parabola occurs at the point where the axis of symmetry intersects the parabola.

   Describe how you could use the construction in the exploration to find the vertex of the parabola.

d. Given the equation of the directrix and the location of the focus, explain how you could find the vertex of the parabola.

e. How does changing the distance from the focus to the directrix change the shape of the resulting parabola?

f. 1. How did locating the focus below the directrix affect the resulting parabola?

   2. How did it affect the equation that defines the parabola?

g. Although the parabolas that you have examined so far are functions, not all parabolas are functions.

   1. Describe how a parabola that is not a function might appear.

   2. Suggest an equation for a parabola that is not a function. Justify your response.

h. How would you change the construction in the exploration to draw a parabola that opened to the left? to the right?

i. As you already know, a parabola—like all the other conics you have studied—can be modeled by an equation. In fact, any conic can be modeled by an equation of the form:

$$Ax^2 + Bxy + Cy^2 + Dx + Ey + F = 0$$

   When coefficients A, B, and C are not all equal to zero, this is the **general quadratic equation.**

   1. Which coefficients in the general quadratic equation equal zero for an ellipse or a hyperbola? Explain your response.

   2. The standard form of the equation of a circle is $(x - h)^2 + (y - k)^2 = r^2$. When expanded, this equation can be written as:

$$x^2 - 2hx + h^2 + y^2 - 2ky + k^2 = r^2$$

      Which are the values of the coefficients in the general quadratic equation for a circle?

3. In the general quadratic equation for a parabola with a horizontal directrix, $A = a$, $B = 0$, $C = 0$, $D = b$, $E = -1$, and $F = c$. What is this equation in terms of y?

Exploration 2

In this exploration, you compare two different forms of equations for parabolas. One is the general equation $y = ax^2 + bx + c$.

The other is the **standard form,** also known as the **vertex form.** As the name implies, the vertex form provides you with specific information about the vertex of the parabola.

mathematics note

The **standard form,** or **vertex form,** of the equation for a parabola with a horizontal directrix and vertex $V(h,k)$ is:

$$y - k = a(x - h)^2$$

When a is positive, the parabola opens upward. When a is negative, the parabola opens downward.

By definition, the distance p from the vertex to the focus is the same as the distance from the vertex to the directrix. As shown in Figure **7-22,** the coordinates of the focus are $(h,k + p)$ and the equation of the directrix is $y = k - p$.

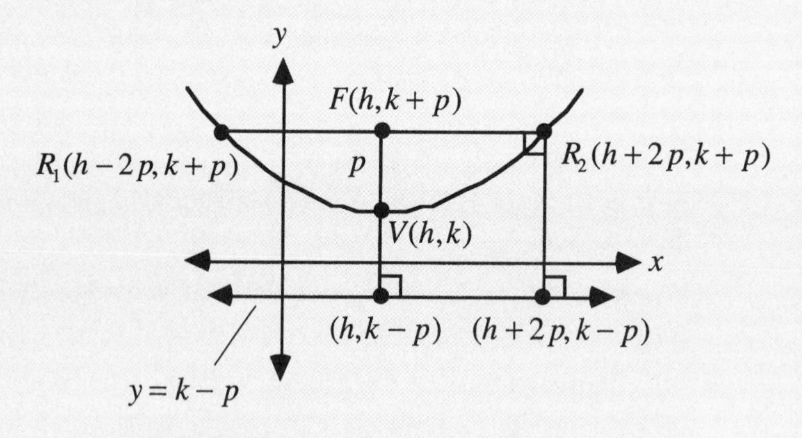

FIGURE 7-22 A parabola with horizontal directrix.

a. Recall that $(x + h)^2 = (x + h)(x + h) = x^2 + 2xh + h^2$. The expression $x^2 + 2hx + h^2$ is called a **perfect square.**

In this case, the perfect square is formed by multiplying the expression $(x + h)$ by itself, or, in other words, squaring $(x + h)$. One way to visualize this perfect square is shown in Figure **7-23** below.

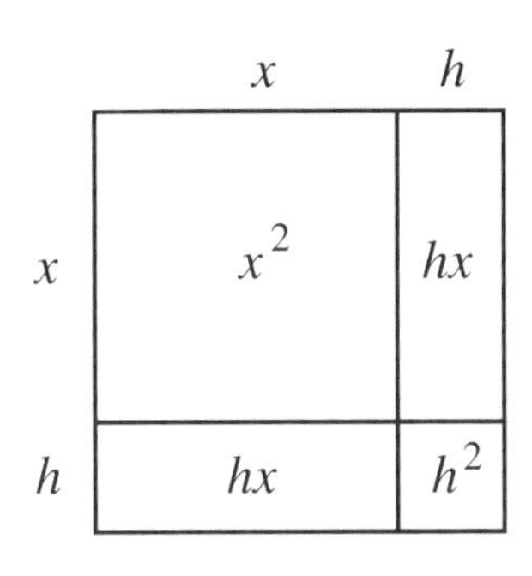

$$(x + h)^2 = x^2 + 2hx + h^2$$

FIGURE 7-23 A perfect square.

Describe the relationship between the diagram and the equation in Figure **7-23.**

b. Draw a picture to represent the fact that $(x + 3)^2 = x^2 + 6x + 9$.

c. Each of the following diagrams shows a perfect square in which the value of h^2 is unknown. Identify each unknown value to "complete the square." Verify your responses by squaring $(x + h)$.

1. $x^2 + 12x +$ ______ $= (x +$ ______$)^2$

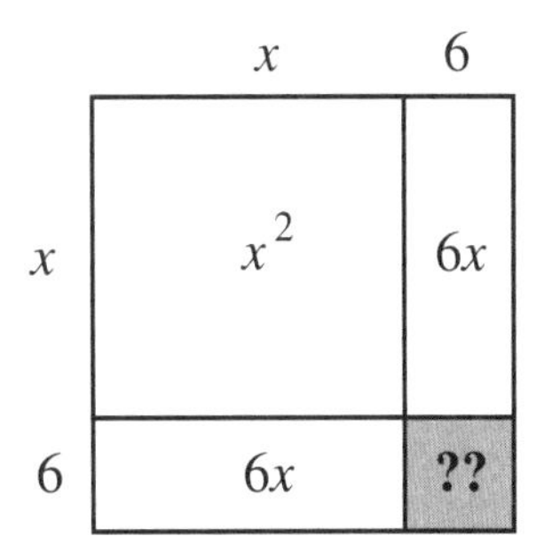

2. $x^2 + 16x +$ ______ $= (x +$ ______$)^2$

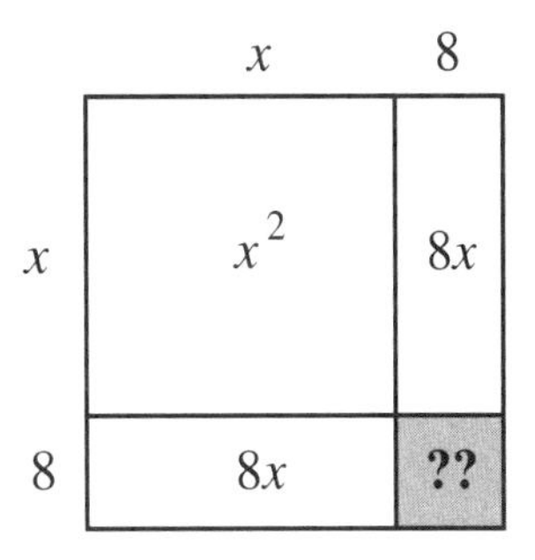

3. $x^2 + 7x +$ ______ $= (x +$ ______$)^2$

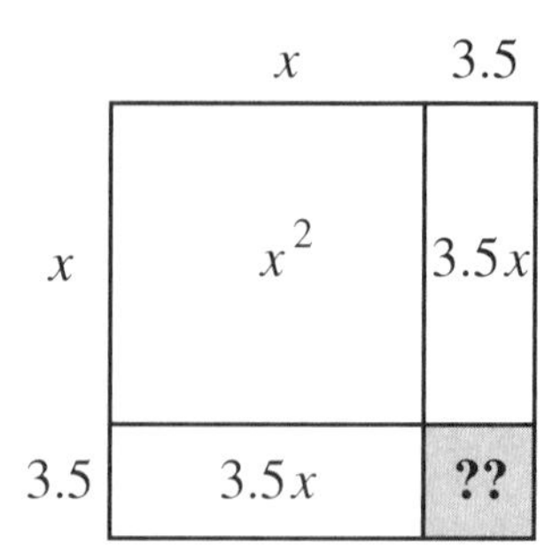

4. $x^2 + 3x +$ ______ $= (x +$ ______$)^2$

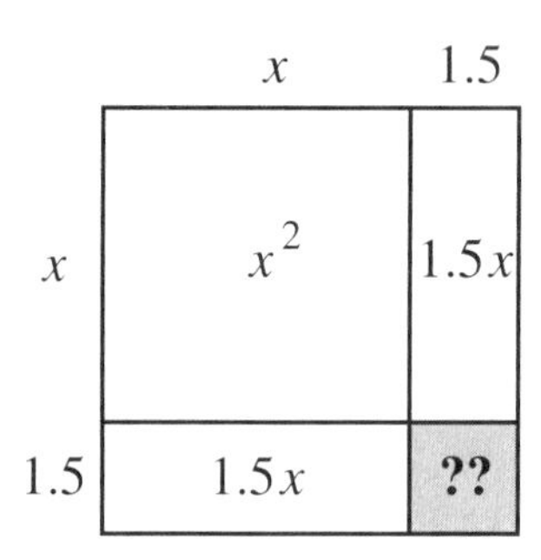

d. The ability to complete the square allows you to rewrite an equation for a parabola in general form to one in vertex form. The example below shows this process for the equation $y = 4x^2 + 12x + 16$.

Describe what has occurred at each step of this process.

$$y - 16 = 4x^2 + 12x$$
$$y - 16 = 4(x^2 + 3x)$$
$$\frac{y}{4} - 4 = x^2 + 3x + \_\_\_\_$$
$$\left(\frac{y}{4} - 4\right) + (1.5)^2 = x^2 + 3x + (1.5)^2$$
$$\frac{y}{4} - 4 + 2.25 = x^2 + 3x + 2.25$$
$$\frac{y}{4} - 1.75 = x^2 + 3x + 2.25$$
$$y - 7 = 4(x + 1.5)^2$$

e. Graph the equations $y = 4x^2 + 12x + 16$ and $y - 7 = 4(x + 1.5)^2$ on the same coordinate plane.

1. Describe the two graphs.
2. Identify the coordinates of the vertex of each graph.
3. Describe how the vertex of each graph relates to the equation in vertex form.

f. 1. Write the equation, in general form, of a parabola other than the one in Part **e.**

   2. Graph the equation and determine the coordinates of its vertex.

   3. Following the process outlined in Part **d,** rewrite the equation in vertex form.

   4. Describe how the coordinates of the vertex relate to the equation you found in Step **3.**

Discussion 2

a. Describe how you determined the values needed to "complete the squares" in Part **c** of Exploration **2.**

b. What value would you add to $x^2 - 20x$ to form a perfect square?

c. Given an equation in vertex form, how would you rewrite it in general form?

d. Why do you think that $y - k = a(x - h)^2$ is called the vertex form of the equation for a parabola?

e. Can you determine the equation of a parabola given only the coordinates of its vertex? If so, how? If not, what other information do you need?

f. Without completing the square, can you determine the equation, in vertex form, of a parabola that represents a translation of $y = 6x^2$ so that the image vertex is located at $(-3,11)$? Justify your response.

g. In the Level 3 module, "It's All in the Family," you explored several transformations of the parent function $y = x^2$.

   1. Where is the vertex of the parabola defined by $y = x^2$?

   2. How does the graph of $y = x^2$ compare to that of $y = -x^2$?

   3. How does the graph of $y = x^2$ compare to that of $y = x^2 + 3$?

   4. How does the graph of $y = x^2$ compare to that of $y = (x - 2)^2$?

h. The shape of each transformed graph in Part **f** is identical to the shape of the parent. How would you modify the equation $y = x^2$ to change the shape of the parabola?

i. Describe how the graph of $y = x^2$ is transformed in the graph of $y - 5 = 3(x - 4)^2$.

j. Describe the graph of the equation $x - 5 = 3(y - 4)^2$.

Warm-Up

1. Identify the coordinates of the vertex for each parabola below.

   a. $y = 4x^2$

   b. $y = (x - 3)^2$

   c. $y - 2 = 6x^2$

   d. $y + 5 = 2(x + 8)^2$

   e. $x - 3 = 5(y + 2)^2$

   f. $\frac{y}{5} - 3 = 2(x + 1)^2$

2. For each of the following expressions, determine the value that must be added to form a perfect square (in other words, complete the square).

   a. $x^2 + 4x$

   b. $y^2 - 8y$

   c. $x^2 - 7x$

   d. $x^2 + 2bx$

   e. $y^2 - dy$

3. Rewrite each of the following equations in vertex form.

   a. $y = -x^2 + 5$

   b. $y = (x - 2)^2$

   c. $y = 4(x - 6)^2 + 5$

   d. $y = x^2 - 7x$

   e. $y = 2x^2 + 8x + 6$

   f. $y - 9 = 3x^2 - 9x + 18$

   g. $y = x^2 + 2bx + c$

4. All of the parabolas described below represent functions. Sketch a graph of each one and write its equation in both vertex form and general form.

   a. The vertex of this parabola is (2,5). One point on the parabola is (3,6).

   b. The vertex of this parabola is (2,5). One point on the parabola is (–3,–6).

   c. The vertex of this parabola is (–2,5). One point on the parabola is (3,6).

   d. The vertex of this parabola is (2,–5). One point on the parabola is (3,–6).

   e. The vertex of this parabola is (–2,–5). One point on the parabola is (–3,6).

Assignment

4.1 Use the diagram of the parabola below to complete Parts **a–e.**

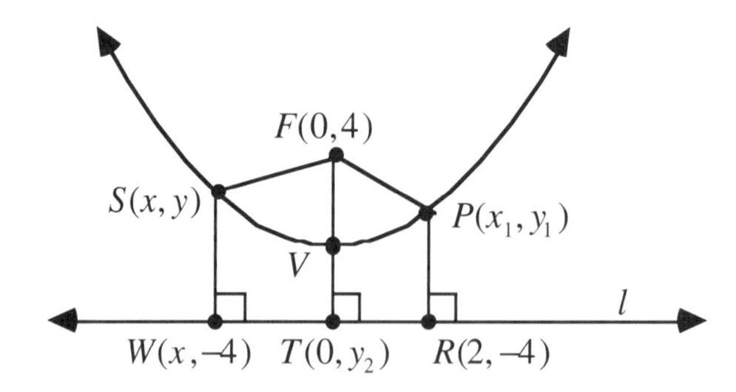

   a. What is the value of y^2?

   b. What are the coordinates of the vertex?

   c. What is the value of x_1?

   d. Use the distance formula to describe the relationship between *PF* and *PR.*

   e. Use the relationship you described in Part **d** to determine the value of y_1.

4.2 Use the parabola shown in Problem **4.1** to complete Parts **a–d.**

a. Why are the x-coordinates of points S and W equal?

b. Use the distance formula to show that $FS = SW$.

c. Use the relationship in Part **b** to determine the equation of the parabola in general form.

d. Verify your equation using the coordinates of P from Problem **4.1.**

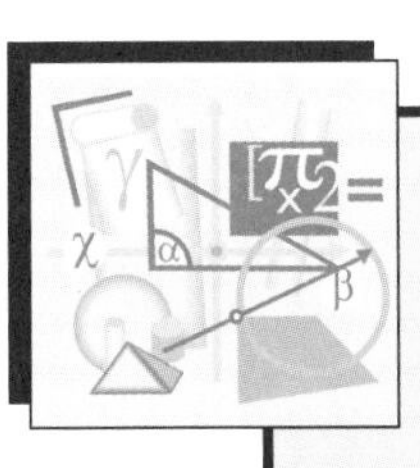

mathematics note

Given the equation of a parabola in vertex form, $y - k = a(x - h)^2$, then

$$|a| = \frac{1}{4p}$$

where p is the distance from the focus to the vertex or the vertex to the directrix.

For example, Figure **7-24** shows a graph of the equation

$$y - 4 = -\frac{1}{8}(x - 8)^2$$

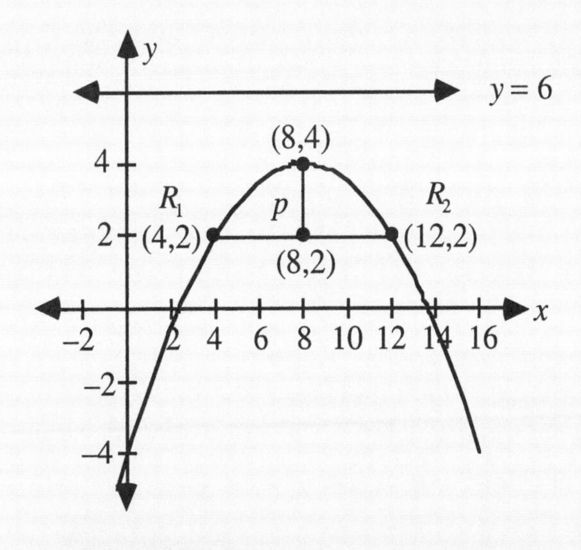

FIGURE 7-24 Graph of $y - 4 = -\frac{1}{8}(x - 8)^2$.

For this parabola, $R_1R_2 = 8$, $p = 2$, and

$$|a| = \frac{1}{4 \bullet 2} = \frac{1}{8}$$

4.3 The equation $x = 3y^2$ describes a parabola that opens to the right.

a. Sketch a graph of this parabola.

b. Determine the coordinates of the focus.

c. Find the equation of the directrix.

d. Is this equation a function? Explain your response.

4.4 **a.** What transformations of the parent function $y = x^2$ are described by $y - k = (x - h)^2$?

b. What additional transformation of the parent function is described by $y - k = a(x - h)^2$?

c. How is the distance R_1R_2 in Figure **7-21** related to a in the equation $y - k = a(x - h)^2$?

d. Write an equation that describes the relationship in Part **c.**

e. Given that $R_1R_2 = 4p$, write an equation that describes the relationship between a and $4p$.

4.5 Consider the parabola with focus at (2,6) and directrix described by the equation $y = 4$.

a. Plot the focus and vertex and draw the directrix.

b. Determine the equation of the parabola.

c. By inspection, determine two points on the parabola (other than the vertex) which have coordinates that are integers.

d. Verify that the points you identified in Part **c** are on the parabola by substituting their coordinates in the equation from Part **b.**

4.6 The path traced by a parabola revolving around its axis of symmetry describes a **paraboloid.** The reflectors used in searchlights and satellite dishes, for example, are paraboloids.

Imagine that you are building a radio telescope with a parabolic dish 10 m deep and 30 m in diameter. The radio receiver will be located at the focus of the paraboloid.

a. To identify the receiver's position, complete Steps **1–5** below.

1. Make a scale drawing of a cross section of the dish on a two-dimensional coordinate system. Place the vertex at the origin.
2. Label a point B on the edge of the dish and identify its coordinates.
3. Substitute the coordinates of B into the following equation and solve for p.

$$y = \frac{1}{4p}x^2$$

4. Write an equation, in general form, for the parabola that describes the cross section of the dish.

5. Determine the coordinates of the focus.

b. During construction of the telescope, cost overruns require you to change the size of the collecting dish. To save money, you must reduce the depth of the dish to 5 m. The diameter of 30 m remains unchanged. Repeat Part **a** for this new design.

4.7 You have been asked to test a headlight for a new car. As shown in the diagram below, the headlight consists of a halogen bulb and a parabolic reflector. The reflector must be 5 cm deep and 15 cm high. According to the manufacturer's specifications, the light-producing filament should be located at the focus of the paraboloid.

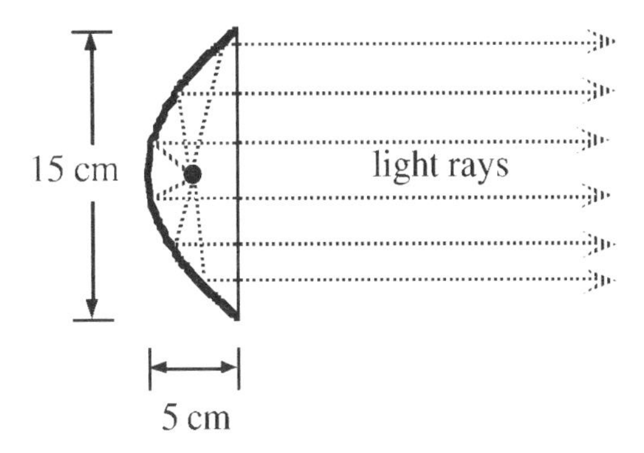

a. When the base of the bulb is mounted on the surface of the reflector, the light-producing filament is 2 cm from the reflective surface. Why is this position incorrect?

b. How would you redesign the headlight to satisfy the manufacturer?

4.8 Consider the parabola with focus at (2,6) and directrix $x = 0$.

a. Determine the equation of the parabola. Write this equation in both vertex and general form.

b. Graph the focus, vertex, and directrix on a sheet of graph paper.

c. By inspection, determine two points on the parabola (other than the vertex) which have coordinates that are integers.

d. Using the coordinates of the points identified in Part **c**, verify the equation you determined in Part **a**.

4.9 **a.** Determine the equation, in vertex form, of the parabola with focus at (–1,2) and directrix $y = 5$.

b. Rewrite the equation for the parabola in general form.

4.10 Light rays emitted from a bulb located at the focus of a paraboloid are reflected parallel to the axis of symmetry of the parabola that generated the shape of the reflector.

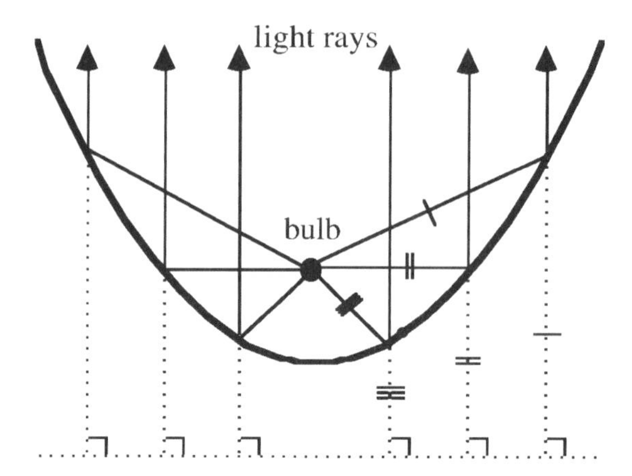

Consider a paraboloid formed by revolving the portion of the parabola $20y = x^2$ between $x = 20$ and $x = -20$ about the y-axis.

a. To use this shape as a light reflector, the bulb should be placed at the focus. Determine the coordinates of the focus.

b. If each unit on the coordinate system represents 1 cm, what is the maximum depth of the reflector?

4.11 Broadcast signals traveling into the opening of a parabolic reflector parallel to its line of symmetry are reflected through the focus of the paraboloid. This property allows an appropriately shaped antenna to collect relatively weak signals.

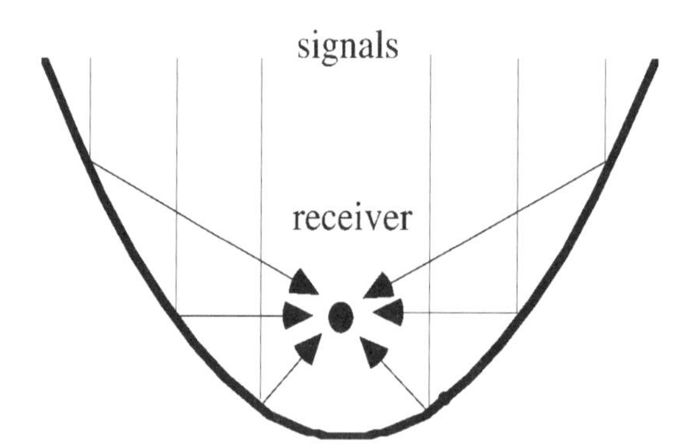

a. Imagine that you have been asked to design a dish antenna at least 180 cm in diameter at its opening, but no more than 60 cm deep. Determine an equation for a parabola that can be used to generate a suitable paraboloid. Write the equation in both general and vertex form and identify the location that you used for the origin.

b. If each unit on the coordinate system represents 1 cm on the antenna, where should the receiver be located?

Summary Assessment

1. Imagine that you have just observed a comet that you cannot find in any star chart or atlas. So that others may observe the comet and verify your discovery, you must describe its orbit. If the comet is indeed a new discovery, it will be named after you.

   From Kepler's laws of planetary motion, you know that the comet's orbit is an ellipse with the sun at one focus. According to your observations, the comet's closest approach to the sun is $9.00 \bullet 10^6$ km, while its farthest distance from sun is $1.79 \bullet 10^9$ km.

   Using an appropriate coordinate system, write an equation that describes the comet's elliptical orbit. On a graph of the equation, label all important points and measurements.

2. In this age of worldwide telecommunications, orbiting satellites reflect television signals back to large sections of the earth.

   Many communications satellites are located about 36,000 km above the equator, in what is known as the Clarke Belt. This region is named for Arthur C. Clarke, author of *2001: A Space Odyssey.* Written in 1945, this popular novel described television signals bouncing off satellites and back to earth more than 10 years before any country launched an object into space.

   Some of these satellites have geosynchronous orbits. This means that they remain above the same locations on earth. To maintain its position, a satellite must follow a nearly circular orbit at the same rate at which the earth rotates.

   The earth's diameter at the equator is about 13,000 km. Write an equation that could be used to model the path followed by a satellite in geosynchronous orbit. Describe any assumptions you make.

3. Because broadcasters often want satellite signals to be available over as large a region as possible, hyperbolic reflectors are used to transmit back to the ground. A cross section of a hyperbolic reflector can be modeled by one branch of a hyperbola.

   Consider a hyperbolic reflector with the focus located 3 m from the vertex. Assuming that the signals transmitted from this reflector can be received at any point on Earth with an unobstructed line of sight to the satellite, determine an equation that describes the curve of the reflector. Create a diagram to support your solution and describe any assumptions you made.

4. The diagram below shows a cross section of a typical dish antenna. Because of a parabola's reflective properties, all signals entering the dish parallel to the axis of symmetry are reflected through a receiving horn located at the focus.

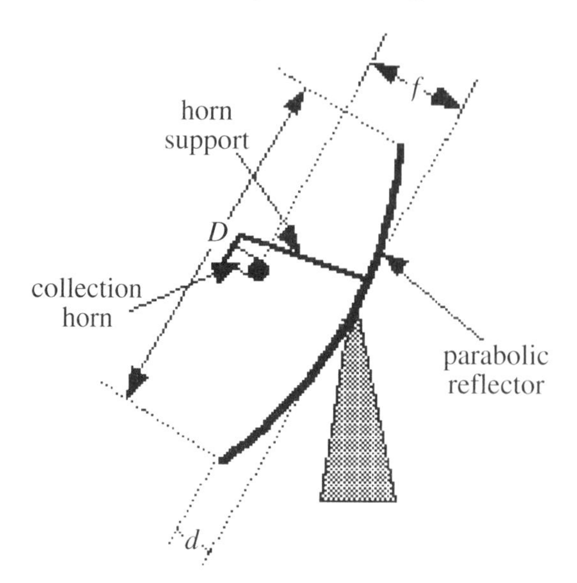

The distance from the focus to the center of the dish is called the focal length (f). The ratio between the focal length and the diameter (D) of the dish is typically between 0.25 and 0.65. The diameter of a home reflector can range from 45 cm to 1 m.

The relationship among f, D, and the depth (d) of the dish at the center is described by the equation below:

$$f = \frac{D^2}{16d}$$

Determine a function that could represent a cross section of a dish. Write the function as an equation in both general and vertex form. Include appropriate intervals for the domain and range and describe any assumptions that you made.

Module Summary

- The set of all points that satisfies one or more given conditions is a **locus** (plural **loci**).
- A **conic section** can be formed by the intersection of a plane with a cone. In a right circular cone, the conic section formed depends on the slope of intersecting plane. The intersection may result in a **circle,** an **ellipse**, a **parabola,** or a **hyperbola,** depending on the placement of the plane.

  Each conic section separates a plane into three regions: the conic section itself, an interior, and an exterior.

  It is also possible for the intersection of a plane and a cone to form a point, a line, or two intersecting lines. These intersections are called **degenerate conic sections.**
- A **circle** is the locus of points in a plane that are a given distance, the **radius,** from a fixed point, the **center.**
- The **standard form** of the equation of a circle with center at (h,k) and radius r is:

$$(x-h)^2+(y-k)^2=r^2$$

- A **tangent line** to a conic is a line in the plane of the conic that intersects the curve at exactly one point and contains no points in the interior. The point at which the conic and the tangent line intersect is the **point of tangency.**
- An **ellipse** is a locus of points in the plane such that the sum of the distances from two fixed points, the **foci,** is a constant.

  An ellipse is symmetric with respect to the lines containing its two axes. The **major axis** is the longer of the two and always contains the foci; the **minor axis** is the shorter of the two. The intersection of the major and minor axes is the **center** of the ellipse. The intersections of the ellipse and the major and minor axes are the **vertices** of the ellipse.
- The **standard form** of the equation of an ellipse with center at (h,k) is:

$$\frac{(x-h)^2}{a^2}+\frac{(y-k)^2}{b^2}=1$$

  The square of the distance along the major axis from the center to each focus is equal to the difference of the square of half the length of the major axis and the square of half the length of the minor axis.
- An **extraneous root** is an incorrect solution that may result from correct algebraic manipulation.

* A **hyperbola** is the locus of points in a plane for which the positive difference of the distances from two designated foci is constant.

  The midpoint of the segment joining the foci is the **center** of the hyperbola. The intersections of the **branches** and this segment are the **vertices** of the hyperbola. The line segment joining the vertices is the **transverse axis.** The perpendicular bisector of the transverse axis lies on the **conjugate axis.**

* The **standard form** of the equation of a hyperbola with center at (h,k) is:

$$\frac{(x-h)^2}{a^2} - \frac{(y-k)^2}{b^2} = 1 \text{ or } \frac{(y-k)^2}{b^2} - \frac{(x-h)^2}{a^2} = 1$$

  where $b^2 = c^2 - a^2$, $2a$ is the distance between the vertices, and c is the distance from the center to each focus.

* An **asymptote** to a hyperbola is a line passing through the center such that the distance from a point P on the hyperbola to the line approaches zero as the distance from P to the center increases without bound. The slopes of the asymptotes for a hyperbola are b/a and $-b/a$.

* The **general quadratic equation** is $Ax^2 + Bxy + Cy^2 + Dx + Ey + F = 0$, where coefficients A, B, and C are not all equal to zero.

* A **parabola** is a locus of points in a plane equidistant from a fixed line and a fixed point not on the line. The fixed line is the **directrix** of the parabola. The fixed point is the **focus** of the parabola. The **vertex** of a parabola occurs where the axis of symmetry for the parabola intersects the parabola.

* The **standard form,** or **vertex form,** of the equation for a parabola with a horizontal directrix and vertex $V(h,k)$ is:

$$y - k = a(x - h)^2$$

  When the coefficient a is positive, the parabola opens up; when a is negative, the parabola opens down.

* The absolute value of the coefficient a is:

$$|a| = \frac{1}{4p}$$

  where p is the distance from the focus to the vertex or the vertex to the directrix.

* Any expression multiplied by itself results in a **perfect square.**

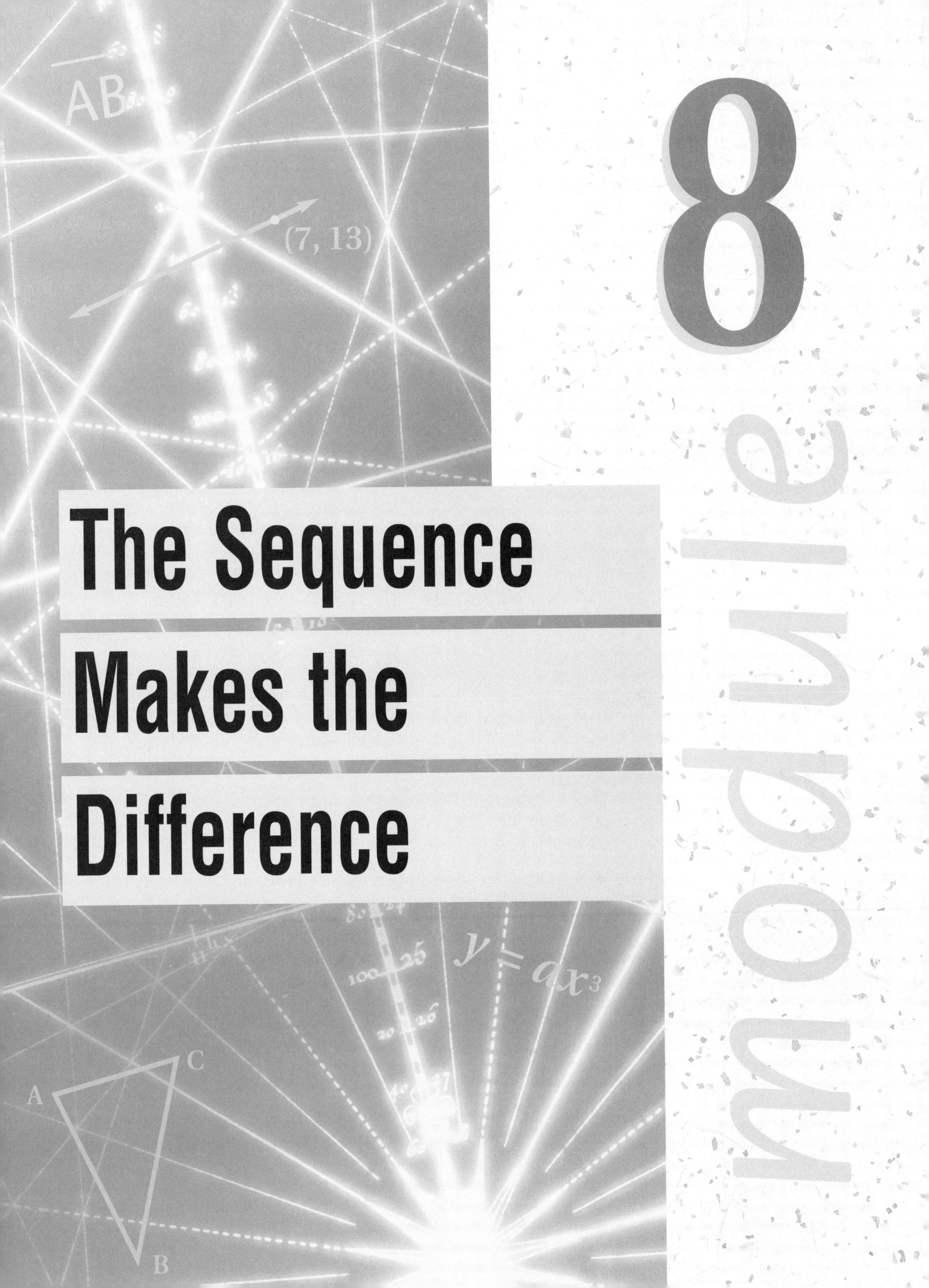

8

module

The Sequence Makes the Difference

Introduction

In this module, you continue your explorations with number patterns. Some of these patterns are easily recognizable. Others are not. If you can recognize a number pattern, then you might be able to identify functions that can generate it.

For example, consider the function $f(n) = 2n$. Over a domain of the natural numbers, this function generates the following sequence:

$$2, 4, 6, 8, \ldots$$

The function $f(n) = 2n$ is a first-degree polynomial (or linear) function. Polynomial functions of other degrees also can be used to generate sequences.

Discussion

a. Recall that the general form of a polynomial function is:

$$f(n) = a_k n^k + a_{k-1} n^{k-1} + a_{k-2} n^{k-2} + \cdots + a_1 n^1 + a_0$$

where k is a natural number. What is the degree of this polynomial?

b. Using a function $f(n)$ and the domain of natural numbers to generate a sequence, what value of n corresponds with the first term t_1 of the sequence? What value of n corresponds with t_k?

c. Over a domain of the natural numbers, a zero-degree polynomial of the form $f(n) = a_0$ generates a **constant sequence.** Give an example of a constant sequence.

d. What is another name for a sequence generated by a linear function, such as 2, 4, 6, 8, . . . ? Explain your response.

e. Sequences also can be generated by second-, third-, and fourth-degree polynomials. Give an example of a sequence generated by each of the following:

   1. a quadratic function
   2. a cubic function
   3. a quartic function.

f. Compare the use of polynomial functions to the use of explicit formulas in defining the terms of sequences.

ACTIVITY 1

A scatterplot of a sequence often can give you a clue about the types of functions that may have generated its terms. However, scatterplots alone might not provide enough information. In this activity, you examine another useful tool: the **finite-difference process.**

Exploration 1

As you have seen in earlier modules, an arithmetic sequence always has a common difference. For example, the common difference for the following arithmetic sequence is 6:

$$14, 20, 26, 32, 38, 44, \ldots$$

In this exploration, you identify differences between successive terms of non-arithmetic sequences.

a. Table **8-1** lists four different degrees of polynomial functions and shows their general forms. Select values for the coefficient(s) and constant in each of these polynomials.

TABLE 8-1 ■ *Four Types of Polynomials*

Type	General Form
linear	$f(n) = a_1n + a_0$
quadratic	$f(n) = a_2n^2 + a_1n + a_0$
cubic	$f(n) = a_3n^3 + a_2n^2 + a_1n + a_0$
quartic	$f(n) = a_4n^4 + a_3n^3 + a_2n^2 + a_1n + a_0$

b. Finding the differences between consecutive terms in a sequence can help you identify how the sequence might have been formed. Listed in order, these differences themselves form a sequence: a **sequence of differences.**

   For example, consider the finite sequence 4, 7, 24, 60, 120, 209. Its first sequence of differences is (7 – 4), (24 – 7), (60 – 24), (120 – 60), (209 – 120), or 3, 17, 36, 60, 89.

   The terms of its second sequence of differences are the differences between consecutive terms in this new sequence: (17 – 3), (36 – 17), (60 – 36), (89 – 60), or 14, 19, 24, 29.

Figure **8-1** shows the results of continuing this process for a third sequence of differences.

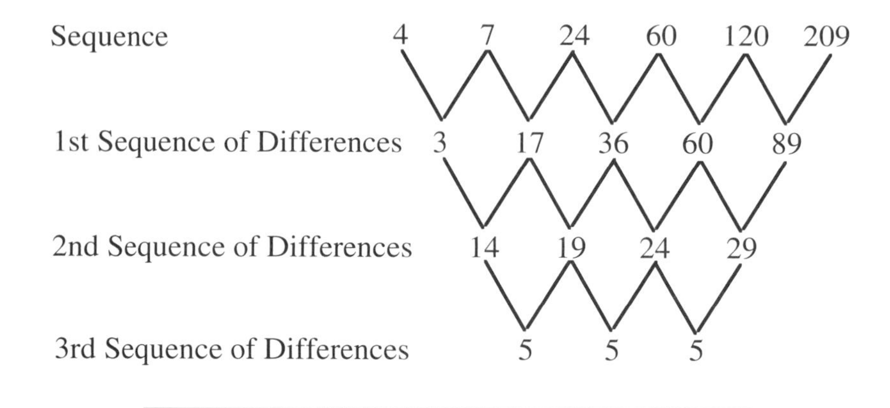

FIGURE 8-1 **Successive sequences of differences.**

1. List at least the first six terms of the sequence generated by the cubic function you wrote in Part **a.**
2. Determine the first sequence of differences for this sequence.
3. Determine the second sequence of differences.
4. If possible, continue the process of finding successive sequences of differences until you obtain a constant sequence.
5. If you obtained a constant sequence in Step **4,** identify the sequence of differences that corresponds with the constant sequence.

c. Repeat Part **b** for the other polynomials you created in Part **a.**

d. Recall that a geometric sequence can be defined using a recursive formula of the form $t_n = rt_{n-1}$, where $n > 1$ and r is the common ratio. Select values for t_1 and r, then repeat Part **b** for at least six terms of the resulting sequence.

e. The first two terms of the **Fibonacci sequence,** named for an Italian merchant also known as Leonardo of Pisa (ca. 1180–1250), are both 1. Successive terms are generated by adding the previous two terms. In other words, the Fibonacci sequence is 1, 1, 2, 3, 5, 8, ...

Any sequence in which successive terms are formed by adding the previous two terms is referred to as a **Fibonacci-type** sequence. A Fibonacci-type sequence can be defined recursively as $t_n = t_{n-1} + t_{n-2}$ where $n > 2$.

Select values for t_1 and t_2, then repeat Part **b** for at least six terms of the resulting sequence.

Discussion 1

a. In Exploration **1**, what type(s) of sequences eventually resulted in a constant sequence of differences?

b. What appears to be the relationship between the degree of a polynomial function that generates a sequence and the corresponding sequences of differences?

mathematics note

A sequence generates a constant sequence of differences if and only if that sequence can be generated by a polynomial function.

If the first constant sequence of differences is the nth sequence of differences, there exists a unique polynomial function of degree n that generates the original sequence.

For example, consider the sequence 4, 7, 24, 60, 120, 209 and its successive sequences of differences (shown in Figure **8-1**). The second sequence of differences is 14, 19, 24, 29. The third sequences of differences is 5, 5, 5. Because the first constant sequence of differences occurs at the third sequence of differences, there is a unique third-degree polynomial that generates the original sequence. In this case, that polynomial function is:

$$f(n) = \frac{5}{6}n^3 + 2n^2 - \frac{53}{6}n + 10$$

where the domain is 1, 2, 3, 4, 5, 6.

c. Do you think that it would be possible to generate an infinite geometric sequence, where $r \neq 1$, using a polynomial function?

d. Given any finite sequence, can you determine with certainty the degree of the polynomial function that generates it? Explain your response.

e. Why would you expect it to be possible to generate every finite sequence using polynomial functions?

Exploration 2

Each sequence of differences that results from a sequence generated by a polynomial function also can be generated by a polynomial function. In this exploration, you explore the relationship among the degree(s) of polynomial functions that generate successive sequence(s) of differences.

a. Determine the first 10 terms of the sequence generated by the quartic function $f(n) = n^4 - 2n^2 + n$.

b. 1. The terms of this sequence's first sequence of differences can be generated by the function $f_1(n) = f(n + 1) - f(n)$. Use this function to calculate the first nine terms of the first sequence of differences.

   2. The function $f_1(n)$ can be expanded, as shown below:

$$\begin{aligned} f_1(n) &= f(n + 1) - f(n) \\ &= \left((n + 1)^4 - 2(n + 1)^2 + (n + 1)\right) - \left(n^4 - 2n^2 + n\right) \end{aligned}$$

   Use the distributive and associative properties to simplify this expression. Record the degree of the function in a table with headings like those in Table **8-2.**

TABLE 8-2 ■ *Degrees of Functions that Generate Sequences of Differences*

Function	Degree
$f_1(n)$	
$f_2(n)$	
$f_3(n)$	
$f_4(n)$	

c. 1. Use the function $f_2(n) = f_1(n + 1) - f_1(n)$ to calculate the first eight terms of the second sequence of differences.

   2. Using the procedure described in Part **b,** determine the degree of $f_2(n)$ and record it in Table **8-2.**

d. 1. Use the function $f_3(n) = f_2(n + 1) - f_2(n)$ to calculate the first seven terms of the third sequence of differences.

   2. Determine the degree of $f_3(n)$ and record it in Table **8-2.**

e. 1. Use the function $f_4(n) = f_3(n + 1) - f_3(n)$ to calculate the first six terms of the fourth sequence of differences. (This should be a constant sequence.)

   2. Determine the degree of $f_4(n)$ and record it in Table **8-2.**

f. Describe a relationship between the degree of a polynomial that generates a sequence and the degrees of polynomials that generate successive sequences of differences.

Discussion 2

a. Given a finite sequence generated by a polynomial function of degree 7, what is the least degree of a polynomial function that generates each of the following:

1. the first sequence of differences?
2. the third sequence of differences?
3. the fifth sequence of differences?
4. the sixth sequence of differences?

b. What is the relationship between the degree of a polynomial function that generates a finite sequence and the degrees of the polynomial functions that generate its successive sequences of differences?

c. Describe how you could use your knowledge of the finite-difference process to determine the terms of a sequence given the following information.

- The first term of the sequence is 17.
- The first term of the first sequence of differences is 9.
- The first term of the second sequence of differences is 6.
- The terms of the third sequence of differences are 5, 5, 5.

Warm-Up

1. Complete a copy of the following table for the finite sequence generated by $t_n = 3n^3 + 4n - 3$, for $n = 1, 2, 3, \ldots, 10$.

n	Sequence	Sequences of Differences		
1		First		
2			Second	
3				Third
4				
⋮				
10				

2. Each column of the previous table contains a sequence that can be generated by a polynomial function. Identify the least degree of polynomial that could generate each sequence.

Assignment

1.1 Create a polynomial function that generates a finite sequence in which the fourth sequence of differences is the first constant sequence of differences.

1.2 **a.** Identify the missing term in the following finite sequence and describe how you determined your answer.

$$2, 9, ?, 65, 126, 217, 344, 513$$

b. Identify the least degree of polynomial function that could generate the sequence in Part **a.**

1.3 Explain why a sequence generated by a fifth-degree polynomial eventually results in a constant sequence of differences.

1.4 Each of the following sequences was generated by a cubic function. Identify the missing term in each one.

a. 4, 15, 38, 79, 144, 239, ?

b. –144, –286, –420, –540, –640, –714, –756, –760, ?

1.5 Use the infinite sequences defined by the following recursive rules to complete Parts **a–c.**

$$\begin{cases} p_1 = 1 \\ p_n = p_{n-1} + n, \ n > 1 \end{cases} \qquad \begin{cases} q_1 = 1 \\ q_n = q_{n-1} + n^2, \ n > 1 \end{cases}$$

a. Determine the first eight terms of each sequence.

b. Determine whether or not each sequence could be generated by a polynomial function.

c. If the sequence could be generated by a polynomial function, determine the least degree of this polynomial.

* * * * *

1.6 Determine the least degree of polynomial function that could have generated each sequence below.

a. 3, 11, 31, 69, 131, 223, 351, 521, 739

b. 1, 4, 9, 16, 25, 36, 49, 64, 81, 100

1.7 **a.** Identify the missing term in the following sequence, given that it was generated by a polynomial:

$$5, -22, -147, ?, -1219, -2550, -4747, -8122, -13035, -19894$$

b. Determine the least degree of polynomial function that could have generated the sequence in Part **a.**

Retailers and builders often stack objects in pyramids. For example, a grocer might display a pyramid of fruit in the produce department, and a builder might store a pyramid of concrete blocks on a job site. In this activity, you examine how sequences generated by polynomial functions can be used to model these situations.

Exploration

a. Create a stack of blocks shaped like a pyramid with a square base, using 25 blocks on the bottom level and 1 block on the top level. When completed, your stack should resemble the diagram in Figure **8-2.**

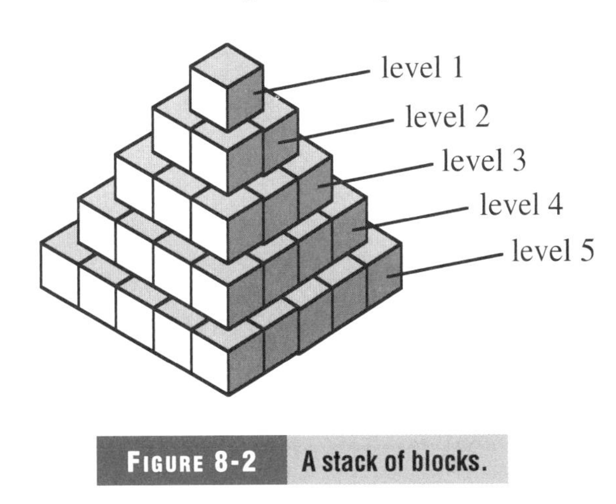

FIGURE 8-2 A stack of blocks.

b. 1. Write a sequence to model the total number of blocks in the pyramid after each level, starting with the top. Let the term number of the sequence equal the level of the pyramid, and let the value of the term equal the total number of blocks in the pyramid after each level.

2. Determine a recursive formula for the sequence.

3. Find the next three terms of the sequence.

c. One method for finding an explicit formula for a polynomial sequence involves using finite differences. Use the finite-difference process to determine the least degree of the polynomial that might generate the sequence found in Part **b.**

d. Once the least degree of the polynomial has been identified using finite differences, the polynomial function itself can be found by solving a system of equations.

For example, Table **8-3** shows the results of using the finite-difference process for the sequence 49, 72, 99, 130, 165.

TABLE 8-3 ■ *Differences for a Sequence Created by a Quadratic*

n	Sequence	Sequences of Differences	
1	49	**First**	
2	72	23	**Second**
3	99	27	4
4	130	31	4
5	165	35	4

Because the second sequence of differences is the first constant sequence, the least degree of the polynomial that generates this sequence is 2.

From Table **8-3,** when $n = 1, f(n) = 49$; when $n = 2, f(n) = 72$; and when $n = 3$, $f(n) = 99$.

These values, along with the general equation for a quadratic polynomial, $f(n) = a_2n^2 + a_1n + a_0$, can be used to create the following system of equations:

$$\begin{cases} 49 = a_2(1)^2 + a_1(1) + a_0 \\ 72 = a_2(2)^2 + a_1(2) + a_0 \\ 99 = a_2(3)^2 + a_1(3) + a_0 \end{cases}$$

Solving this system for a_2, a_1, and a_0, results in the polynomial function that generates the sequence: $f(n) = 2n^2 + n - 6$.

Use this process to determine a polynomial that generates the sequence in Part **b.**

e. Another method for identifying a polynomial that generates a sequence involves curve-fitting techniques.

   1. Create a scatterplot of term value versus term number for the sequence in Part **b.**

   2. Considering your response to Part **c,** use a polynomial regression to find an explicit formula for the sequence.

Discussion

a. Compare the two polynomial functions you identified in Parts **d** and **e** of the exploration.

b. 1. How can a recursive formula be used to find the 100th term of a sequence?

   2. How can an explicit formula be used to find the 100th term of a sequence?

c. Given only the first few terms, what assumption must be made to predict the 100th term of a sequence?

d. Consider the sequence 1, 2, 4, 8, 16 . . . .

   1. Predict the sixth term of this sequence and describe how you made your prediction.

   2. The sequence given above could be generated by the following polynomial function:

$$f(n) = \frac{41}{120}n^5 - \frac{61}{12}n^4 + \frac{691}{24}n^3 - \frac{911}{12}n^2 + \frac{1393}{15}n - 40$$

   In this case, what would be the sixth term of the sequence?

e. What do your responses to Part **d** above imply about the reliability of making predictions about subsequent terms in a given sequence?

f. Suppose that you know the recursive formula for an infinite sequence. The pattern revealed by the first several terms indicates that it can be generated by a polynomial. Would you expect there to be more than one polynomial that could generate this sequence?

Warm-Up

1. Suggest a polynomial function for generating each sequence below and use it to predict the next three terms.

   a. 1, 6, 18, 40, 75, 126, 196, . . .

   b. 6.5, 17, 36.5, 65, 102.5, . . .

   c. 8.9, –43.6, –215.1, –631.6, –1469.5, –2955.6, . . .

   d. –1, 2, 3, 2, –1, –6, –13, –22, . . .

2. Are the functions you suggested in Problem **1** the only polynomials that could have generated the corresponding sequences? Explain your response.

Assignment

2.1 A pipe manufacturer stores its products in piles like the one shown in the diagram below.

a. The total number of pipes after any row, beginning with the top row, defines a sequence. For example, after 1 row, there is 1 pipe; after 2 rows, there are 3 pipes; and so on.

   Do you think that this sequence can be generated by a polynomial function? Explain your response.

b. The warehouse manager would like to develop a method for determining the total number of pipes in a pile by counting the number of pipes in the bottom row.

   Find a formula that describes the total number of pipes in a pile given the number of pipes in the bottom row.

c. The warehouse has a pile with 40 pipes in the bottom row. How many pipes are in this pile?

2.2 Consider the sequence 1, 2, 3, ...

a. Predict the fourth term in the sequence.

b. Determine a polynomial function that could be used to generate the sequence containing your four terms.

c. Suggest a value for the fourth term other than the one you predicted in Part **a.**

d. Use the first four terms of the sequence from Part **c** and the general form of a cubic function, $f(x) = a_3x^3 + a_2x^2 + a_1x + a_0$, to determine a polynomial that could be used to generate these four terms.

e. Compare the fifth terms of the sequences generated by the polynomials in Parts **b** and **d.**

2.3 Consider an arrangement of the natural numbers in a triangular pattern, as shown below.

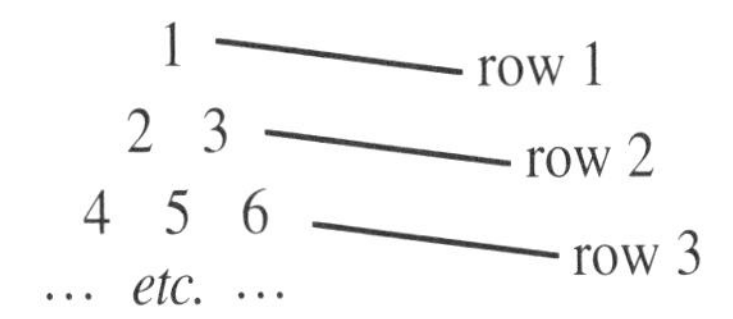

a. Generate the next two rows of the triangular pattern.

b. Which row will contain the number 1000?

c. What is the sum of the numbers in the 100th row?

2.4 Grocery stores often display fruit in stacks shaped like tetrahedrons. The diagram below shows such a display, with 15 oranges on the bottom level and 1 orange on the top level.

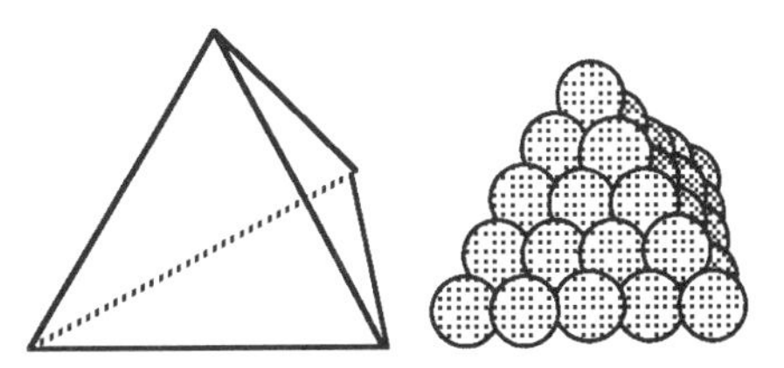

a. Determine the number of oranges that could be displayed in a tetrahedral stack with 10 levels.

b. A produce department has 7 cases of oranges. Each case contains 48 oranges. If the manager decides to display these oranges in a tetrahedral stack, how many levels will it have?

2.5 A box manufacturer creates clothing boxes from a template like the one shown below.

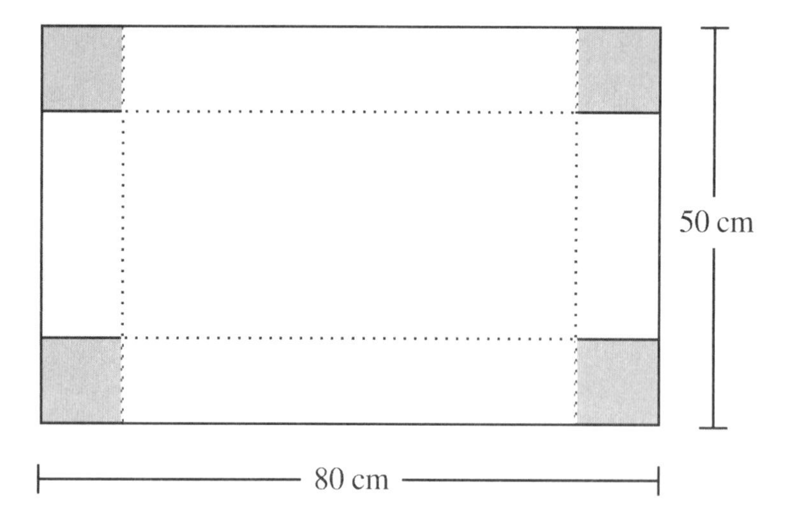

Cuts are made along the solid lines and folds are made along the dotted lines. The square tabs (shaded areas) are folded and glued inside to form the box. The machinery that makes the cuts will cut only square tabs with dimensions measured in whole centimeters.

a. Create a sequence in which the term number represents the length of the side of the square tab and the terms describe the surface area of the resulting box.

b. Create a sequence in which the term number represents the length of the side of the square tab and the terms describe the volume of the resulting box.

c. Determine the dimensions of the square tabs that result in a box with the largest possible surface area.

d. Determine the dimensions of the square tabs that result in a box with the largest possible volume.

* * * * *

2.6 According to a popular holiday song, "The Twelve Days of Christmas," a "true love" gives an increasing number of gifts on 12 consecutive days. On the first day, the true love gives a partridge in a pear tree. On the second day, the true love gives two turtledoves and a partridge in a pear tree. On the third day, the true love gives three French hens, two turtledoves, and a partridge in a pear tree. This pattern continues.

a. On the 12th day, how many gifts does the true love give? Justify your response.

b. During the entire 12 days, how many gifts does the loved one receive? Explain your response.

2.7 Quilts sometimes are created by starting with a hexagonal piece of cloth, then adding rings of hexagons, as shown below.

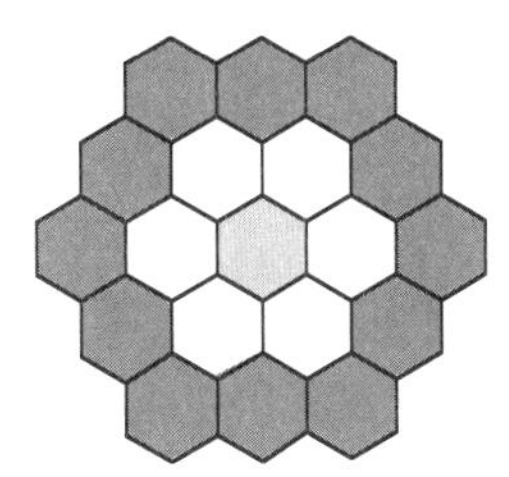

a. Write a sequence for the number of hexagons in each of the first 10 rings of this quilt pattern.

b. How many hexagons would there be in the 21st ring of such a quilt?

2.8 **a.** Create a sequence by following the steps below.

1. Construct a circle. Construct one point on the circle. Record the number of regions in the interior of the circle.
2. Construct a circle. Construct a diameter of the circle. Record the number of regions in the interior of the circle.
3. Construct a circle. Inscribe an equilateral triangle in the circle and connect each vertex to every other vertex with a line segment. Record the number of regions in the interior of the circle.
4. Construct a circle. Inscribe a square in the circle and connect each vertex to every other vertex with a line segment. Record the number of regions in the interior of the circle.
5. Construct a circle. Inscribe a regular pentagon in the circle and connect each vertex to every other vertex with a line segment. Record the number of regions in the interior of the circle.

b. Determine a pattern in the numbers of interior regions formed.

c. Predict the numbers of regions formed by each of the following:

1. inscribing a regular hexagon in a circle and connecting each vertex to every other vertex with a line segment
2. inscribing a regular heptagon in a circle and connecting each vertex to every other vertex with a line segment.

d. Verify your predictions from Part **c.**

Research Project

The Tower of Hanoi is a classic game involving sequences. The goal of the game is to move all the rings from one peg to another peg, retaining the same order, in a minimum number of moves. The game is subject to the following restrictions:

- Only one ring may be moved at a time.
- Once a ring is removed from one peg, it must be placed on one of the other two pegs.
- A ring may not be placed on top of a smaller ring.

Figure **8-3** shows the starting positions for 8 rings, an intermediate step, and the final positions of the rings.

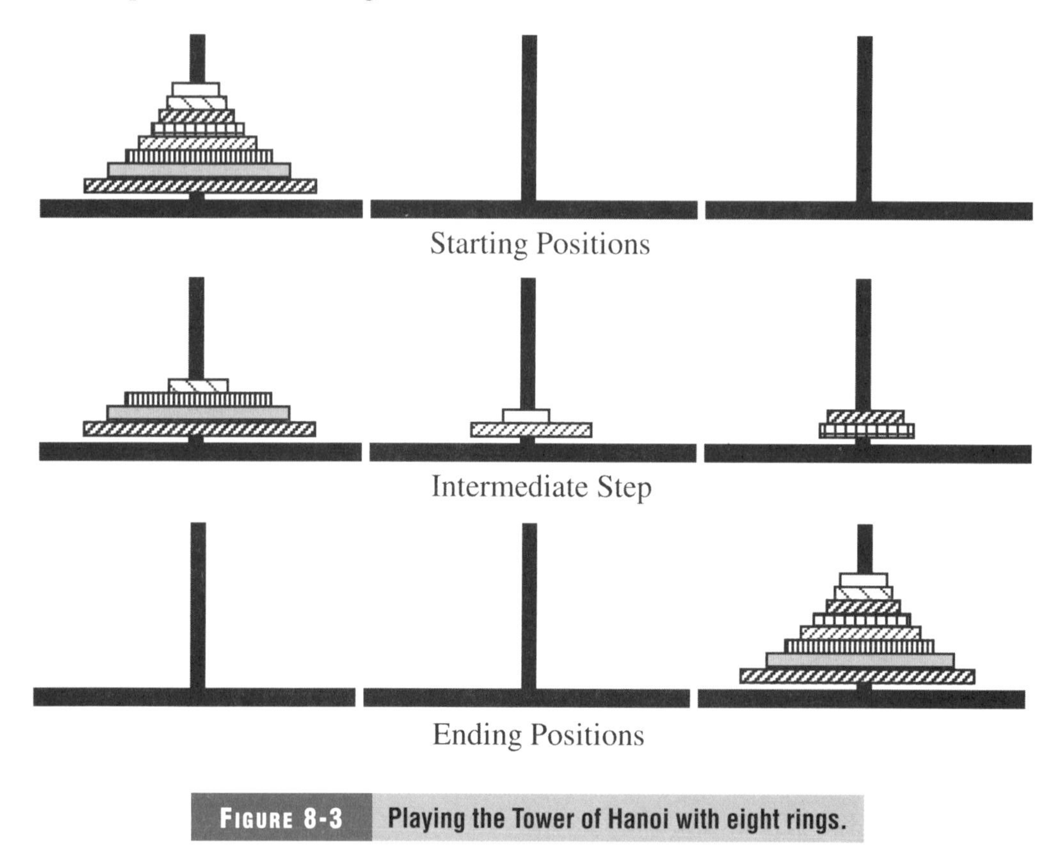

FIGURE 8-3 **Playing the Tower of Hanoi with eight rings.**

a. Determine the minimum number of moves needed to move a stack of n rings from one peg to another while retaining the same order.

b. Determine the relationship between the number of rings and the minimum number of moves necessary to complete the task. Express this relationship as:

   1. a recursive formula
   2. an explicit formula.

Summary Assessment

Imagine that you are an engineer for a company that manufactures paper bags. Your department has been asked to design a bag with a capacity of at least 12,500 cm^3. For advertising purposes, the bag also must have the largest possible outside surface area.

The bag must be cut and folded from a rectangular sheet of paper measuring 100 cm by 45 cm, as shown in the following diagram.

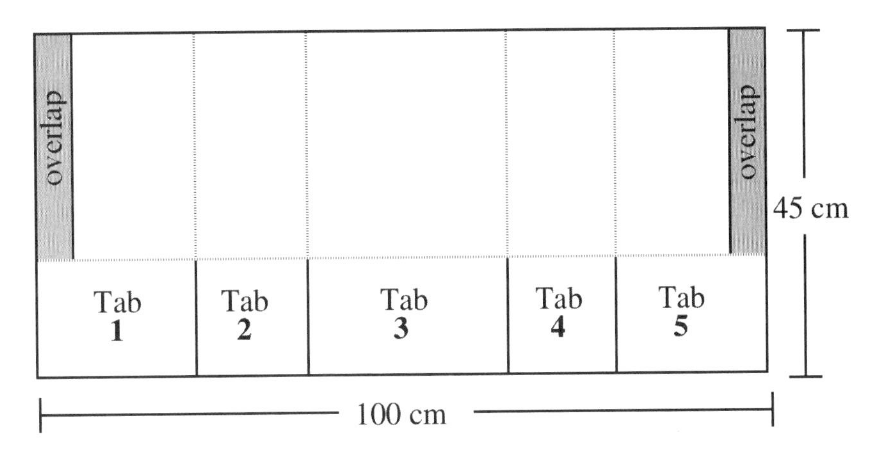

The solid lines on the template indicate cuts; the dotted lines indicate folds. Tabs **2** and **4** are squares of equal measure. Tabs **1** and **5** are 3/4 the length of Tab **3.** (This creates an overlap for gluing and strength.) The dimensions of the base of the bag are the length of Tab **2** by the length of Tab **3.** Due to the nature of the machinery that makes the cuts, the dimensions of the tabs must be in whole centimeters.

Once you have designed an acceptable bag, you must make a presentation to the company's board of directors. Your presentation should include the dimensions of the bag, a description of the method you used to determine these dimensions, and a paragraph that explains why you believe your bag is the best one possible. As part of your presentation, include a scale model made from a sheet of notebook paper.

Module Summary

* The first two terms of the **Fibonacci sequence,** named for an Italian merchant also known as Leonardo of Pisa (ca. 1180–1250), are both 1. Successive terms are generated by adding the previous two terms. In other words, the Fibonacci sequence is 1, 1, 2, 3, 5, 8, ...
* Any sequence in which successive terms are formed by adding the previous two terms is referred to as a **Fibonacci-type** sequence. A Fibonacci-type sequence can be defined recursively as $t_n = t_{n-1} + t_{n-2}$ where $n > 2$.
* A **sequence of differences** can be generated from a finite sequence $t_1, t_2, t_3, t_4, t_5, \ldots, t_n$ by taking the differences of consecutive terms. The first sequence of differences is $t_2 - t_1, t_3 - t_2, t_4 - t_3, t_5 - t_4, \ldots, t_n - t_{n-1}$.
* The process of finding successive sequences of differences is called the **finite-difference process,** which continues until the first constant sequence of differences is found.
* A sequence generates a constant sequence of differences if and only if that sequence can be generated by a polynomial function.
* If the first constant sequence of differences is the nth sequence of differences, there exists a unique polynomial function of degree n that generates the original sequence.

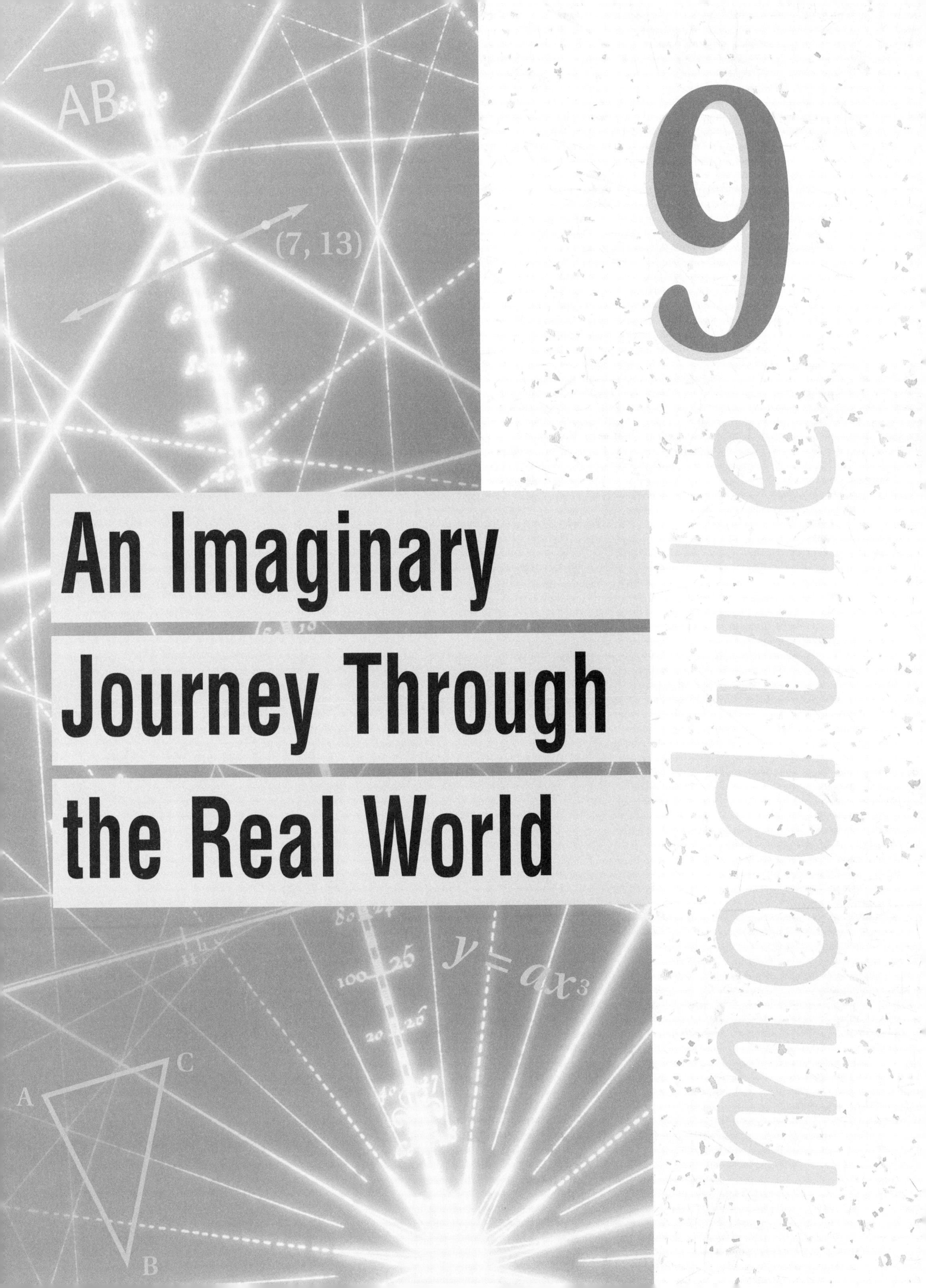
module
9
An Imaginary
Journey Through
the Real World
AB
(7, 13)
y = ax3
A
B
C

Introduction

You are familiar with many different sets of numbers: the natural numbers, the whole numbers, the integers, the rational numbers, and the real numbers. Each set was developed as a social—or mathematical—need arose.

Written symbols for the natural numbers 1, 2, 3, . . . are at least as old as the pyramids. Around 200 A.D., the number 0 was introduced in India to represent an empty column in a counting board that resembled an abacus. The set of numbers consisting of 0 and the natural numbers make up the set of whole numbers.

The need for negative numbers emerged in China in the 6th and 7th centuries, though they were not used in Europe until the 15th century. The natural numbers, their opposites (negatives), and zero make up the set of integers.

The ancient Greeks introduced the positive rational numbers to represent fractional parts of a quantity. The term *rational* was coined to describe numbers that are ratios of two natural numbers, where the denominator is not 0. During this time, the Greeks believed that rational numbers could be used to precisely describe all measurements in the physical world.

This hypothesis about rational numbers was incorrect. When Greek mathematicians tried to find a rational number to describe the length of the diagonal of a square like the one shown in Figure **9-1,** they realized that no such rational number existed.

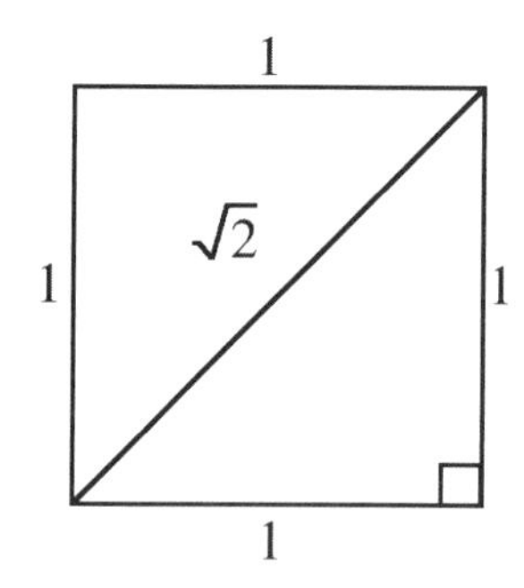

FIGURE 9-1 **A square and one of its diagonals.**

As a result, the Greeks extended their number system to include irrational numbers. Eventually, the sets of rational and irrational numbers were combined to form the set of real numbers.

Is the set of real numbers sufficient to describe everything in the physical—or mathematical—world? In this module, you will investigate situations in which another set of numbers is useful.

Exploration 1

In the Level 4 module "It's Napped Time," you converted the equations of parabolas from the general form to vertex form by a process called **completing the square.** This method can be used to solve any quadratic equation.

In this exploration, you investigate the roots of second-degree polynomial equations of the form $y = ax^2 + bx + c$, where a, b, and c are real numbers and $a \neq 0$.

a. Recall that when the roots or zeros of a quadratic function are known, the function can be written as a product of factors: $f(x) = a(x - r_1)(x - r_2)$.

   1. Identify real-number values for a, b, and c so that the roots of $y = ax^2 + bx + c$ are two different rational numbers.

   2. To check your results, substitute your values for a, b, and c into the general equation $y = ax^2 + bx + c$. Graph this equation, then use the graph to determine its zeros.

b. Repeat Part **a** so that $y = ax^2 + bx + c$ has only one rational root.

   Note: If r is the only solution to $0 = ax^2 + bx + c$, then $f(x) = a(x - r)(x - r)$. This solution is a double root.

c. The example below shows how to solve the quadratic equation $3x^2 + 10x - 8 = 0$ by completing the square.

$$3x^2 + 10x - 8 = 0$$

$$3x^2 + 10x = 8$$

$$3\left(x^2 + \frac{10}{3}x\right) = 8$$

$$x^2 + \frac{10}{3}x + \_\_\_\_\_ = \frac{8}{3}$$

$$x^2 + \frac{10}{3}x + \left(\frac{1}{2} \bullet \frac{10}{3}\right)^2 = \frac{8}{3} + \left(\frac{1}{2} \bullet \frac{10}{3}\right)^2$$

$$x^2 + \frac{10}{3}x + \frac{100}{36} = \frac{8}{3} + \frac{100}{36}$$

$$\left(x + \frac{10}{6}\right)^2 = \frac{96}{36} + \frac{100}{36}$$

$$\sqrt{\left(x + \frac{10}{6}\right)^2} = \sqrt{\frac{196}{36}}$$

$$\left|x + \frac{10}{6}\right| = \frac{\sqrt{196}}{6}$$

$$\text{so } x + \frac{10}{6} = \frac{\sqrt{196}}{6} \quad \text{or} \quad -\left(x + \frac{10}{6}\right) = \frac{\sqrt{196}}{6}$$

$$x = -\frac{10}{6} + \frac{\sqrt{196}}{6} \quad \text{or} \quad x = -\frac{10}{6} \quad \frac{\sqrt{196}}{6}$$

$$x = -\frac{10}{6} + \frac{14}{6} \quad \text{or} \quad x = -\frac{10}{6} \quad \frac{14}{6}$$

$$x = \frac{2}{3} \quad \text{or} \quad x = -4$$

Use this process to solve the quadratic equations you wrote in Parts **a** and **b.**

Discussion 1

a. Given the two roots of a quadratic equation $y = ax^2 + bx + c$, can you identify the values of a, b, and c? Explain your response.

b. Describe the first step you would take to solve the following equation by completing the square.

$$4x - 3 = 2x^2 - 7x + 5$$

c. How are the solutions to each quadratic function in Parts **a** and **b** of Exploration **1** related to the x-intercept(s) of its graph?

d. The zeros of the function $y = ax^2 + bx + c$ are equal to the solutions of the equation $0 = ax^2 + bx + c$. Explain why this must be true.

e. 1. In general, when completing the square, taking the square root of a quantity that has been squared results in $\sqrt{n^2} = |n|$. Why is $\sqrt{n^2}$ not equal to n?

   2. The steps below were included in the example given in Part **c** of Exploration **1.** Why are there two possibilities in the step following the absolute-value equation?

$$\left|x + \frac{10}{6}\right| = \frac{\sqrt{196}}{6}$$

$$\text{so } x + \frac{10}{6} = \frac{\sqrt{196}}{6} \quad \text{or} \quad -\left(x + \frac{10}{6}\right) = \frac{\sqrt{196}}{6}$$

f. A quadratic expression that can be written in the form $x^2 - a^2$ is a **difference of squares.** In general, such expressions have two factors: $(x - a)$ and $(x + a)$. In other words, $x^2 - a^2$ can be factored as $(x - a)(x + a)$.

   1. Given this fact, what are the solutions to a polynomial equation of the form $x^2 - a^2 = 0$?

   2. What are the solutions to the equation $x^2 - 2 = 0$?

   3. What are the factors of the polynomial $x^2 - 2$?

Exploration 2

In the previous exploration, you investigated second-degree polynomials with rational roots. However, not all quadratics have rational solutions. In this exploration, you examine some other possibilities.

a. 1. Identify real-number values for a, b, and c so that the roots of $y = ax^2 + bx + c$ are two different irrational numbers, r_1 and r_2.

   2. To check your results, substitute the values you used for a, b, and c into the general equation $y = ax^2 + bx + c$. Graph this equation, then use the graph to determine its zeros.

b. Repeat Part **a** so that $y = ax^2 + bx + c$ has only one irrational root r.

c. Experiment with values of a, b, and c to identify a function $y = ax^2 + bx + c$ that has no x-intercepts.

d. Find the roots of the quadratic equations you identified in Parts **a–c** by completing the square.

e. Use your ability to complete the square to solve the general quadratic equation $ax^2 + bx + c = 0$, where $a \neq 0$. This general solution is called the **quadratic formula.**

f. Use the quadratic formula to find the roots of each equation you identified in Parts **a–c.** Compare the solutions with your results in Part **d.**

Discussion 2

a. Describe how you could use a graph to demonstrate that a quadratic function has each of the following:

   1. two real roots

   2. one double root

   3. no real roots.

b. How do the roots of the quadratic equation that you identified in Part **c** of Exploration **2** differ from those in Parts **a** and **b**?

c. Are there any real-number roots for the equation that you wrote in Part **c** of Exploration **2**? Explain your response.

The notation for the **imaginary unit *i***, where $i = \sqrt{-1}$ and $i^2 = -1$, was first introduced by Swiss mathematician Leonhard Euler (1707–1783). The adoption of i by Gauss in his classic *Disquisitiones arithmeticae* in 1801 secured its use in mathematical notation. This notation was generalized to define the square root of any negative number as: $\sqrt{-a} = \sqrt{-1} \bullet \sqrt{a} = i\sqrt{a}$ for any number $a > 0$.

For example, $\sqrt{-3} = \sqrt{-1} \bullet \sqrt{3} = i\sqrt{3}$ and $\sqrt{-9} = \sqrt{9} \bullet \sqrt{-1} = 3i$.

A **complex number** is any number in the form $a + bi$, where both a and b are real numbers. For example, $4.3 + i\sqrt{5}$ and $\pi = 2i$ are complex numbers. So are $7i$ and 11, because they may be represented as $0 + 7i$ and $11 + 0i$, respectively.

A **pure imaginary number** is a complex number $a + bi$ for which $a = 0$ and $b \neq 0$. For example, $5i$, $8i$, and $i\sqrt{5}$ are pure imaginary numbers.

A real number is a complex number $a + bi$ for which $b = 0$. For example, $5 + 0i = 5$ and $-3 + 0i = -3$ are real numbers.

The Venn diagram in Figure **9-2** shows the relationships among the sets of complex numbers, pure imaginary numbers, and real numbers.

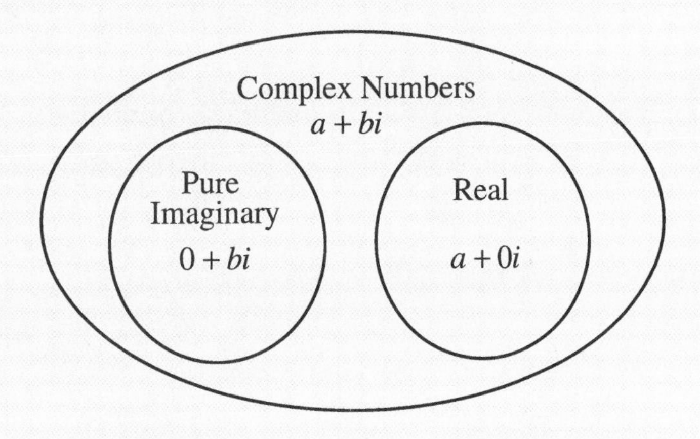

FIGURE 9-2 **Venn diagram of complex numbers.**

In the set of complex numbers, $a + bi = c + di$ if and only if $a = c$ and $b = d$.

d. Are all real numbers also complex numbers? Explain your response.

e. 1. Use $i = \sqrt{-1}$ to describe the solutions to the equation you wrote in Part **c** of Exploration **2**.

   2. Compare these solutions to those of others in the class. How are each pair of complex-number solutions related?

f. 1. Considering the information given in the previous mathematics note, along with the factors of a difference of squares, determine the factors of $x^2 + 4$.

2. What are the solutions to the equation $x^2 + 4 = 0$?

g. Describe how you could factor any expression of the form $x^2 + a^2$ and identify its zeros.

h. 1. Describe your solution to the general quadratic equation in Part **e** of Exploration **2.**

2. Describe how you would apply the quadratic formula to the equation $3x^2 + 10x - 8 = 0$.

3. Describe how you would apply the quadratic formula to the equation $2x - 7 = x^2 + 3x$.

mathematics note

Second-degree polynomial equations of the form $ax^2 + bx + c = 0$ with $a \neq 0$, always have two solutions when solved over the complex numbers:

$$x = \frac{-b}{2a} + \frac{\sqrt{b^2 - 4ac}}{2a} \quad \text{and} \quad x = \frac{-b}{2a} - \frac{\sqrt{b^2 - 4ac}}{2a}$$

These two solutions make up the **quadratic formula.**

When a, b, and c are real numbers and $a \neq 0$, the expression $b^2 - 4ac$ is known as the **discriminant.** When the discriminant is less than 0, the solutions are complex and occur in pairs called **complex conjugates.** Complex conjugates are in the form $m + ni$ and $m - ni$. Each complex number in the pair is said to be the **conjugate** of the other.

For example, consider the quadratic equation $x^2 + 2x + 5 = 0$. In this case, the discriminant $b^2 - 4ac = -16$. Because $-16 < 0$, $x^2 + 2x + 5 = 0$ has two complex-number solutions:

$$x = \frac{-2}{2} + \frac{\sqrt{2^2 - 4\bullet 5}}{2} = -1 + 2i \quad \text{and} \quad x = \frac{-2}{2} - \frac{\sqrt{2^2 - 4\bullet 5}}{2} = -1 - 2i$$

These two roots, $-1 + 2i$ and $-1 - 2i$, are complex conjugates.

i. As described in the mathematics note above, the discriminant can help you determine whether the roots of a quadratic equation are real or complex. Explain why this is true.

j. A polynomial is **reducible** over the real numbers if it can be expressed as the product of two or more polynomials of degree 1 and with real coefficients. Is every second-degree polynomial reducible over the real numbers? Explain your response.

Warm-Up

1. Identify the discriminant of each quadratic equation below. Use the discriminant to determine if the equation has two complex but non-real roots, two real roots, or a double root.

   a. $x^2 + 4 = 0$
   b. $x^2 - 3 = 0$

   c. $9x^2 - 6x + 1 = 0$
   d. $9x^2 - 30x + 1 = 0$

   e. $2x^2 + 8 = 5x + 1$
   f. $x^2 + 13 = 6x$

2. Solve each of the following quadratic equations by completing the square. Write any non-real solutions in the form $a + bi$.

   a. $x^2 + 4x + 3 = 0$
   b. $2x^2 - 6x - 5 = 0$

   c. $3x^2 + 9x + 15 = 0$
   d. $8x - 12 = 2x^2$

3. Solve each of the following quadratic equations using the quadratic formula. Write any non-real solutions in the form $a + bi$.

   a. $4x^2 - 3x + 2 = 0$
   b. $6x^2 - 10 = 11x$

   c. $2x - 3 = 4x^2 + 1$
   d. $3x^2 - 5x + 4 = 2x^2 - 11x - 5$

4. Write each radical expression as a complex number in the form $a + bi$.

   a. $\sqrt{25}$
   b. $4\sqrt{-36}$

   c. $3 - \sqrt{16}$
   d. $-2 + \sqrt{-49}$

5. Write each complex number below using the square root of a single real number.

   a. $3i$
   b. $-5i$

   c. $6i^2$
   d. $2 + i$

Assignment

1.1 Determine the roots of each equation below in the set of complex numbers and write the equation in factored form.

   a. $y = x^2 - 28$

   b. $y = x^2 + 28$

1.2 Describe the roots of each quadratic equation graphed below.

a.

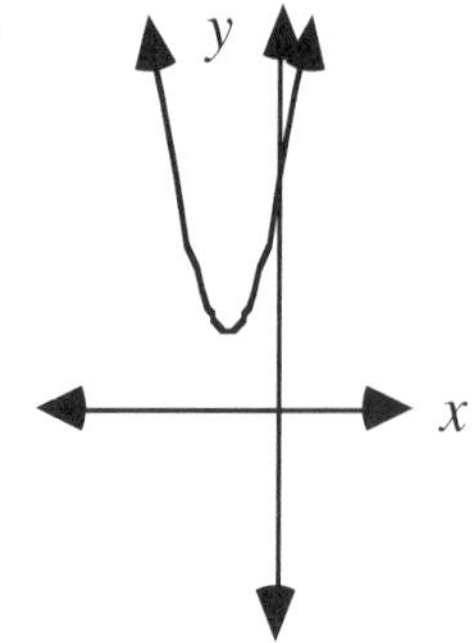

b.

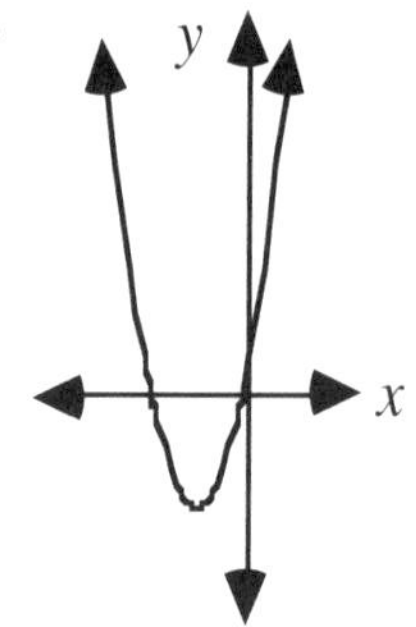

c.

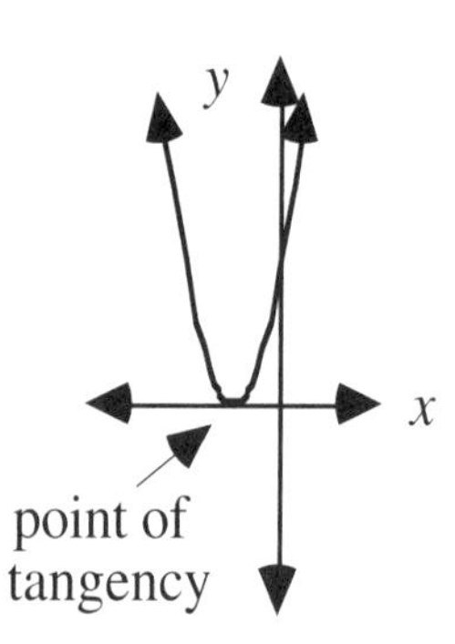

1.3 For each expression below, write an equation with real coefficients for which that expression is a solution.

a. $5i$

b. $2i\sqrt{7}$

c. $6-7i$

1.4 Use two different methods to show that the solutions to the equation $x^2+27=0$ are $x=3i\sqrt{3}$ and $x=-3i\sqrt{3}$.

1.5 **a.** Another way to solve a quadratic equation of the form $x^2+n=0$ uses the difference of squares. For example, the equation $x^2+27=0$ can be solved as shown below. Write a justification for each step in this solution.

1. $x^2-(-27)=0$

2. $x^2-\left(\sqrt{-27}\right)^2=0$

3. $\left(x-\sqrt{-27}\right)\left(x+\sqrt{-27}\right)=0$

4. $\left(x+\sqrt{-27}\right)=0$ or $\left(x+\sqrt{-27}\right)=0$

5. $x=\sqrt{-27}$ or $x=-\sqrt{-27}$

6. $x=i\sqrt{27}$ or $x=-i\sqrt{27}$

7. $x=3i\sqrt{3}$ or $x=-3i\sqrt{3}$

b. Use the difference of squares to solve each of the following equations.

1. $x^2+4=0$

2. $x^2+5=0$

c. Verify your solutions in Part **b** using the quadratic formula.

1.6 As you may recall, the following function can be used to model the height of a projectile over time:

$$h(t) = -0.5gt^2 + v_0t + h_0$$

In this equation, h_0 represents the initial height in meters, v_0 represents the initial velocity in meters per second, and t represents time in seconds. The constant g represents the acceleration due to gravity. On earth, this value is approximately 9.8 m/sec^2.

a. If a ball is thrown straight up from a height of 1.5 m at an initial velocity of 17.9 m/sec, when will it hit the ground?

b. Approximately when will the ball reach a height of 15 m?

c. Approximately when will the ball reach a height of 20 m?

1.7 A container company has received an order for paper trays of varying sizes. As shown in the diagram below, the trays will be made by cutting congruent squares from each corner of a sheet of paper, then folding the remaining tabs. The sheet of paper measures 22 cm by 28 cm.

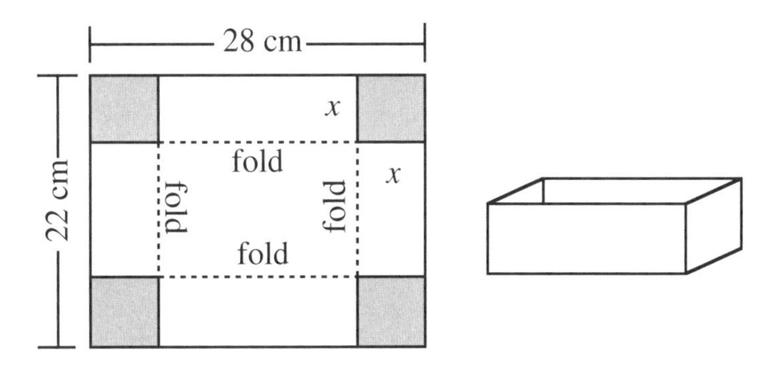

a. Write a function $A(x)$ to represent the surface area of the outside of the tray, including the bottom.

b. If squares with sides of 8 cm are cut from the paper, what will be the surface area of the outside of the tray?

c. If the outside surface area is 260 cm^2, what are the dimensions of the squares?

d. If the outside surface area is 1000 cm^2, what are the dimensions of the squares?

* * * * *

1.8 For each expression below, write an equation with real coefficients for which that expression is a solution.

a. $2i$

b. $-3i\sqrt{5}$

c. $3+9i$

d. $-6i+4$

1.9 **a.** Without solving the equation $x^2+12=0$, describe its solutions over each of the following:

1. the set of real numbers
2. the set of complex numbers.

b. Solve the equation $x^2+12=0$ using the difference of squares.

c. Verify your responses using the quadratic formula.

1.10 A housing company plans to develop a rectangular piece of land measuring 10 ha. **Note:** A hectare is a metric unit typically used to measure land area. One hectare (1 ha) equals 10,000 m^2.

The land borders a road for 250 m. According to local zoning regulations, 10% of the property must be designated as open space. The developer plans to create a rectangular park in the center of the property, with its boundaries equidistant from each side. To access the park, the developer must construct a lane from the existing road to the park boundary. How many meters long should the new lane be?

The set of complex numbers has many of the same characteristics as the set of real numbers. For example, it is possible to add, subtract, multiply, and divide them.

When you perform these operations on the complex numbers, do you think that the result will always be another complex number? If this is true, the complex numbers have the **closure property** under these operations.

Some sets of numbers exhibit the closure property only under certain operations. For example, consider the set of even natural numbers. If you add any two even natural numbers, you obtain an even natural number. Therefore, this set of numbers is closed under addition.

However, if you divide two even natural numbers, the result is not always even. For example, $18/2=9$. Because 9 is not an even natural number, this set is not closed under division.

Does the set of complex numbers have the closure property under addition? Is it closed under multiplication? Does each complex number have a multiplicative inverse? In this activity, you answer these questions and more.

Discussion 1

a. Using your knowledge of the distributive property of multiplication over addition and subtraction, describe how you would find the sum and the difference of the complex numbers $s + ti$ and $r + qi$, expressing the results in the form $a + bi$.

b. In any complex number $a + bi$, the values of a and b are always real numbers. The set of real numbers is closed under addition and subtraction. In other words, if you add or subtract two real numbers, the result is always a real number.

   Given these facts, do you think that the complex numbers are closed under addition and subtraction? Explain your response.

c. In previous modules, you used the distributive property of multiplication over addition to multiply polynomials such as $(ax + b)(cx + d)$. Based on your experience with polynomials, suggest a method for multiplying two complex numbers.

d. Recall from the definition of the imaginary unit that $i = \sqrt{-1}$ and $i^2 = -1$. Considering this definition, how could you determine the values of i^3 and i^4?

e. Given the roots of a quadratic r_1 and r_2, you can determine a corresponding equation by multiplying $(x - r_1)(x - r_2)$. How does this support the fact that complex solutions to quadratic equations with real coefficients occur as conjugate pairs?

Exploration

By definition, the reciprocal of a complex number such as $(3 + 4i)$ is $(a + bi)$ if and only if $(a + bi)(3 + 4i) = 1 + 0i$. If complex numbers behave like real numbers, then the reciprocal of $3 + 4i$ can be written as:

$$\frac{1}{3 + 4i}$$

In the following exploration, you discover how this reciprocal also can be represented in the form $a + bi$.

a. 1. Expand the left-hand side of the equation below by multiplying the complex numbers.

$$(a + bi)(3 + 4i) = 1 + 0i$$

   2. Write the product on the left in the form $m + ni$.

b. For the complex number $m + ni$ found in Part **a** to equal $1 + 0i$, the real part (m) must equal 1 and the imaginary part (n) must equal 0.

1. Write each of these relationships as an equation.
2. Solve these two equations to find the values of a and b in the complex number $a + bi$ that is the reciprocal of $3 + 4i$.

c. Verify that the complex number found in Part **b** is the reciprocal of $3 + 4i$ by determining that its product with $3 + 4i$ is 1.

d. The conjugate plays an important role in writing the reciprocal of a complex number in the form $m + ni$.

Use technology to evaluate $1/(3 + 4i)$. Write the result so that m and n are reduced fractions.

e. 1. Evaluate the following expression:

$$\left(\frac{1}{3 + 4i}\right)\left(\frac{3 - 4i}{3 - 4i}\right)$$

2. Compare the result to the complex number determined in Part **b** and your response to Part **d.**
3. Suggest a method for finding the reciprocal of a complex number $a + bi$ using the conjugate.

f. In the set of real numbers, division by a non-zero number can be interpreted as the product of the dividend and the reciprocal of the non-zero divisor. In other words,

$$a \div b = a \bullet \frac{1}{b}$$

where $b \neq 0$. In the complex numbers, division can be interpreted in the same way. Use this information to perform the following division:

$$\frac{7 - 5i}{3 + 4i}$$

Discussion 2

a. Does the set of natural numbers have the closure property under subtraction? Explain your response.

b. In the real-number system, the commutative property of addition is stated as $a + b = b + a$. How could you show that the commutative property of addition is preserved in the set of complex numbers?

c. In the real-number system, the associative property of addition is stated as $a + (b + c) = (a + b) + c$. How could you show that the associative property of addition is preserved in the set of complex numbers?

d. In the real-number system, the commutative property of multiplication is stated as $ab = ba$. How could you show that the commutative property of multiplication is preserved in the set of complex numbers?

e. In the real-number system, the associative property of multiplication is stated as $a(bc) = (ab)c$. How could you show that the associative property of multiplication is preserved in the set of complex numbers?

f. Describe how you would perform division in the set of complex numbers.

g. 1. Describe how you would represent zero as a complex number in the form $a + bi$.

   2. Is it possible to divide by zero in the set of complex numbers? Explain your response.

   3. Is the set of complex numbers closed under division? Explain your response.

Warm-Up

1. Recall that $i = \sqrt{-1}$ and $i^2 = -1$. Using the laws of exponents, it follows that $i^3 = i^2 \bullet i = -1 \bullet i = -i$.

   Use the laws of exponents to write each power of i below in simplest form.

   a. i^4
   b. i^5
   c. i^6
   d. i^7
   e. i^8
   f. i^9
   g. i^{10}

2. Using your knowledge of the distributive property of multiplication over addition and subtraction, find the sum and the difference of each pair of complex numbers below. (Find the difference by subtracting the second complex number from the first.) Write each result in the form $a + bi$.

   a. i and $9i$
   b. 4 and $7 + 3i$
   c. $21 - 6i$ and $15i$
   d. $-13 + 4i$ and $3 - i$
   e. $12 + 5i$ and $12 - 5i$

3. Multiply and divide each of the following pairs of complex numbers. (Find the quotient by dividing the first complex number by the second.) Write each result in the form $a + bi$.

   a. i and 3
   b. $2i$ and i
   c. 7 and $6 - 11i$
   d. $5 + i$ and $6 - 3i$

Assignment

2.1 Find the sum and the difference of $a + bi$ and $c + di$. (Find the difference by subtracting the second complex number from the first.) Write each result in the form $m + ni$.

2.2 **a.** Multiply $a + bi$ and $c + di$. Write the result in the form $m + ni$.

b. Divide $a + bi$ and $c + di$. Write the result in the form $m + ni$.

2.3 Recall that complex conjugates are pairs of complex numbers in the form $a + bi$ and $a - bi$.

a. Create a pair of complex conjugates.

b. Find the sum and product of the numbers in Part **a**.

c. Suggest a method for finding the sum and product of complex conjugates.

2.4 In the set of real numbers, the multiplicative identity is 1. In other words, when a is a real number, $a \bullet 1 = 1 \bullet a = a$. Demonstrate that $1 + 0i$ is the multiplicative identity in the set of complex numbers.

* * * * *

2.5 Write each of the following expressions in the form $a + bi$.

a. $\sqrt{-49} + \sqrt{-1} + \sqrt{-9}$

b. $\sqrt{-25} - 5\sqrt{-9}$

c. $(3 - 4i) + (-8 + 6i)$

d. $(8 - 7i) - (2 + 6i)$

2.6 In Problem **1** of the Warm-Up, you found the values of $i^1, i^2, \ldots, i^{10}$.

a. Describe any patterns you observe in these values.

b. Write i^{90} in its simplest form.

c. Describe a rule for evaluating i^n for any positive integer n.

2.7 Write each of the expressions below in the form $a + bi$.

a. $(-9i)(22i)$

b. $(4 - i)(7 + 2i)$

c. $i^3(5 + 7i)(3 - 4i)$

2.8 Using the method developed in the exploration in this activity, simplify each expression below to the form $a + bi$.

a. $\dfrac{3}{5 - 6i}$

b. $\dfrac{-8 - i}{-3 - 9i}$

ACTIVITY 3

As you discovered in Activity **1,** quadratic equations of the form $ax^2 + bx + c = 0$, where a, b, and c are real numbers and $a \neq 0$, do not always have real-number solutions. However, such equations always have two complex-number solutions that form a conjugate pair.

What do you think will be true of the zeros of higher-degree polynomials? In this activity, you investigate the roots of polynomial equations with degrees greater than 2.

Exploration

In this exploration, you investigate the solutions to polynomial equations of degrees 3 and 4 with real-number coefficients.

a. If the third-degree polynomial equation $ax^3 + bx^2 + cx + d = 0$, where $a \neq 0$, has roots r_1, r_2, and r_3, then the equation can be expressed in the form:

$$a(x - r_1)(x - r_2)(x - r_3) = 0$$

Using this fact, find a combination of three distinct, real-number roots such that $a(x - r_1)(x - r_2)(x - r_3)$ results in a third-degree polynomial with real coefficients.

Check your response by graphing the resulting equation.

b. As you found in previous activities, equations with real coefficients can have non-real solutions. When these complex roots occur, they are conjugate pairs. Repeat Part **a** where r_1 is a real root and r_2 and r_3 are complex roots that are not real.

c. Consider fourth-degree polynomial equations of the form $ax^4 + bx^3 + cx^2 + dx + e = 0$ where a, b, c, d, and e are real numbers and $a \neq 0$.

Find a combination of four distinct, real-number roots such that $a(x - r_1)(x - r_2)(x - r_3)(x - r_4)$ results in a fourth-degree polynomial with real coefficients.

Check your response by graphing the resulting equation.

d. Repeat Part **c** where r_1 and r_2 are distinct, real roots and r_3 and r_4 are complex roots that are not real.

e. Repeat Part **c** where r_1, r_2, r_3, and r_4 are complex roots that are not real.

Discussion

a. 1. How many real-number solutions are possible for an equation of the form $ax^3 + bx^2 + cx + d = 0$, where a, b, c, and d are real numbers and $a \neq 0$?

2. How many complex-number solutions are possible?

3. Describe how graphs can be used to characterize the solutions to a cubic equation of the form $ax^3 + bx^2 + cx + d = 0$, where a, b, c, and d are real numbers and $a \neq 0$?

b. 1. How many real-number solutions are possible for an equation of the form $ax^4 + bx^3 + cx^2 + dx + e = 0$ where a, b, c, d and e are real numbers and $a \neq 0$?

2. How many complex-number solutions are possible? How many of these may be non-real?

3. Describe how graphs can be used to characterize these solutions.

4. Given the graph of a fourth-degree equation that is tangent to the x-axis, can you tell how many duplicate roots exist? Explain your response.

c. Describe the relationship among the complex solutions of the form $a + bi$, where $b \neq 0$, of a polynomial equation when that equation has real-number coefficients.

mathematics note

The **fundamental theorem of algebra** states that every polynomial equation of degree $n \geq 1$ with complex coefficients has at least one root that is a complex number.

One consequence of the fundamental theorem of algebra is that nth-degree polynomial equations have exactly n roots in the set of complex numbers. This total may include some multiple roots. For example, the roots of the fifth-degree polynomial $x^5 - 4x^4 - 15x^3 + 50x^2 + 64x - 96 = 0$ are –3, –2, 1, and 4. One of these (4) is a double root. Therefore, the polynomial has a total of five roots in the set of complex numbers.

d. Describe the number of real solutions possible for polynomial equations of the form $ax^5 + bx^4 + cx^3 + dx^2 + ex + f = 0$, where the coefficients are real numbers and $a \neq 0$.

e. In general, how many complex roots of the form $a + bi$, where $b \neq 0$, can an nth-degree polynomial equation with real coefficients have? How are these complex roots related?

f. For what type of polynomial equations must there always be at least one real root? Explain your response.

Warm-Up

1. Describe the possible numbers and kinds of roots for polynomial equations with real coefficients of each of the following degrees:

   a. 5

   b. 6

   c. 7

   d. 8

2. Each of Parts **a–d** below, shows the graph of a polynomial equation, along with its degree. Describe the numbers and kinds of roots for each one.

   a. degree 5

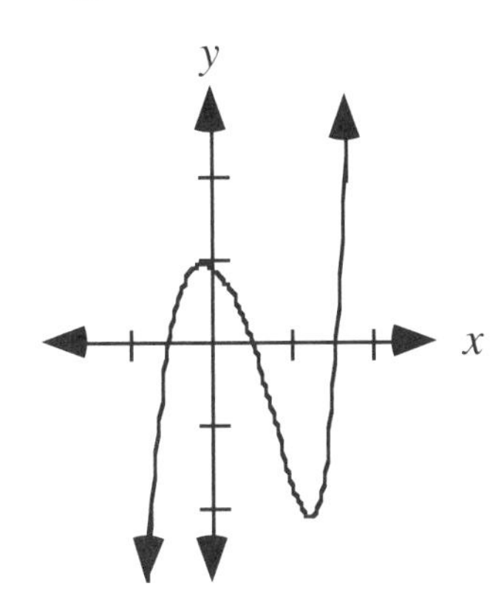

   b. degree 4

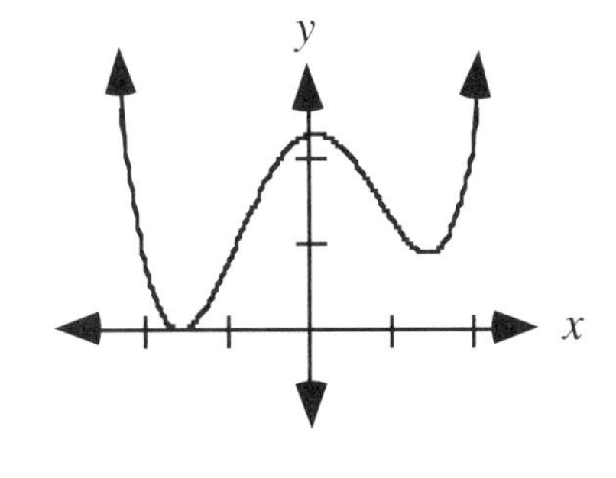

   c. degree 3

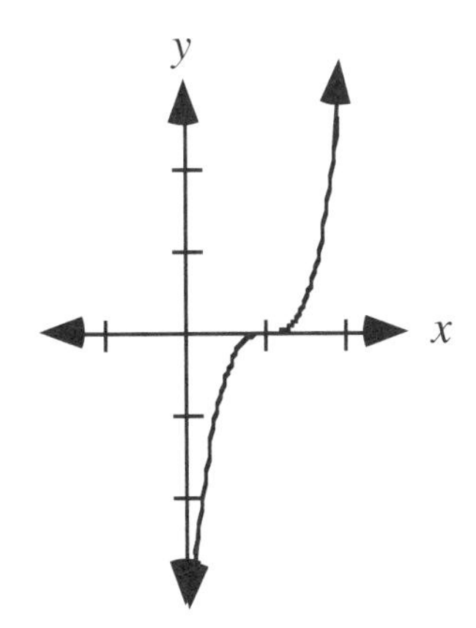

   d. degree 6

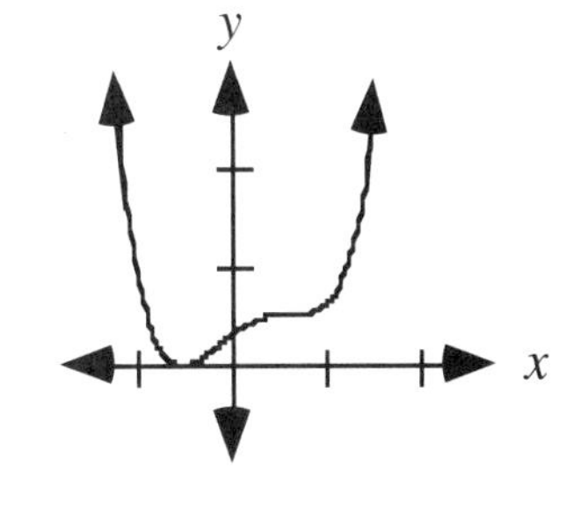

Assignment

3.1 Determine the solutions to each of the following equations over the complex numbers. Use these solutions to express each equation as the product of first-degree polynomials.

a. $9x^2 + 12x + 4 = 0$

b. $9x^2 + 35x - 4 = 0$

c. $x^2 + 4x + 9 = 0$

d. $3x^3 - 12x^2 + 12x - 48 = 0$

e. $2x^4 - 6x^3 + 12x^2 + 4x - 120 = 0$

3.2 When considering solutions to polynomial equations with real coefficients, the fact that the product of a complex number and its conjugate is a real number has special significance.

a. Find a polynomial equation of the form $ax^2 + bx + c = 0$ with real coefficients that has solutions $r_1 = 2 + i$ and $r_2 = 2 - i$.

b. Find the solutions to $x^2 - 6x + 13 = 0$. Describe the relationship between the two solutions.

c. Determine four complex-number solutions for an equation of the form $ax^4 + bx^3 + cx^2 + dx + e = 0$, where $a \neq 0$, that result in coefficients that are real numbers. Give the values of these coefficients.

3.3 If $2 + 3i$, 2, and -5 are solutions to the polynomial equation $x^4 - x^3 + cx^2 + 79x - 130 = 0$, determine the value of c. Describe how you made this determination.

3.4 Write a paragraph describing the different numbers of real solutions that are possible for sixth-degree polynomial equations of the form $ax^6 + bx^5 + cx^4 + dx^3 + ex^2 + fx + g = 0$, where the coefficients are real numbers and $a \neq 0$.

* * * * *

3.5 Two zeros of a polynomial function are -1 and $5i + 3$.

a. Find a third-degree polynomial with a lead coefficient of 2 that has these zeros. Justify your response.

b. If one of the roots is a double root, find a fourth-degree polynomial with a lead coefficient of -1 that has these zeros. Justify your response.

c. If you were told that both of these roots were double roots, what is the least degree that a polynomial with real coefficients could have with these zeros? Justify your response.

ACTIVITY

The use of the word *imaginary* reflects some of the original uneasiness that mathematicians had with numbers involving $\sqrt{-a}$, where a is a positive real number. However, the phrase "imaginary numbers" seems inappropriate in today's world, where such numbers are routinely used in analyzing electrical circuits, in cartography, and in quantum mechanics.

mathematics note

Swiss clerk Jean Robert Argand (1768–1822) and Danish mathematician Caspar Wessel (1745–1818) were the first two people to graph complex numbers on a plane. They represented a complex number $a + bi$ as an ordered pair (a,b) where a is the real part and b is the imaginary part.

Each complex number can be graphed as a point in the complex plane. Any point on the horizontal axis is a real number and any point on the vertical axis is a pure imaginary number.

For example, Figure **9-3** shows the graphs of the ordered pairs (2,3), (0,3), (3,0) and (4,–3), which represent the complex numbers $2 + 3i$, $0 + 3i$, $3 + 0i$, and $4 - 3i$, respectively.

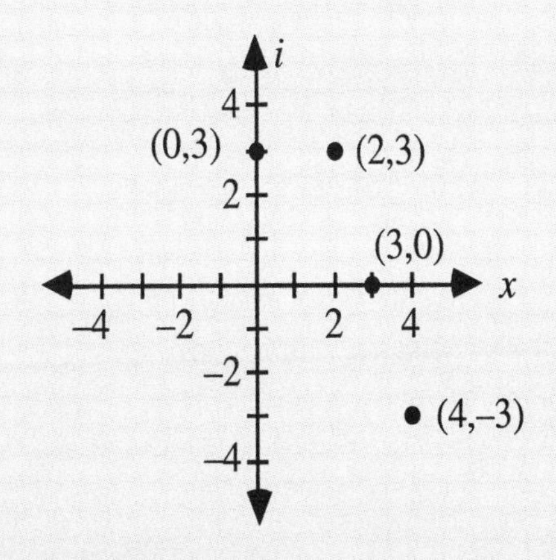

FIGURE 9-3 The complex plane.

Exploration

Argand's geometric interpretation of complex numbers provides many advantages when exploring the complex-number system. In this exploration, you will examine how multiplication of complex numbers affects their graphical representation.

a. Graph a complex number of the form $a + 0i$ on the complex plane.

b. 1. Multiply the number by i and graph the result as a point.

   2. Multiply the result from Step **1** by i and graph the resulting point. Continue this process of multiplying by i to obtain two more points.

c. Make a conjecture about the effects of multiplying by i with respect to the movement of a point on the complex plane.

d. 1. Predict the result of multiplying $a + 0i$ by $-i$.

   2. Test your prediction by repeating Parts **a** and **b** using the factor $-i$.

e. 1. Multiply $a + bi$ by i.

   2. Does your conjecture from Part **c** appear to apply to all complex numbers? If not, revise it so that it does.

Discussion

a. Describe the transformation that occurs when a complex number is multiplied by each of the following:

   1. i

   2. $-i$

b. How do the transformations in Part **a** affect the ordered pair that represents $a + 0i$?

c. Describe what occurs when $0 + 0i$ is multiplied by $-i$.

Warm-Up

1. Multiply the complex number $3 + 2i$ by the each of the following numbers. Write the products as ordered pairs (a,b).

   a. i

   b. i^2

   c. i^3

   d. i^4

2. Plot the products from Problem **1** on a square grid. What is the geometric relationship among these points?

3. Consider the sequences defined by the rule $a_n + b_n i = i(a_{n-1} + b_{n-1}i)$. Given each of the following first terms, use this rule to write terms 2–5.

   a. $a_1 + b_1 i = 0 + i$

   b. $a_1 + b_1 i = 1 - i$

   c. $a_1 + b_1 i = 2 - 3i$

   d. $a_1 + b_1 i = -3 + 5i$

4. Plot the first five terms of each sequence in Problem **3** as ordered pairs on the complex plane.

Assignment

4.1 Describe how complex conjugates are related in terms of their graphs in the complex plane.

4.2 Consider $u = 4 + 9i$ and $v = 5 + 4i$.

   a. Find $u + v$ and $u - v$.

   b. Graph u, v, $u + v$, and $u - v$ as ordered pairs on the complex plane.

   c. Define the addition and subtraction of complex numbers $a + bi$ and $c + di$ using ordered pairs.

4.3 **a.** Consider the polynomial equation $x^3 - x^2 + x - 1 = 0$. Determine which of the following are solutions to this equation: 1, –1, i, or $-i$.

   b. Rewrite $x^3 - x^2 + x - 1 = 0$ as a product of factors in the form $(x - k)$ where k is a root of the equation.

   c. Multiply the factors to verify your response to Part **b.**

* * * * *

4.4 Julia sets are sets of complex numbers that often make interesting patterns when graphed on the complex plane. One type of Julia set is generated by the recursive formula below, where n is a natural number.

$$a_n + b_n i = (a_{n-1} + b_{n-1} i)^2 + a_1 + b_1 i$$

a. The second term of the Julia set where $a_1 + b_1 i = 2 + 3i$ is:

$$\begin{aligned} a_2 + b_2 i &= (2 + 3i)^2 + 2 + 3i \\ &= 4 + 6i + 6i + 9i^2 + 2 + 3i \\ &= -3 + 15i \end{aligned}$$

Find the third term of this Julia set.

b. To create a scatterplot of a Julia set using technology, each term is written as an ordered pair. The first two terms of the Julia set from Part **a** can be written as (2,3) and (–3,15). Write the third term of this Julia set as an ordered pair.

c. **1.** Expand the recursive formula given above, writing the result in the form indicated below:

$$\begin{aligned} a_n + b_n i &= (a_{n-1} + b_{n-1} i)^2 + a_1 + b_1 i \\ &= \text{real part} + \text{imaginary part} \end{aligned}$$

2. Write the nth term as an ordered pair in the form (a_n, b_n).

d. The following graph shows a scatterplot of the first 400 terms of a Julia set where $a_1 = -0.63$ and $b_1 = -0.37$:

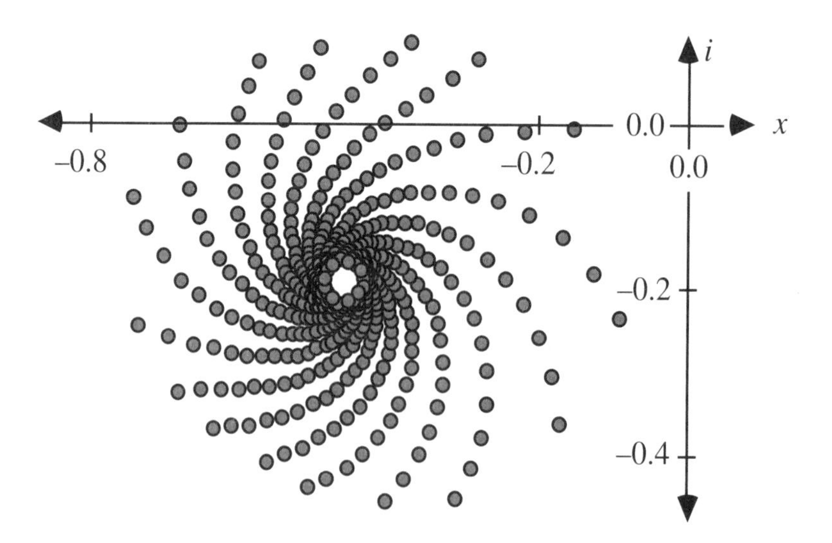

The table below shows the first six terms (rounded to the nearest 0.0001) of a Julia set with $a_1 = -0.63$ and $b_1 = -0.37$.

Term Number (n)	Real Part (a_n)	Imaginary Part (b_n)
1	–0.6300	–0.3700
2	–0.3700	0.0962
3	–0.5024	–0.4412
4	–0.5723	0.0733
5	–0.3079	–0.4539
6	–0.7412	–0.0906
⋮	⋮	⋮

1. Use a spreadsheet to extend the table to 200 terms.
2. Create a scatterplot of the ordered pairs (a_n, b_n) on the complex plane.

e. Small changes in the first term of a Julia set result in a dramatically different set.

1. Create a scatterplot of the first 200 terms of the Julia set where $a_1 = -0.63$ and $b_1 = -0.38$.
2. Create new scatterplots by making small modifications in a_1 and b_1.

f. The table below shows the first terms in some other Julia sets. Use these first terms to explore patterns in the resulting scatterplots.

(a_1)	(b_1)
0.2477	0.5600
–0.6100	–0.4050
0.2900	0.4500
–1.1950	0.4500
–1.2000	0.1500

4.5 Consider the set of matrices of the form below, where a and b are real numbers.

$$\begin{bmatrix} a & b \\ -b & a \end{bmatrix}$$

a. Show that this set of matrices has the closure property under addition. In other words, show that if any two matrices in this set are added together, the sum is a matrix from the set.

b. Show that this set of matrices is closed under multiplication.

c. Find an additive identity and a multiplicative identity for this set of matrices.

d. Find the multiplicative inverse of the following matrix, if it exists:

$$\begin{bmatrix} a & b \\ -b & a \end{bmatrix}$$

e. The arithmetic of the set of matrices defined in Parts **a–d** behaves almost exactly the same as arithmetic with real numbers. However, this arithmetic has one property that arithmetic with real numbers does not. Square the following matrix and describe how the result compares to the multiplicative identity for the set of matrices.

$$\begin{bmatrix} 0 & 1 \\ -1 & 0 \end{bmatrix}$$

f. Considering your results in Part **e,** the arithmetic of this set of matrices behaves like the arithmetic of the set of complex numbers. Now suppose that every complex number of the form $a + bi$ can be identified with the matrix below.

$$\begin{bmatrix} a & b \\ -b & a \end{bmatrix}$$

What is the matrix representation of the complex number $0 + i$?

g. Recall that multiplication by a matrix of the form below produces a rotation of θ about the origin.

$$\begin{bmatrix} \cos\theta & -\sin\theta \\ \sin\theta & \cos\theta \end{bmatrix}$$

What matrix produces a 90° rotation about the origin?

h. Compare the matrices found in Parts **f** and **g.**

ACTIVITY 5

In Activity **4,** you used ordered pairs of the form (a,b) to represent complex numbers. However, when performing multiplication of complex numbers, it can be more convenient to use their **trigonometric form.** Using the trigonometric form also can simplify finding powers of complex numbers.

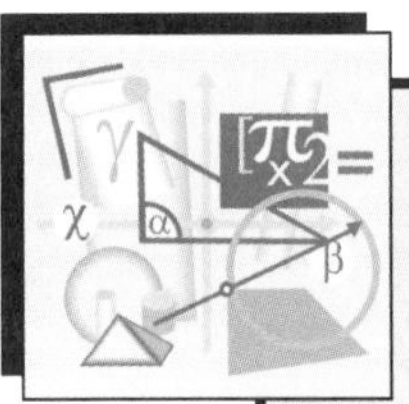

mathematics note

Figure **9-4** shows the complex number $a + bi$ represented as the ordered pair (a,b).

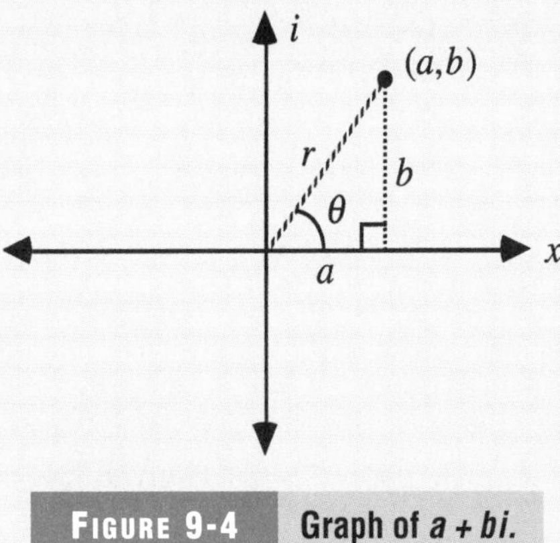

FIGURE 9-4 **Graph of $a + bi$.**

A complex number $a + bi$ can be written in **trigonometric form** as follows:

$$a + bi = (r\cos\theta) + (r\sin\theta)i = r(\cos\theta + i\sin\theta)$$

The value of r is the **absolute value** or **modulus** of the complex number and is determined by $r = \sqrt{a^2 + b^2}$. Note that r is always a non-negative number and represents a distance from the origin.

The angle θ is an **argument** of the complex number and is measured from the positive portion of the real axis. Angles generated by counterclockwise rotations are assigned positive measures; those generated by clockwise rotations are assigned negative values.

The ray passing through the point (a,b) representing the number $a + bi$ is the **terminal ray** of the argument.

For example, consider the complex number $\sqrt{3} + i$ represented by the point $(\sqrt{3},1)$. Using right-triangle trigonometry, an argument is $\theta = \tan^{-1}(1/\sqrt{3}) = \pi/6$. The absolute value is

$$r = \sqrt{\left(\sqrt{3}\right)^2 + 1^2} = \sqrt{4} = 2.$$

Therefore, the trigonometric form of $\sqrt{3} + i$ is:

$$2\left(\cos\frac{\pi}{6} + i\sin\frac{\pi}{6}\right)$$

Because θ can be any angle measured from the positive portion of the real axis whose terminal ray contains $(\sqrt{3},1)$, the trigonometric form of $\sqrt{3} + i$ is not unique. In this case, θ can be any angle of the form $\theta = \pi/6 + 2n\pi$, where n is an integer. Considering that $n = 1$, for example, $\theta = \pi/6 + 2\pi$. As a result, $\sqrt{3} + i$ also can be represented in trigonometric form as $2(\cos(13\pi/6) + i\sin(13\pi/6))$. For $n = -1$, $\theta = \pi/6 - 2\pi$ and $\sqrt{3} + i$ can be represented as $2(\cos(-11\pi/6) + i\sin(-11\pi/6))$.

Exploration 1

In this exploration, you begin your investigation of the trigonometric form of complex numbers by examining arguments.

a. The following complex numbers are written in the form $a + bi$. Evaluate $\tan^{-1}(b/a)$ for each number. Use the resulting angle measure to determine an argument of the given number.

1. $1 + \sqrt{3}i$
2. $-1 + \sqrt{3}i$
3. $-1 - \sqrt{3}i$
4. $1 - \sqrt{3}i$

b. Determine the measure of two additional positive arguments and two additional negative arguments for each of the complex numbers in Part **a.**

Discussion 1

a. Given the complex number $a + bi$, in which quadrants can the point (a,b) be located if $\theta = \tan^{-1}(b/a)$ is an argument of $a + bi$?

b. If $\theta = \tan^{-1}(b/a)$ is not an argument of $a + bi$, how can an argument be determined using $\tan^{-1}(b/a)$?

c. Describe the methods you used to determine the additional positive and negative arguments in Part **b** of Exploration **1.**

mathematics note

If the graph of a complex number $a + bi$ is in the first or fourth quadrants, $\theta = \tan^{-1}(b/a)$ is an argument of the number and every argument is represented by the expression $\theta = \tan^{-1}(b/a) + 2n\pi$, where n is any integer.

For complex numbers represented by points in the second and third quadrants, arguments have the form $\theta = (\tan^{-1}(b/a) + \pi) + 2n\pi$, where n is an integer.

For example, the graph of the complex number $-2 + 2i$ is in the second quadrant. In this case, its arguments can be found as follows, where n is an integer:

$$\theta = \left(\tan^{-1}(2/-2) + \pi\right) + 2n\pi = 3\pi/4 + 2n\pi$$

d. 1. Figure **9-5** below shows a graph of a unit circle. Use this graph to explain why all arguments of complex numbers $a + bi$ in the first or fourth quadrants can be represented by $\theta = \tan^{-1}(b/a) + 2n\pi$, where n is an integer.

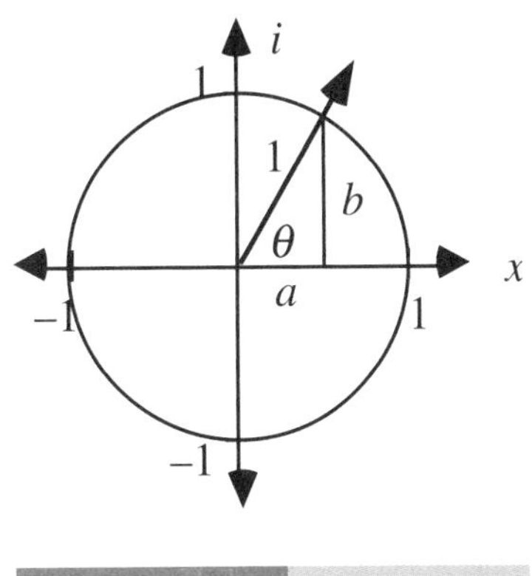

FIGURE 9-5 **A unit circle.**

2. Explain why it is necessary to add π for the complex numbers in the second and third quadrants.

Exploration 2

In Activity **4,** you learned that points on the complex plane are rotated when multiplied by i or $-i$. In this activity, you multiply complex numbers to discover other patterns.

a. Multiply each of the following pairs of complex numbers. Plot each pair of complex numbers and their product as points on a complex plane.

1. $v = 2 + i$ and $s = 2 + 3i$
2. $t = 0 + 2i$ and $u = -1 + i$
3. $m = -1 + 2i$ and $w = -2 - i$
4. $g = 3 + 2i$ and $h = 2 + 4i$

b. For each complex number in Part **a,** determine its absolute value and an argument (to the nearest 0.01 radians) between -2π and 2π. Leave the absolute value in radical form, even if the square root is an integer. Record these values in a table with headings like those in Table **9-1** below.

TABLE 9-1 ■ *Complex Numbers and Their Products*

Number	$a + bi$	Absolute Value	Argument
v	$2 + i$		
s	$2 + 3i$		
$v \bullet s$			
t	$0 + 2i$		
u	$-1 + i$		
$t \bullet u$			
m			
w			
$m \bullet w$			
g			
h			
$g \bullet h$			

c. Select at least three conjugate pairs of complex numbers. Repeat Parts **a** and **b** using these pairs.

d. 1. Use a symbolic manipulator to verify the following rule for multiplying complex numbers in trigonometric form:

$$[a(\cos x + i \sin x)] \bullet [b(\cos y + i \sin y)] = ab[\cos(x + y) + i \sin(x + y)]$$

2. Using the terms *absolute value* and *argument,* describe the rule for multiplying complex numbers in trigonometric form.

3. Determine if this rule is illustrated in Table **9-1.**

e. 1. Write $1 - i$ and $-2 + i$ in trigonometric form, rounding both r and θ to the nearest 0.01.

2. Use the rule from Part **d** to multiply the trigonometric forms of $1 - i$ and $-2 + i$.

3. Write the product in the form $a + bi$.

4. Use the distributive property to multiply $1 - i$ and $-2 + i$.

5. Compare the products in Steps **3** and **4.**

Discussion 2

a. Describe the relationship between conjugates when they are expressed in trigonometric form.

b. What is the argument of the product when a complex number and its conjugate are multiplied?

c. Is multiplication of complex numbers in trigonometric form commutative? Justify your response.

d. Compare the process of multiplying complex numbers in the form $a + bi$ with the process of multiplying the same numbers in trigonometric form.

Warm-Up

1. Multiply each complex number below by its respective conjugate. Write the products in trigonometric form.

   a. $3(\cos(\pi/12) + i\sin(\pi/12))$

   b. $11(\cos(8.83) + i\sin(8.83))$

   c. $\sqrt{7}(\cos(-\pi/15) + i\sin(-\pi/15))$

2. Use the rule developed in Exploration **2** to multiply the following pairs of complex numbers. Write each product in trigonometric form.

   a. $3(\cos(\pi/2) + i\sin(\pi/2))$ and $2(\cos(2\pi/3) + i\sin(2\pi/3))$

   b. $5(\cos(-2.35) + i\sin(-2.35))$ and $(\cos(8.85) + i\sin(8.85))$

   c. $\sqrt{6}(\cos(-11\pi/6) + i\sin(-11\pi/6))$ and $3\sqrt{2}(\cos(-5\pi/4) + i\sin(-5\pi/4))$

Assignment

5.1 **a.** Describe a general rule for finding the product of a complex number and its conjugate and writing the product in trigonometric form.

b. When writing the product of a complex number and its conjugate in trigonometric form, the angle found in the product is always the same. Explain why this is true.

5.2 Use the rule developed in Exploration **2** to multiply the general pair of complex numbers $r_1(\cos\theta_1 + i\sin\theta_1)$ and $r_2(\cos\theta_2 + i\sin\theta_2)$. Write your answer in trigonometric form.

5.3 The ordered pairs $(-1,2)$ and $(3,-2)$ represent two complex numbers on the complex plane.

a. Find their product using two different methods.

b. Compare the results and explain any differences you observe.

5.4 Multiplication by the complex number $2(\cos(\pi/6) + i\sin(\pi/6))$ can be thought of as a dilation by a scale factor of 2 and a rotation of $\pi/6$ with center at $(0,0)$. What complex number produces the same dilation but the opposite rotation? Describe the relationship between these two numbers.

5.5 **a.** Evaluate $(3-4i)^2$ by converting the expression to trigonometric form before multiplying.

b. Find the trigonometric form of $(3-4i)^3$ by multiplying the trigonometric form of $(3-4i)^2$ by the trigonometric form of $(3-4i)$.

c. Write $(3-4i)^5$ in trigonometric form.

d. Express $(3-4i)^n$, where n is an integer, in trigonometric form.

5.6 Given that the trigonometric form of $a + bi$ is $r(\cos\theta + i\sin\theta)$, write the trigonometric forms of $(a+bi)^2$, $(a+bi)^3$, $(a+bi)^4$, and $(a+bi)^n$.

* * * * *

5.7 In previous modules, you have used several different methods to draw regular polygons. In this assignment, you investigate another way to construct regular polygons.

a. Consider the complex number $3 + 4i$. What is the modulus r of this number?

b. Plot the complex number $3 + 4i$ on a square grid.

c. What is the radius of the circle with center at the origin that contains the point $3 + 4i$?

d. What is the measure θ of a central angle of a regular pentagon?

e. To construct a regular pentagon with the point representing $3 + 4i$ as a vertex, one could rotate the point (and its successive images) by θ, with center at the origin.

To do this, multiply $3 + 4i$ by a complex number in the form $\cos\theta + i\sin\theta$. Plot the coordinates of the product. Continue this process to find the five vertices of the regular pentagon.

5.8 Use the process described in Problem **5.7** to construct a regular hexagon whose sides measure 3 units.

5.9 When designing circuits for use with alternating current, electrical engineers use the complex-number form of Ohm's law:

$$I = \frac{V}{Z}$$

where I is the effective current (a measure of the number of electrons moving in the wires), V is the effective voltage (a measure of the force moving the electrons), and Z is the impedance (a measure of the resistance to the flow of electrons caused by magnetic fields). In this relationship, I, V, and Z are complex numbers.

In Parts **a–c,** write each response in the same form as the original numbers.

a. Determine the effective voltage in a circuit if the effective current is $4(\cos(\pi/18) + i\sin(\pi/18))$ and the impedance is $29(\cos(\pi/9) + i\sin(\pi/9))$.

b. Find the effective current in a circuit if the effective voltage is $120(\cos 0 + i\sin 0)$ and the impedance is $44(\cos(11\pi/36) + i\sin(11\pi/36))$.

c. Find the impedance of a circuit when the effective voltage is $77 + 77i$ and the effective current is $2.9 - 0.35i$.

Evaluating $(a + bi)^n$ for large values of n can be a long and difficult task. As you learned in the previous activity, however, expressing complex numbers in trigonometric form can greatly simplify the process.

In this activity, you examine some other advantages of expressing complex numbers in trigonometric form.

mathematics note

De Moivre's theorem states that the non-zero powers of any complex number $a + bi$ can be found in the following manner:

$$(a + bi)^n = \left[r(\cos\theta + i\sin\theta)\right]^n = r^n(\cos n\theta + i\sin n\theta)$$

Abraham De Moivre (1667–1754) developed this theorem for positive integer values of n. Later work found it to be true for all real-number values of n. For example,

$$(2 + 0i)^3 = [2(\cos 0 + i\sin 0)]^3 = 2^3(\cos(3 \bullet 0) + i\sin(3 \bullet 0))$$

Exploration

In previous activities, you examined the square roots of negative numbers. In this activity, you investigate some additional roots of complex numbers.

a. 1. Graph $2(\cos 0 + i\sin 0)$ on a square grid.

   2. On the same plane, graph the image of $2(\cos 0 + i\sin 0)$ under a counterclockwise rotation of $\pi/2$ with center at (0,0).

   3. Repeat Step **2** with each new image until points begin to repeat. Using this process, determine the coordinates of each unique point generated.

b. 1. Describe the geometric relationships among the points in Part **a.**

   2. Determine the trigonometric form of the complex number represented by each point.

c. Use De Moivre's theorem to raise each complex number in Part **b** to the fourth power. Convert each result to a number in the form $a + bi$.

d. 1. If the graph of the complex number $2(\cos 0 + i\sin 0)$ represents one vertex of a regular pentagon centered at the origin, determine the angle of counterclockwise rotation about the origin required to locate the next consecutive vertex of the pentagon.

   2. Determine the complex numbers that correspond to the five vertices obtained by repeating this rotation on each image. Write these numbers in trigonometric form. **Note:** Save this data for use in the assignment.

e. Use De Moivre's theorem to raise each complex number from Part **c** to the fifth power. Convert each result to a number in the form $a + bi$.

f. Select any complex number $a + bi$ where $a \neq 0$ and $b \neq 0$. Determine the cube roots of this number and write them in trigonometric form.

g. Graph the cube roots found in Part **f** on a square grid. Describe any geometric relationship among these points.

mathematics note

From the fundamental theorem of algebra, the equation $x^n - z = 0$ has n roots in the set of complex numbers.

For example, $x^3 - 8 = 0$ has three roots: $2, -1 + i\sqrt{3}$, and $-1 - i\sqrt{3}$. The solutions to this equation are the cube roots of 8. Thus, there are 3 cube roots of 8 in the set of complex numbers. In a similar manner, there are 4 fourth roots of 8 and 5 fifth roots of 8. In general, there are exactly n distinct nth roots of any complex number.

Discussion

a. Describe the significance of your results in Part **c** of the exploration in terms of the fourth roots of a number.

b. Describe the significance of your results in Part **e** of the exploration in terms of the fifth root of a number.

c. Using the examples from the exploration, describe the relationship between the modulus of a complex number in trigonometric form and the modulus of its roots in trigonometric form.

d. Using the examples from the exploration, describe the relationship between the argument of a complex number and the argument of its roots.

e. Describe any errors you observe in the following calculations.

$$\begin{aligned}(-2)^3 &= (-2 + 0i)^3 \\ &= [-2(\cos \pi + i \sin \pi)]^3 \\ &= (-2)^3(\cos 3\pi + i \sin 3\pi) \\ &= (-8)(-1 + 0i) \\ &= 8 + 0i \\ &= 8\end{aligned}$$

f. Evaluate $r(\cos\theta + i\sin\theta)$ for each of the following values of θ:

1. $\theta = 0$
2. $\theta = \pi/2$

g. What effect did the initial value of θ have on the polygons formed in the exploration?

mathematics note

If a complex number $z = a + bi$ is written as $z = r(\cos\theta + i\sin\theta)$, then the nth roots of z can be found using the following formula:

$$\sqrt[n]{z} = \sqrt[n]{r}\left(\cos\left(\frac{\theta}{n} + \frac{k \bullet 2\pi}{n}\right) + i\sin\left(\frac{\theta}{n} + \frac{k \bullet 2\pi}{n}\right)\right)$$

where $k = 0, 1, 2, \ldots, n - 1$. There will be exactly n of these roots.

For example, $z = 8 + 0i$ can be written as $z = 8(\cos 0 + i\sin 0)$. The three cube roots of z are:

$$r_1 = 2\left(\cos\left(\frac{0}{3} + \frac{0 \bullet 2\pi}{3}\right) + i\sin\left(\frac{0}{3} + \frac{0 \bullet 2\pi}{3}\right)\right) = 2 + 0i$$

$$r_2 = 2\left(\cos\left(\frac{0}{3} + \frac{1 \bullet 2\pi}{3}\right) + i\sin\left(\frac{0}{3} + \frac{1 \bullet 2\pi}{3}\right)\right) \approx -1 + 1.73i$$

$$r_3 = 2\left(\cos\left(\frac{0}{3} + \frac{2 \bullet 2\pi}{3}\right) + i\sin\left(\frac{0}{3} + \frac{2 \bullet 2\pi}{3}\right)\right) \approx -1 - 1.73i$$

h. It can be possible to find the nth root of a complex number using a calculator and fractional exponents. Describe one disadvantage to using this method.

Warm-Up

1. Evaluate each of the following expressions. Write your answers in both trigonometric form and $a + bi$ form.

   a. $(-5)^3$

   b. $(2i)^4$

   c. $(-2\sqrt{3} + 2i)^3$

   d. $(3 - 4i)^2$

   e. $(1 + 6i)^5$

2. Identify all possible values for the roots given below. Express your answers in both trigonometric form and $a + bi$ form.

   a. $\sqrt[4]{-625}$

   b. $\sqrt{16i}$

   c. $\sqrt{-6 + 6i\sqrt{3}}$

   d. $\sqrt[3]{-8 + 8i}$

3. Each of the following graphs represents the roots of a complex number. Identify each complex number and write the root in the form $\sqrt[n]{a + bi}$.

a.

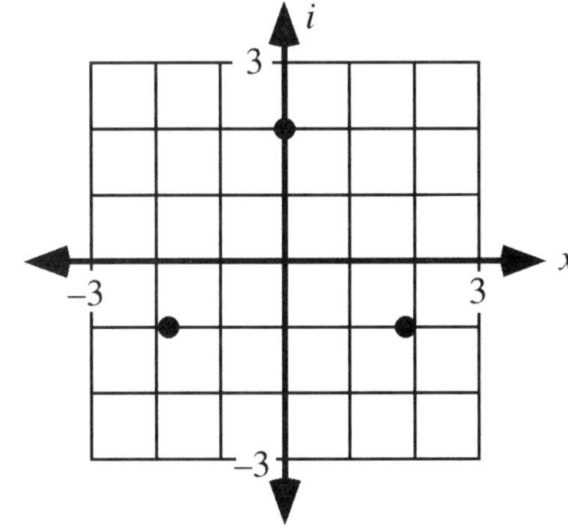

b.

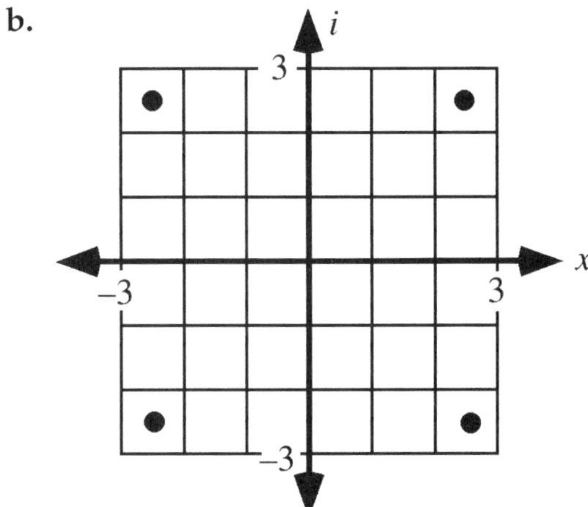

c.

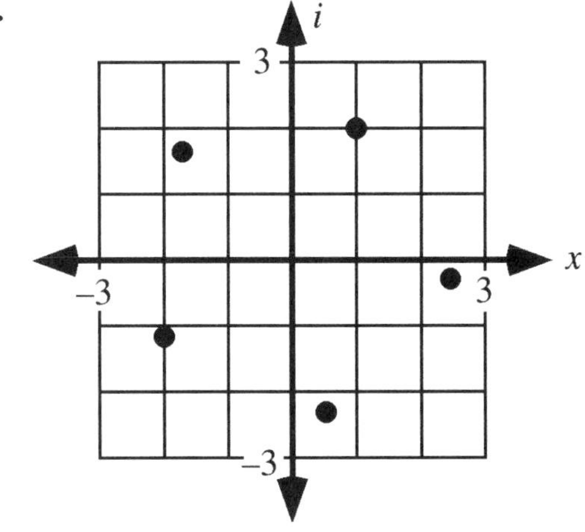

Assignment

6.1 **a.** Evaluate $(2\sqrt{3} + 2i)^3$ using the distributive property.

b. Convert $2\sqrt{3} + 2i$ to trigonometric form and cube it using De Moivre's theorem. Round the argument to the nearest 0.001 radians.

6.2 The 4 fourth roots of 81 are evenly spaced on a circle in the complex plane centered at the origin.

a. What is the radius of the circle?

b. By how many radians are consecutive roots separated?

c. Graph all 4 fourth roots. Include the circle containing the vertices in your graph.

d. Write each fourth root in the form $a + bi$.

6.3 **a.** Pick a complex number of the form $a + bi$ where $a \neq 0$ and $b \neq 0$.

b. Find the three cube roots of this complex number.

c. Write each cube root in trigonometric form.

d. Sketch a graph of the cube roots on a complex coordinate plane.

6.4 Solve the equation $z^8 = -2 + 3i$ for z and write the roots as ordered pairs (a,b).

6.5 One of the cube roots of 64 is 4, which can be written as $4\cos 0 + 4i\sin 0$.

a. The point (4,0) in the complex plane represents the complex number $4\cos 0 + 4i\sin 0$. Determine the counterclockwise rotation of the point (4,0) about the origin required to locate the next consecutive cube root of 64.

b. Graph the three cube roots of 64 on the complex plane.

* * * * *

6.6 **a.** Find the three cube roots of 1 in the form $r(\cos\theta + i\sin\theta)$ and write each cube root in the form $a + bi$.

b. Verify that the roots obtained are in fact cube roots of 1.

6.7 **a.** If the graph of $3(\cos(3\pi/4) + i\sin(3\pi/4))$ defines one vertex of a regular octagon centered at the origin of the complex plane, what numbers correspond to the other seven vertices?

b. What do the complex numbers corresponding to each vertex of this octagon represent?

Research Project

Besides introducing the imaginary unit *i*, Swiss mathematician Leonhard Euler made many other contributions to mathematics. Read more about Euler's life and work. Complete the following tasks in your report.

a. Describe Euler's formula.

b. Explain how Euler's formula can be used to represent complex numbers in exponential form.

c. Show how substituting π into Euler's formula results in a natural logarithm for -1.

d. Demonstrate that natural logarithms of negative numbers exist in the set of complex numbers.

Summary Assessment

1. Write a paragraph describing the number of real roots possible for the equation $a_n x^n + a_{n-1} x^{n-1} + \cdots + a_1 x + a_0 = 0$, where the coefficients are real numbers and $a_n \neq 0$.

2. a. Use a symbolic manipulator to find the roots of the polynomial equation $x^4 - 2x^3 + x^2 + 4x - 6 = 0$.

   b. Use the results from Part **a** to express the polynomial $x^4 - 2x^3 + x^2 + 4x - 6$ as a product of one or more polynomials such that the constant term in each factor is:

   1. a complex number 2. a real number 3. a rational number.

3. According to the binomial theorem:

$$(a + b)^n = C(n, n) \bullet a^n b^0 + C(n, n-1) \bullet a^{n-1} b^1 + C(n, n-2) \bullet a^{n-2} b^2$$
$$+ \cdots + C(n, 1) \bullet a^1 b^{n-1} + C(n, 0) \bullet a^0 b^n$$

   where $C(n,r)$ is the combination of n things, taken r at a time.

   a. Expand $(1 + i)^8$ using the binomial theorem.

   b. Simplify the expression from Part **a.**

   c. Write $(1 + i)$ in trigonometric form.

   d. Use the trigonometric form to evaluate $(1 + i)^8$. Write the result in standard form.

   e. Compare the binomial theorem and De Moivre's theorem as methods for raising complex numbers to a power.

4. The coordinates of the vertices of $\triangle ABC$ in a complex coordinate plane are $A(2,1)$, $B(4,1)$, and $C(3,2)$. The image of $\triangle ABC$ has vertices with coordinates $A'(-5,5)$, $B'(-7,9)$, and $C'(-8,6)$.

   The transformation from $\triangle ABC$ to $\triangle A'B'C'$ is produced by multiplying by the complex number z, then adding z. For example, A is transformed to A' by $(2,1) \bullet z + z = (-5,5)$.

   a. Plot $\triangle ABC$ and its image in the complex plane. Describe the geometric relationship between these two triangles.

   b. What is the ratio of $A'B'/AB$? What does this ratio reveal about the number z that produced the transformation?

   c. Find the trigonometric forms of $B - A$ and $B' - A'$. What do these reveal about the number z that produced the transformation?

   d. Find z. Pick a point on $\triangle ABC$ and show that it is transformed appropriately.

Module Summary

- The **imaginary unit** is ***i*** where $i = \sqrt{-1}$ and $i^2 = -1$.
- A **complex number** is defined as any number in the form $a + bi$, where both a and b are real numbers.
- A **pure imaginary number** is a complex number $a + bi$ for which $a = 0$ and $b \neq 0$.
- A real number is a complex number $a + bi$ for which $b = 0$.
- In the set of complex numbers, $a + bi = c + di$ if and only if $a = c$ and $b = d$.
- **Complex conjugates** are pairs of complex numbers of the form $a + bi$ and $a - bi$. The sum of complex conjugates is a real number. The product of complex conjugates also is a real number.
- The **reciprocal** of a complex number $a + bi$ is $1/(a + bi)$. To express this reciprocal in complex form $m + ni$, it can be multiplied by

$$\frac{a - bi}{a - bi}$$

  where $a - bi$ is the conjugate of $a + bi$.
- A complex number $a + bi$ can be represented by the ordered pair (a,b) where a is the real part and b is the imaginary part. Using the horizontal axis as the real axis and the vertical axis as the imaginary axis, this ordered pair can be graphed as a point on the complex plane.
- Second-degree polynomial equations of the form $ax^2 + bx + c = 0$ with $a \neq 0$, always have two solutions when solved over the complex numbers:

$$x = \frac{-b}{2a} + \frac{\sqrt{b^2 - 4ac}}{2a} \quad \text{and} \quad x = \frac{-b}{2a} - \frac{\sqrt{b^2 - 4ac}}{2a}$$

  These two solutions make up the **quadratic formula.**
- When a, b, and c are real numbers and $a \neq 0$, the expression $b^2 - 4ac$ in the quadratic formula is known as the **discriminant.** When the discriminant is less than 0, the solutions are complex and occur in conjugate pairs.
- The fundamental theorem of algebra states that every polynomial equation of degree $n \geq 1$ with complex coefficients has at least one root in the set of complex numbers.
- One consequence of the fundamental theorem of algebra is that nth-degree polynomial equations have exactly n roots in the set of complex numbers.

* A complex number $a + bi$ can be written in **trigonometric form** as:

$$r \cos \theta + ri \sin \theta = r(\cos \theta + i \sin \theta)$$

The value of r is the **absolute value** or **modulus** of the complex number and is determined by $r = \sqrt{a^2 + b^2}$. The modulus is always a non-negative number and represents a distance from the origin.

The angle θ is an **argument** of the complex number and is measured from the positive portion of the real axis to the point (a,b) in the complex plane.

If the graph of the complex number $a + bi$ is in the first or fourth quadrants, $\theta = \tan^{-1}(b/a)$ is an argument of the number and every argument is represented by the expression $\theta = \tan^{-1}(b/a) + 2n\pi$ where n is any integer.

For complex numbers $a + bi$ represented by points in the second and third quadrants, arguments have the form $\theta = (\tan^{-1}(b/a) + \pi) + 2n\pi$ where n is any integer.

* **De Moivre's theorem** states that the powers of any complex number $a + bi$ can be found in the following manner:

$$(a + bi)^n = [r(\cos \theta + i \sin \theta)]^n = r^n(\cos n\theta + i \sin n\theta)$$

* Another consequence of the fundamental theorem of algebra is that the equation $x^n - z = 0$ has n roots in the set of complex numbers.

* If a complex number $z = a + bi$ is written as $z = r(\cos\theta + i\sin\theta)$, then the nth roots of z can be found using the following formula:

$$\sqrt[n]{z} = \sqrt[n]{r}\left(\cos\left(\frac{\theta}{n} + \frac{k \bullet 2\pi}{n}\right) + i \sin\left(\frac{\theta}{n} + \frac{k \bullet 2\pi}{n}\right)\right)$$

where $k = 0, 1, 2, \ldots, n - 1$. There will be exactly n of these roots.

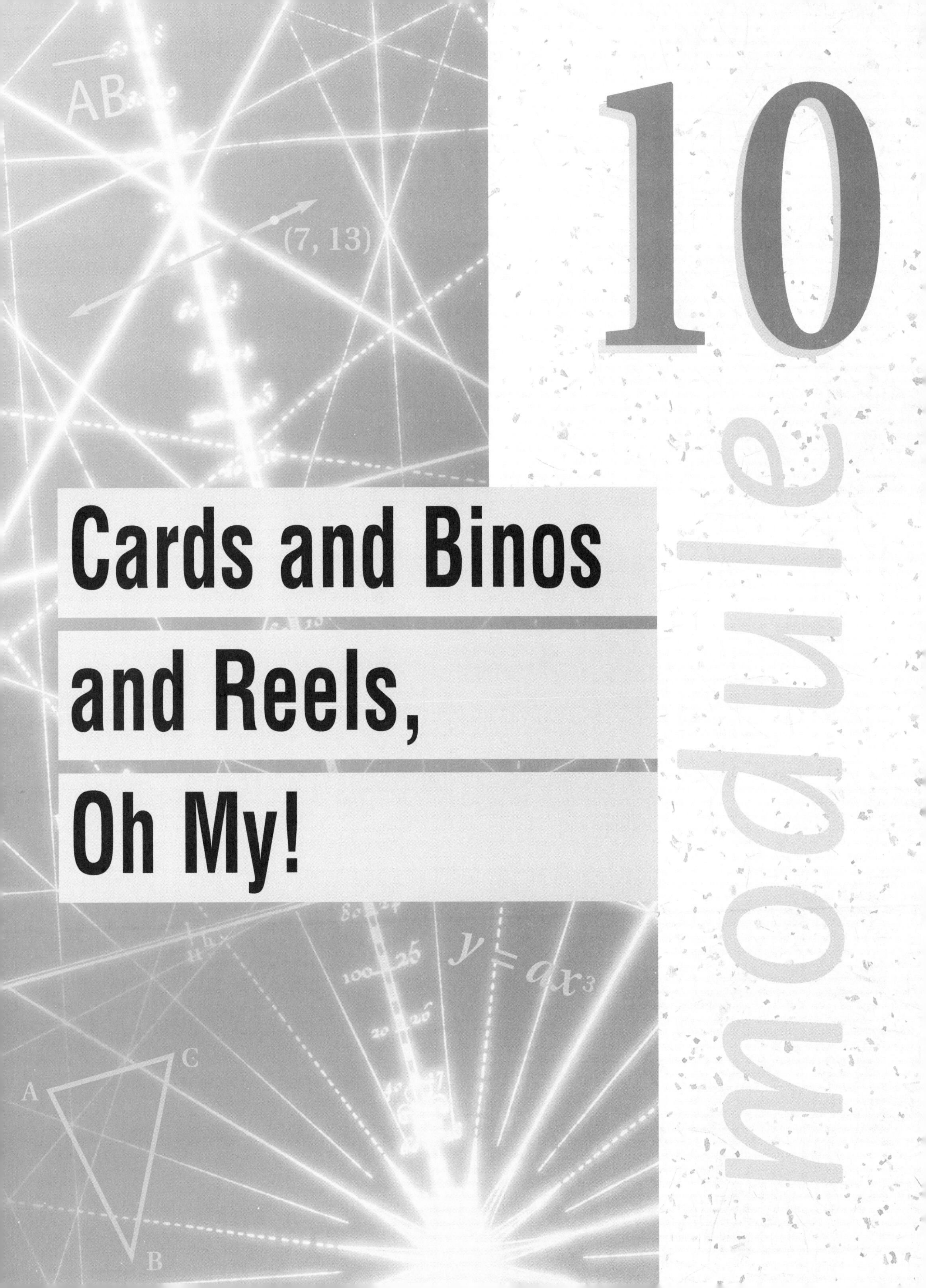

module 10

Cards and Binos and Reels, Oh My!

Introduction

High Tech Games designs and markets video gaming machines. As shown in Figure **10-1,** the video screen for Cards of Chance displays 16 cards face down. These cards include four from each suit, placed in a random order.

FIGURE 10-1 Arrangement of cards for Cards of Chance.

Cards of Chance offers the possibility of winning at three different levels involving two, three, and four cards, respectively.

To play Cards of Chance, a player inserts tokens in the machine. When the opening screen appears, the player selects one card and turns it face up. The player then selects any one of the remaining cards and turns it face up. (This constitutes play at the two-card level.)

A player wins credits at each level if all cards turned face up are the same color. If the combination of cards does not meet this condition, the game is over. More credits may be earned at the third level than the second, and more at the fourth level than at the third.

Successful players at the two-card level may collect the credits they have earned or draw a third card, beginning play at the three-card level. Successful players at the three-card level may collect their credits or draw a fourth card. The game ends at the four-card level. Winning players may then collect their earned credits. If a player loses at any level, then all credits earned to that point are lost. Figure **10-2** shows some possible card combinations for three sample games.

	two-card level	three-card level	four-card level
Game 1 win at all levels	♦ ♥	♦ ♥ ♦	♦ ♥ ♦ ♥
Game 2 win at all levels	♦ ♦	♦ ♦ ♦	♦ ♦ ♦ ♦
Game 3 win at two-card level, loss at three-card level	♠ ♠	♠ ♠ ♦	play stopped with loss at three-card level

FIGURE 10-2 **Card combinations in three sample games.**

Exploration

In this exploration, you investigate the probabilities of winning Cards of Chance at the two-card level.

a. Select 16 cards, 4 from each suit, from a deck of ordinary playing cards. To simulate the game, shuffle the 16 cards and draw 2 randomly.

b. Play 10 games of Cards of Chance, stopping each game at the two-card level and shuffling the cards between games. Record your wins and losses.

c. Determine the experimental probability of winning a game of Cards of Chance at the two-card level.

d. Compile the class results. Use the class data to determine the experimental probability of winning at the two-card level. **Note:** Save your data for use in Activity **1.**

e. List all the possible outcomes for Cards of Chance at the two-card level.

f. Determine the theoretical probability of each possible outcome.

g. Recall that for two events A and B, the theoretical probability of either A or B occurring can be found as follows:

$$P(\text{A or B}) = P(\text{A}) + P(\text{B}) - P(\text{A and B})$$

Given this fact, determine the theoretical probability of winning Cards of Chance at the two-card level.

Discussion

a. Describe how you determined the theoretical probabilities in Part **f** of the exploration.

b. What is the theoretical probability of winning at the two-card level? Explain your response.

mathematics note

According to the **law of large numbers,** as the number of trials increases, the experimental probability of an event tends to approach its theoretical probability.

For example, when tossing a fair coin, the theoretical probability that the coin lands heads up is 0.5. As the number of tosses increases, the experimental probability that the coin lands heads up will tend to get closer to 0.5.

c. How should increasing the number of times you play the game affect the experimental probability of winning?

Video gaming machines are designed to be durable, not portable. They are usually too big and too heavy for easy transportation. Imagine that you are a sales representative for High Tech Games. To make a sales pitch to potential buyers, you need a quick, creative simulation of the game that can be presented easily.

In this activity, you develop your own simulation of Cards of Chance and determine theoretical probabilities for the three-card level.

Exploration

a. Develop a simulation of Cards of Chance that could be used in a presentation to prospective buyers. The model must demonstrate the rules of the game, provide representative sample results, and be easy to transport.

b. Use your simulation to play 10 games at the three-card level. Use the results to calculate the experimental probability of winning at the three-card level.

c. 1. Compile the class results. Use this data to determine the experimental probability for winning at the three-card level.

2. Compare this probability with the experimental probability for winning at the two-card level obtained in the introduction.

mathematics note

Conditional probability is the probability of an event occurring, given that an initial event, or **condition,** has already occurred. The probability of event B occurring, given that event A has already occurred, is denoted $P(B|A)$.

In an experiment involving conditional probabilities, the probability of both A and B occurring is found by multiplying the probability of A by the conditional probability of B given A:

$$P(\text{A and B}) = P(\text{A}) \bullet P(\text{B}|\text{A})$$

For example, consider drawing two playing cards from a standard deck, one at a time, without replacement, and observing their colors. The cards may be either red (R) or black (B). The tree diagram in Figure **10-3** shows the probabilities in this situation.

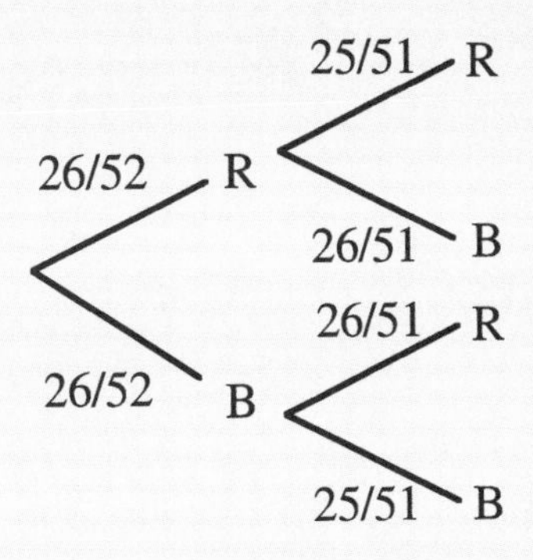

FIGURE 10-3 **Tree diagram for drawing two cards without replacement.**

In this case, the conditional probability of obtaining a red card on the second draw, given that the first card is black, is $P(\text{R}|\text{B}) = 26/51$. The conditional probability of obtaining a red card on the second draw, given that the first card is also red, is $P(\text{R}|\text{R}) = 25/51$.

The probability of obtaining two red cards is:

$$P(\text{RR}) = P(\text{R}) \bullet P(\text{R}|\text{R}) = \frac{26}{52} \bullet \frac{25}{51} = \frac{25}{102}$$

d. Create a tree diagram showing each possible outcome and its probability for the three-card level of Cards of Chance. **Note:** Save your work for use in the assignment.

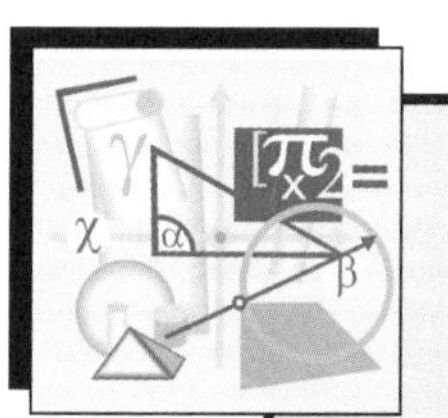

mathematics note

An experiment is **random** if individual outcomes are chance events.

A **random variable** X is a variable that takes on each of its possible values with a specific probability. Given possible values for X of $x_1, x_2, \ldots, x_k$, each has its corresponding probability $p_1, p_2, \ldots, p_k$. The sum of these probabilities is 1.

For example, rolling an ordinary six-sided die is a random experiment because the outcome of the roll is uncertain. If the outcomes of the experiment are assigned to the random variable X, then the possible values for X are 1, 2, 3, 4, 5, or 6. The probability of each outcome is 1/6.

A **probability distribution** for a random variable X assigns probabilities $p_1, p_2, \ldots, p_k$ to the values $x_1, x_2, \ldots, x_k$ for X.

Table **10-1** shows the probability distribution of the random variable X when rolling a six-sided die.

TABLE 10-1 ■ *Probability Distribution of Random Variable X*

Value of X (x_i)	1	2	3	4	5	6
Probability (p_i)	1/6	1/6	1/6	1/6	1/6	1/6

e. Make a table that shows the probability distribution for all possible outcomes of Cards of Chance at the three-card level.

f. Calculate the theoretical probability of winning at the three-card level.

Discussion

a. Is the theoretical probability of winning Cards of Chance at the two-card level the same as winning at the three-card level? Explain your response.

b. What is the sum of all the probabilities in a probability distribution? What does this sum represent?

c. In Cards of Chance, the first draw and the second draw are not independent events. How does this affect the probabilities of drawing two cards of the same color?

d. How could you change the rules for Cards of Chance so that the game involves independent events?

e. What is the probability of each of the following events in the three-card level of Cards of Chance?

1. drawing a black card, given that the first two cards are black
2. drawing a black card, given that the first two cards are red
3. drawing a black card, given that the first two cards are different colors

Warm-Up

1. **a.** What is the theoretical probability of drawing three red cards at the three-card level of Cards of Chance?

   b. Describe how you could use your tree diagram from the exploration to determine the probability in Part **a.**

2. **a.** Consider a game that involves drawing two cards from a standard deck, one at a time with replacement. Is obtaining an ace on the first draw independent of obtaining an ace on the second draw?

   b. For two independent events A and B, $P(\text{B} | \text{A}) = P(\text{B})$. How does this fact support your response to Part **a**?

   c. If each card is not replaced after it is drawn, does the game still involve independent events? Explain your response.

Assignment

1.1 **a.** Extend the tree diagram from the exploration to the four-card level of Cards of Chance.

b. Make a table that shows the probability distribution for all possible outcomes at the four-card level.

1.2 **a.** Determine the probability of drawing a fourth card of the same color, given that three cards of the same color were drawn at the three-card level.

b. Determine the probability of losing at the four-card level, given that three cards of the same color were drawn at the three-card level.

c. Determine the probability of winning at the four-card level, with no previous conditions given. Justify your response.

d. Determine the probability of losing at the four-card level, with no previous conditions given. Justify your response.

1.3 The Reel Game is another product of High Tech Games. As shown below, each machine has three spinning reels. Each reel has three equally likely symbols—a diamond, a square, and a circle. A player wins by matching the symbols on all three reels when the reels stop.

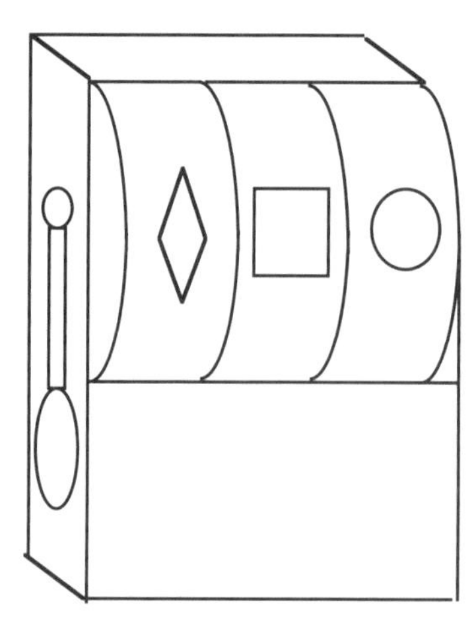

a. Draw a tree diagram that shows all the possible outcomes of the Reel Game. Label each branch with the appropriate probability.

b. Find the probability of getting a diamond on the second reel.

c. Find the probability of getting a diamond on the third reel.

d. Are getting a diamond on the second reel and a diamond on the third reel independent events? Explain your response.

e. Determine the probability of winning the Reel Game described with three diamonds, given that two diamonds have already appeared on the first two reels.

f. How does $P(3 \text{ diamonds} \mid 2 \text{ diamonds})$ compare to the probability of getting a diamond on the third reel?

1.4 Given rules similar to those of the Reel Game in Problem **1.3,** determine the probability of winning each of the following:

a. a game with two spinning reels, each having two symbols, a diamond and a triangle

b. a game with three spinning reels, each having three symbols, a square, a diamond, and a circle.

1.5 Consider a game that involves rolling two standard dice. If the sum of the faces is greater than 10, the player earns 10 points. If the sum equals 7, the player earns 5 points. Any other roll of the dice is worth 0 points. Show the probability distribution for the random variable S, where S represents the number of points won.

* * * * *

1.6 A history test contains 5 multiple-choice questions. Each question has 5 possible responses, only 1 of which is correct. To pass this test, students must answer at least 4 of the questions correctly.

If a student selects responses at random, what is the probability of each of the following events?

a. All 5 questions are answered correctly.

b. None of the questions are answered correctly.

c. Exactly 4 of the questions are answered correctly.

d. The student passes the test.

e. The student does not pass the test.

1.7 Consider a game in which 26 cards, each labeled with a different letter of the alphabet, are placed in a container and mixed thoroughly. If cards are drawn without replacement, what is the probability of each of the following?

a. When three cards are drawn, all three cards are vowels.

b. When five cards are drawn, all five cards are consonants.

c. Given that two vowels have been drawn, the next card is a vowel.

d. Given that three vowels and two consonants have been drawn, the next card is a vowel.

e. When seven cards are drawn, they include the letters of the word *fortune.*

1.8 Louis has four $1 bills, three $5 bills, and two $10 bills in his pocket. If he randomly draws two bills from his pocket, one at a time without replacement, what is the probability that the total is $15?

ACTIVITY 2

To expand its share of the market, High Tech Games is developing another kind of gaming machine, the binostat. As shown in Figure **10-4,** a binostat game involves dropping a ball through a triangular grid. At each level of the grid, the ball deflects to the right or left of a peg with equal probability, until it enters a numbered slot. For example, the ball in Figure **10-4** passed through the grid and landed in slot 2.

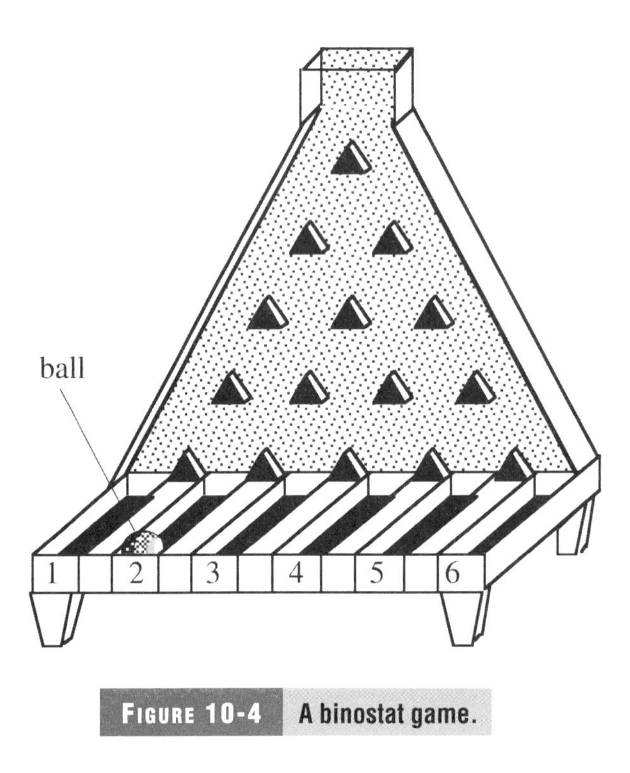

FIGURE 10-4 A binostat game.

To play a binostat game, a player inserts tokens in the machine and selects a slot number. The player then drops the ball into the top of the machine and watches as it falls through the grid. If the ball lands in the selected slot, the player wins the game and earns credits. If the ball lands in any other slot, the game is over and the player loses the tokens or credits played.

Exploration

In this exploration, you develop a method for finding probabilities in situations that have the same characteristics as a binostat. To determine the probabilities in a complicated setting, it is often helpful to observe simpler examples, then identify a pattern.

Figure **10-5** shows a simple binostat with only one level. In this binostat, a ball falling through the grid deflects either to the right or to the left. If it deflects to the left, it ends up in slot 1. If it deflects to the right, it ends up in slot 2.

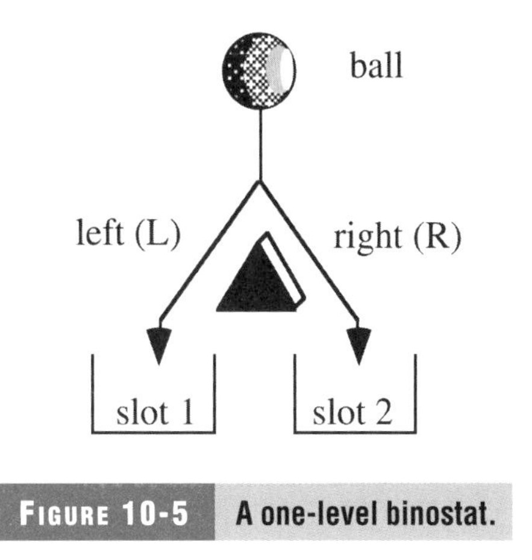

FIGURE 10-5 A one-level binostat.

a. In the one-level binostat game shown in Figure **10-5,** a ball falling through the grid has only two possible paths: right (R) or left (L).

   For a ball to reach slot 1 in the two-level binostat game shown in Figure **10-6,** the ball must deflect left and then left again (LL). To reach slot 2, a ball can deflect left and then right (LR), or it can deflect right and then left (RL). To reach slot 3, the ball must deflect right and then right again (RR).

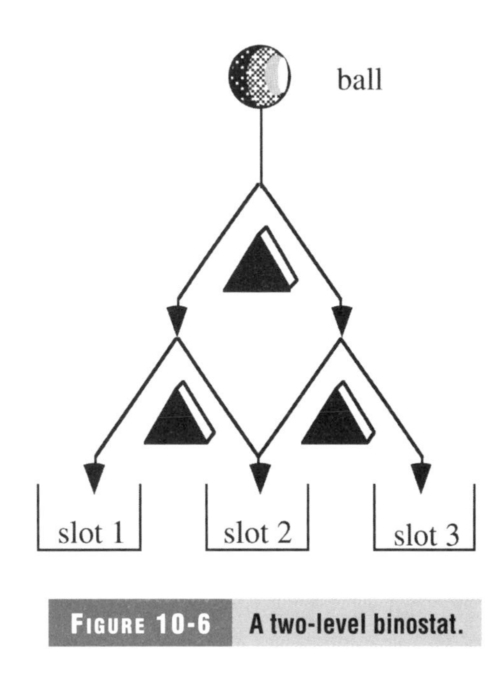

FIGURE 10-6 A two-level binostat.

In other words, there are a total of four ways—LL, LR, RL, and RR—to reach the three slots. Two of these paths lead to slot 2.

List all the paths in a binostat game with each of the following:

1. three levels
2. four levels.

b. At each junction in the binostat, the probability of going left is equal to the probability of going right. Determine the probability of the ball landing in each slot in a one-level binostat. Express each probability as a fraction in which the denominator equals the number of possible paths.

c. Repeat Part **b** for two-level, three-level, and four-level binostat games.

d. Obtain a template of the binostat paths shown in Figure **10-7.**

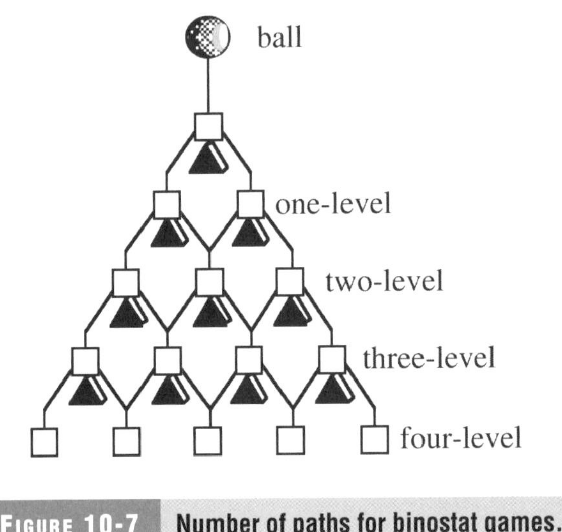

FIGURE 10-7 **Number of paths for binostat games.**

1. Fill in each square with the number of paths that can be taken to get to that particular slot.
2. Describe any patterns you observe in this figure.

e. In a one-level binostat, there are a total of 2 possible paths. In a two-level binostat, there are a total of 4 possible paths.

1. Use your results from Part **d** to express the total number of paths as a power of 2 for one-level, two-level, three-level, and four-level binostats.
2. Describe any relationship you observe between the total number of paths and the corresponding level of the binostat.

f. Use the patterns you observed in Parts **d** and **e** to extend the template through the 10th level.

mathematics note

The diagram you developed in the exploration is part of a pattern of numbers known as **Pascal's triangle.** Figure **10-8** shows the first five rows of Pascal's triangle.

				1					Row 0
			1		1				Row 1
		1		2		1			Row 2
	1		3		3		1		Row 3
1		4		6		4		1	Row 4

FIGURE 10-8 A portion of Pascal's triangle.

Discussion

a. Describe how you could generate any row of Pascal's triangle, given the previous row.

b. Explain how you could use your diagram to find the number of paths a ball can take to land in a particular slot of a binostat game.

c. Explain how you could use your diagram to find the total number of paths in a binostat game of any level.

d. In Part **e** of the exploration, the total number of paths in a given row was expressed as a power of 2. Explain why 2 was chosen as the base.

e. Explain how you could use your diagram to find the probability of a ball landing in slot x of an n-level binostat.

f. Why is a 1-level binostat like tossing a fair coin?

Warm-Up

1. List the numbers in each of the following rows of Pascal's triangle.
   - **a.** row 5
   - **b.** row 6
   - **c.** row 1

2. Consider a three-level binostat game.
   - **a.** How many slots does this game have?
   - **b.** How many different paths are possible for the ball?
   - **c.** How many paths can the ball take to land in slot 2?
   - **d.** What is the probability of the ball landing in slot 2?

Assignment

2.1 **a.** Determine the sum of the theoretical probabilities for the slots of each of the following.

1. a one-level binostat

2. a two-level binostat

3. a three-level binostat

b. Explain your responses to Part **a.**

2.2 **a.** How could you use exponential notation to express the theoretical probability of a ball landing in slot 1 in a one-, two-, or three-level binostat game?

b. What is the theoretical probability of a ball landing in slot 1 of a 10-level binostat?

2.3 **a.** Complete the probability distribution table below for each slot in a three-level binostat game.

Slot	1	2	3	4
Probability				

b. Can you use Pascal's triangle to create a probability distribution for each slot in an n-level binostat game? If so, how?

2.4 Create a probability distribution table for a six-level binostat.

* * * * *

2.5 An industrial plant has 8 robots for use on its assembly line. Six of the robots must be functioning for the plant to be operational.

a. If "I" represents an inoperable robot and "O" represents an operable robot, then one possible situation can be written as [OIOOIOOI]. Find the total number of situations that can occur.

b. Which row of Pascal's triangle corresponds with your response to Part **a**?

c. Use Pascal's triangle to find the number of outcomes in which exactly 6 out of 8 robots are operational.

d. Use Pascal's triangle to find the number of outcomes in which at least 6 out of 8 robots are operational.

2.6 Consider an experiment in which 10 supermarket customers are selected at random and asked to taste 2 different brands of tomato soup. Each person must state a preference for one brand or the other. The company sponsoring the taste test would like to claim that 80% of consumers prefer their brand over their competitor's brand.

a. Find the number of possible outcomes for the experiment. Which row of Pascal's triangle corresponds with this total?

b. Use Pascal's triangle to find the number of ways that exactly 8 of the 10 customers could choose a specific brand.

c. Use Pascal's triangle to find the number of ways that at least 8 of 10 customers could choose a specific brand.

Although Pascal's triangle can be used to calculate the probabilities of winning and the numbers of possible paths in binostat games, High Tech Games wants a mathematical model to determine the probabilities for its machines.

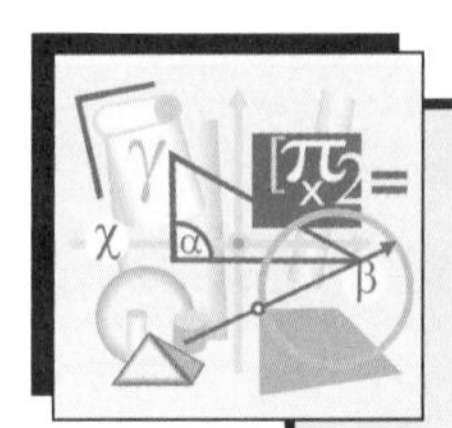

mathematics note

A **binomial experiment** has the following characteristics:

- It consists of a fixed number of repetitions of the same action. Each repetition is a **trial.**
- The trials are independent of each other. In other words, the result of one trial does not influence the result of any other trial in the experiment.
- Each trial has only two possible outcomes: a success or a failure. (The prefix *bi-* means "two.")
- The probability of a success remains constant from trial to trial.
- The total number of successes is observed.

For example, consider an experiment that consists of tossing a fair coin 3 times and observing the number of heads that occur. In this case, there is a fixed number of trials, 3. For each trial, there are only two possible outcomes: either heads or tails. The probability that heads occurs remains constant for each toss, and the result of one toss does not influence the result of any other. Therefore, this represents a binomial experiment.

Discussion 1

a. Explain whether or not each of the following represents a binomial experiment.

1. A fair coin is flipped six times. The total number of heads is recorded.
2. Two cards are drawn from a standard deck of playing cards, one at a time with replacement. The total number of diamonds is recorded.
3. Two cards are drawn from a standard deck of playing cards, one at a time without replacement. The total number of diamonds is recorded.

b. Given *P*(success) for any trial in a binomial experiment, describe how to find *P*(failure).

Exploration

Consider a ball falling through the four-level binostat in Figure **10-9.** Before reaching a slot, the ball makes a total of four deflections. At each peg, the ball has an equal probability of deflecting to the right or to the left.

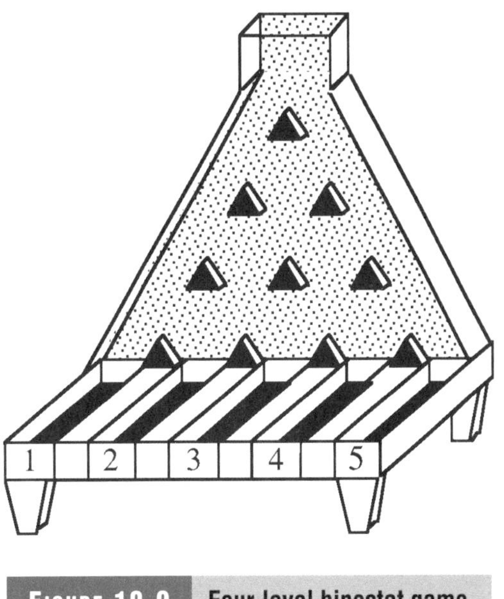

FIGURE 10-9 Four-level binostat game.

Using Pascal's triangle, you can determine that there is one possible path to slot 1, four possible paths to slot 2, six possible paths to slot 3, four possible paths to slot 4, and one possible path to slot 5.

a. To land in slot 2, the ball can make only one deflection to the right out of a total of four deflections. The four possibilities are RLLL, LRLL, LLRL, and LLLR.

   Recall that an arrangement of r items out of n items, where order is not important, is a **combination.** Use the notation $C(n,r)$, where n is the total number of deflections and r is the number of deflections to the right, to describe the number of paths the ball can take to land in slot 2.

b. List the possible paths the ball can take to land in each of the other slots of a four-level binostat. What patterns exist between the number of deflections to the left or right for each path to a given slot?

c. Use combination notation to describe the number of paths possible for each of the following slots in a four-level binostat.

   1. slot 1
   2. slot 3
   3. slot 4
   4. slot 5

d. As noted previously, there are four possible paths to slot 2. Each path has a total of four deflections, with only one deflection to the right: RLLL, LRLL, LLRL, and LLLR.

Since the probability of a deflection to the left or to the right is 1/2, the probability that the ball will take path RLLL can be found as follows:

$$\begin{aligned} P(\text{RLLL}) &= P(\text{R}) \bullet P(\text{L}) \bullet P(\text{L}) \bullet P(\text{L}) \\ &= [P(\text{R})]^1 \bullet [P(\text{L})]^3 \\ &= \left(\frac{1}{2}\right)^1 \bullet \left(\frac{1}{2}\right)^3 = \frac{1}{16} \end{aligned}$$

Similarly, the probability for each of the other three paths to slot 2 is also $[P(\text{R})]^1 \bullet [P(\text{L})]^3$, or 1/16. Because there are 4 possible paths, each with a probability of $[P(\text{R})]^1 \bullet [P(\text{L})]^3$, the probability of the ball landing in slot 2 can be expressed as follows:

$$\begin{aligned} P(\text{slot } 2) &= 4 \bullet [P(\text{R})]^1 \bullet [P(\text{L})]^3 \\ &= 4 \bullet \left(\frac{1}{2}\right)^1 \bullet \left(\frac{1}{2}\right)^3 \\ &= \frac{4}{16} = \frac{1}{4} \end{aligned}$$

Using the process described for slot 2, determine the probabilities for slots 1, 3, 4, and 5.

e. Use combinations and exponents to write a formula for the probability of a ball ending in slots 1, 2, 3, 4, and 5.

Discussion 2

a. How can you use Pascal's triangle to determine the number of possible paths that include r deflections to the right in an n-level binostat?

b. How can you use the notation $C(n,r)$ to represent any element of Pascal's triangle?

mathematics note

A **binomial distribution** is the probability distribution associated with repeated trials of a binomial experiment.

The probability of obtaining r successes in n trials can be determined using the following formula, where p is the probability of success in any one trial:

$$P(r \text{ successes in } n \text{ trials}) = C(n, r) \bullet p^r \bullet (1 - p)^{n-r}$$

For example, consider a binomial experiment that involves rolling a fair die. In this experiment, rolling a six is designated a success while any other roll is designated a failure. In 7 trials, the probability of getting 3 sixes is:

$$P(3 \text{ successes}) = C(7, 3) \bullet \left(\frac{1}{6}\right)^3 \bullet \left(\frac{5}{6}\right)^4 = 35 \bullet \frac{625}{279{,}936} \approx 8\%$$

c. Using the process described in Part **e** of the exploration, how can you use combinations to express the probability of a ball landing in a slot that requires each of the following?

1. r deflections to the right in an n-level binostat
2. r deflections to the left in an n-level binostat

d. Can you use the formula for a binomial distribution to calculate the probability of getting at least 3 twos with 5 rolls of a fair die? If so, how?

Warm-Up

1. Which of the following are binomial experiments? Justify your responses.

   a. A die is tossed three times. After each toss, the number that appears on the top face is recorded.

   b. Two playing cards are drawn from a deck of 16 cards, one at a time, without replacement. After each card is drawn, its color is recorded.

   c. A coin is flipped until it lands heads up.

2. Use the formula for a binomial distribution to calculate the probabilities of a ball landing in each of the slots of a five-level binostat game. Check your answers using Pascal's triangle.

Assignment

3.1 Experimental data shows that when a thumbtack is tossed in the air, it will land point up 75% of the time, and point down 25% of the time.

a. Does tossing a thumbtack in the air and observing the outcome represent a binomial experiment?

b. What is the probability that when a tack is tossed 10 times, it lands point down exactly 6 times?

3.2 Consider a reel game with five reels. Each reel has the same five symbols—a diamond, a club, a heart, a spade, and an automobile. Each of the five symbols is equally likely to appear on each reel.

a. If you wanted to get an automobile on each reel, how would you define a "success" in this game?

b. What is the probability of a "success" on any one reel?

c. What is the probability of a "failure" on any one reel?

3.3 Consider the reel game described in Problem **3.2.**

a. What is the probability of getting a diamond on every reel?

b. What is the probability of getting a heart on exactly three of the reels?

c. What is the probability of getting a heart on at least three reels?

d. The middle reel on one machine always sticks, displaying a diamond. Calculate the probability of getting three diamonds on this machine.

3.4 Binomial expressions such as $(x + y)^3$ can be expanded using the distributive property. For example, the expanded forms of several binomial expressions are shown below:

$$(x + y)^0 = 1$$

$$(x + y)^1 = x + y$$

$$(x + y)^2 = x^2 + 2xy + y^2$$

$$(x + y)^3 = x^3 + 3x^2y + 3xy^2 + y^3$$

$$(x + y)^4 = x^4 + 4x^3y + 6x^2y^2 + 4xy^3 + y^4$$

a. Examine the expanded form of each of the binomial expressions above. Describe the sum of the exponents on each term in the expanded form with respect to the exponent of the original expression.

b. For each expression, describe the relationship between the coefficients of each term and Pascal's triangle.

c. Rewrite the expanded form of $(x + y)^4$ using the notation for combinations, $C(n,r)$.

d. Use your results in Parts **a–c** to suggest an expanded form for the general binomial $(x + y)^n$.

3.5 Consider an airplane with two engines. Assume that the probability of engine failure during a transcontinental flight is 0.001, and that the event of one engine failing is independent of the other engine failing. Given these conditions, determine the probability of each of the following outcomes.

a. A transcontinental flight is completed without engine failure.

b. Both engines fail.

c. At least one engine fails.

* * * * *

3.6 A married couple plans to have four children. Assuming that the probability that each child is a girl is 0.5, what is the probability that their four children will include:

a. 3 boys and 1 girl?

b. 4 girls?

c. 2 boys and 2 girls?

3.7 On January 28, 1986, the space shuttle *Challenger* exploded shortly after launch. The cause of this tragedy was traced to the failure of 1 of the 6 sealed joints on the booster rockets. Assuming that each joint has a 0.977 success rate, and that the failure of any one joint is independent of the failure of any of the others, calculate the probability that at least 1 of the 6 joints fails.

3.8 According to the **binomial theorem,** the expansion of $(x + y)^n$, where n is a whole number, is the sum of $(n + 1)$ terms, as follows:

$$(x + y)^n = C(n, n)x^n + C(n, n - 1)x^{n-1}y + C(n, n - 2)x^{n-2}y^2 + \cdots + C(n, 0)y^n$$

Use the binomial theorem to expand each of the expressions below.

a. $(x - y)^6$

b. $(x^2 + 3y)^3$

c. $(2xy - 5)^4$

ACTIVITY 4

The video gaming machine industry is highly competitive. Besides designing games that keep players interested and entertained, High Tech Games must also ensure that its products generate a profit.

Whenever someone uses a gaming machine, there are costs involved. For the player, the cost is the price required to play. For the machine's owners, the costs include paying off the credits earned by successful players.

mathematics note

The **expected value** or **mean** of a random variable X, denoted $E(X)$, is the sum of the products of each possible value of X and its corresponding probability.

$$E(X) = x_1p_1 + x_2p_2 + \cdots + x_kp_k$$

In mathematics, a sum often is denoted using the Greek letter *sigma*, Σ. Using this notation, the expected value of X can be written as follows:

$$E(X) = \sum_{i=1}^{k} x_ip_i$$

This indicates that the values of x_ip_i are added as i increases from 1 to k.

For example, consider a game that consists of rolling a fair die. A roll of one is worth 1 point, a roll of two is worth 2 points, and so on. The expected value for this game can be calculated as shown below:

$$E(X) = \sum_{i=1}^{6} x_ip_i = 1 \bullet \frac{1}{6} + 2 \bullet \frac{1}{6} + 3 \bullet \frac{1}{6} + 4 \bullet \frac{1}{6} + 5 \bullet \frac{1}{6} + 6 \bullet \frac{1}{6} = \frac{21}{6} = 3.5$$

In this case, an exact value of 3.5 cannot be obtained on any single roll of the die. However, according to the law of large numbers, if the die is rolled many times, the mean of all the rolls is likely to be close to 3.5.

Exploration

In the following exploration, you investigate a five-level binostat that costs 100 tokens to play.

a. To players, the expected value for a game is its expected payoff. This can be determined by multiplying the payoff for each outcome by its theoretical probability, then finding the sum of these products.

The payoffs (in tokens) for each slot in the five-level binostat are shown in Table **10-2** below. From the exploration in Activity **2,** the probabilities of the ball landing in slot 1, 2, 3, 4, 5, or 6 are 1/32, 5/32, 5/16, 5/16, 5/32, or 1/32, respectively. Determine the expected payoff for this game.

TABLE 10-2 ■ *Payoffs for Five-Level Binostat Game*

Slot	1	2	3	4	5	6
Payoff	200	20	10	10	20	200

b. In a **fair game,** the expected payoff equals the cost of playing the game. The game described in Part **a** is not a fair game. Use a spreadsheet to determine a set of payoffs that make this five-level binostat game a fair one.

c. In High Tech's home market, state law requires a 70% minimum return to players. Determine a set of payoffs that satisfies the state requirements, while providing a profit for the owners of the gaming machines.

Discussion

a. For the binostat game represented in Table **10-2,** the payoffs for landing in slots 1 or 6 are much higher than those of the other slots. What is the relationship between the probabilities for each of the six outcomes and their corresponding payoffs?

b. Is there more than one way to assign payoffs to make the game fair? Explain your response.

c. What changes did you make in your payoff scheme to turn your fair game into a legal and profitable one?

d. Describe a payoff scheme that might attract players, yet still make the game profitable for owners.

e. Consider a game that costs 100 tokens to play. A local regulation requires that the expected payoff be at least 70% of the cost to play.

1. What is the minimum number of tokens in the expected payoff?
2. The probability distribution for this game is shown in Table **10-3** below. Which outcome would you expect to have the greatest single payoff?

TABLE 10-3 ■ *Probability Distribution for a Game*

Outcome A	Outcome B	Outcome C	Outcome D	Outcome E
1/9	2/9	1/3	2/9	1/9

3. Suppose that the payoff for outcome C is x tokens. If there is an inverse relation between probability and payoff for each outcome, how would you describe the payoffs for the other outcomes in terms of x?
4. Using the probability distribution in Table **10-3** and the payoffs you described in Step **3,** how would you represent the game's expected value in terms of x?
5. If the game's expected value equals the expected payoff in Step **1,** what is the value of x? What is the corresponding payoff for each outcome?

Warm-Up

1. The spinner below is used in a carnival game. If the arrow lands in the unshaded sector, the player receives 50 points. If it lands in the shaded sector, the player receives 5 points. The central angle of the unshaded sector measures 30°. Determine the expected value (in points) for this game.

2. In most games, outcomes with lower probabilities have higher payoffs than outcomes with higher probabilities. This can make the game attractive to players, yet still profitable.

   a. Suppose that the payoff for the first slot of a six-level binostat is 457 tokens, as shown in the table below. Determine the payoffs for each remaining slot using an inverse relationship between the probability and the payoff. For example, the probability of landing in slot 2 is 6 times the probability of landing in slot 1. To determine the payoff for slot 2, multiply the payoff for slot 1 by 1/6, or $457 \bullet 1/6 \approx 76$.

Slot	1	2	3	4	5	6	7
Probability	1/64	6/64	15/64	20/64	15/64	6/64	1/64
Payoff	457	76					

   b. What should be the cost to play to make this a fair game?

Assignment

4.1 Consider a six-level binostat that costs 50 tokens to play. If local regulations require a minimum 70% return for players, determine a set of payoffs that would make this game both legal and profitable. To attract players, the payoff for each slot should be inversely related to its probability.

4.2 Suppose that Cards of Chance costs 50 tokens to play. If local regulations require a minimum 70% return for players, determine a set of payoffs for the entire game—from the two-card level to the four-card level—that would make it both legal and profitable.

4.3 Consider a three-level binostat game that costs 50 tokens to play. If local regulations require a minimum 70% return for players, determine a set of payoffs that would make this game both legal and profitable. The payoff for each slot should be inversely related to its probability.

4.4 As part of a market analysis for High Tech Games, you have been asked to compare Cards of Chance, reel games, and binostat games in terms of complexity, player interest, and potential profitability. Write a summary of your comparisons.

* * * * *

4.5 A three-reel game costs 50 tokens to play. Each reel has three distinct symbols, and players must match at least two symbols to earn tokens. If local regulations require a minimum of 70% return for players, determine a set of payoffs that would make this game both legal and profitable. The payoff for each slot should be inversely related to its probability.

4.6 An insurance company offers an accident/illness policy with the following benefits.

- If a policyholder becomes seriously ill during the year, the company will pay $1000.
- If a policyholder has an accident, the company will pay $2000.
- If a policyholder has an accident and becomes seriously ill, the company will pay $7500.

The annual premium for this policy is $200.

a. According to the company's statistics, the probability of becoming seriously ill in any one year is 0.06, while the probability of having an accident is 0.04. Assuming that these are independent events, determine the probability of each of the following:

1. a policyholder does not become ill or have an accident

2. a policyholder becomes ill, but does not have an accident

3. a policyholder does not become ill, but does have an accident

4. a policyholder becomes ill and has an accident.

b. What is the company's expected annual profit per policyholder?

Summary Assessment

High Tech Games is developing a new video gaming machine called Flip-o-Mania. To begin the game, players insert tokens in the machine. The game then electronically "flips" a coin. The player continues flipping coins electronically. For play to continue, each successive coin flipped must match the first coin. When a coin appears that does not match the others, the game is over. The player wins credits based on the number of coins flipped successfully.

Although High Tech has not yet determined how many coins players should have the option of flipping, the company plans to market a test version of Flip-o-Mania soon. As director of marketing, you must make a presentation at next week's board meeting about the new machine.

1. Design a simulation for Flip-o-Mania that you could use to demonstrate how the game works.

2. a. An initial study suggests that players should be offered the chance to flip at least 4 coins, but no more than 10. If each flip is considered a level in the game, determine at what level Flip-o-Mania should conclude.

   b. Determine the probabilities of winning at each level.

3. If local regulations require a 70% minimum return to players, determine an appropriate set of payoffs for Flip-o-Mania, given that the cost to play is 10 tokens.

4. Write a report that defends your recommendations and findings in Problems **1–3.** Your report should include a discussion of probability distribution tables, binomial experiments, binomial probabilities, and expected value.

Module Summary

- According to the **law of large numbers,** as the number of trials increases, the experimental probability of an event tends to approach its theoretical probability.
- **Conditional probability** is the probability of an event occurring, given that an initial event, or **condition,** has already occurred. The probability of event B occurring, given that event A has already occurred, is denoted $P(B|A)$.
- In an experiment involving conditional probabilities, the probability of both A and B occurring is found by multiplying the probability of A by the conditional probability of B given A:

$$P(\text{A and B}) = P(\text{A}) \bullet P(\text{B}|\text{A})$$

- An experiment is **random** if individual outcomes are chance events.
- A **random variable** X is a variable that takes on each of its possible values with a specific probability. Given possible values for X of $x_1, x_2, \ldots, x_k$, each has its corresponding probability $p_1, p_2, \ldots, p_k$. The sum of these probabilities is 1.
- A **probability distribution** for a random variable X assigns probabilities $p_1, p_2, \ldots, p_k$ to the values $x_1, x_2, \ldots, x_k$ for X.
- The triangular pattern of numbers shown below is called **Pascal's triangle:**

```
            1              Row 0
          1   1            Row 1
        1   2   1          Row 2
      1   3   3   1        Row 3
    1   4   6   4   1      Row 4
  ⋮   ⋮   ⋮   ⋮   ⋮   ⋮
```

- A **binomial experiment** has the following characteristics:
  1. It consists of a fixed number of repetitions of the same action. Each repetition is a **trial.**
  2. The trials are independent of each other. In other words, the result of one trial does not influence the result of any other trial in the experiment.
  3. Each trial has only two possible outcomes: a success or a failure. (The prefix *bi-* means "two.")
  4. The probability of a success remains constant from trial to trial.
  5. The total number of successes is observed.

* A **binomial distribution** is the probability distribution associated with repeated trials of a binomial experiment. The probability of obtaining r successes in n trials can be determined using the following formula, where p is the probability of success in any one trial:

$$P(r \text{ successes in } n \text{ trials}) = C(n, r) \bullet p^r \bullet (1 - p)^{n-r}$$

* The **expected value** or **mean** of a random variable X, denoted $E(X)$, is the sum of the products of each possible value of X and its corresponding probability.

$$E(X) = x_1p_1 + x_2p_2 + \cdots + x_kp_k$$

  In mathematics, a sum is often denoted using the Greek letter *sigma*, Σ. Using this notation, the expected value of X can be written as follows:

$$E(X) = \sum_{i=1}^{k} x_ip_i$$

  This indicates that the values of x_ip_i are added as i increases from 1 to k.

* In a **fair game,** the expected payoff equals the cost of playing the game.

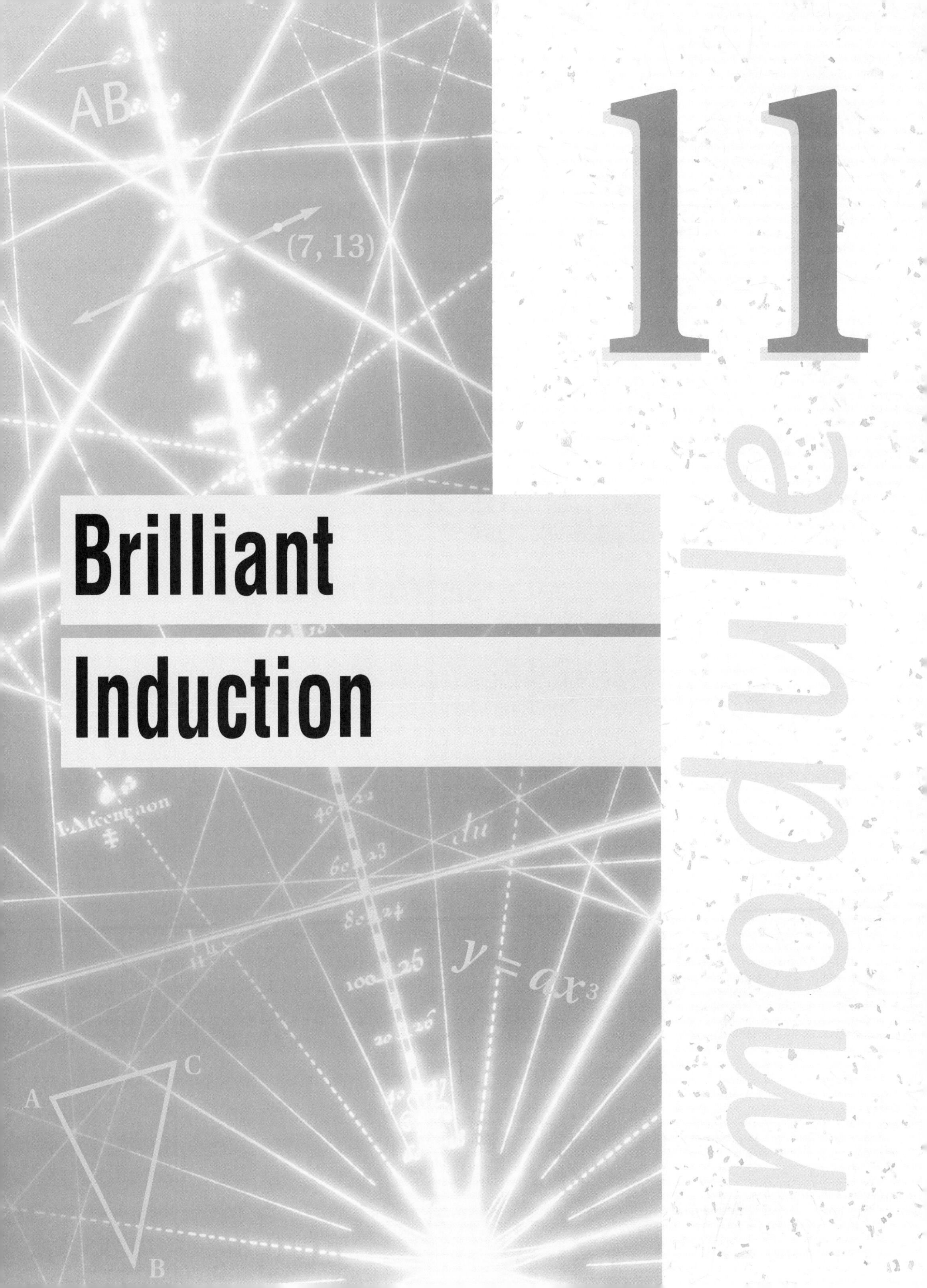

module 11

Brilliant Induction

Introduction

When dominoes are stood on end, each one slightly behind another, tipping over the first domino will cause the second one to fall. As the second domino falls, it will cause the next one to fall, and so on. Figure **11-1** shows this chain of events.

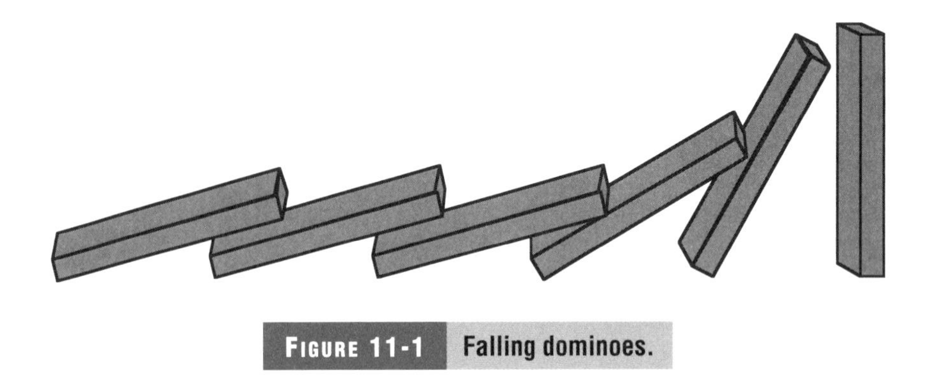

Figure 11-1 Falling dominoes.

A process in which each falling domino causes the next one to fall resembles in some ways a method of proof known as **mathematical induction.** This technique has been in use at least since the 16th century, and might have been recognized much earlier, perhaps by the Pythagoreans. In this module, you explore the conditions under which such a method of proof might work, and investigate situations where it does not apply.

Discussion

a. When 100 dominoes are stood on end, what conditions are necessary for all the dominoes to fall when the first one is knocked over?

b. The process that causes the 50th domino to fall is similar to the process that causes the 5th domino to fall. Describe the similarities.

c. How could you prove, without actually knocking the first domino over, that all the dominoes will fall if the first one falls?

d. Many situations involve the successful completion of a chain of similar events. In a 400-m relay, for example, the first person must run 100 m, then successfully pass the baton to the second person. The second person also must run 100 m and successfully pass the baton to the next person, and so on, until the race ends. Describe the different ways in which a 400-m relay team might not finish a race.

e. To climb to the top of a ladder, you must start on the first rung, then advance to the second. Once on the second rung, you can advance to the third, and so on. Describe how this process is similar to the one that causes dominoes to fall.

In this activity, you consider the conditions necessary to prove a statement using mathematical induction.

Exploration 1

Figure **11-2** shows a point on a line. Disregarding the point itself, it can be thought of as separating the line into two regions R_1 and R_2: one on either side of the point.

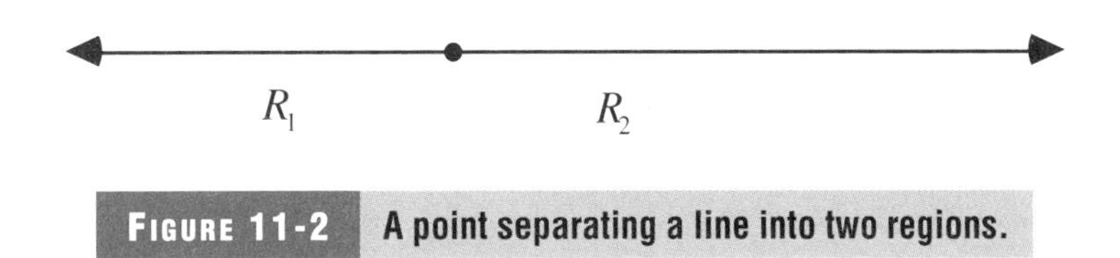

FIGURE 11-2 **A point separating a line into two regions.**

In the following steps, you consider the number of regions into which n distinct points separate a line.

a. Draw a picture showing the number of regions formed when a second distinct point is placed on the line. Label each region as in Figure **11-2.**

b. Suppose that a third distinct point is placed on the line. Does the number of regions formed depend on the location of the point?

c. Repeat the process described in Parts **a** and **b** for three more points. Record the results in a table with headings like those in Table **11-1** below.

TABLE 11-1 ■ *Number of Regions into Which n Distinct Points Separate a Line*

Number of Distinct Points (n)	Number of Regions Added with Each Additional Point	Total Number of Regions
1		2
2		
3		
4		
5		
6		

Discussion 1

a. Judging from your results in Exploration **1**, what happens to the number of regions formed when an additional point is placed on the line?

b. Does it matter where each additional point is placed on the line, if each one is distinct from any previous points?

c. Do you think that your response to Part **b** is true regardless of the number of points already placed on the line?

d. If you knew that your conjecture in Part **a** was true for all points up to and including some kth point, how would you argue that the conjecture was true when another point, the $(k + 1)$th, is placed on the line?

Exploration 2

Figure **11-3** shows three rectangles constructed with toothpicks. Each rectangle has dimensions $1 \times n$, where n is 1, 2, or 3 toothpicks. The total number of toothpicks required to build each rectangle with dimensions $1 \times n$ can be described by the following formula: $a_n = 2n + 2$ for $n = 1, 2, 3$.

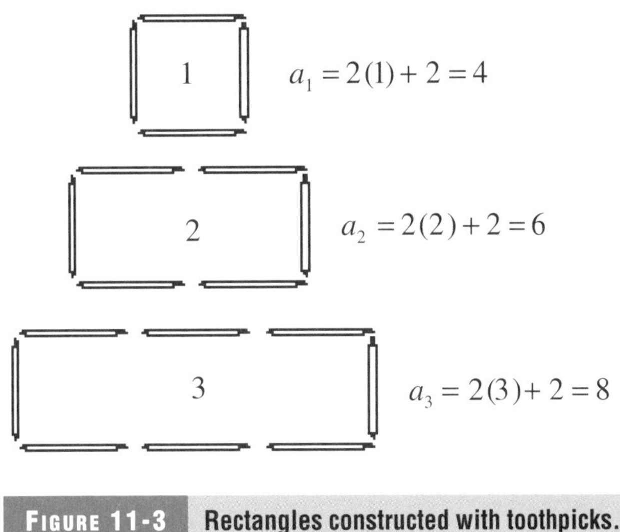

FIGURE 11-3 **Rectangles constructed with toothpicks.**

Suppose that the pattern shown in Figure **11-3** is continued for all natural numbers. Does the formula still work for $n = \{1, 2, 3, \ldots\}$?

a. To argue that the formula $a_n = 2n + 2$ is correct for all natural numbers n, you must start by examining the first rectangle of dimensions $1 \times n$. When $n = 1$, the rectangle requires four toothpicks. Therefore, $a_1 = 4$.

   1. What could you do to the first rectangle to create the second rectangle?
   2. How is a_2 related to a_1?

b. Explain how the process you described in Part **a** can be used to create a third rectangle given the second rectangle, and determine a_3 given a_2.

c. Suppose that the process you described in Parts **a** and **b** continues to work for all natural numbers up to k. Do you think that it then can be used to determine a_{k+1} given a_k? Explain your response.

d. The number of toothpicks required to build each rectangle in Figure **11-3** describes a sequence: a_1, a_2, a_3, where $a_1 = 4$, $a_2 = 6$, and $a_3 = 8$. The corresponding series S_3 represents the total number of toothpicks required to build three rectangles.

   Determine S_1, S_2, S_3, S_4, and S_5.

e. Using the techniques you learned in the Level 4 module, "The Sequence Makes the Difference," verify that one possible formula for S_n is $S_n = n(n + 3)$.

f. Note that $S_1 = a_1$ and $a_n = 2n + 2$. Use this fact to verify that the formula suggested in Part **e** is true for S_1.

g. Because $S_2 = S_1 + a_2$ and $a_n = 2n + 2$, the algebraic process below demonstrates that the formula $S_n = n(n + 3)$ is true for $n = 2$, given that it is true for $n = 1$.

$$\begin{aligned} S_2 &= S_1 + a_2 \\ &= 1(1 + 3) + 2(2) + 2 \\ &= 4 + 6 \\ &= 10 \\ &= 2(2 + 3) \end{aligned}$$

1. Use the same process to verify that the formula $S_n = n(n + 3)$ is true for $n = 3$, given that it is true for $n = 2$.

2. Verify that the formula is true for S_4, given that it is true for S_3.

h. 1. Assuming that the formula is true for S_{100}, the total number of toothpicks required to build the first 100 rectangles, verify that it also is true for S_{101}.

2. Assuming that the formula is true for S_{752}, verify that it also is true for S_{753}.

Discussion 2

a. Is it possible to prove that the formulas in Exploration **2** are true by checking them for every possible value of n?

b. Describe how you could verify that the formula $S_n = n(n + 3)$ is true for S_{k+1} given that it is true for S_k. *Hint:* The process is the same as the one used in verifying that the formula is true for S_2 given that it true for S_1.

Warm-Up

1. At a very young age, the mathematician Carl Gauss (1777–1855) devised a method for adding consecutive natural numbers $1 + 2 + 3 + \cdots + n$. This method has many applications.

   By examining a pattern or using the methods developed in "The Sequence Makes the Difference," suggest a formula for the sum of the first n natural numbers.

2. **a.** Assume that your formula in Problem **1** is true for $n = 100$. Use this assumption to verify that the formula also is true for $n = 101$.

   b. Assuming that the formula is true for $n = 101$, show that it also is true for $n = 102$.

   c. Assuming that the formula is true for $n = 102$, show that it also is true for $n = 103$.

3. Describe how your work in Problem **2** is similar to the following statement: "If the 100th domino falls, so will the 101st, the 102nd, and the 103rd."

4. Each of the following mathematical statements is false. To prove that each is false, identify a counterexample for each one.

   a. $1 \bullet 2 \bullet 3 \bullet \cdots \bullet n = n^n - 2^{n-1}$ for all natural numbers n

   b. $5^n \geq n^5$ for all natural numbers n

   c. 8 is a factor of $12^n - 8^n$ for all natural numbers n

   d. $2n + 1$ is prime for all natural numbers n

Assignment

1.1 a. A student has suggested the following formula for the sum of the first n natural numbers:

$$1 + 2 + 3 + \cdots + n = \frac{n(n+1)}{2} + 1$$

Show that if this conjecture is true for some natural number k, then it also is true for the next natural number $k + 1$.

b. Show that the conjecture is in fact false when $n = 1$.

c. Your responses to Parts **a** and **b** are comparable to showing that if the first domino in a row of dominoes is knocked down, then all the others will fall, when in fact, the first one cannot be knocked down.

Use a truth table to illustrate how a false hypothesis leads to a true conditional statement.

d. Is there any way to prove that the conjecture in Part **a** is true? Explain your response.

1.2 Consider the following inequality: $2^{(n+1)} < 3^n$, where n is a natural number. This relationship is not true for $n = 1$ but is true for $n = 2$.

a. Graph the sequences $t_n = 2^{(n+1)}$ and $t_n = 3^n$ on the same coordinate system for $n = \{2, 3, 4, 5\}$.

b. Does the inequality appear to be true for $n \geq 2$?

c. Assuming that the inequality is true for $n = 577$, explain how the following steps verify that it also is true for $n = 578$.

$$\begin{aligned} 2^{(578+1)} &= 2^{(577+1)} \bullet 2^1 \\ &< 3^{577} \bullet 2^1 \\ &< 3^{577} \bullet 3^1 = 3^{578} \end{aligned}$$

d. Make a conjecture about the set of natural numbers for which the inequality is true.

1.3 Consider a meeting room containing the members of a civic group. Each person shakes hands with every other person in the room. When 2 people are in the room, 1 handshake occurs. When 3 people are in the room, 2 handshakes occur.

Suggest a formula for the number of handshakes that occur when n people are in the room.

1.4 Consider the following conjecture: "The quantity $3^n + 1$ is divisible by 2 for all natural numbers n."

a. Assuming that the conjecture is true for $n = 10{,}003$, show that it also is true for 10,004 using the steps described below.

1. The expression $3^{10{,}004} + 1$ can be rewritten as follows:

$$\begin{aligned} 3^{10{,}004} + 1 &= 3^{10{,}003+1} + 1 \\ &= 3^{10{,}003} \bullet 3^1 + 1 \end{aligned}$$

Using the fact that $3^1 = 2 + 1$, rewrite the above expression.

2. Argue that the result is divisible by 2, given that the conjecture is true for $n = 10{,}003$.

b. Does your work in Part **a** alone guarantee that the conjecture is always true? Explain your response.

1.5 A sequence can be defined by the recursive formula below:

$$\begin{cases} a_1 = 3 \\ a_n = a_{n-1} + 4, \ n > 1 \end{cases}$$

a. Determine the first five terms of the sequence.

b. Write an explicit formula for the sequence.

c. Assume that the explicit formula is true for $n = 35$. Use this assumption to show that the formula also is true for $n = 36$.

1.6 Consider the inequality $(n - 3)^2 \leq 3n$, where n is a natural number.

a. Assume that this inequality is true for $n = 7$. Use this assumption to show that it also is true for $n = 8$.

b. Graph the sequences $t_n = (n - 3)^2$ and $t_n = 3n$ on the same coordinate system.

c. Make a conjecture about the set of natural numbers for which the inequality is true.

1.7 Consider the conjecture: "The quantity $2^n - 2$ is divisible by n whenever n is a positive odd integer."

a. Find a value of n that supports this conjecture.

b. Does the evidence you provided in Part **a** constitute a proof? Explain your response.

1.8 The diagram on the right shows a sequence of three figures constructed with toothpicks.

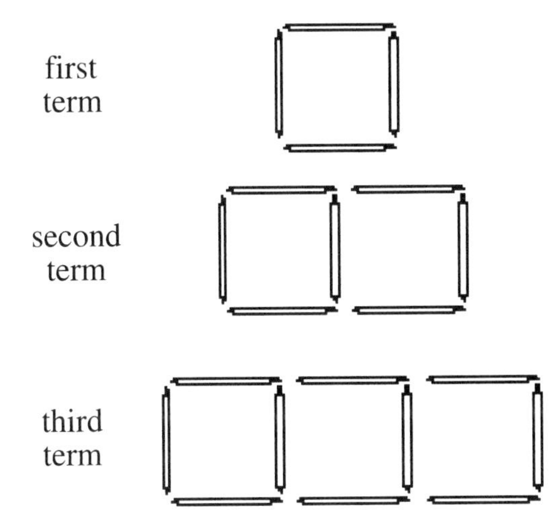

a. Describe the process required to create successive terms in this sequence.

b. Develop a formula for the number of toothpicks needed to construct a figure with n congruent squares.

c. Assuming that the formula is true for $n = 50$, show that it also is true for $n = 51$.

As you observed in Activity **1,** many conjectures can be verified for a finite number of cases. However, this does not necessarily prove that a conjecture is true for all cases. In this activity, you use what you have learned to investigate a proof by mathematical induction.

Discussion 1

a. Consider an endless row of dominoes standing on end, each one slightly behind another. Describe how this arrangement ensures that if the first domino in the row is tipped over, then:

1. the millionth domino will fall
2. the rest of the dominoes also will continue to fall.

b. Describe the results in Part **a** if the fifth domino in the row is tipped over instead of the first.

c. Consider a non-empty subset T of the natural numbers with the following property: for any natural number that is in T, the next consecutive natural number also is in T.

Explain how the "domino effect" described in Part **a** guarantees that T contains all natural numbers greater than the least natural number in T.

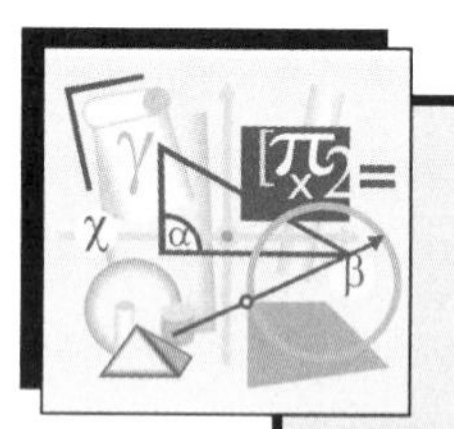

mathematics note

The principle of **mathematical induction** can be described as follows:

Suppose that for any natural number n, $P(n)$ is a mathematical statement involving n. If,

- $P(1)$ is true, and
- whenever k is a natural number such that $P(k)$ is true, $P(k + 1)$ also is true

then $P(n)$ is true for all natural numbers n.

For example, consider the following conjecture: "The square of each natural number n is the sum of the first n odd numbers." Figure **11-4** shows a geometric representation of this conjecture for $n = \{1, 2, 3, 4\}$.

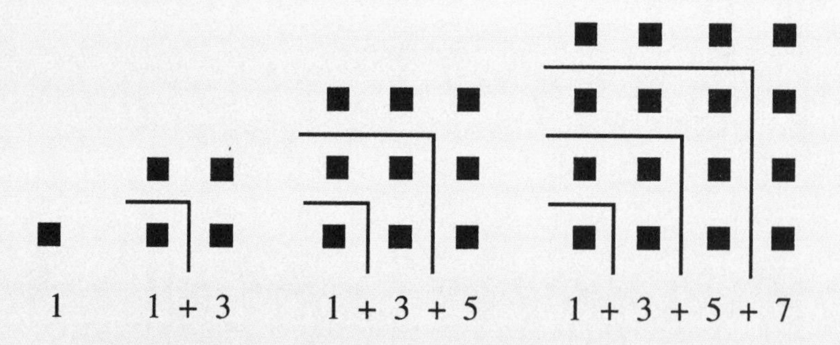

FIGURE 11-4 Geometric depiction of square numbers.

The numbers of dots in the terms of this sequence are 1, 4, 9, and 16, respectively, or $1^2, 2^2, 3^2$, and 4^2. Because the sum of the first n odd numbers can be represented as the series $S_n = 1 + 3 + 5 + \cdots + (2n - 1)$, the conjecture can be expressed as follows: $1 + 3 + 5 + \cdots + (2n - 1) = n^2$.

This conjecture can be proven true for all natural numbers n using mathematical induction, as described below.

- Show $P(1)$ is true:

$$S_1 = 2(1) - 1 = 1 = 1^2$$

- Showing that $P(1)$ implies that $P(2)$ is true may suggest a method for proving that $P(k)$ implies that $P(k + 1)$ is true. In this case, $P(1)$ can be used to prove that $P(2)$ is true as follows:

$$\begin{aligned} S_2 &= S_1 + (2 \bullet 2 - 1) \\ &= 1 + (2 \bullet 2 - 1) \\ &= 2 \bullet 2 + 1 - 1 \\ &= 2 \bullet 2 \\ &= 2^2 \end{aligned}$$

- Let k be a natural number such that whenever $P(k)$ is true,

$$1 + 3 + 5 + \cdots + (2k - 1) = S_k = k^2$$

Use this assumption to prove that $P(k + 1)$ is true.

$$\begin{aligned} S_{k+1} &= S_k + (2(k + 1) - 1) \\ &= k^2 + (2(k + 1) - 1) \\ &= k^2 - 1 + 2k + 2 \\ &= (k - 1)(k + 1) + 2(k + 1) \\ &= (k - 1 + 2)(k + 1) \\ &= (k + 1)^2 \end{aligned}$$

Because it has been shown that $P(1)$ is true, and that if $P(k)$ is true, then $P(k + 1)$ also is true, $P(n)$ is true for all natural numbers n.

d. 1. Consider a non-empty subset T of the integers with the same property described in Part **c** of this discussion: for any integer that is in T, the next consecutive integer also is in T.

Could the principle of mathematical induction be used to show that a set contains all integers greater than the least integer in the set? Explain your response.

2. Could it be used to show that a set contains all real numbers greater than the least in the set? Explain your response.

e. Consider the following conjecture: "The inequality $2^{n+1} < 3^n$ is true for all natural numbers n." Could the principle of mathematical induction be used to prove this conjecture? Justify your response.

f. Describe how you could prove the following conjecture using a process similar to mathematical induction: "The inequality $2^{n+1} < 3^n$ is true for all natural numbers greater than 1."

Exploration

In Exploration **2** of Activity **1,** you examined the series $S_n = 4 + 6 + 8 + \cdots + (2n + 2)$ and suggested a possible formula for it. In the following exploration, you use mathematical induction to prove that $S_n = n(n + 3)$ for all natural numbers n.

a. In Activity **1,** you showed that the following conjecture is true for $n = 1$ and $n = 2$. It also is true for some other natural numbers.

$$S_n = 4 + 6 + 8 + \cdots + (2n + 2) = n(n + 3)$$

Assume that this conjecture is true for any natural number k. Write the equation that is implied by this assumption.

b. Use the equation you wrote in Part **a** to show that if k is a natural number and $P(k)$ is true, then $P(k + 1)$ also is true.

Hint: Begin by adding the next term of the sequence, $(2(k + 1) + 2)$, to both sides of the equation. Then manipulate the right-hand side of the equation until it is equal to $(k + 1)((k + 1) + 3)$.

Discussion 2

a. How does manipulating the right-hand side of the equation in Part **b** of the exploration until it is equivalent to $(k + 1)((k + 1) + 3)$ verify that $P(k + 1)$ is true?

b. In Activity **1,** you verified that $P(1)$ is true. You also showed that if $P(1)$ is true, then $P(2)$ is true. Do these verifications, along with the steps in the exploration, constitute a proof that the conjecture is true for all natural numbers?

c. Consider the false conjecture: "The inequality $(n + 1)! > 2^{n+3}$ is true for all natural numbers n." How could this conjecture be disproved?

d. Describe the steps needed for a proof by mathematical induction.

e. How do the requirements for proof by mathematical induction guarantee that a conjecture is true for all natural numbers?

Warm-Up

1. Consider the following conjecture: $2 + 4 + 6 + \cdots + 2n = n(n + 1)$, for all natural numbers n. Complete the following steps to prove, by mathematical induction, that this conjecture is true.

a. Show that $P(1)$ is true.

b. Show that your response to Part **a** implies that $P(2)$ also is true.

c. Suppose the conjecture is true for a natural number k. Write the equation that is implied if $P(k)$ is true.

d. Write the equation that is implied if $P(k+1)$ is true.

e. Prove that if $P(k)$ is true, then $P(k+1)$ also is true. *Hint:* Manipulate the right-hand side of the equation from Part **d.**

2. Consider the conjecture below for all natural numbers n:

$$1 + 2 + 3 + \cdots + n = \frac{n(n+1)}{2}$$

Explain what is wrong with the following proof of this conjecture.

- As shown below, $P(1)$ is true:

$$S_1 = 1 = \frac{1(1+1)}{2}$$

- Given that $P(1)$ is true, $P(2)$ also is true:

$$\begin{aligned} S_2 &= S_1 + 2 \\ &= \frac{1(1+1)}{2} + 2 \\ &= 3 \\ &= \frac{2(2+1)}{2} \end{aligned}$$

- Assuming that $P(k+1)$ is true, it can be shown that $P(k)$ is true:

$$\begin{aligned} 1 + 2 + 3 + \cdots + n + (n+1) &= \frac{(n+1)((n+1)+1)}{2} \\ 1 + 2 + 3 + \cdots + n + (n+1) &= \frac{(n+1)(n+2)}{2} \\ 1 + 2 + 3 + \cdots + n + (n+1) &= \frac{n(n+1) + 2(n+1)}{2} \\ 1 + 2 + 3 + \cdots + n + (n+1) &= \frac{n(n+1)}{2} + (n+1) \\ 1 + 2 + 3 + \cdots + n &= \frac{n(n+1)}{2} \end{aligned}$$

- Therefore, by the principle of mathematical induction, the conjecture is true for all natural numbers.

Assignment

2.1 In Problem **1.4,** you examined the conjecture, "The quantity $3^n + 1$ is divisible by 2 for all natural numbers n." This can be restated as follows: "For all natural numbers n, $3^n + 1 = 2p$, where p is some integer."

a. Show that $P(1)$ is true.

b. Show that your response to Part **a** implies that $P(2)$ also is true.

c. Continue using the principle of mathematical induction to prove that the conjecture is true for all natural numbers.

2.2 The diagram below shows the first four terms of a sequence generated by combining unit squares into triangular patterns.

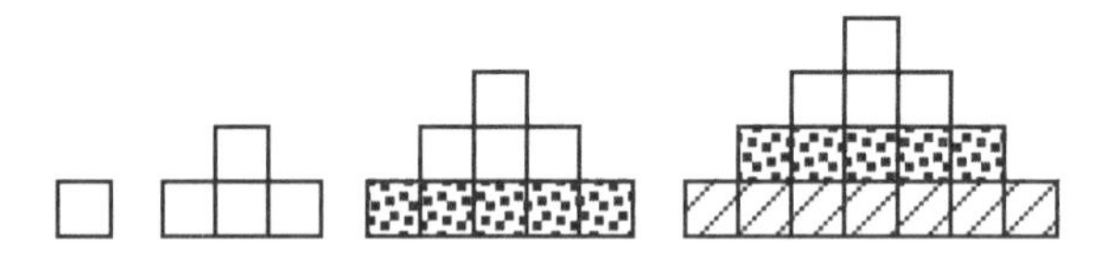

a. Make a conjecture about an explicit formula for S_n, the number of unit squares in the nth term of the sequence.

b. Use mathematical induction to prove that your conjecture is true for all natural numbers n.

2.3 Use mathematical induction to prove that the following conjecture is true for all natural numbers n.

$$\begin{bmatrix} a & 0 \\ 0 & b \end{bmatrix}^n = \begin{bmatrix} a^n & 0 \\ 0 & b^n \end{bmatrix}$$

2.4 Use mathematical induction to prove that the following conjecture is true for all natural numbers n: "3 is a factor of $n^3 + 5n + 6$."

2.5 To prove a conjecture using mathematical induction, you must prove first that the statement $P(1)$ is true. However, some conjectures might be true only for a subset of the natural numbers (for example, $n \geq 2$).

In such cases, it might be possible to prove the conjecture for a particular subset of natural numbers using a form of induction in which the first statement is not $P(1)$. After showing that the conjecture is true for some initial natural number, the conjecture is proven true for the next natural number. From there, you can generalize and prove that if $P(k)$ is true, then $P(k + 1)$ also is true.

a. Consider the following conjecture: $n! > 2^n$. This conjecture is not true for $P(1)$, because $1! \not> 2^1$.

1. Find the first value of n for which the conjecture is true by graphing the sequences $t_n = n!$ and $t_n = 2^n$ on the same coordinate system for $n \geq 1$.
2. Show that the conjecture is true for the value of n you identified in Step **1.** This is the first step of the induction process.
3. Does the conjecture appear to be true for all values of n greater than the number you identified in Step **1**?

b. The second step of the induction process is to show that $P(5)$ is true, given that $P(4)$, or $4! > 2^4$, is true. This can be done as follows:

$$(4+1)! = 5! = 5 \bullet 4! > 2 \bullet 4! > 2^1 \bullet 2^4 = 2^5$$

So, $5! > 2^5$ is true.

Use the same method to show that if $P(k)$ is true, then $P(k+1)$ also is true. This is the final step of the induction process.

* * * * *

2.6 Use mathematical induction to prove that the following conjecture is true for all natural numbers n:

$$7 + 11 + 15 + \cdots + (4n+3) = 2n^2 + 5n$$

2.7 The diagram below shows a geometric model of a sequence. In each rectangular array of dots, the length is always 1 greater than the width.

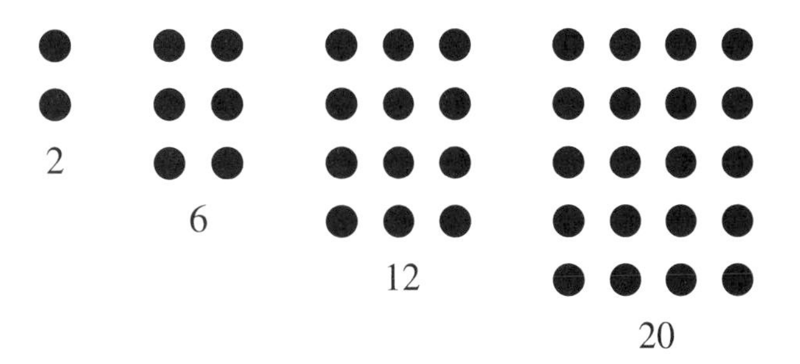

a. Determine a_n explicit formula for a_n, the number of dots in each array.

b. Use mathematical induction to prove that your formula is true for all natural numbers n.

2.8 **a.** A diagonal of a polygon connects two non-adjacent vertices. As the number of sides of a polygon increases, the number of diagonals also increases. To explore the patterns created by this situation, complete the following table.

Term No. (n)	No. of Sides in Polygon	No. of Additional Diagonals	Total No. of Diagonals (a_n)
1	3		0
2	4		
3	5		
4	6		
5	7		

b. Determine a recursive formula for a_n, the total number of diagonals.

c. Either prove or disprove the conjecture that an explicit formula for the total number of diagonals is as follows:

$$a_n = \frac{(n + 2)(n - 1)}{2}$$

Summary Assessment

1. **Concurrent lines** are two or more lines that intersect at a common point. Two angles are **supplementary** if the sum of their measures is 180°.

   a. Given n concurrent lines, how many pairs of supplementary angles are formed, if none of the angles are right angles? To identify a pattern, examine the diagram below and complete the following table.

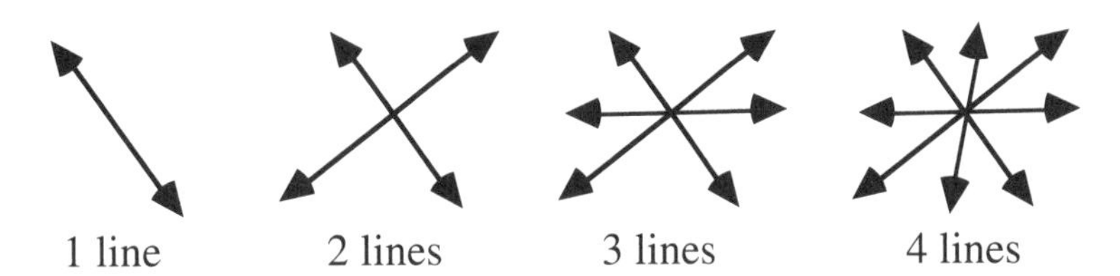

No. of Lines (n)	Additional Pairs of Supplementary Angles	Total No. of Pairs of Supplementary Angles (a_n)
1		0
2	4	4
3		
4		

   b. Describe the recursive pattern in the number of pairs of supplementary angles formed.

   c. Use the pattern described in Part **b** to find the number of pairs of supplementary angles for five concurrent lines.

   d. Write a recursive formula for a_n.

2. Prove the conjecture that the explicit formula for the number of pairs of supplementary angles for n concurrent lines is $a_n = 2n(n-1)$.

Module Summary

✷ The principle of **mathematical induction** can be described as follows:

Suppose that for any natural number n, $P(n)$ is a mathematical statement involving n. If,

- $P(1)$ is true, and
- whenever k is a natural number such that $P(k)$ is true, $P(k + 1)$ also is true

then $P(n)$ is true for all natural numbers n.

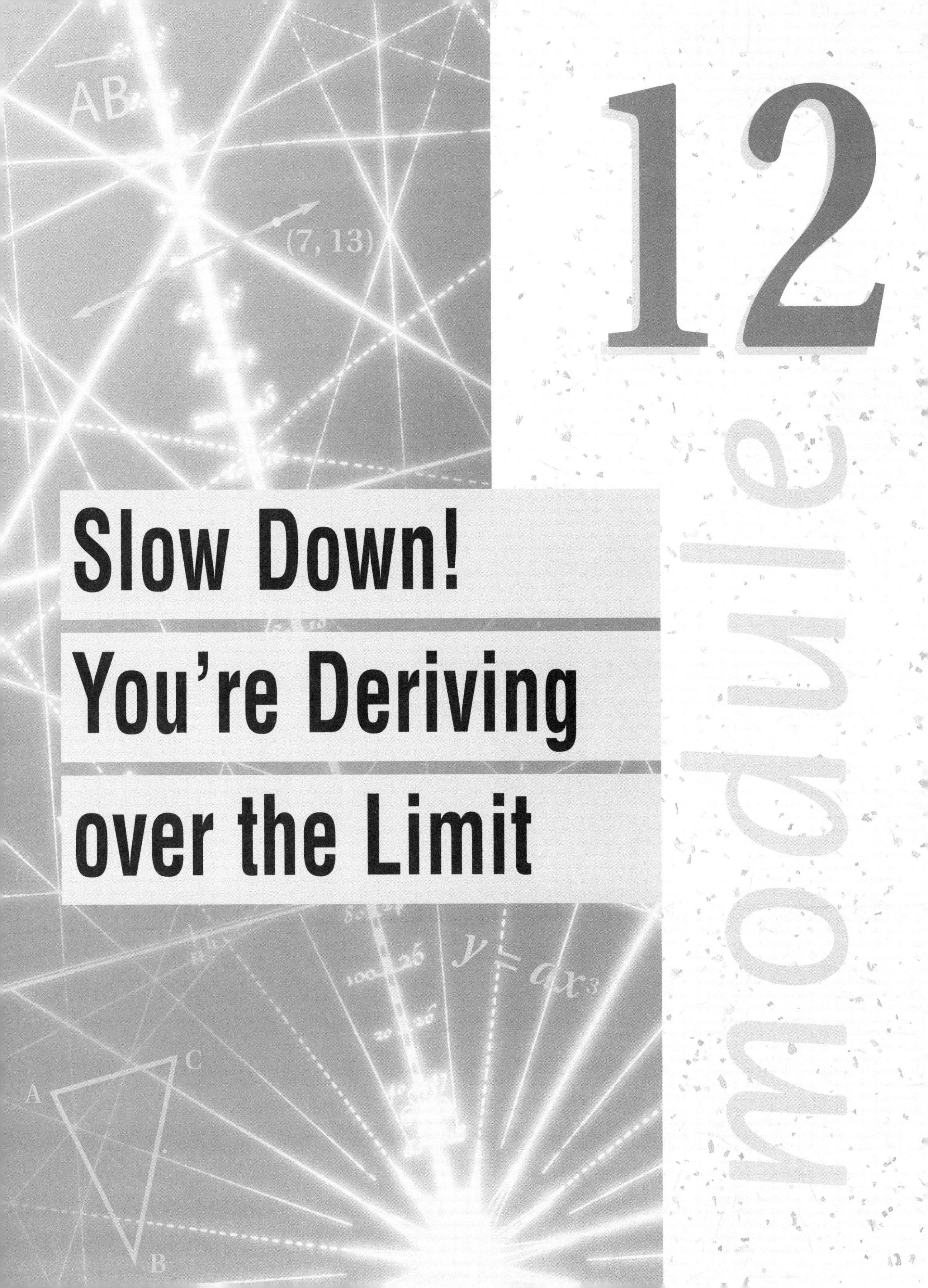

Module 12

Slow Down! You're Deriving over the Limit

Introduction

Recall that freely falling objects are acted on only by the force of gravity. Ignoring air resistance, for example, a ball dropped from some initial height is a freely falling object, as is a ball thrown with some initial velocity. In this module, you continue your exploration of this type of motion.

Discussion

a. Consider a ball dropped from an initial height of 100 m. What would a graph of the ball's height versus time look like? Explain your response.

b. 1. Recall that velocity describes an object's change in position with respect to time. After 1 sec, the ball described in Part **a** is 95.1 m from the ground. Describe the ball's average velocity during this interval.

   2. In this case, what does the sign of the velocity indicate?

c. Will the ball travel the same distance during each second of its fall? Explain your response.

ACTIVITY 1

In this activity, you collect data on the motion of a freely falling object and determine an equation that models its height with respect to time.

Exploration

a. Drop an object from an initial height of 2 m. As it falls, use a range finder and science interface device to collect data on the object's height with respect to time.

b. Create a scatterplot of the object's height versus time.

c. Determine an appropriate equation to model the data. **Note:** Save this equation, the scatterplot from Part **b,** and your data for use in Activity **2.**

d. Graph your function from Part **c** on the scatterplot from Part **b.**

e. Use your equation to predict the time required for the object to reach a height of 0 m.

f. The acceleration due to gravity is 9.8 m/sec^2 in a direction toward Earth's center. Estimate the ball's velocity at the time it hit the ground.

Discussion

a. Describe your scatterplot of the data for the falling object.

b. What is represented by the slope of a line containing any two points on the scatterplot?

c. 1. Describe the equation that you obtained in the exploration.

   2. How well does your equation appear to model the data?

d. Recall that the height of a freely falling object after t sec can be described by the following equation:

$$h(t) = -\frac{1}{2}gt^2 + v_0t + h_0$$

where g is the acceleration due to gravity, v_0 is the object's initial velocity in the vertical direction, and h_0 is the object's initial height.

1. Given this general equation, describe a function that would model the height with respect to time of a ball dropped from the same initial height as in the exploration.
2. Compare this equation to the one you obtained in the exploration.

e. Figure **12-1** shows a graph of height versus time for a ball thrown straight into the air.

1. During what time interval is the ball's velocity positive?
2. During what time interval is the ball's velocity negative?
3. What is the ball's velocity when it reaches its highest point?

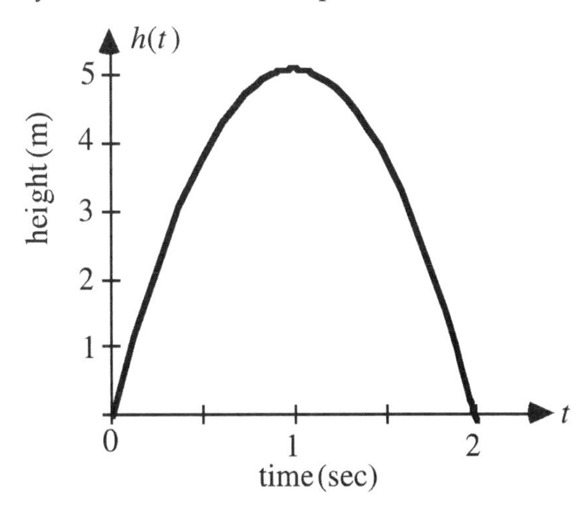

FIGURE 12-1

Graph of distance versus time.

Warm-Up

1. Consider an object propelled upward at a velocity of 49 m/sec from the top of a 98-m tower.

   a. Determine a function $h(t)$ that models the object's height with respect to time and graph it.

   b. Identify the interval for which the object's velocity is positive.

   c. Identify the interval for which the object's velocity is negative.

2. **a.** What is the greatest height reached by the object described in Problem **1**?

   b. How long will it take the object to reach this height?

   c. What is the velocity of the object when it reaches this height?

   d. How many seconds will it take the ball to return to its initial height of 98 m?

3. **a.** Describe how to solve the following equation for x: $2x^2 + 12x + 16 = 0$.

   b. What do the solutions from Part **a** represent in terms of a graph of the function $f(x) = 2x^2 + 12x + 16$?

Assignment

1.1 A ball dropped from the top of a tower strikes the ground after 3 sec.

   a. How tall is the tower?

   b. Determine an equation that describes the ball's height with respect to time.

1.2 **a.** If an object is propelled straight up from the ground with an initial velocity of 34.3 m/sec, how long will it remain in the air?

   b. What will the object's velocity be just before it strikes the ground?

   c. If a similar object remained in the air for 6 sec, what was its initial velocity?

1.3 Consider a ball thrown straight up from the ground with a velocity of 49 m/sec.

   a. Write an equation that models the ball's height with respect to time.

   b. Determine how long the ball will remain in the air.

   c. Determine the height of the ball at the end of each second of its flight.

d. Determine the ball's average velocity during each 2-sec interval of its flight. Record these values in a table like the one shown below.

Interval (sec)	Average Velocity
[0, 2)	
[2, 4)	
⋮	

e. What do the values in the table from Part **d** indicate about the ball's flight?

1.4 Consider a wind-up toy moving along a linear track. The graph below shows its displacement over time. In this case, a positive displacement indicates movement to the right of the starting position. Assume that the toy's initial velocity is 0 m/sec.

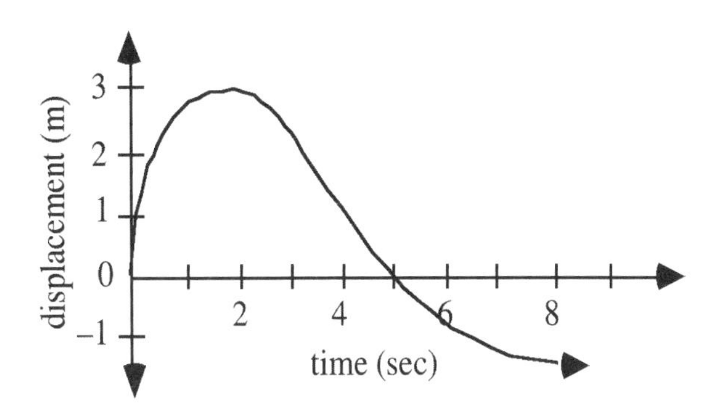

a. During what time interval is the toy's velocity positive? During what interval is its velocity negative? Explain your response.

b. What is the toy's average velocity during the first 2 sec?

c. When did the toy change direction? Describe how this change is indicated on the graph.

d. When did the toy return to its starting position? Describe how this is indicated on the graph.

e. During which 1-sec interval does the magnitude of the toy's velocity appear to be the greatest? How is this indicated on the graph?

f. Describe the toy's motion from the time it started moving until the time it stopped.

* * * * *

1.5 The Empire State Building in New York City is approximately 381 m high. Consider the motion of an object dropped from the top of this building.

a. Write an equation that models the height of the object over time.

b. Determine the time required for the object to reach the ground.

c. Estimate the object's velocity just before it reaches the ground.

d. Because of the danger to pedestrians, it is illegal to drop objects from tall buildings. Write a statement explaining how such laws protect the public.

1.6 The height of a ball in meters after t seconds can be modeled by the following equation: $h(t) = 24.5 + 19.6t - 4.9t^2$.

a. From what height was the ball thrown?

b. What initial velocity was given to the ball?

c. How long was the ball in the air?

d. What was the maximum height reached by the ball?

e. What was the ball's velocity just before it struck the ground?

In Activity **1**, you investigated the change in position with respect to time for a falling object, and its average velocity over particular intervals of time. In this activity, you examine one method for approximating an object's velocity at any given instant. This is known as **instantaneous velocity.**

Exploration

a. Examine your scatterplot of the falling-ball data from Activity **1.** Select a subset of the data that appears to accurately describe the motion of the ball for approximately 0.5 sec. Identify a data point A so that there are an equal number of data points before and after A.

b. One way to estimate the ball's instantaneous velocity at point A is to examine the average velocities for intervals that include A.

1. Using your chosen subset of data, identify the data point P that is farthest to the left of A.
2. Draw the line that contains A and P. Your graph should now resemble the one shown in Figure **12-2** below.

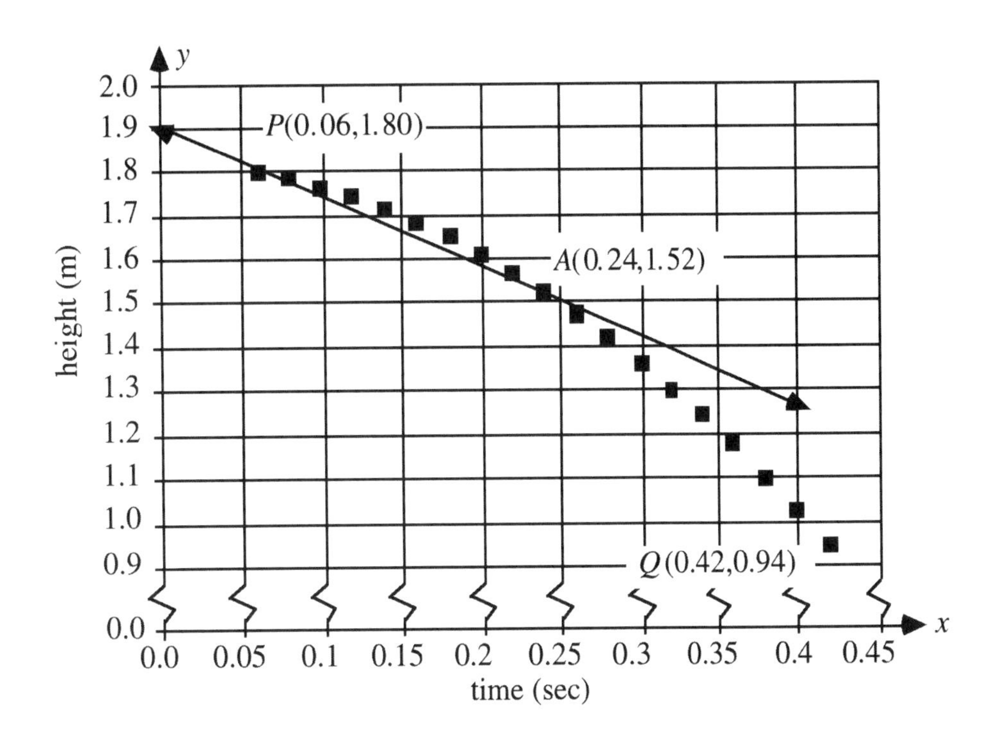

FIGURE 12-2 **Graph of sample falling-ball data.**

3. Calculate the difference d in the x-coordinates of this pair of points. For A and P in Figure **12-2,** for example, this value is $0.24 - 0.06 = 0.18$ sec.
4. Determine the slope of the line from Step **2** and describe what this value represents in terms of the falling ball.

c. Draw a line through A and a data point Q that is d sec to the right on the scatterplot. In Figure **12-2,** for example, this is the point (0.42,0.94). Determine the slope of this line and describe what its value represents in terms of the falling ball.

Record your findings from Parts **b** and **c** in a table with headings like those in Table **12-1.** In this case, $(x - d)$ is the x-coordinate of a point P to the left of A, while $(x + d)$ is the x-coordinate of a point Q to the right of A. (The cells in the first row of Table **12-1** show the appropriate sample values from Figure **12-2.**)

TABLE 12-1 ■ *Approximating Velocity at Point A(x,y)*

Value of d	$(x - d)$	y-coord. of P	Slope of $\overleftrightarrow{PA}$	$(x + d)$	y-coord. of Q	Slope of $\overleftrightarrow{AQ}$
0.18	0.06	1.80	–1.56	0.42	0.94	–3.22
0.16						
0.14						
⋮						
0.04						
0.02						

d. What is the relationship among the slope of $\overleftrightarrow{PA}$, the slope of $\overleftrightarrow{AQ}$ and the instantaneous velocity of the ball at A? Explain your response.

e. Repeat Parts **b** and **c,** using a pair of points P and Q that are closer to A. Record your results in Table **12-1.**

f. Continue the process described in Parts **b** and **c** for each successive pair of points, until you have used the pair closest to A.

g. Use your results in Parts **b–f** to estimate the ball's instantaneous velocity at point A.

Discussion

a. The slope of the line that passes through the first and last data points in Figure **12-2** is:

$$m = \frac{1.80 - 0.94}{0.06 - 0.42} \approx -2.39$$

Describe what this value represents in terms of the falling ball.

b. Describe how you approximated the instantaneous velocity of the falling ball at point A.

c. In Activity **1,** you used a regression equation to model the data for the falling ball. Figure **12-3** shows the graph of a function, $f(x) = -4.65x^2 - 0.14x + 1.82$, that models the scatterplot in Figure **12-2.**

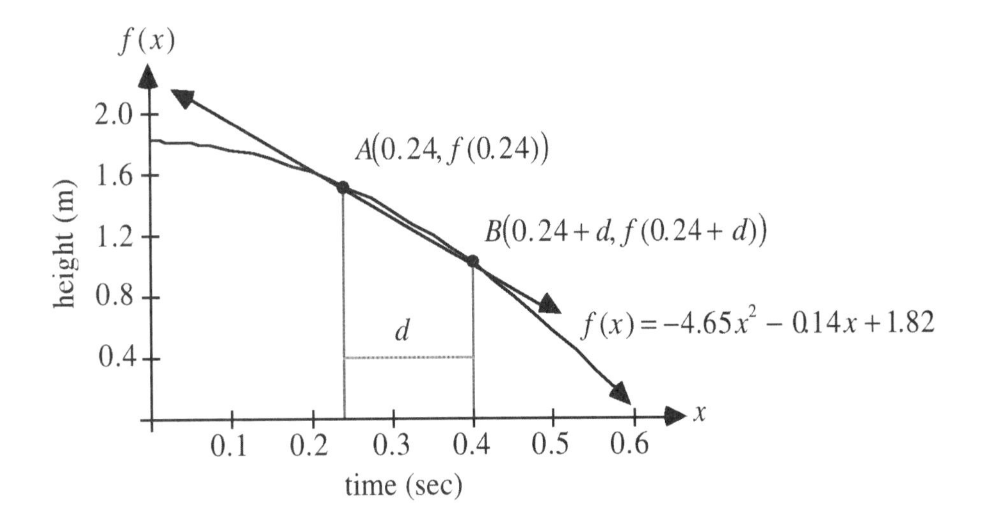

FIGURE 12-3 **Regression equation for sample data.**

1. A **secant** is a line that intersects a curve in at least two points. Describe how a secant such as $\overleftrightarrow{AB}$ in Figure **12-3** can be used to approximate the velocity of the falling ball at 0.24 sec.

2. In Figure **12-3,** the coordinates of B are given in terms of d and the coordinates of A. How does the value of d affect the estimate of instantaneous velocity?

3. Recall that a **tangent** to a conic is a line in the plane of the conic that intersects the curve at exactly one point and contains no points in the interior.

   As d approaches 0, the slope of $\overleftrightarrow{AB}$ approaches the slope of the line tangent to the parabola at point A. What does the slope of the line tangent to the parabola at A represent?

d. Table **12-2** on the next page lists the slopes of some secant lines through A (0.24,1.52) on the curve in Figure **12-3.** The values in the columns labeled "Slope" were calculated using the following formulas, where $x = 0.24$:

$$\frac{f(x-d)-1.52}{(x-d)-0.24} \quad \text{and} \quad \frac{f(x+d)-1.52}{(x+d)-0.24}$$

Describe how you could use this table to approximate the ball's instantaneous velocity at 0.24 sec.

TABLE 12-2 ■ *Slopes of Secant Lines through A*

d	$(x - d)$	$f(x - d)$	Slope	$(x + d)$	$f(x + d)$	Slope
0.18	0.06	1.798	–1.54	0.42	0.942	–3.21
0.16	0.08	1.781	–1.63	0.40	1.023	–3.11
0.14	0.10	1.762	–1.73	0.38	1.097	–3.02
0.12	0.12	1.739	–1.83	0.36	1.168	–2.93
0.10	0.14	1.711	–1.91	0.34	1.236	–2.84
0.08	0.16	1.682	–2.03	0.32	1.300	–2.75
0.06	0.18	1.646	–2.10	0.30	1.360	–2.67
0.04	0.20	1.608	–2.20	0.28	1.417	–2.58
0.02	0.22	1.566	–2.30	0.26	1.471	–2.45

e. What information would allow you to obtain a better approximation of the velocity of the ball at 0.24 sec? Explain your response.

f. Is it possible for a moving object to have a velocity of 0? Explain your response.

Warm-Up

1. Consider a projectile shot upward with an initial velocity of 98 m/sec from a height of 196 m above the ground.

   a. Write a function $h(t)$ that models the height of the projectile with respect to time.

   b. Graph the function in Part **a.**

2. Find the average velocity of the projectile in Problem **1** during each of the following intervals:

   a. from $t = 0$ sec to $t = 2$ sec

   b. from $t = 18$ sec to $t = 20$ sec

   c. from $t = 2$ sec to $t = 18$ sec

3. The total distance traveled by the projectile from $t = 2$ sec to $t = 18$ sec is approximately 628 m. Half of this distance is in the direction away from Earth's surface, while the other half is directed towards Earth's surface.

   Explain why the average velocity for this interval cannot be calculated as shown below:

$$\frac{628 \text{ m}}{16 \text{ sec}} = 39.25 \text{ m/sec}$$

4. Approximate the instantaneous velocity of the projectile in Problem **1** at $t = 16$ sec.

Assignment

2.1 A group of students obtained the following data during a ball-drop experiment.

Time (sec)	Height (m)
0.22	1.564
0.23	1.542
0.24	1.519
0.25	1.494
0.26	1.469
0.27	1.443
0.28	1.416

a. Determine the quadratic regression equation that models the data above and create a graph of this equation.

b. Choose an instant in time x. Use the quadratic regression equation to predict the ball's height y at that time. Plot this point (x,y) on the graph from Part **a.**

c. Use a spreadsheet with headings like those in Table **12-2** to approximate the ball's instantaneous velocity at this point.

d. Describe what the instantaneous velocity represents in terms of the line tangent to the parabola at this point.

2.2 **a.** Select three more instants in time on the graph of the regression equation from Problem **2.1.** Approximate the ball's instantaneous velocities at these times and record these values, along with the one from Problem **2.1c,** in a table like the one below.

Time (sec)	Velocity (m/sec)

b. Use your results in Part **a** to create a scatterplot of velocity versus time.

c. Describe any trends you observe in the scatterplot and determine an appropriate model for the data.

d. What does your model in Part **c** indicate about the ball's change in velocity with respect to time?

2.3 The diagram below shows an experiment designed to measure the acceleration of a ball rolling down a ramp.

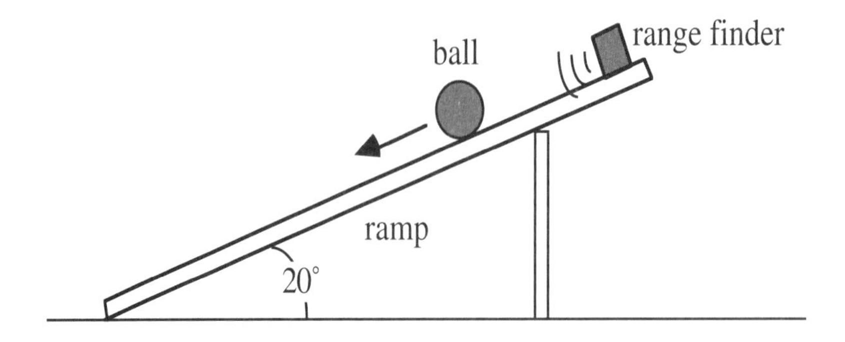

The following table shows some of the data collected in this experiment.

Time (sec)	Distance (m)	Time (sec)	Distance (m)
0.0	0.443	1.0	2.607
0.1	0.571	1.1	2.931
0.2	0.718	1.2	3.276
0.3	0.885	1.3	3.640
0.4	1.072	1.4	4.024
0.5	1.279	1.5	4.427
0.6	1.505	1.6	4.850
0.7	1.751	1.7	5.293
0.8	2.016	1.8	5.755
0.9	2.302	1.9	6.238

a. Predict the shape of a scatterplot of this data.

b. Create a scatterplot of the data and compare its shape with your prediction.

c. Determine an appropriate regression model for the data and graph it on the scatterplot from Part **b.**

d. Use your model to determine the distance the ball has traveled after 1 sec, 2 sec, 3 sec, and 4 sec. Approximate the ball's instantaneous velocity at each of these points.

e. Use your results in Part **d** to create a scatterplot of velocity versus time.

f. Determine an appropriate model for the scatterplot in Part **e.**

g. What does your model in Part **f** indicate about the ball's change in velocity with respect to time?

* * * * *

2.4 As a train sounding its whistle approaches and passes an observer, the pitch of the sound changes. (This is known as the Doppler effect.)

a. The following diagram shows the locations of the observer and the train at the moment when the train was first heard ($t = 0$ sec). What is the distance d between the observer and the train at this time?

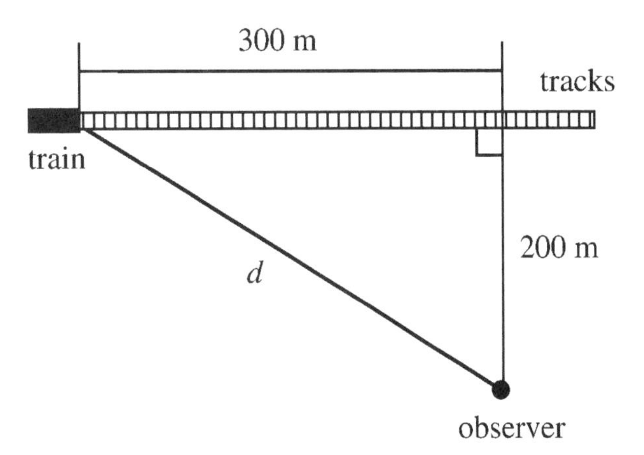

b. The train is traveling at a constant velocity of 30 m/sec. When will it be closest to the observer?

c. Write an equation that describes the distance from the train to the observer with respect to time.

d. Do you believe that the rate at which the distance between the observer and the train changes is constant? Explain your response.

e. Graph the equation from Part **c** and explain whether or not the graph confirms your response to Part **d.**

f. Approximate the instantaneous rate of change in the distance from the observer to the train at $t = 5$ sec and at $t = 10$ sec.

ACTIVITY 3

In the previous activity, you used the average velocity over smaller and smaller intervals to approximate instantaneous velocity. In this activity, you investigate a method of determining a precise rate of change at any given instant.

Exploration

Figure **12-4** shows a portion of a graph of a semicircle in the first quadrant, a point on the semicircle $(x, f(x))$, and two secant lines u and t. As described in Activity **2,** the slope of the line tangent to the conic at $(x, f(x))$ can be approximated using the slope of u or t. Better approximations of the slope are found for values of h near 0.

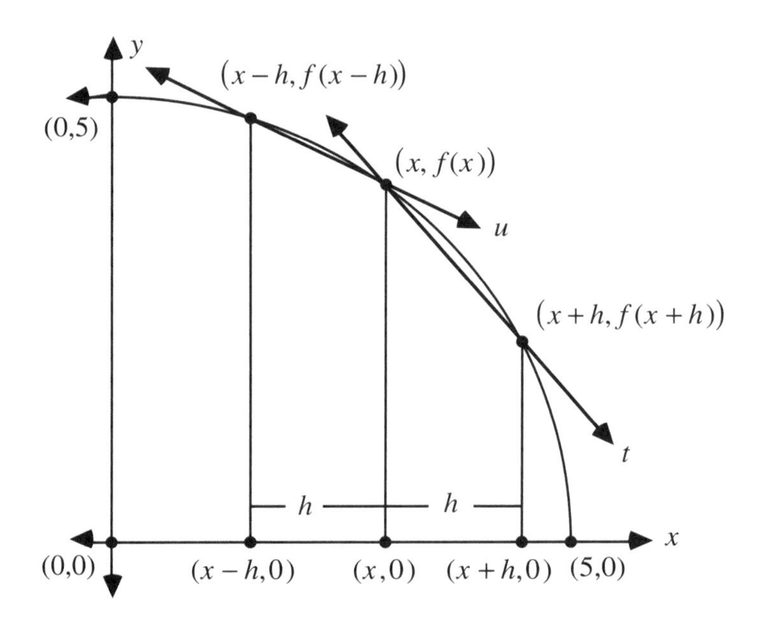

FIGURE 12-4 **Approximating the slope of a tangent line.**

a. 1. Construct a circle with center at the origin of a two-dimensional coordinate system and a radius of 5 units.

   2. As shown in Figure **12-4,** construct a point $(x, f(x))$ on the circle. Record its coordinates.

   3. Construct a line perpendicular to the x-axis through $(x, f(x))$. Label the point of intersection with the axis $(x,0)$.

b. 1. Construct a moveable point $(x + h, 0)$ on the x-axis between $(x,0)$ and $(5,0)$.

   2. Construct the point $(x - h, 0)$ by reflecting the point $(x + h, 0)$ in the line created in Part **a.** (This guarantees that the distance from $(x + h, 0)$ and $(x - h, 0)$ to $(x,0)$ will be the same, h units.)

c. 1. The point $(x + h, f(x + h))$ is the intersection of the circle with the line perpendicular to the x-axis passing through $(x + h, 0)$. Construct the point $(x + h, f(x + h))$.

   2. The point $(x - h, f(x - h))$ is the intersection of the circle with the line perpendicular to the x-axis passing through $(x - h, 0)$. Construct the point $(x - h, f(x - h))$.

d. 1. Construct two secant lines: one passing through $(x, f(x))$ and $(x + h, f(x + h))$, the other through $(x, f(x))$ and $(x - h, f(x - h))$.

   2. Measure and record the slopes of the two secants.

e. To decrease the size of h, move the point $(x + h, 0)$ toward the point $(x,0)$. As you move $(x + h, 0)$, the point $(x - h, 0)$ should move the same distance towards $(x,0)$.

   As the points move closer together, the secant lines approach the tangent line through the point $(x, f(x))$. Observe the measures of the slopes of the secant lines as h approaches 0.

   Use your construction to approximate the slope of the line tangent to the circle at $(x, f(x))$.

f. Use the construction to approximate the slopes of the lines tangent to three other points on the circle.

Discussion

a. If $f(x)$ represents distance and x represents time, how is the slope of a secant line related to average velocity?

mathematics note

Figure **12-5** shows a secant line passing through two points on the graph of a function $f(x)$. Note that h is depicted as a positive real number.

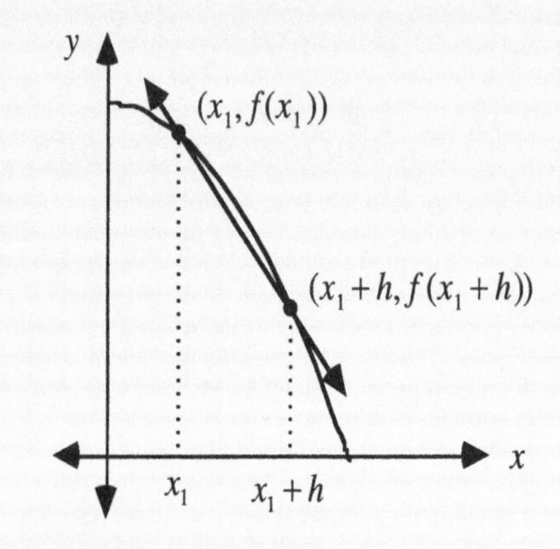

FIGURE 12-5 A secant to a curve.

The slope of the secant line can be expressed as follows:

$$\frac{f(x_1 + h) - f(x_1)}{h}$$

By assigning a value to h that is close to 0, the point with coordinates $(x_1 + h, f(x_1 + h))$ can be moved very close to the point $(x_1, f(x_1))$. When this occurs, the slope of the secant line is a good approximation of the slope of a tangent line at $(x_1, f(x_1))$. A better approximation can be obtained by assigning h a value even closer to 0. This process can be repeated indefinitely and provides the basis for the following definition.

The **tangent** to a curve at $(x, f(x))$ is defined as the line with the following slope:

$$\lim_{h \to 0} \frac{f(x + h) - f(x)}{h}$$

provided that this limit exists.

If this limit exists, it is the **derivative** of the function $f(x)$ at x and represents the **slope of the curve** at the point $(x, f(x))$. The derivative of f at x is denoted by $f'(x)$.

For example, consider an object dropped from a height of 10 m. The height of the object with respect to time is described by the function $f(t) = -4.9t^2 + 10$, where t represents time in seconds. In this case, the slope of the curve at the point $(t, f(t))$ represents the instantaneous velocity at t.

To find the function that describes instantaneous velocity with respect to time, you can determine the derivative $f'(t)$ as follows:

$$f'(t) = \lim_{h \to 0}\left(\frac{f(t+h) - f(t)}{h}\right)$$

$$= \lim_{h \to 0}\left(\frac{-4.9(t+ h)^2 + 10 - (4.9t^2 \quad 10)}{h}\right)$$

$$= \lim_{h \to 0}\left(\frac{-4.9t^2 - 9.8ht \quad 4.9h^2 \quad 10 \quad 4.9t^2 \quad 10}{h}\right)$$

$$= \lim_{h \to 0}\left(\frac{-9.8ht - 4.9h^2}{h}\right)$$

$$= \lim_{h \to 0}\left(\frac{h(-9.8t - 4.9h)}{h}\right)$$

$$= \lim_{h \to 0}(-9.8t - 4.9h)$$

$$= -9.8t$$

b. How is the slope of a curve at a given point related to the slope of the tangent at that point?

c. Figure **12-6** shows a third-degree polynomial curve.

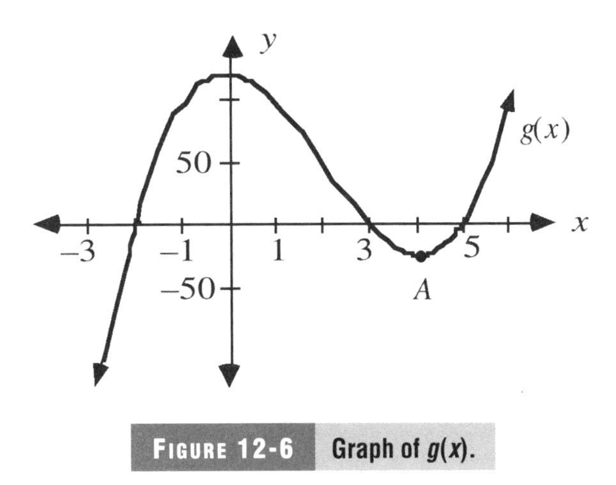

FIGURE 12-6 **Graph of $g(x)$.**

1. Describe the line tangent to this curve at point A.
2. Does this line intersect the curve at any other points? If so, does this conflict with the definition of a tangent to a curve given in the previous mathematics note?

d. Figures **12-7–12-9** show the graphs of three different functions for which no derivative exists at a point P. In each graph, the points $(x - h, f(x - h))$ and $(x + h, f(x + h))$ are moving closer and closer to P. In each case, use the graph to explain why the derivative at P does not exist.

1. In Figure **12-7** below, P is located at the "peak" of the function.

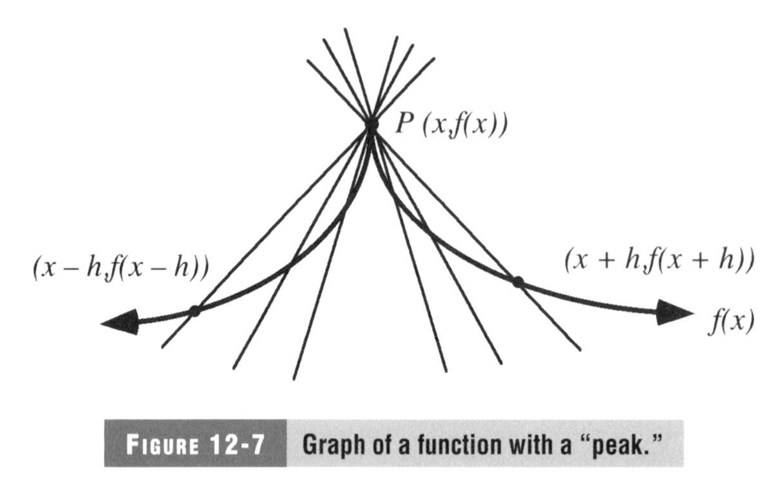

FIGURE 12-7 Graph of a function with a "peak."

2. In Figure **12-8** below, P is located at a "corner" of the function.

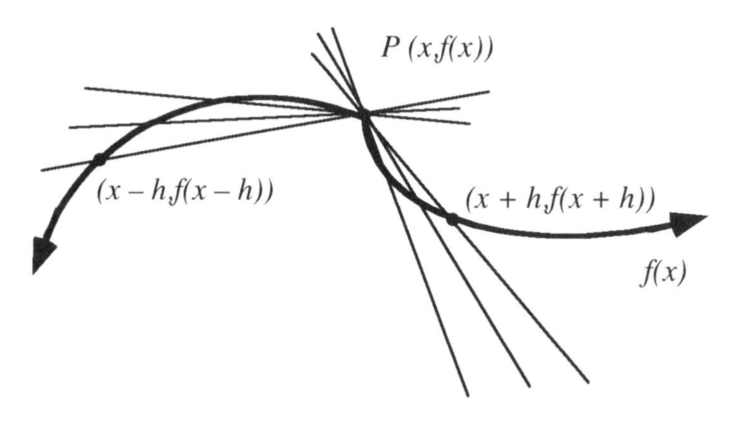

FIGURE 12-8 Graph of a function with a "corner."

3. In Figure **12-9** below, P is located at a "break" in the function.

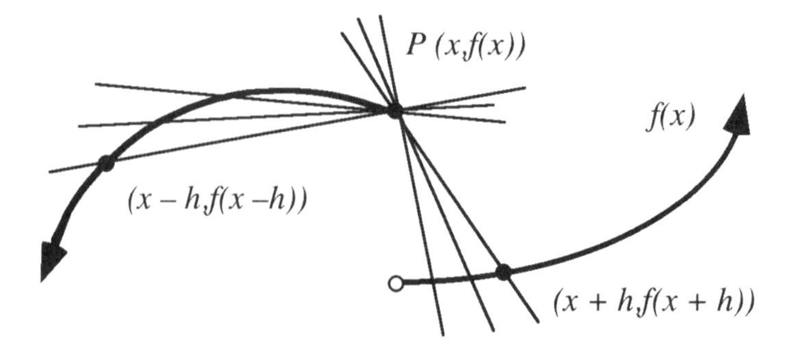

FIGURE 12-9 Graph of a function with a "break."

e. On Earth, the height of a freely falling object after t sec can be described by the equation $h(t) = -4.9t^2 + v_0 t + h_0$, where v_0 is the object's initial velocity in the vertical direction, and h_0 is the object's initial height.

   In this situation, what does the derivative $h'(t) = -9.8t + v_0$ represent?

f. Consider the linear function $f(x) = -2x + 3$. Explain why $f'(x) = -2$.

g. Figure **12-10** shows a graph of height versus time for an object propelled upward with an initial velocity of 9.8 m/sec from a height of 196 m. Explain why $h'(t) = 0$ when the object reaches its highest point.

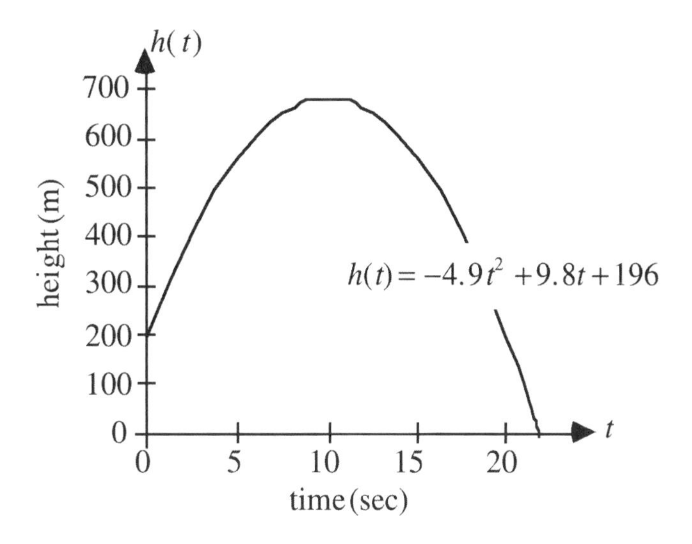

FIGURE 12-10 Graph of $h(t) = -4.9t^2 + 9.8t + 196$.

Warm-Up

1. Evaluate the following expression:

$$\lim_{h \to 0}\left(\frac{2h(5 + h)}{h}\right)$$

2. **a.** Use the definition given in the previous mathematics note to find the derivative of the linear equation $f(x) = 3x - 5$.

   b. How is the derivative of $f(x)$ related to the slope of the line?

   c. Compare the degree of $f(x)$ with the degree of its derivative $f'(x)$.

3. **a.** Use the definition given in the previous mathematics note to find the derivative of $f(x) = x^2$.

   b. Use a symbolic manipulator to verify your response to Part **a.**

   c. Find the slope of the graph of $f(x)$ at $x = -3$ and at $x = 15$.

   d. For what value of x is the slope of the graph 0? What is the significance of the point that corresponds to this value of x?

Assignment

3.1 The regression equation $h(t) = -4.65t^2 - 0.14t + 1.82$ was used to model data collected in a ball-drop experiment.

a. Find its derivative $h'(t)$.

b. Graph $h(t)$ and $h'(t)$ on the same coordinate system.

c. Describe what the coordinates of corresponding points on each graph represent in terms of the falling ball.

d. Compare the degree of $h(t)$ to the degree of its derivative $h'(t)$.

3.2 Consider a quadratic function whose derivative is $f'(x) = 2x - 7$.

a. For what value of x does the slope of the graph of $f(x)$ equal 0?

b. Over what interval are the values of $f(x)$ increasing?

c. Over what interval are the values of $f(x)$ decreasing?

3.3 **a.** The graph of a semicircle with center at the origin and radius 5 is defined by the function $f(x) = \sqrt{25 - x^2}$. Use technology to find the derivative of this function.

b. Evaluate the derivative at $x = 1.5$, $x = 2.5$, and $x = 3.5$.

c. Recall that a radius of a circle is perpendicular to the tangent at the point of tangency. On a coordinate plane, two lines are perpendicular if the product of their slopes is –1.

Use these facts to demonstrate that the derivative is the slope of the tangent at the three points described in Part **b.**

3.4 **a.** Write a function $f(r)$ that describes the volume of a cylinder in terms of the radius r when its height is twice the radius.

b. Graph the function found in Part **a.**

c. What does $f'(r)$ represent?

3.5 Consider the general linear equation $f(x) = mx + b$.

a. Use the definition of a derivative to find $f'(x)$.

b. What is the mathematical meaning of $f'(x)$ for a linear equation?

* * * * *

3.6 The following graph models the number of fruit flies in a laboratory population over time.

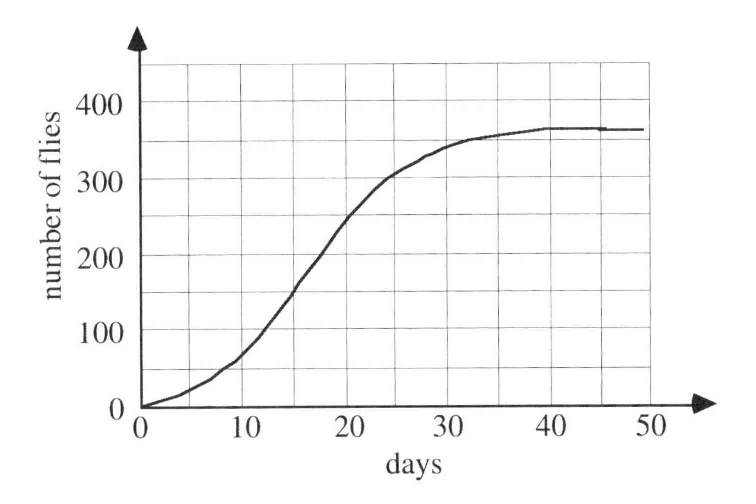

a. Determine the average rate of change in the fruit fly population from day 15 to day 35.

b. Determine the instantaneous rate of change in the population on day 25.

3.7 Consider the following graph of the function $f(x) = 0.2x^5 - 5x^3 + 5x^2 + 24x$.

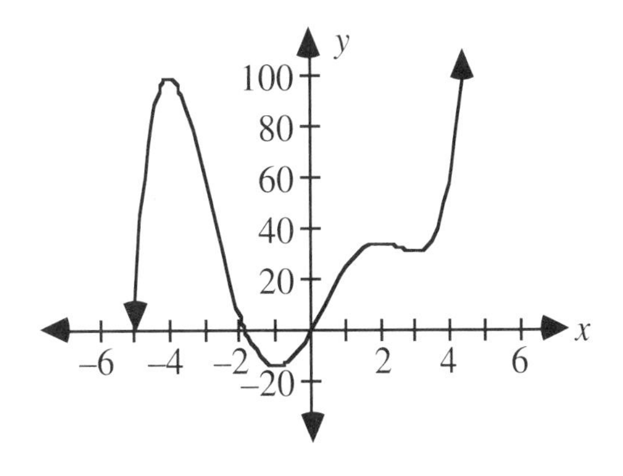

a. Describe the intervals on the graph where the slopes of the tangents to the curve are:

1. positive 2. negative.

b. Use the intervals you described in Part **a** to predict the points for which the derivative of the function is 0.

c. Use technology to determine the derivative of the function, then test your predictions from Part **b.**

d. Describe the significance of the points where the slope of the tangent to the curve is 0 in terms of the graph of the function.

Summary Assessment

Understanding rates of change is important in business and economics. To most companies, for example, the bottom line means profit. The relationship between profit (P), sales or revenue (R), and costs (C) can be described by the equation $P = R - C$. For manufacturers, these quantities can be described by functions in terms of the number of units (x) produced and sold.

The derivative of a profit function determines the instantaneous rate of change in the profit for a given number of units. This is known as *marginal profit*. Similarly, the derivative of a cost function determines marginal cost, the instantaneous rate of change in the cost for a given number of units. In the same manner, the derivative of the revenue function determines the marginal revenue.

1. Consider a company that makes only one product. The cost of producing x of these items can be described by the function $C(x) = x^2 + \$80{,}000$ for $x > 0$.
   a. The company sells each item it produces for \$750. Write an expression for R in terms of x.
   b. Given that $P = R - C$, write an expression for P in terms of x.
2. a. Graph $P(x)$, $R(x)$, and $C(x)$ on the same coordinate system.
   b. Explain what the graphs show about the relationship between profit, revenue, and cost for the company.
3. Determine the equations for the marginal profit, the marginal revenue, and the marginal cost.
4. Because the derivative of a cost function for a particular x is the instantaneous rate of change in the cost, the marginal cost approximates the additional cost of producing one more item ($x + 1$). If the company already has produced 200 items, what is the additional cost of producing the 201st item?
5. Determine the number of items for which the company will receive the maximum profit. Compare the marginal revenue and marginal cost for this number of items.
6. Imagine that you are a business consultant. How many items would you advise the company to produce? Explain your response.

Module Summary

- A **secant** is a line that intersects a curve in at least two points.
- The **tangent** to a curve at $(x, f(x))$ is defined as the line with the following slope:

$$\lim_{h \to 0} \frac{f(x+h) - f(x)}{h}$$

  provided that this limit exists.
- The **derivative** of a function at the point $(x, f(x))$, denoted by $f'(x)$, is

$$\lim_{h \to 0} \frac{f(x+h) - f(x)}{h}$$

  This value is the slope of the tangent line to the function at $(x, f(x))$ and represents the instantaneous rate of change in the function with respect to x.

module 13

Mathematics in Motion

Introduction

The forest is on fire. Crews on the ground are battling the blaze, but they need more equipment. The dispatcher orders a plane to deliver a crate of supplies.

The crate is designed to be dropped without a parachute. As the plane flies toward the target zone, its crew must decide when to drop the crate. To do this, however, they must be able to predict the path of the falling crate. In this module, you use parametric equations to explore this and other types of motion.

Discussion 1

a. 1. What factors influence the path of a crate during its fall?

   2. Describe the effect of each of these factors on the crate's path.

b. What do you think the path of a falling crate will look like?

c. Should the crew drop the crates when the plane is directly over the target area? Explain your response.

Exploration

In the following exploration, you investigate the motion of two falling objects: one dropped straight down, and one projected horizontally. Both objects begin their fall from the same height.

a. 1. Fold an index card over a flexible meterstick or ruler. Secure the card to the meterstick with a binder clip.

   2. Fold the index card to form a platform on each side of the meterstick, parallel to the ground, as shown in Figure **13-1.**

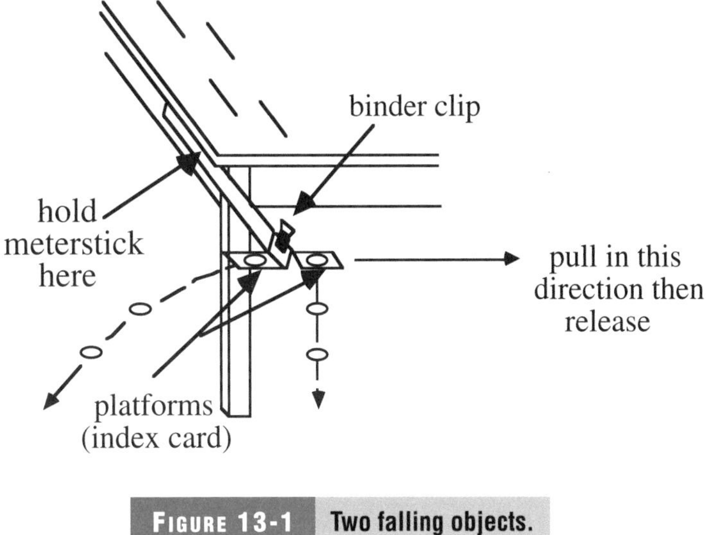

FIGURE 13-1 **Two falling objects.**

b. 1. Hold the opposite end of the meterstick against the side of a table.

   2. Place a dense object, such as a coin, on each platform. (Using dense objects lessens the effects of air resistance.)

   3. Measure and record the height of the objects from the floor.

   4. Pull the free end of the meterstick in the direction indicated in Figure **13-1,** then release it.

   5. Observe the path of each object, and note when each hits the floor. Record your observations, including a sketch of each path.

c. Repeat Part **b** two or three times, varying the amount of tension on the meterstick.

d. Repeat Parts **b** and **c** with two dense objects that are not alike.

Discussion 2

a. Compare the paths of the two like objects in Part **b** of the exploration.

b. Did both objects fall from the same height?

c. Compare the time required for the two objects to reach the floor.

d. Does the time required for an object to reach the ground appear to be affected by its path?

e. How did your observations change when using two unlike objects?

f. If a feather and a coin are dropped from a height of 10 m, would you expect them to reach the floor at the same time? Explain your response.

science note

One of Galileo Galilei's (1564–1642) more famous accomplishments is his description of the motion of falling objects. While first investigating free fall, he is said to have simultaneously dropped a 10-kg cannonball and a 1-kg stone off the Leaning Tower of Pisa. He discovered that the objects hit the ground at approximately the same time.

About 75 years later, Isaac Newton (1642–1727) developed three laws of motion. Using his own second law of motion and the laws of planetary motion developed by Johannes Kepler (1571–1630), Newton proved that, in the absence of air resistance, any two objects dropped from the same height hit the ground at exactly the same time.

ACTIVITY 1

In the introduction, you investigated the paths of freely falling objects. In this activity, you model these paths with parametric equations.

Exploration

Consider two freely falling objects. One is dropped straight down from a height of 10 m. At the same instant, the other is projected horizontally from the same initial height.

a. The graph in Figure **13-2** shows the position of each object at intervals of 0.2 sec. Use the graph to approximate ordered pairs (x,y) for these positions, where x represents the horizontal distance and y represents the vertical distance.

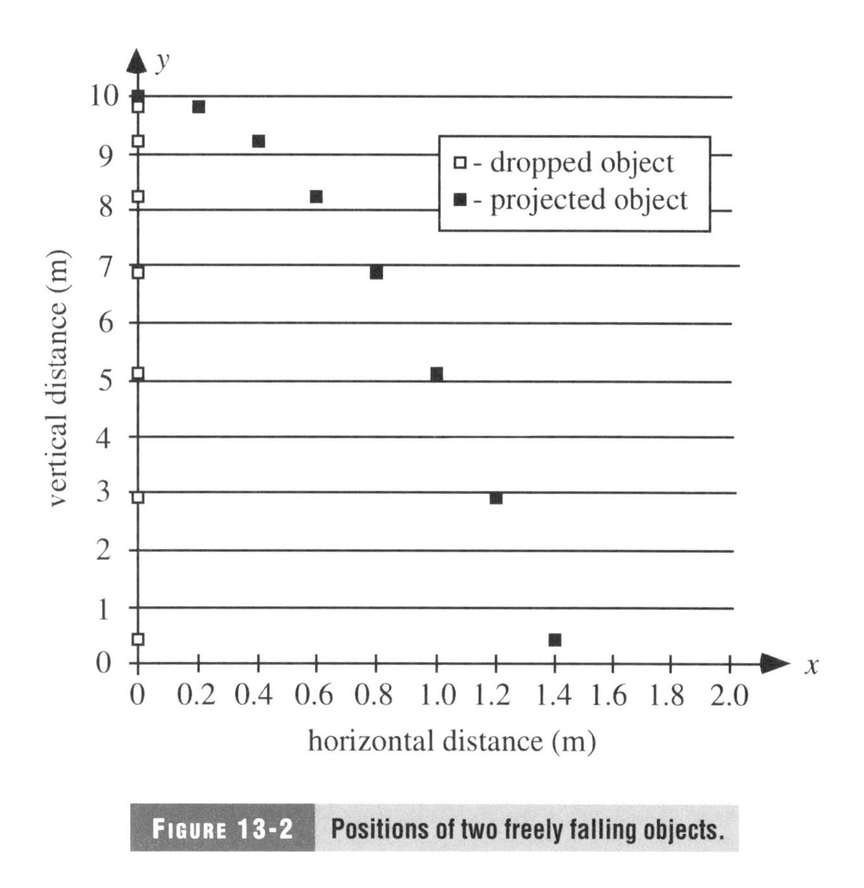

FIGURE 13-2 Positions of two freely falling objects.

b. Record the values from Part **a,** along with the corresponding times, in a spreadsheet with headings like those in Table **13-1.**

TABLE 13-1 ■ *Positions of Objects Over Time*

	Object Dropped from Rest (□)		Object Projected Horizontally (■)	
Time (sec)	Horizontal Distance (m)	Vertical Distance (m)	Horizontal Distance (m)	Vertical Distance (m)
0.0				
0.2				
⋮				
1.4				

c. 1. Calculate the change in horizontal position between consecutive points for each falling object.

   2. The average velocity of an object can be calculated as follows:

$$\text{average velocity} = \frac{\text{change in position}}{\text{change in time}}$$

   Determine the average horizontal velocity (v_x) between consecutive points for each object.

   3. Write a function $x(t)$ that describes each object's horizontal position with respect to time t.

d. 1. Calculate the change in vertical position between consecutive points for each falling object.

   2. Determine the average vertical velocity between consecutive points for each object. Record these values in a spreadsheet with headings like those in Table **13-2** below.

TABLE 13-2 ■ *Vertical Velocity of Objects Over Time*

Time Interval (sec)	Object Dropped from Rest (m/sec)	Object Projected Horizontally (m/sec)
[0, 0.2)		
[0.2, 0.4)		
⋮		
[1.2, 1.4)		

e. **Acceleration** describes an object's change in velocity per unit time. The average acceleration of an object can be calculated as follows:

$$\text{average acceleration} = \frac{\text{change in velocity}}{\text{change in time}}$$

Use the spreadsheet to calculate the average vertical acceleration between consecutive points for each object.

f. The acceleration due to gravity near Earth's surface is approximately 9.8 m/sec^2 in a direction toward Earth's center. Compare the average acceleration you determined in Part **e** to this value.

g. When a freely falling object has no initial velocity in the vertical direction, its height after t sec can be described by the following function, where g is the acceleration due to gravity and h_0 is the initial height:

$$y(t) = -\frac{1}{2}gt^2 + h_0$$

1. Write a function $y(t)$ that describes the vertical position of each object in Figure **13-2** with respect to time t. Recall that the initial height for both objects was 10 m.

2. Check your equations by substituting 0.2, 0.8, and 1.2 for t and comparing the resulting values of $y(t)$ to those in Table **13-1.**

mathematics note

Parametric equations allow rectangular coordinates to be expressed in terms of another variable, the **parameter.** In an xy-plane, for example, both x and y can be expressed as functions of a third variable, t:

$$\begin{cases} x = f(t) \\ y = g(t) \end{cases}$$

In these parametric equations, the independent variable is the parameter t. The dependent variables are x and y. In other words, each value of t in the domain corresponds with an ordered pair (x,y).

For example, consider an object projected horizontally at a velocity of 15 m/sec off a cliff 20 m high. This object's position after t sec can be described by the following parametric equations, where $x(t)$ represents the horizontal distance traveled and $y(t)$ represents the height above the ground:

$$\begin{cases} x(t) = v_x t = 15t \\ y(t) = -\dfrac{1}{2}gt^2 + h_0 = -\dfrac{1}{2}(9.8)t^2 + 20 = -4.9t^2 + 20 \end{cases}$$

At $t = 2$ sec, the ordered pair generated by these equations is (30,0.4). This indicates that 2 sec after leaving the cliff, the object has traveled 30 m horizontally and is 0.4 m off the ground.

h. Write parametric equations to describe the position of each object in Figure **13-2** with respect to time.

i. Set your graphing utility to graph parametric equations simultaneously.

1. Using appropriate intervals for x, y, and the parameter t, graph both pairs of equations from Part **h.**

2. Experiment with different increments for t. Record your observations.

3. Use the trace feature to observe and record the values of x, y, and t at various locations on each graph.

Discussion

a. Describe the graphs you created in the exploration.

b. Does the speed with which the graphs are drawn appear to be related to the actual speed of the objects? Explain your response.

c. 1. How could you determine the time required for each object to reach the ground?

   2. Describe how you could find the location of each object after half this time has passed.

d. Describe how you could determine the maximum horizontal distance traveled by the object that was projected horizontally.

e. Considering an object whose height above the ground can be described by the function $y(t)$, is it reasonable to consider negative values for $y(t)$? Explain your response.

Warm-Up

1. Identify the family of functions to which each of the following equations belongs and describe the general shape of its graph.

   a. $x(t) = vt$

   b. $y(t) = -4.9t^2 + vt + h_0$

2. Solve each equation below for x.

   a. $-25 = 100 - 5x^2$

   b. $4x^2 - 2x + 1 = 7$

   c. $y = h - 0.5gx^2$

Assignment

1.1 While practicing at a target range, an archer shoots an arrow parallel to the ground at a velocity of 42 m/sec. At the moment the arrow is released, the strap on the archer's wristwatch breaks and the watch falls toward the ground. The initial height of both the arrow and the watch is 1.6 m.

a. Write a pair of parametric equations, $x(t)$ and $y(t)$, to describe each of the following:

1. the position of the watch after t sec

2. the position of the arrow after t sec.

b. Graph the equations from Part **a.**

c. Determine the height of each object after 0.25 sec.

d. Determine how long it will take for each object to hit the ground.

e. Determine the horizontal distance traveled by the arrow at the time it hits the ground.

1.2 In the introduction to this module, you discussed the airlift of a crate of supplies to some firefighters. Suppose that the plane is traveling at a horizontal velocity of 250 km/hr and the crate is dropped from a height of 100 m.

a. Write a set of parametric equations, $x(t)$ and $y(t)$, to model the path of the crate, where t represents time in seconds. *Hint:* The units for distance should be the same in each equation.

b. Determine how long it will take for the crate to hit the ground.

c. Determine the horizontal distance traveled by the crate during its time in the air.

d. If the plane continues to travel at the same velocity, where will it be located in relation to the crate when the crate hits the ground?

1.3 Two mountain climbers are stranded by a blizzard at an elevation of 1690 m. A search-and-rescue plane locates the climbers but cannot land to pick them up. Flying due east at a velocity of 90 m/sec and an elevation of 1960 m, the crew drops a package of food and supplies.

a. How long (to the nearest 0.1 sec) will it take for the package to reach the ground if it lands at the same elevation as the climbers?

b. How far should the plane be from the target site when the rescue team releases the package?

* * * * *

1.4 Under the watchful eye of your skydiving instructor, you step out of a plane. The plane is traveling at a constant velocity of 65 m/sec and an altitude of 1300 m. You wait 10 sec before pulling the ripcord of your parachute.

a. Ignoring air resistance, describe your path during the 10 sec of free fall.

b. Write a set of parametric equations that models your path during this interval.

c. Determine how far you have fallen vertically before pulling the ripcord.

d. Determine the horizontal distance you have traveled before pulling the ripcord.

e. At the time you pull the ripcord, where is the airplane relative to your position? Explain your response.

1.5 The object of the game "Sure-Aim" is to roll a marble off a table and into a cup. The height of the table is 0.8 m. The cup is 0.1 m high, with a diameter of 5 cm. The horizontal distance from the table to the cup's rim is 0.75 m.

Determine the approximate velocity at which a marble must leave the table to land in the cup. Defend your response.

In Activity **1,** you explored the motion of objects falling from rest or projected with a horizontal velocity. In this activity, you investigate the motion of objects projected into the air at an angle.

Discussion 1

a. When a batter hits a ball, what forces are involved?

b. What factors influence the distance that the ball travels?

Exploration

While watching a videotape of herself in the batting cage, Kami noticed that she hit the ball at many different angles of elevation, from line drives to pop-ups. After speaking with her fast-pitch softball coach, she wondered what angle of elevation would make her hits travel as far as possible.

In this exploration, you develop a vector model to help answer Kami's question.

mathematics note

A **vector** is a quantity that has both magnitude (size) and direction. In printed work, a vector is typically symbolized by a bold, lowercase letter, such as vector **u**. In handwritten work, the same vector can be symbolized by $\vec{u}$. The magnitude of a vector **u** is denoted by $|\mathbf{u}|$.

The pair of horizontal and vertical vectors that when added result in a given vector are the **components** of that vector. The horizontal component of a vector **u** is denoted by $\mathbf{u}_x$ (read "u sub x"); its vertical component is denoted by $\mathbf{u}_y$.

For example, the arrowhead on vector **a** in Figure **13-3** indicates its direction. The length of vector **a** indicates its magnitude. Its horizontal and vertical components are $\mathbf{a}_x$ and $\mathbf{a}_y$, respectively.

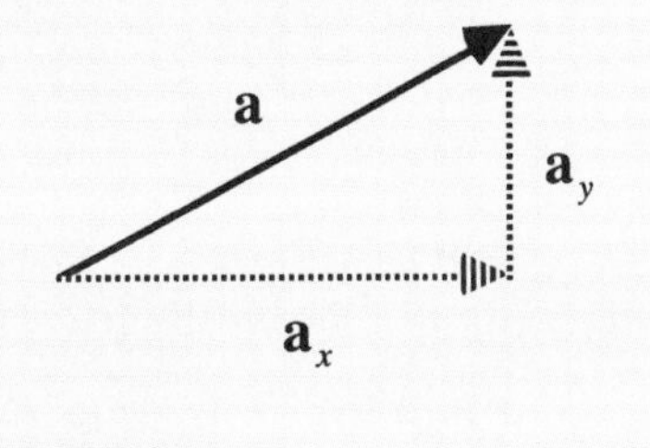

FIGURE 13-3 Vector a and its components.

a. To analyze the paths of the hit balls, Kami ignores air resistance and assumes that each ball leaves the bat at the same speed of 40 m/sec.

   When the initial velocity of a hit ball is represented by a vector **v**, the vector's direction is determined by the angle θ at which the ball leaves the bat. Its magnitude is the velocity at which the ball is hit. Figure **13-4** shows vector **v** and its components.

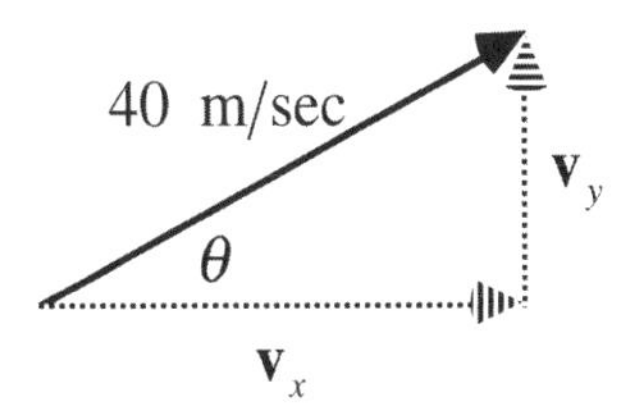

FIGURE 13-4 Vector v and its components.

1. Write an expression for the horizontal velocity $\mathbf{v}_x$ in terms of the initial velocity of 40 m/sec and the angle θ.
2. Write an expression for the vertical velocity $\mathbf{v}_y$ in terms of the initial velocity and θ.

b. Complete Table **13-3** for softballs hit at angles of elevation between 0° and 90°, in increments of 5°.

TABLE 13-3 ■ *Component Velocities of a Softball*

Initial Velocity (m/sec)	Angle of Elevation (degrees)	Horizontal Component (v_x)	Vertical Component (v_y)
40	0	40	0
40	5	39.85	3.49
⋮	⋮	⋮	⋮
40	90		

c. In general, the height of a projectile above the ground at any time t can be modeled by the following function:

$$h(t) = -\frac{1}{2}gt^2 + \mathbf{v}_y t + h_0$$

where g is the acceleration due to gravity, $\mathbf{v}_y$ is the vertical component of the initial velocity, and h_0 is the initial height.

1. Consider a softball hit with an initial velocity of 40 m/sec at a 30° angle of elevation from an initial height of 1 m. Write a function that models the height of this softball with respect to time.
2. Determine the height of the softball 4 sec after it is hit.

d. The softball's horizontal motion can be analyzed independently of its vertical motion. In general, the horizontal distance traveled at any time t can be modeled by the following function:

$$x(t) = \mathbf{v}_x t$$

where $\mathbf{v}_x$ is the horizontal component of the initial velocity.

1. Write a function that models the horizontal distance traveled by the softball described in Part **c.**
2. Find the horizontal distance traveled by the softball 4 sec after it is hit.

e. Graph the parametric equations from Parts **c** and **d.** Use the graph to determine the horizontal distance traveled by the softball before it hits the ground.

f. Repeat Parts **c–e** using several different values for θ, the angle of elevation. Estimate the measure of the angle that will allow a hit ball to travel the farthest distance.

Discussion 2

a. Describe the paths of the softball in Part **e** of the exploration.

b. Given the initial velocity and angle of elevation for a hit softball, how could you determine each of the following?

1. the maximum horizontal distance traveled by the softball
2. the time required for the softball to reach its maximum height
3. the maximum height reached by the softball.

c. What angle of elevation appears to result in the maximum horizontal distance for a hit ball?

d. Suppose that the wind is blowing when Kami hits the ball.

1. Does wind affect the horizontal or vertical component of a ball's velocity? Explain your response.
2. How would the ball's velocity be affected if the wind is blowing toward Kami? Use vectors to justify your response.
3. How would the ball's velocity be affected if the wind is blowing away from Kami? Use vectors to justify your response.

Warm-Up

1. Describe two different techniques for adding vectors.

2. Vector **w** in the diagram below has a magnitude of 5 units. Determine its horizontal and vertical components.

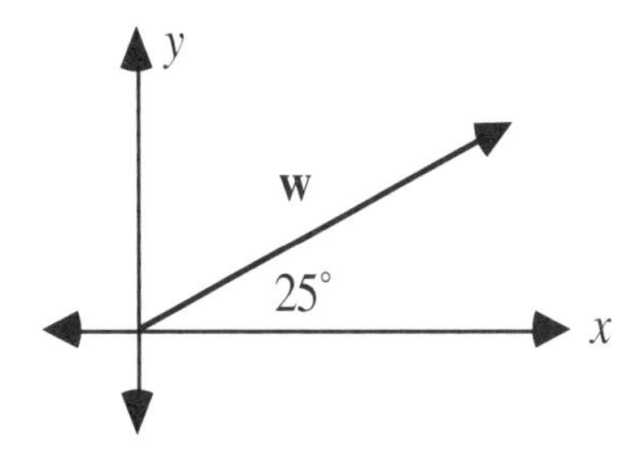

3. The diagram on the right shows vector **v** and its components.

a. Determine the magnitude of vector **v**.

b. Determine the value of θ.

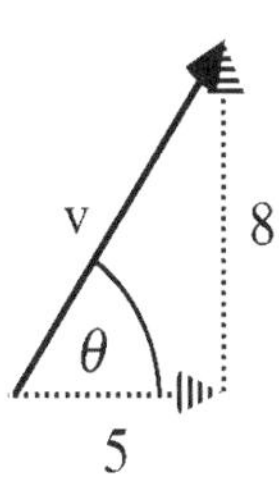

Assignment

2.1 While watching the videotape of herself in the batting cage, Kami noticed that she hit one pitch especially well. Estimating that the angle of elevation measured 20°, she wondered if that hit would have been a home run.

Assume that the softball left the bat with an initial velocity of 40 m/sec at a height of 1 m.

a. At what time would the softball have reached its maximum height?

b. What would have been its maximum height?

c. The outfield fence is 2 m high and 80 m from home plate. Would the ball have cleared the fence? If so, determine the distance by which the ball would have cleared the fence. If not, determine the distance by which the ball would have fallen short.

2.2 Imagine that the wind is blowing directly toward home plate at 8.5 m/sec. If Kami hits the ball as in Problem **2.1,** will the ball clear the fence? Check your response using a graph of the appropriate parametric equations.

2.3 The distance traveled by a ski jumper is measured from the base of the ramp to the landing point. As shown in the diagram below, the end of the ramp is 4 m above the snow. The angle formed by the plane of the landing area and the horizontal is 20°. Ignoring air resistance, find the horizontal velocity that the skier would need to jump 55 m.

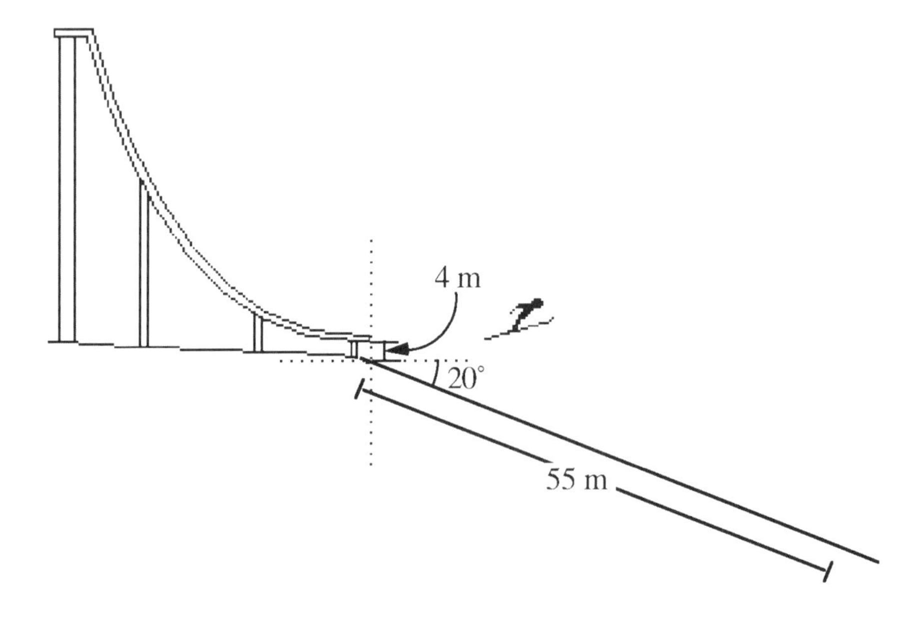

2.4 Imagine that you are an engineer for the Buildaroad Construction Company. To widen a highway, the company must blast through a mountain. You have been asked to determine a safe distance from the blast for the construction workers on the site. The charge of dynamite will propel rocks and debris at a maximum initial velocity of 55 m/sec. Write a report explaining your recommendations, including a minimum "safe" distance.

* * * * *

2.5 At the circus, Rowdy the Riot is shot out of a cannon and into a square net that measures 10 m on each side. To land safely, Rowdy must land at least 2 m from the edge of the net. The barrel of the cannon is 2 m off the ground and has a 40° angle of elevation. The net is 1 m off the ground. Its nearest edge is 30 m from the cannon.

Ignoring air resistance, determine an interval of initial velocities that will allow Rowdy to land safely in the net. Justify your response by showing an appropriate vector analysis of the situation.

2.6 When Lief hits a golf ball, the distance it travels depends on which golf club he uses. The following table shows the ball's angle of elevation and initial velocity when hit with four different golf clubs.

Golf Club	Angle of Elevation	Initial Velocity
six iron	32°	44.5 m/sec
seven iron	36°	41.5 m/sec
eight iron	40°	38.5 m/sec
nine iron	44°	36.5 m/sec

From his position on the fairway, Lief wants to hit a golf ball so that it lands in the middle of the green. The front of the green is 162 m away and the back is 181 m away. Use the information in the table to determine which club Lief should select.

In the previous activities, you used parametric equations to model parabolic paths. In this activity, you use parametric equations to investigate circular and elliptical paths.

Exploration 1

Recall from the Level 3 module, "Controlling the Sky with Parametrics," that a circle with center at point (h,k) and radius r can be defined by the following pair of parametric equations:

$$\begin{cases} x(\theta) = h + r\cos\theta \\ y(\theta) = k + r\sin\theta \end{cases}$$

where θ is the measure of the central angle formed by two radii of the circle, one of which is parallel to the x-axis. As shown in Figure **13-5,** each value of θ corresponds with a specific point on the circle.

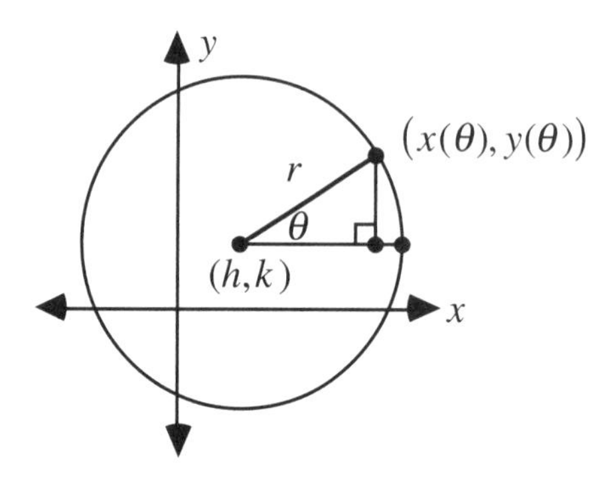

FIGURE 13-5 **A circle with center at (h,k) and radius r.**

a. Figure **13-6** shows a toy airplane attached by a string to a weighted base. As the plane flies, it follows a circular path whose radius is the length of the string.

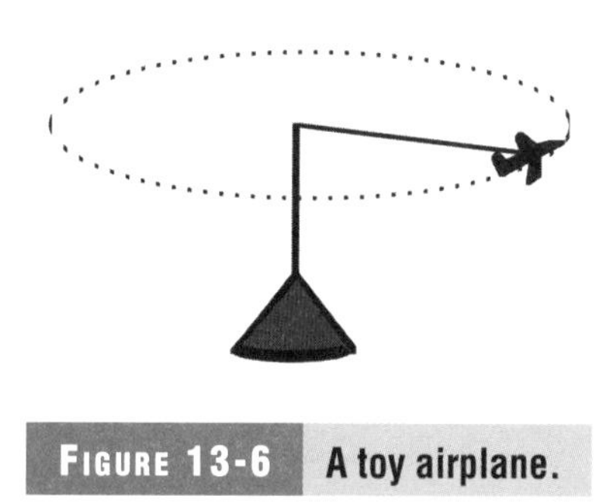

FIGURE 13-6 **A toy airplane.**

1. Use parametric equations to model the path of the airplane, given that the length of the string is 2 m long and the end attached to the base is at the origin.

2. Graph your equations from Step **1. Note:** Remember to set your graphing utility to measure angles in radians.

b. The plane completes 1 revolution in 1 sec. Determine its average speed in meters per second.

mathematics note

The average **angular speed** of a moving point P, relative to a fixed point O, is the measure of the angle θ through which the line containing O and P passes per unit time. For example, consider the wheel in Figure **13-7** below.

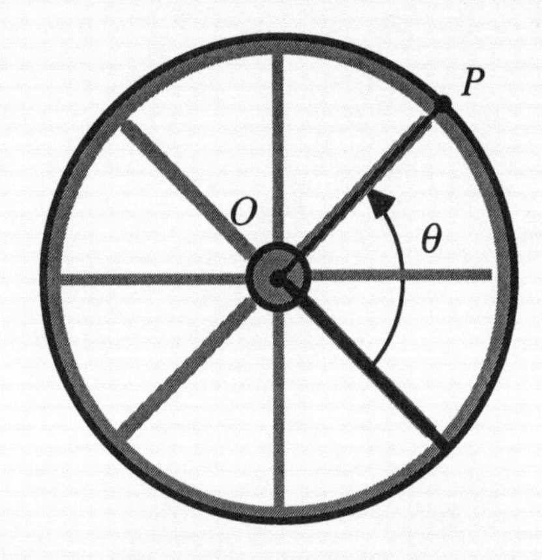

FIGURE 13-7 **Point *P* on a wheel.**

Suppose P moves $1/4$ the circumference of the wheel in 2 sec. In this case, the line containing O and P has passed through an angle measure of $2\pi/4$ or $\pi/2$ radians in 2 sec. Therefore, the average angular speed of P is:

$$\frac{\pi/2 \text{ radians}}{2 \text{ sec}} = \frac{\pi}{4} \text{ radians/sec}$$

c. Determine the plane's average angular speed in radians per second.

mathematics note

The position of an object traveling counterclockwise at a constant angular speed c, on a circle with center at point (h,k) and radius r, can be modeled by the following parametric equations:

$$\begin{cases} x(t) = h + r\cos(ct) \\ y(t) = k + r\sin(ct) \end{cases}$$

where t represents time.

For example, consider a chair on a Ferris wheel with a radius of 10 m, where the center of the wheel is 12 m off the ground. The Ferris wheel completes 1 revolution every 20 sec. In this case, the angular speed c is $2\pi/20$, or $\pi/10$ radians/sec. If the origin is located on the ground directly below the wheel's center, the chair's position with respect to time can be modeled by the following parametric equations:

$$\begin{cases} x(t) = 10\cos\left(\dfrac{\pi}{10}t\right) \\ y(t) = 12 + 10\sin\left(\dfrac{\pi}{10}t\right) \end{cases}$$

d. Each of the following pairs of parametric equations models the position with respect to time of a toy airplane at the end of a 2-m string, where t represents time in seconds. Determine how long it takes each plane to complete 1 revolution.

1. $\begin{cases} x(t) = 2\cos(\pi t) \\ y(t) = 2\sin(\pi t) \end{cases}$

2. $\begin{cases} x(t) = 2\cos(2\pi t) \\ y(t) = 2\sin(2\pi t) \end{cases}$

3. $\begin{cases} x(t) = 2\cos\left(\dfrac{2\pi}{3}t\right) \\ y(t) = 2\sin\left(\dfrac{2\pi}{3}t\right) \end{cases}$

e. Determine a pair of parametric equations that models the position with respect to time of a toy airplane that completes 1 revolution in each of the following intervals:

1. 2.5 sec
2. 0.8 sec
3. a sec.

f. For each pair of parametric equations in Part **e**, determine the average speed of the toy in meters per second.

Discussion 1

a. Is the speed at which the graph is plotted related to the actual speed of the object moving around the circle? Explain your response.

b. Using parametric equations of the form given in the previous mathematics note, what is the position of the object when $t = 0$? Justify your response.

c. Figure **13-8** below shows three different points on a circle: A, B, and C. How would you model an object's position with respect to time, given its initial position at each one of these points?

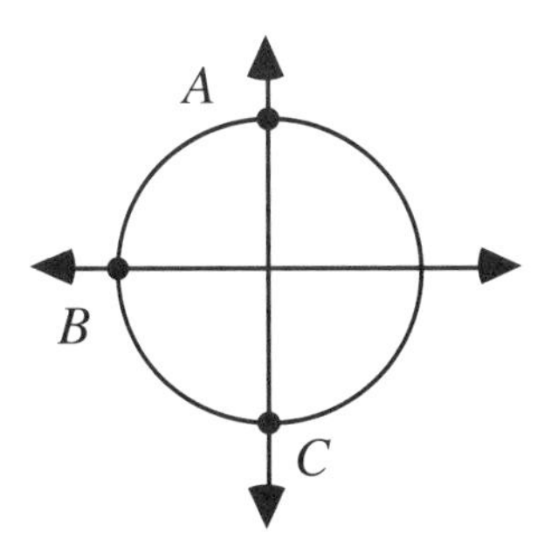

FIGURE 13-8 A circle with center at the origin.

d. Consider an object moving on a circle with center at (–4,3) and radius 7 units. If the object completes 1 revolution every 5 sec, describe how to use parametric equations to model its position over time.

e. Describe how to determine the speed of an object whose position with respect to time can be modeled by the parametric equations below, where t represents time in hours:

$$\begin{cases} x(t) = 9\cos(6t) \\ y(t) = 9\sin(6t) \end{cases}$$

f. Figure **13-9** on the right shows two concentric circles and a segment OP containing a point Q.

1. Compare the speeds of P and Q as the segment rotates about O.
2. Compare the angular speeds of P and Q as the segment rotates about O.

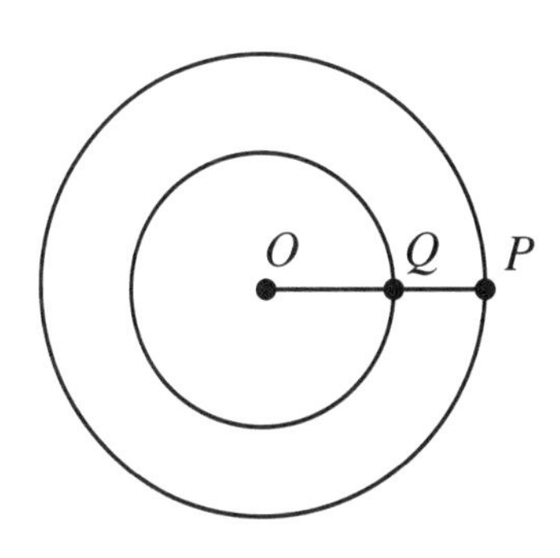

FIGURE 13-9
Two concentric circles.

Exploration 2

Parametric equations also can be used to model elliptical paths. In this exploration, you discover how to use parametric equations to define an ellipse.

a. Use a geometry utility to complete the following steps.

1. On a two-dimensional coordinate system, construct two circles with center at the origin O and different radii. Create a moveable point on the outer circle. Label this point A.
2. Draw a ray from O through A. Locate the point of intersection of the ray and the inner circle. Label this point B.
3. From A, construct a segment perpendicular to the x-axis. Locate the intersection of the perpendicular and the x-axis. Label this point C.
4. From B, construct a segment perpendicular to the x-axis and a line perpendicular to the y-axis. Label the line perpendicular to the y-axis m. Locate the intersection of the perpendicular segment and the x-axis. Label this point E.
5. Locate the point of intersection of $\overline{AC}$ and line m. Label this intersection D. This point represents one point on your graph of an ellipse. Your construction now should resemble the diagram in Figure **13-10.**

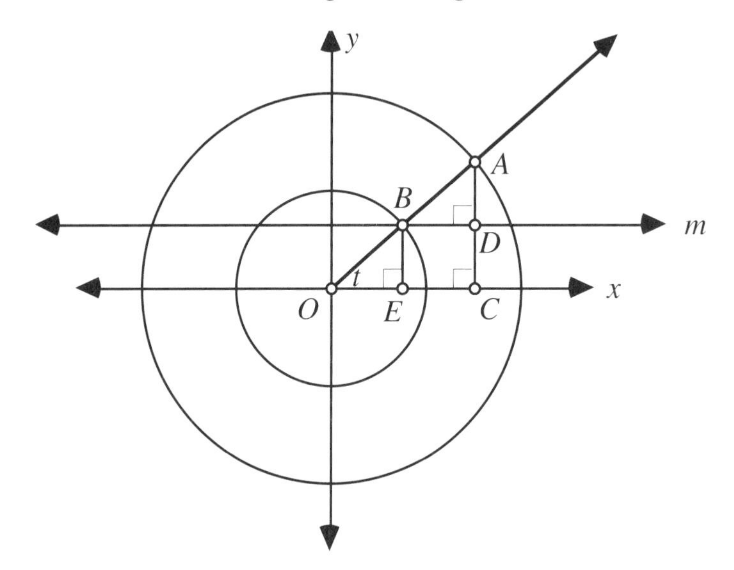

FIGURE 13-10 Construction for modeling an ellipse.

b. Trace the locus of point D as point A moves about the outer circle.

c. Using your construction, let t represent $m\angle BOE = m\angle AOC$. Let (x,y) represent the coordinates of point D.

1. Express x in terms of t and OA.
2. Express y in terms of t and OB.

d. Suppose that the radius of the larger circle in Figure **13-9** is 4 units, and the radius of the smaller circle is 2 units. Write parametric equations that model the paths of points A, B, and D as A moves about the larger circle.

Discussion 2

a. Compare your construction with those of your classmates. What differences do you observe?

b. 1. Compare the parametric equations that you found in Part **d** of Exploration **2** with those of your classmates.

   2. Describe a method you could use to determine these equations.

An ellipse with center at the origin can be defined parametrically by the equations

$$\begin{cases} x(t) = a \cos t \\ y(t) = b \sin t \end{cases}$$

where a is the positive x-intercept of the ellipse and b is the positive y-intercept.

For example, consider an ellipse with center at the origin that intersects the positive x-axis at (12,0) and the positive y-axis at (0,7). In this case, $a = 12$ and $b = 7$. Therefore, the parametric equations of the ellipse are $x(t) = 12 \cos t$ and $y(t) = 7 \sin t$.

c. Consider the locus of points traced by D in Part **b** of Exploration **2.** Does a graph of these points appear to be a function? Explain your response.

d. When the locus of points traced by point D is expressed using parametric equations, its graph is a function of t.

   1. Describe the domain and range of this function.

   2. Explain why it is a function.

e. How are the values of a and b in the equations $x = a \cos t$ and $y = b \sin t$ related to the lengths of the axes of an ellipse?

f. Describe the type of ellipse formed when $a = b$.

g. What advantages are there in using parametric equations to sketch ellipses?

h. The parametric equations $x = a\cos t$ and $y = b\sin t$ define the coordinates of the points of an ellipse. Solving these equations for $\cos t$ and $\sin t$, respectively, results in the following: $\cos t = x/a$ and $\sin t = y/b$.

If these equations are squared and added together, how is the resulting equation related to an ellipse? *Hint:* Recall from the Level 4 module, "Ostriches are Composed," that $\sin^2 x + \cos^2 x = 1$ is true for all values of x.

Warm-Up

1. Assume that the radius of the larger circle in Exploration **2** is 5 units, and the radius of the smaller circle is 3 units.

   a. Write parametric equations that describe the locus of points traced by D in terms of the sine and cosine of the angle t. (See Figure **13-10** for reference.)

   b. Graph the equations from Part **a** on a graphing utility. Describe the resulting figure, including the locations of its foci.

   c. Graph the parametric equations $x(t) = 3\cos t$ and $y(t) = 5\sin t$. Describe the resulting figure, including the locations of its foci.

2. Use your response to Part **h** of Discussion **2** to complete the following.

   a. An ellipse can be represented parametrically by the equations $x = 12\cos t$ and $y = 7\sin t$. Write the equation of this ellipse in standard form.

   b. Write a set of parametric equations for the ellipse defined by the following equation:

$$\frac{x^2}{36} + \frac{y^2}{4} = 1$$

Assignment

3.1 The diagram below shows a Ferris wheel with a radius of 8 m. The bottom of the Ferris wheel is 2 m above the ground.

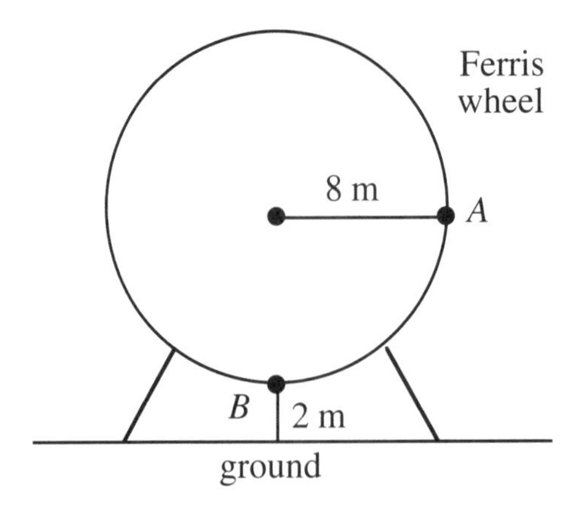

a. The wheel completes 1 revolution every 20 sec. Determine the speed and angular speed of a chair on this Ferris wheel.

b. **1.** Consider a chair whose initial position is at point *A*. Use parametric equations to model the position of this chair over time.

2. How high above the ground will this chair be if the wheel stops 10 sec after the chair passes point *A*? Explain your response.

3. How long will it take for this chair to reach a height of 16 m?

c. Describe how you could model the movement of a chair whose initial position is at point *B*.

3.2 The following diagram shows two toy trains traveling on concentric sets of circular tracks.

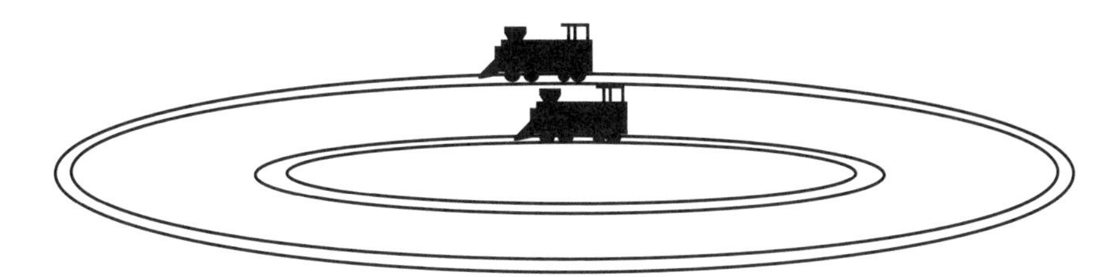

The train on the outer track is 1 m from the center, while the one on the inner track is 0.5 m from the center.

a. Suppose that each train completes 1 lap around its respective track in 15 sec.

1. Determine the angular speed of each train.

2. Determine the speed of each train.

3. Model each train's position over time with parametric equations, given that at $t = 0$, both trains are located on the positive x-axis of a two-dimensional coordinate system.

b. Suppose that each train travels at a constant speed of 0.25 m/sec.

1. Model each train's position over time with parametric equations.

2. How long will it take the train on the inner track to gain a one-lap lead over the train on the outer track?

3.3 **a.** Write a set of parametric equations that define an ellipse with center at (2,3), a major axis with a length of 7 units, and a minor axis with a length of 3 units.

b. At what points does a graph of this ellipse intersect the lines $x = 2$ and $y = 3$?

c. Write a set of parametric equations for an ellipse with center at (h,k), a major axis with length $2a$, and a minor axis with length $2b$.

mathematics note

The **area** of an ellipse can be calculated using the formula $A = \pi ab$, where $2a$ and $2b$ are the lengths of the axes.

For example, consider the ellipse defined parametrically by $x(t) = 6\cos t$ and $y(t) = 11\sin t$. In this case, the length of the major axis is 22 units, while the length of the minor axis is 12 units. The area of this ellipse is $6(11)\pi = 66\pi$ units^2.

3.4 **a.** Select positive real-number values for a and b, where $a \neq b$. Graph an ellipse defined by parametric equations of the form $x(t) = a\cos t$ and $y(t) = b\sin t$.

b. Use the formula $A = \pi ab$ to calculate the area of this ellipse.

c. How is the formula for the area of an ellipse related to the formula for the area of a circle?

* * * * *

3.5 Johannes Kepler's (1571–1630) first law of planetary motion states that the planets move in elliptical orbits in which the sun is located at one focus of the ellipse, as shown in the following diagram.

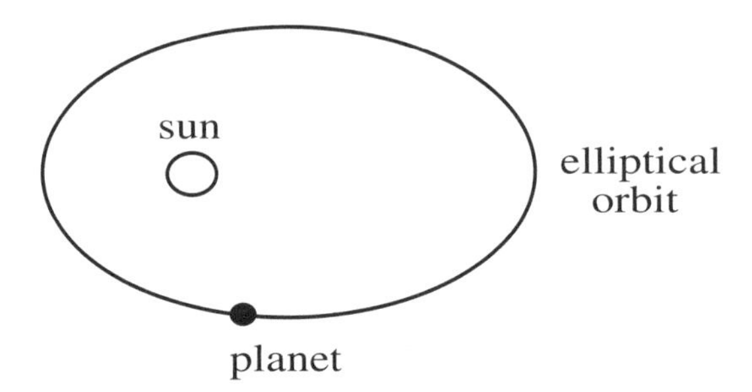

The shape of Earth's elliptical orbit can be modeled parametrically by the equations $x(t) = (1.4958 \bullet 10^8)\cos t$ and $y(t) = (1.4955 \bullet 10^8)\sin t$, where x and y represent distances in kilometers and t represents angle measures.

Johannes Kepler approximated the circumference of an ellipse using the equation $\pi(a + b)$.

a. Explain why this formula provides a reasonable approximation for Earth's orbit by comparing it to the formula for the circumference of a circle.

b. Using Kepler's approximation, how far does Earth travel in its yearly orbit?

3.6 Kepler's second law of planetary motion states that a ray drawn from the sun to a planet will sweep out equal areas in equal times.

In the diagram below, for example, the time required for a planet to travel from A to B equals the time it takes for the planet to move from C to D. Therefore, according to Kepler's second law, the two shaded areas are equal.

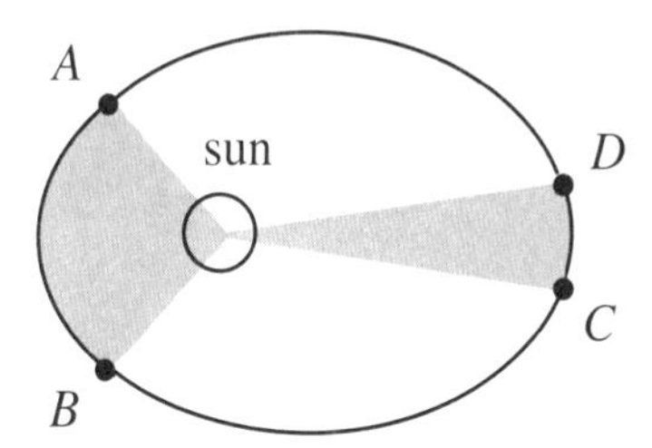

Use Kepler's second law to approximate the area that a ray drawn from the sun to Earth would sweep in 30 days.

3.7 The following diagram shows a belt and two circular pulleys. The radius of pulley A is 10 cm, and the radius of pulley B is 6 cm.

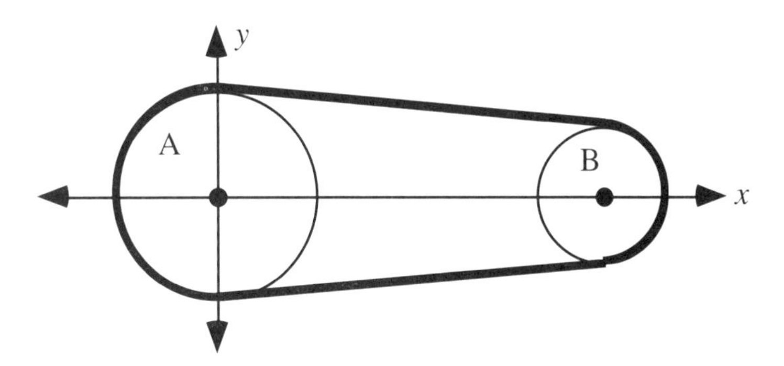

The center of pulley A is located at the origin of a two-dimensional coordinate system. The center of pulley B is 40 cm to the right of the origin on the x-axis.

a. Suppose that pulley A completes 1 revolution every 0.1 sec. Determine the speed of a point on the circumference of pulley A.

b. Write parametric equations to model the movement of a point on pulley A.

c. When either pulley turns, the belt causes the other pulley to turn also. Given this fact, which quantities would you expect to be equal: the pulleys' speeds, or their angular speeds? Explain your response.

d. Write parametric equations to model the movement of a point on pulley B.

Summary Assessment

1. A motorcycle stunt rider is planning to jump a line of cars arranged side by side, as shown in the diagram below. The approach ramp is 14.4 m long and 2.5 m high, and the motorcycle will have a velocity of 130 km/hr when it leaves the ramp.

The average width of each car is 1.7 m, and the last car in line is 1.5 m high. Determine the maximum number of cars that the stunt rider could clear (ignoring air resistance). Justify your response.

2. The following diagram shows a water wheel with eight paddles.

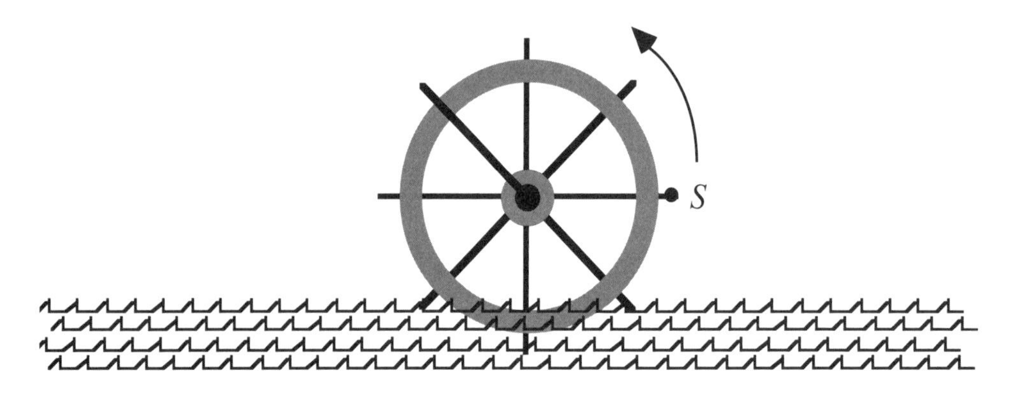

The center of the wheel is 1.2 m above the water's surface. The distance from the wheel's center to the end of each paddle is 1.8 m. The current flows at a speed of 4.5 km/hr.

a. Assuming that the speed of point S equals the speed of the current, use parametric equations to model the position of S with respect to time.

b. Determine how long point S is under water during each revolution of the wheel.

c. Given that the eight paddles are evenly spaced, how long are two consecutive paddles under water during a single turn of the wheel? Explain your response.

3. The orbits of planets can be modeled by ellipses with one focus at the sun. Orbits often are described by their *aphelion* (farthest point from the sun), *perihelion* (closest point to the sun), and orbital *eccentricity.*

   Eccentricity is a measure of the orbit's elongation, and is equal to the ratio of the distance c between the center and one focus to half the length of the major axis. In other words, $e = c/a$.

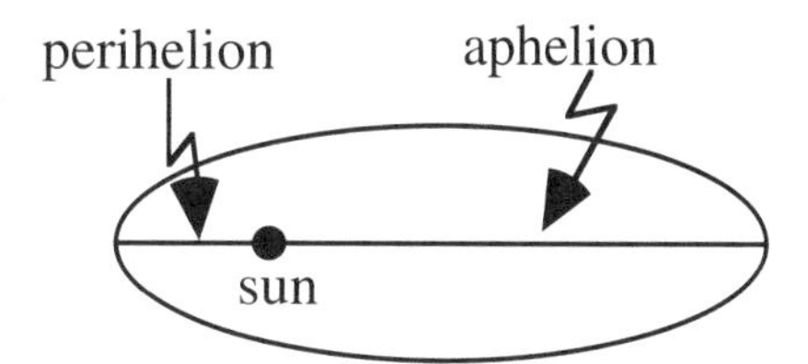

   In our solar system, Pluto has the most elongated orbit. Its orbital eccentricity is 0.2482. Pluto's aphelion and perihelion are $7.3812 \bullet 10^9$ km and $4.4458 \bullet 10^9$ km, respectively.

   Determine parametric equations to model Pluto's orbit. Graph these equations and describe the shape of the orbit.

Module Summary

* **Acceleration** describes an object's change in velocity per unit time. The average acceleration of an object can be calculated as shown below:

  average acceleration = change in velocity/change in time

* The height h of a falling object after t sec can be described by the function:

$$h(t) = -\frac{1}{2}gt^2 + h_0$$

  where g is the acceleration due to gravity and h_0 is the object's initial height. The acceleration due to gravity on earth is about 9.8 m/sec^2 in a direction toward Earth's center.

* **Parametric equations** allow rectangular coordinates to be expressed in terms of another variable, the **parameter.** In an xy-plane, for example, both x and y can be expressed as functions of a third variable, t:

$$\begin{cases} x = f(t) \\ y = g(t) \end{cases}$$

  In these parametric equations, the independent variable is the parameter t. The dependent variables are x and y. In other words, each value of t in the domain corresponds with an ordered pair (x,y).

* A **vector** is a quantity that has both magnitude (size) and direction. In printed work, a vector is typically symbolized by a bold, lowercase letter, such as vector **u.** In handwritten work, the same vector can be symbolized by $\vec{u}$. The magnitude of a vector **u** is denoted by $|\mathbf{u}|$.

* The pair of horizontal and vertical vectors that when added result in a given vector are the **components** of that vector. The horizontal component of a vector **u** is denoted by $\mathbf{u}_x$ (read "u sub x"), while its vertical component is denoted by $\mathbf{u}_y$.

* In general, the height of a projectile above the ground at any time t is described by the function:

$$h(t) = -\frac{1}{2}gt^2 + \mathbf{v}_y t + h_0$$

  where g is the acceleration due to gravity, $\mathbf{v}_y$ is the vertical component of the velocity, and h_0 is the initial height.

- A circle with center at point (h,k) and radius r can be defined by the following pair of parametric equations:

$$\begin{cases} x(\theta) = h + r\cos\theta \\ y(\theta) = k + r\sin\theta \end{cases}$$

  where θ is the measure of the central angle formed by two radii of the circle, one of which is parallel to the x-axis.

- The average **angular speed** of a moving point P, relative to a fixed point O, is the measure of the angle θ through which the line containing O and P passes per unit time.

- The position of an object traveling counterclockwise at a constant angular speed c, on a circle with center at point (h,k) and radius r, can be modeled by the following parametric equations:

$$\begin{cases} x(t) = h + r\cos(ct) \\ y(t) = k + r\sin(ct) \end{cases}$$

  where t represents time.

- An ellipse with center at the origin can be defined parametrically by the equations

$$\begin{cases} x(t) = a\cos t \\ y(t) = b\sin t \end{cases}$$

  where a is the positive x-intercept of the ellipse and b is the positive y-intercept.

- The **area** of an ellipse can be calculated using the formula $A = \pi ab$, where $2a$ and $2b$ are the lengths of the axes.

module 14

How Sure Are You?

Introduction

Most of the choices you make each day contain some degree of uncertainty. When things go wrong, the consequences of a mistake can range from almost insignificant to very grave. The process of using statistics to help make these choices—and measure the consequences—is known as **statistical inference.**

There are two basic types of statistical inference. One uses **confidence intervals** like those you encountered in the Level 4 module "Building Confidence." The other uses **tests of significance.** In both cases, a hypothesis is stated about a population parameter or a sample statistic.

When using confidence intervals, researchers make an estimate about a population parameter based on a simple random sample. To characterize the uncertainty associated with this estimate, they assign a **margin of error.**

When applying tests of significance, researchers use the characteristics of a **normal distribution** to gather evidence that will help them to reject—or fail to reject—a hypothesis. Although the proper use of statistics cannot guarantee that you will never make a mistake, it can allow you to measure the risk of an error.

Discussion

a. Consider each of the following scenarios. For each one, describe the possible consequences of a wrong decision.

   1. You are a member of a jury. The defendant in the case has been accused of murder. You must decide if this person is innocent or guilty.

   2. You are the president of a tire manufacturing company. A consultant has recommended that you increase the tread life of your tires. You must decide whether to approve the additional spending required for this upgrade.

   3. You are editor of a high school newspaper. On the recent Scholastic Aptitude Test (SAT), the senior class scored slightly higher than the national average on the mathematics portion. A reporter has submitted an article claiming that the school's seniors are better at mathematics than students nationally. You must decide whether or not to publish the article.

b. Which of the scenarios described above could be analyzed statistically? If an analysis is possible, explain briefly how it might be done.

c. When deciding how to treat a patient's illness, doctors often rely on test results. Many of these tests are not 100% accurate. Given this fact, why do doctors use such tools?

d. During Olympic and other world-class competitions, athletes must undergo testing for drugs and other banned substances.

1. If athletes test positive for a specific substance, does this guarantee that they have used the drug?
2. How would you expect a rules committee to react to the news of a positive drug test?

mathematics note

Statisticians often make hypotheses or claims about the parameters of a population, then use sampling techniques to test their claims. If a researcher assumes that a population parameter has a specific value, then a hypothesis can be formed about the consequences of that assumption.

In statistical analysis, there are two types of hypotheses. A **null hypothesis (H_0)** is a statement about one or more parameters. The **alternative hypothesis (H_a)** is the statement that must be true if the null hypothesis is false. The null hypothesis usually involves a claim of no relationship or no difference. When stated using mathematical symbols, it typically contains an equals sign. In many situations, the null hypothesis and alternative hypothesis are negations of each other, but this is not always the case.

For example, consider a researcher who wants to test the claim that the mean income of a population is $25,000. In this setting, the null hypothesis would be that the mean income of the population does not differ from the claim, or, in other words, that the mean income equals $25,000. The alternative hypothesis would be that the mean income does not equal $25,000. Symbolically, this can be represented as shown below:

$$H_0: \mu = \$25,000$$
$$H_a: \mu \neq \$25,000$$

e. Suppose that a consumer group wants to test a manufacturer's claim that its light bulbs have a mean life of 1000 hr. The study team formulates the null hypothesis "H_0: $\mu = 1000$," where μ represents the population mean.

   1. What is the negation of this null hypothesis?

   2. In this situation, the study team decides to use the alternative hypothesis "H_a: $\mu < 1000$." Why do you think these researchers did not use the negation of the null hypothesis as their alternative hypothesis?

f. 1. Give examples of null and alternative hypotheses for a situation in which an athlete undergoes a drug test.

   2. Would you expect to use the negation of the null hypothesis as the alternative hypothesis in this case? Explain your response.

   3. If your null hypothesis (H_0) is false, what type of evidence would you expect to observe in the drug test?

Statisticians are seldom 100% confident of their findings. In this activity, you explore how uncertainty affects hypothesis testing.

mathematics note

A **hypothesis test** may consist of the following steps.

- State null and alternative hypotheses about a parameter of a population.
- If the null hypothesis is true, predict what this implies about a sample of the population.
- Take a sample of the population and compare the results with your prediction.
- If the results are inconsistent with the prediction, then you can conclude, with some level of certainty, that the null hypothesis is false and, therefore, reject it.
- If the results are consistent with the prediction, you fail to reject the null hypothesis. The failure to reject the null hypothesis does not guarantee that the null hypothesis is true, but only suggests that it might be true.

Exploration

In the following exploration, you use a population of coins to investigate how uncertainty affects your interpretation of test results.

a. Place a nickel in each of 18 envelopes. Place a penny in one additional envelope, and a quarter in another envelope. **Note:** For the remainder of this exploration, these 20 envelopes will be referred to as the "test envelopes."

b. Randomly select one of the test envelopes. You will use this test envelope, along with a balance, to identify an unknown coin.

   1. What is the probability that the test envelope contains a nickel?

   2. What is the probability that the test envelope contains a penny or a quarter?

c. Obtain an envelope from your teacher containing an unknown coin. In this situation, the null and alternative hypotheses can be stated as follows:

H_0: The unknown coin is a nickel.
H_a: The unknown coin is not a nickel.

   1. If the unknown coin is a nickel, what would you expect to occur when this envelope and the test envelope are placed on opposite sides of a balance?

   2. What would you expect to occur if the unknown coin is not a nickel?

d. Place the test envelope and the envelope containing the unknown coin on opposite sides of a balance. Use your observations to decide whether to reject, or fail to reject, the null hypothesis.

e. Describe the conclusions you can make as a result of your hypothesis test.

Discussion

a. Do you think that the unknown coin is a nickel? Explain your response.

b. 1. If the two envelopes in Part **c** of the exploration balance, can you be sure that the unknown coin is a nickel?

   2. If the two envelopes do not balance, can you be sure that the unknown coin is not a nickel?

c. What is the probability of selecting a test envelope that does not contain a nickel?

d. Given only the results of a single test, is there any way to remove the uncertainty from your conclusions? Explain your response.

mathematics note

Whenever a sample is taken from a population about which there is some uncertainty, it is possible that the sample is not representative of the population. Therefore, when performing a hypothesis test by sampling, it is always possible to make an incorrect decision about the null hypothesis (H_0).

Two possible errors can occur: (1) rejecting a true null hypothesis and (2) failing to reject a false null hypothesis, as shown in Figure **14-1** below.

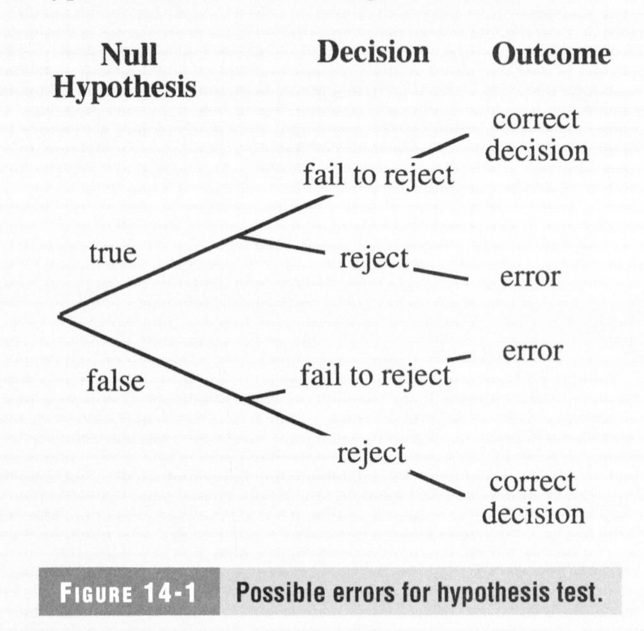

Figure 14-1 **Possible errors for hypothesis test.**

In the exploration, for example, it is likely that the test envelope contains a nickel. If the unknown coin is a nickel, then you would expect the two envelopes to balance. If the test envelope contains a penny, however, it will not balance with an envelope containing a nickel. This would lead you to reject a true null hypothesis.

e. 1. Why does the rejection of the null hypothesis result in the acceptance of the alternative hypothesis?

2. Does acceptance of the alternative hypothesis guarantee that it is true? Explain your response.

f. 1. Does failing to reject the null hypothesis prove it is true? Use the tree diagram in Figure **14-1** to support your answer.

2. If you reject a null hypothesis, does that prove that it is false? Explain your response.

Warm-Up

1. Write a null and an alternative hypothesis for each situation described below.
   a. The advertised mass of a box of cereal is 458 grams. You want to know if this claim is true.
   b. The local newspaper reports that the mean score on the mathematics portion of the ACT at your school is 19. You think the mean score is higher than 19.
   c. The student council collects data on the wages for summer jobs of males and females in your school. You think there is a difference in the mean wages of males and females.
   d. A report states that children spend 20 or more hours watching television in a week. You think this value is higher than the actual amount.
2. Use mathematical notation to represent each pair of hypotheses in Problem **1** above, then determine if each pair consists of negations of each other.

Assignment

1.1 Consider an experiment that involves drawing one marble from a bag of 30 marbles, recording its color, then replacing it in the bag.

   a. If the first marble you draw is green, would you be justified in concluding that all 30 marbles are green? Explain your response.
   b. Suppose that you repeat the experiment 30 times. Each time the marble is green. Does this guarantee that all the marbles are green? Explain your response.
   c. By simply repeating this experiment, could you ever be sure that all the marbles in the bag were green? Justify your response.

1.2 While studying a developing economy, researchers formulated the following null hypothesis: "The mean annual salary in the population is $10,000."

   a. What is the alternative hypothesis in this situation?
   b. Use mathematical notation to represent both the null and alternative hypotheses and determine if each is the negation of the other.

1.3 A mail-order catalog claims that customer satisfaction is guaranteed. Write the null and alternative hypotheses that you would use in testing this claim.

1.4 Using statistical analysis, it is not typically possible to guarantee a correct decision when choosing to fail to reject a null hypothesis. Explain why this is true.

1.5 Consider a set of 20 test envelopes: 19 contain a nickel and 1 contains a quarter. Using the procedure described in the exploration and an envelope containing an unknown coin, you test the null hypothesis: "The unknown coin is a nickel." If the two envelopes balance, how certain can you be of your conclusion?

* * * * *

1.6 In 1994, a U.S. state began collecting a tax on tourism. The state's current governor wants to compare spending by tourists before and after the tax was enacted.

a. Write null and alternative hypotheses for this situation.

b. Describe the types of errors that might occur when testing the null hypothesis in Part **a.**

1.7 A standard deck of 52 playing cards contains 26 red cards and 26 black cards. Suppose that you wanted to determine the proportion of red cards in an unknown deck by sampling. In this situation, the null hypothesis might be: "The proportion of red cards in the deck is 0.5."

a. What is the alternative hypothesis that must be accepted if the null hypothesis is rejected?

b. To test your null hypothesis, you select a random sample of 6 cards from the deck. What outcomes might lead you to suspect that the proportion of red cards in the deck is not 0.5?

c. What is the probability of drawing a random sample of 6 cards, all of which are the same color, from a standard deck?

d. If your sample of 6 cards from this deck were all the same color, would you reject the null hypothesis? Explain your response.

Researchers, pollsters, and statisticians collect samples to gain information about populations. Using **confidence intervals,** along with the **central limit theorem,** they can make reasonable estimates about a population. No matter how carefully they design their studies, however, errors are possible. In this activity, you examine how to quantify and minimize the risk of making mistakes.

mathematics note

The **central limit theorem** states that even if the population from which samples are taken is not normally distributed, the distribution of the means of all possible samples of the same size will be approximately normal. In other words, if you collect many samples of size n, where $n \geq 30$, and create a relative frequency histogram and polygon of the sample means, the graph will tend to assume the bell shape of a normal curve. Figure **14-2** shows an example of such a distribution.

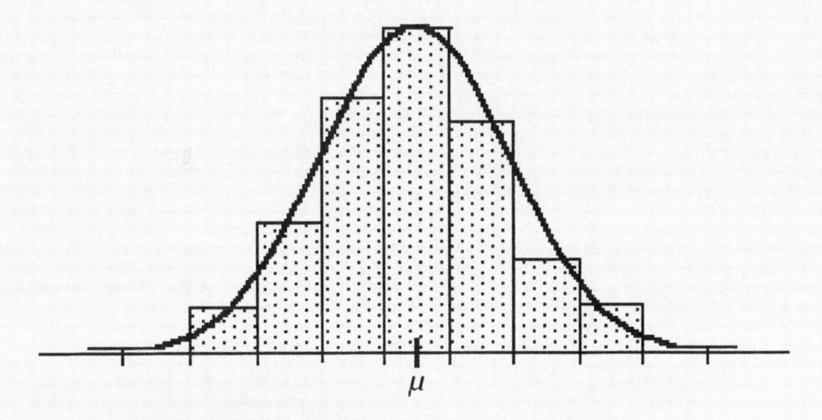

FIGURE 14-2 Normal distribution of sample means.

Statisticians generally agree that for $n \geq 30$, the distribution of sample means can be modeled reasonably well by a normal curve. This approximation becomes more accurate as n increases. A sample size of at least 30 is not required if the population itself is normally distributed.

The mean of the distribution of all sample means, $\mu_{\bar{x}}$, equals the population mean μ. The **standard deviation of all sample means,** denoted $\sigma_{\bar{x}}$, can be calculated using the following formula:

$$\sigma_{\bar{x}} = \frac{\sigma}{\sqrt{n}}$$

where σ is the standard deviation of the population and n is the sample size. The value of $\sigma_{\bar{x}}$ is sometimes called the **standard error of the mean.**

For example, consider a population in which some characteristic is not normally distributed, with $\mu = 35$ and $\sigma = 5$. The standard error of the mean for all samples of size 40 can be calculated as follows:

$$\sigma_{\bar{x}} = \frac{5}{\sqrt{40}} \approx 0.79$$

Discussion 1

a. How does the sample size n affect the shape of the distribution of all possible sample means? Explain why this occurs.

b. When sampling a population, how can a researcher be reasonably sure that the sample mean is a good estimate of the population mean?

mathematics note

A **confidence interval** for a population mean μ is an interval of numbers in which you would expect to find the value of μ. The 68–95–99.7 rule for a normal distribution implies the following:

- For approximately 68% of all sample means $\bar{x}$, the confidence interval $[\bar{x} - \sigma_{\bar{x}}, \bar{x} + \sigma_{\bar{x}}]$ contains the population mean μ. This interval also can be written as $\bar{x} \pm \sigma_{\bar{x}}$.
- For approximately 95% of all sample means $\bar{x}$, the confidence interval $[\bar{x} - 2\sigma_{\bar{x}}, \bar{x} + 2\sigma_{\bar{x}}]$ contains the population mean μ. This interval also can be written as $\bar{x} \pm 2\sigma_{\bar{x}}$.
- For approximately 99.7% of all sample means $\bar{x}$, the confidence interval $[\bar{x} - 3\sigma_{\bar{x}}, \bar{x} + 3\sigma_{\bar{x}}]$ contains the population mean μ. This interval also can be written as $\bar{x} \pm 3\sigma_{\bar{x}}$.

The values $\pm\sigma_{\bar{x}}$, $\pm 2\sigma_{\bar{x}}$, and $\pm 3\sigma_{\bar{x}}$ are the **margins of error** for the estimate of the population parameter.

For example, consider a sample of 40 pennies with a mean age $\bar{x}$ of 9 yr and a standard deviation s of 3 yr. In this case, $\sigma_{\bar{x}}$ can be estimated by $3/\sqrt{40} \approx 0.47$. Using the 68–95–99.7 rule, you can be 68% confident that the population mean μ is in the interval $[9 - 0.47, 9 + 0.47]$, 95% confident that μ is in the interval $[9 - 2(0.47), 9 + 2(0.47)]$, and 99.7% confident that μ is in the interval $[9 - 3(0.47), 9 + 3(0.47)]$.

c. What is the 68–95–99.7 rule for a normal distribution?

d. What is meant by a "95% confidence interval?"

e. How often would you expect a 95% confidence interval to not contain the population mean? Explain your response.

f. Suppose that a researcher surveys a random sample of 100 high school graduates and calculates their mean annual income. What other information is necessary to give a reasonable estimate of how close the sample mean is to the population mean?

g. The graph on the right shows three normal curves with the same mean (μ), but different standard deviations.

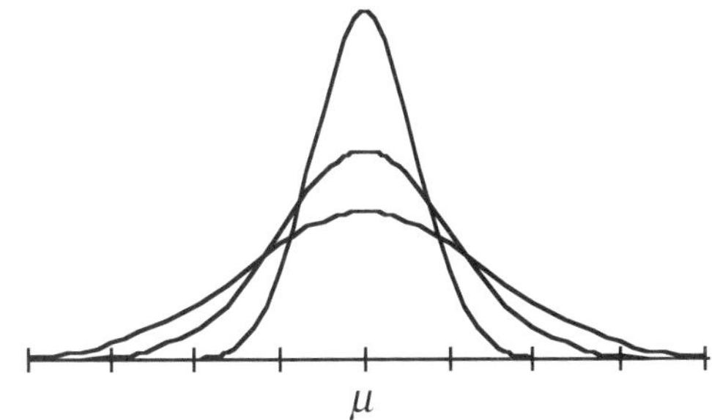

1. Which curve represents the population with the largest standard deviation? Justify your response.
2. Suppose that you randomly select one point beneath each curve to estimate the value of the population mean. Which curve provides the best chance of giving a reasonable estimate for μ? Justify your response.

Exploration 1

Finding the actual mean of a large population can be difficult, so it is often necessary to use statistics to make predictions about a population. In this exploration, you investigate the use of confidence intervals in estimating a population mean.

Imagine that your school business club is completing a survey of the mean incomes of high school graduates in your state. The club has budgeted enough money to conduct a telephone survey of 30 former students. The information gathered in the survey is shown in Table **14-1:**

TABLE 14-1 ■ *A Sample of 30 Incomes (in Dollars)*

4000	17,400	10,900	15,600	8000
9800	10,000	19,400	14,400	42,000
32,000	4500	46,000	90,400	24,400
112,000	19,600	25,400	7000	16,000
16,800	23,600	26,200	19,600	28,400
14,800	19,400	13,500	18,200	6600

a. Construct 68%, 95%, and 99.7% confidence intervals of the sample mean of this data. (Estimate $\sigma_{\bar{x}}$ using the sample standard deviation s.)

b. Create a number line that ranges from \$0 to \$50,000. Graph and label your confidence intervals above the number line, as shown in Figure **14-3.** The graph of each confidence interval should show its endpoints and the mean. **Note:** Save this graph for use in Exploration **2.**

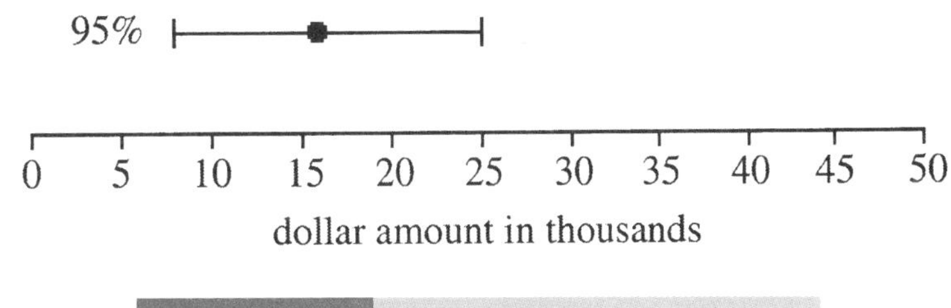

FIGURE 14-3 **Graph of a confidence interval.**

c. Write a statement, including the margin of error, about the actual mean income of high school graduates in this population for each of the following confidence levels:

1. 68%

2. 95%

3. 99.7%

Discussion 2

a. Which confidence interval is most likely to include the actual mean income of high school graduates in your state? Explain your response.

b. Which confidence level has the least range of estimates of the actual average income of the graduates? Explain your response.

c. What is the relationship between interval size and the probability of making an error?

d. How could the confidence intervals be narrowed without increasing the chances of making an error? Explain your response.

e. Describe some of the advantages and disadvantages of using:

1. a 99.7% confidence level

2. a 68% confidence level.

3. a 95% confidence level

f. Explain why it is just as important to use a random sample to estimate a confidence interval as it is to use a random sample to estimate the population mean.

Exploration 2

Roberto is writing an article for the school newspaper. Based on the study by the school business club, he wants to claim that the mean income for high school graduates in the state is $36,000. However, the editor of the newspaper disagrees. She believes that a better value for the mean income is $16,000. Who is right? In this exploration, you use confidence intervals and hypothesis testing techniques to assess both claims.

Recall that a **hypothesis test** may consist of the following steps.

- State null and alternative hypotheses about a parameter of a population.
- If the null hypothesis is true, predict what this implies about a sample of the population.

- Take a sample of the population and compare the results with your prediction.
- If the results are inconsistent with the prediction, then you can conclude, with some level of certainty, that the null hypothesis is false and, therefore, reject it.
- If the results are consistent with the prediction, you fail to reject the null hypothesis. The failure to reject the null hypothesis does not guarantee that the null hypothesis is true, but only suggests that it might be true.

a. State the null and alternative hypotheses for Roberto's claims about the mean income for high school graduates.

b. On your graph of the 68%, 95%, and 99.7% confidence intervals of the income data from Table **14-1** (from Part **b** of Exploration **1**), draw a vertical line to represent Roberto's claim about the average income.

c. Record the confidence intervals that include Roberto's predicted mean.

d. Determine whether you would reject or fail to reject the hypotheses from Part **a** at the 68%, 95%, and 99.7% confidence levels.

e. Repeat Parts **a–d** for the editor's claim that the average income for high school graduates is $16,000.

Discussion 3

a. Given your results in Exploration **2,** what can you conclude about the claims of Roberto and his editor? Explain your response.

b. What is the difference between "failing to reject" a null hypothesis and "accepting" a null hypothesis?

c. Why does the rejection of the null hypothesis result in the acceptance of the alternative hypothesis?

d. Does failing to reject a null hypothesis prove that it is true? Explain your response.

e. Does rejecting a null hypothesis prove that it is false? Justify your response.

f. Scientists often require at least a 95% confidence level to reject a hypothesis. Using this standard, state conclusions about the editor's and Roberto's hypotheses.

g. After Roberto discovers that his hypothesis cannot be rejected at a 99.7% confidence level, he exclaims, "This shows that there is a 99% chance that my hypothesis is right." Explain what is wrong with Roberto's reasoning.

Warm-Up

1. In Parts **a–c** below, determine the specified confidence interval for a sample of size 40 with the given mean and standard deviation.

   a. 68% confidence interval; $\bar{x} = 3$; $s = 0.45$

   b. 99.7% confidence interval; $\bar{x} = 2{,}546$; $s = 153$

   c. 95% confidence interval; $\bar{x} = 462$; $s = 27$

2. Each set of data in Parts **a–c** represents a sample from a *normally distributed* population. Use each sample to estimate the population mean and identify the margin of error at the 95% confidence level.

   a. {25, 35, 44, 32, 33, 46, 47, 22, 23, 19, 51, 34}

   b. {25, 35, 44, 32, 33, 46, 47, 22, 23, 19, 51, 34, 25, 35, 44, 32, 33, 46, 47, 22, 23, 19, 51, 34}

   c. {25, 35, 44, 32, 33, 46, 47, 22, 23, 19, 51, 34, 25, 35, 44, 32, 33, 46, 47, 22, 23, 19, 51, 34, 25, 35, 44, 32, 33, 46, 47, 22, 23, 19, 51, 34}

Assignment

2.1 To test her null hypothesis, Roberto's editor conducted a survey of 30 acquaintances who recently graduated from high school. Their incomes (in dollars) are shown in the table below.

6200	9400	22,300	6200	18,000	38,000
17,100	21,500	17,300	27,500	11,900	23,200
19,000	11,000	13,200	16,500	13,800	13,400
15,500	8700	33,000	34,000	16,200	9500
14,000	11,000	32,000	14,700	6400	3400

a. The editor claimed that the mean income is $16,000. Use the data in the table above to test her null hypothesis at a confidence level of your choice.

b. Based on your test in Part **a,** state your conclusions.

c. Does this test prove that the editor's claim is correct? Explain your response.

d. Roberto complains that the editor's sample is not representative of high school graduates in their state. Describe some possible sources of bias in the sample.

2.2 Roberto decides to survey his own sample of 30 graduates. He telephones the class presidents from each of the past 30 years and records their incomes in the table below.

74,200	29,500	17,000	74,000	44,500	31,000
26,000	19,000	36,000	12,500	32,000	21,000
6100	27,700	34,000	29,000	72,100	30,500
93,000	12,000	19,000	31,000	26,200	33,200
34,000	31,000	23,400	46,300	35,400	6200

a. Recall that Roberto claimed that the mean income is $36,000. Use the data in the table above to test his claim at a 95% confidence level.

b. Based on your test in Part **a,** state your conclusions.

c. What possible sources of bias are there in Roberto's sample?

2.3 In its advertisements, the Shiny Bright Company claims that its 60-watt bulbs have an average life expectancy of 1250 hr. They based this conclusion on a sample of 1000 light bulbs in which the mean life span was 827 hr, with a standard deviation of 424 hr.

According to the company, their advertised value is within 1 standard deviation of the sample mean. Therefore, their claim cannot be rejected. What is wrong with their logic?

2.4 In tests conducted by outside experts, Shiny Bright's "Best Bulb" had an average life expectancy of 2000 hr, with a standard deviation of 300 hr. The Hi-Glow Company claims their "Long-Life" bulbs are better because they last even longer. Both companies decide to test the hypothesis that the mean life expectancy of Long-Life bulbs is 2000 hr.

Using a random sample of 100 Long-Life bulbs, Shiny Bright found a mean life span of 2040 hr, with a standard deviation of 470 hr. The firm concluded that the mean life of Long-Life bulbs is the same as that of their Best Bulbs.

Hi-Glow tested 10,000 Long-Life bulbs and found a mean life span of 2010 hr, with a standard deviation of 400 hr. They concluded that the mean life span of their bulbs is not the same as that of Shiny Bright's bulbs. Perform a hypothesis test at the 95% confidence level to determine which company you think is right.

* * * * *

2.5 Cereal boxes often display the following disclaimer: "Package filled by weight, not by volume. Some settling may occur during shipping."

A high school statistics class decides to examine this claim. The students obtain a random sample of 40 boxes of the same brand of cereal. The advertised weight of the cereal in each box is 397 g.

The table below shows the observed mass of the cereal in each box, rounded to the nearest gram:

402	397	404	384	390	395	397	385	392	399
380	390	408	403	389	389	393	381	402	401
383	403	383	392	400	392	395	395	406	396
408	383	381	390	401	385	382	404	409	387

a. State the null and alternative hypotheses for this experiment.

b. Test the hypothesis at the 95% confidence level.

c. Decide whether to reject or fail to reject the null hypothesis. Justify your reasoning.

d. Explain what conclusion the class should reach about the net mass of the boxes of cereal.

In the previous exploration, you used hypothesis testing to compare statistics taken from the same population. However, it is sometimes necessary to compare statistics from different populations.

Because different populations typically have different means and different standard deviations, such a task can seem as difficult as comparing apples and oranges. For example, consider the results of two different mid-year exams. In the science test, the scores are normally distributed with a mean of 70 and a standard deviation of 5. In the math test, scores are normally distributed with a mean of 72 and a standard deviation of 3. Roberto receives a score of 76 on both tests. On which one did he perform better?

In this activity, you develop a method for answering such questions.

Exploration

Table **14-2** shows a student's scores on two different tests, along with the mean and standard deviation for each test.

TABLE 14-2 ■ *Test Means, Standard Deviations, and Scores*

	Test Score (x)	Mean (μ)	Standard Deviation (σ)
Test A	57	50	5
Test B	64	60	3

a. Which score do you think is the more exceptional? Justify your response.

b. Because standard deviation provides a measure of the spread in a population, one way to evaluate a score's exceptionality involves this parameter.

   In Test A, for example, the mean is 50 and the standard deviation is 5. A score of 55, therefore, is 1 standard deviation from the mean.

   1. In Test A, how many standard deviations from the mean is a score of 57?
   2. Identify a ratio that can be used to determine the number of standard deviations from the mean for any score x on Test A.

c. 1. In Test B, how many standard deviations from the mean is a score of 64?
   2. Identify a ratio that can be used to determine the number of standard deviations from the mean for any score x on Test B.

d. Identify a ratio that can be used to determine the number of standard deviations from the mean for any score x, where μ is the mean and σ is the standard deviation.

Discussion

a. Considering your results in Parts **b** and **c** of the exploration, which score was the more exceptional? Explain your response.

b. Using the terms *score, mean,* and *standard deviation,* describe a ratio that can be used to determine the number of standard deviations from the mean for any score from a given population.

mathematics note

Any value x from a normally distributed population with mean μ and standard deviation σ can be represented by a **standardized score** or ***z*-score.** A *z*-score describes the number of standard deviations that the value is above or below the mean. The formula for determining a *z*-score is shown below:

$$z = \frac{x - \mu}{\sigma}$$

This equation transforms normally distributed values of x to a normal distribution with a mean of 0 and a standard deviation of 1. Because the percentage of values lower than an individual *z*-score can provide useful information, these percentages are commonly available in books and tables. A portion of such a table is shown in Table **14-3** below.

TABLE 14-3 ■ *Portion of a z-Score Table*

z	0.00	0.01	0.02	0.03	0.04	0.05	0.06	0.07	0.08	0.09
1.5	0.9332	0.9345	0.9357	0.9370	0.9382	0.9394	0.9406	0.9418	0.9429	0.9441
1.6	0.9452	0.9463	0.9474	0.9484	0.9495	0.9505	0.9515	0.9525	0.9535	0.9545
1.7	0.9554	0.9564	0.9573	0.9582	0.9591	0.9599	0.9608	0.9616	0.9625	0.9633

In this table, the left-hand column lists *z*-scores from 1.5 to 1.7 by tenths. The hundredths place for each of these values is displayed in the top row. Each four-digit decimal value in the table represents the area in the normal distribution that lies to the left of the corresponding value of z. **Note:** A complete table of *z*-scores and their corresponding areas appears at the end of this module.

For example, consider a set of normally distributed test scores with a mean of 80 and a standard deviation of 3. In this situation, a test score of 85 can be represented by the following *z*-score: $z = (85 - 80)/3 \approx 1.67$. From the table, a *z*-score of 1.67 corresponds with a decimal of 0.9525. This means that approximately 95.25% of the test scores in this population are below a test score of 85. In other words, the probability that a test score from this population is less than 85 is approximately 95.25%. Conversely, the probability that a test score from this population is greater than 85 is $1 - 0.9525 = 0.0475$, or approximately 4.75%.

c. How does the ratio you identified in Part **d** of the exploration compare with the formula for z?

d. Is it possible for z to be negative? If so, when? If not, why not?

e. In the example described in the previous mathematics note, the probability that a score is greater than 85 was reported as $1 - 0.9525$. Why is 0.9525 being subtracted from 1?

f. From the portion of the z-score table in Table **14-3,** it appears that 95% of the normal distribution lies 1.645 standard deviations from the mean. However, a 95% confidence interval encloses a region 2 standard deviations from the mean. How can you explain this difference?

g. According to the 68–95–99.7 rule for normal distributions, approximately 95% of the area falls within 2 standard deviations of the mean.

   1. Describe how you could use a z-score table to identify a more accurate interval that contains 95% of the area under the normal curve. (**Note:** A complete table of z-scores and their corresponding areas appears at the end of this module.)

   2. From the z-score table, what percentage of the area actually falls within 2 standard deviations of the mean?

h. The introduction to this activity describes two tests on which Roberto received the same score: a science test with a mean of 70 and a standard deviation of 5, and a math test with a mean of 72 and a standard deviation of 3.

   1. Based on the number of standard deviations above the mean, which is the better score: a 76 on the science test or a 76 on the math test? Justify your response.

   2. Based on the percentage of scores below 76, which is the better score? Justify your response.

i. A set of examination scores is normally distributed with a mean of μ and a standard deviation of σ. Describe how to find the probability that a score selected at random from this set is less than or equal to 64, given each of the following values for μ and σ.

   1. $\mu = 71$ and $\sigma = 4$

   2. $\mu = 75$ and $\sigma = 5$

   3. $\mu = 48$ and $\sigma = 5$

Warm-Up

1. In each of the following graphs, estimate the percentage of the total area under the curve represented by the shaded region(s) using the 68–95–99.7 rule. Then determine a more accurate percentage using a table of *z*-scores.

a.

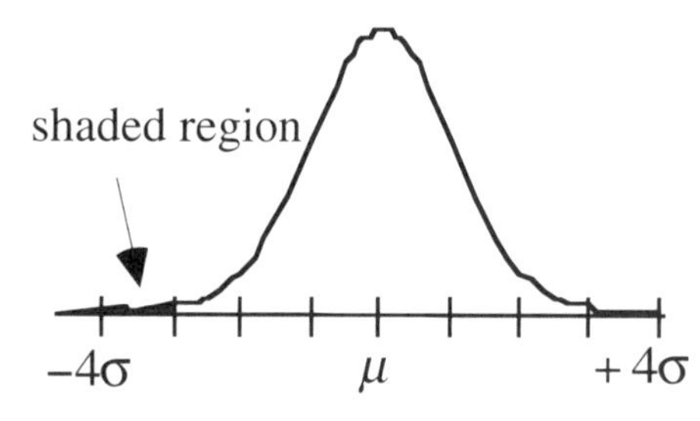

b.

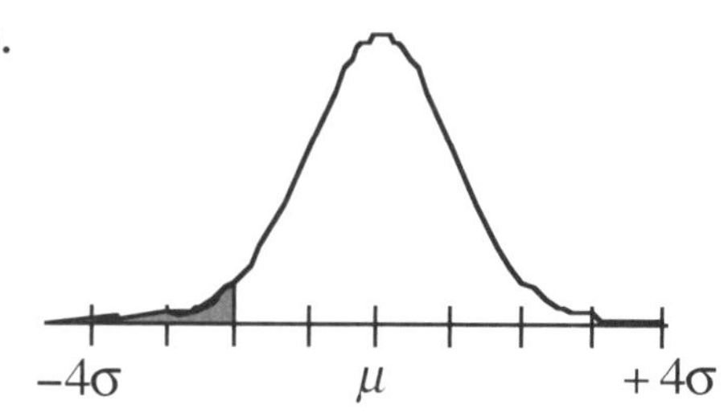

c.

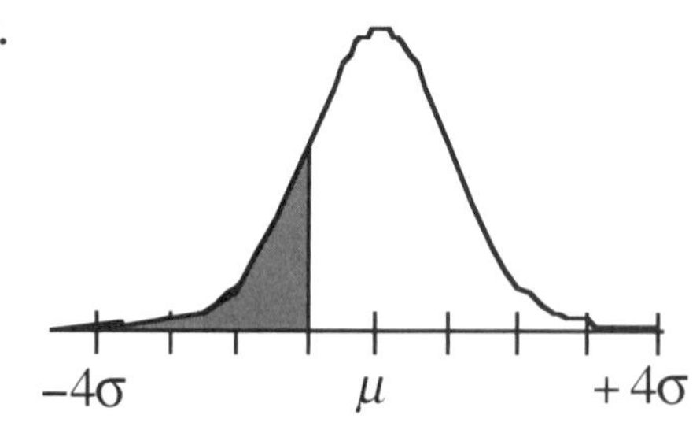

d.

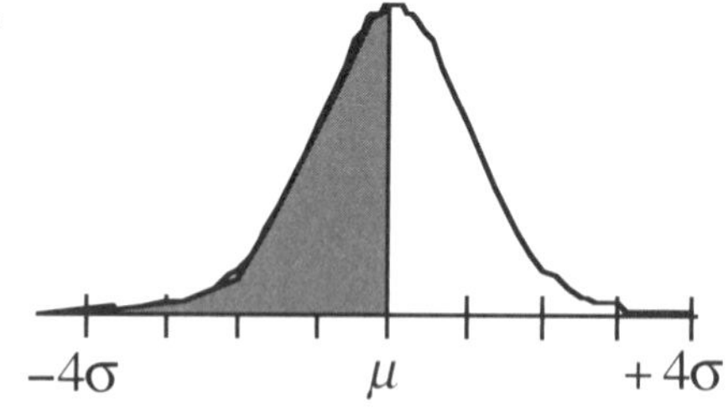

e.

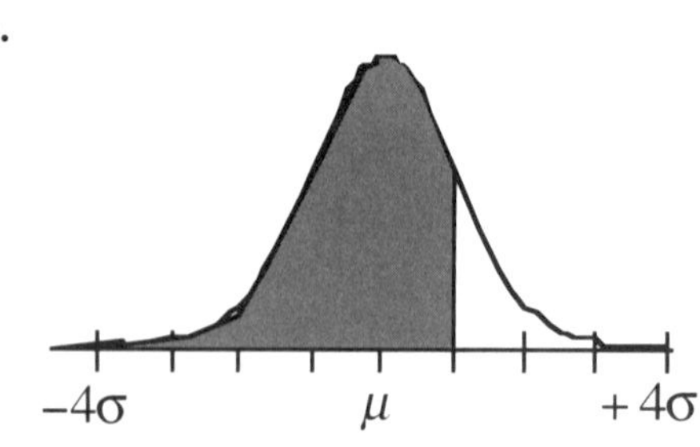

f.

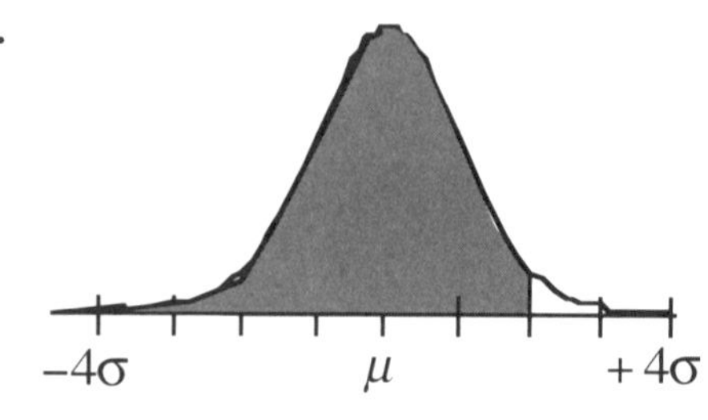

g.

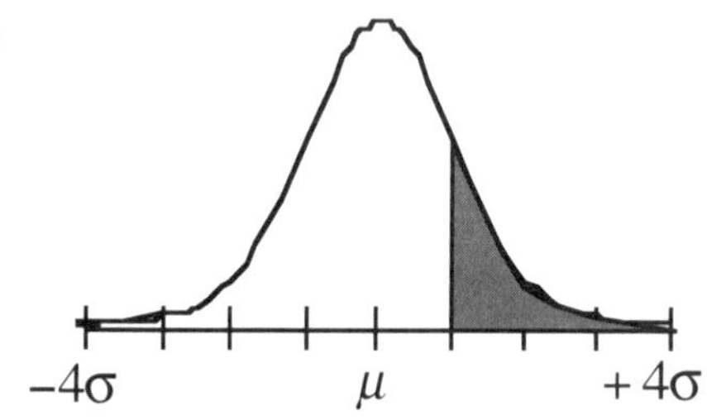

h.

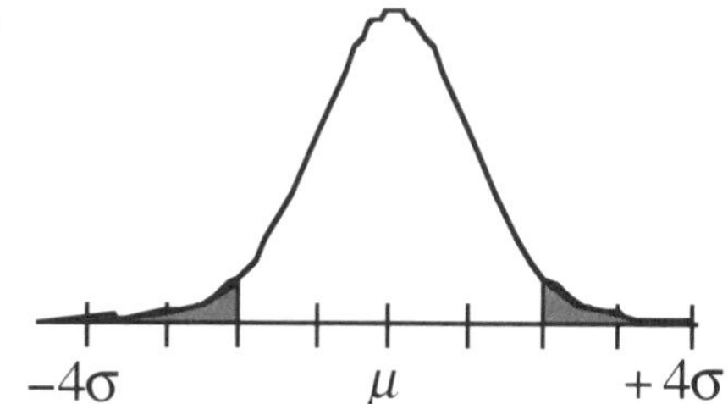

2. Identify the percentage of a normal distribution that corresponds with each of the following:

   a. left of $\mu - 3\sigma$

   b. left of $\mu - \sigma$

   c. left of $\mu + 2\sigma$

   d. right of $\mu - 2\sigma$

   e. right of μ

   f. right of $\mu + \sigma$

   g. right of $\mu + 3\sigma$

3. Determine the probability that the value of x is as described in each case below.

   a. $x < \mu - 1.25\sigma$

   b. $x > \mu + 0.54\sigma$

   c. $\mu - 2.34\sigma < x < \mu + 1.36\sigma$

Assignment

3.1 Rolf earned an 82 on an English exam that was normally distributed with $\mu = 80$ and $\sigma = 5$. Dena received a 77 on a physics exam that was normally distributed with $\mu = 72$ and $\sigma = 3$.

Rolf claims, "My score is better because 82 is greater than 77." Dena says, "No way! My score is better because the physics exam was tougher." Defend either Rolf's or Dena's position.

3.2 Consider a set of normally distributed test scores with $\mu = 79$ and $\sigma = 5$. What is the probability that a randomly selected score from this set is:

a. less than 70?

b. less than 85?

c. between 74 and 84?

d. between 75 and 90?

e. greater than 83?

3.3 In 1993, 1,044,465 students took the mathematics portion of the SAT. The test scores were normally distributed with $\mu = 478$ and $\sigma = 125$.

a. What percentage of students scored below 500 on the exam? (This is the percentile rank associated with a score of 500.)

b. Approximately how many people scored above 500 on the exam?

c. To be considered for a distinguished scholarship at the local university, a candidate must score in the 90th percentile or better (without rounding) on the mathematics portion of the SAT. In 1993, what score did a candidate have to obtain to be eligible for this award?

3.4 Is it possible for two sets of examination scores to exist in which a score of 90 on one test is not as good as a score of 47 on the other? Justify your response with examples.

* * * * *

3.5 A set of test scores is normally distributed with $\mu = 72$ and $\sigma = 3$.

a. If one test score is selected at random from this set, what is the probability that this score is:

1. greater than 74?
2. greater than 82?
3. greater than 68?
4. greater than 70?

b. Maeve scored 74 on this test. She claims she performed significantly better than the others who took the exam. Support or refute her claim.

3.6 The mean body temperature of a healthy person is approximately 37°C. Assume that body temperatures are normally distributed about this mean, with a standard deviation of 0.12°C. Within what range of values would you expect the temperature of 95% of healthy people fall?

Dena is writing an article on SAT scores for the John F. Kennedy High School student newspaper. While conducting research for her story, Dena obtains a random sample of 32 scores from the senior class. Although this sample does not include the scores of all seniors at John F. Kennedy High School, Dena believes that it will provide a good estimate of the population mean. Is she right?

Discussion 1

a. Recall that $\bar{x}$ represents the sample mean, μ the population mean, and $\mu_{\bar{x}}$ the mean of the sampling distribution of sample means. How do $\bar{x}$, μ, and $\mu_{\bar{x}}$ compare?

b. The standard deviation of the sampling distribution is denoted by $\sigma_{\bar{x}}$. How do σ and $\sigma_{\bar{x}}$ compare?

c. According to the central limit theorem, the distribution of sample means for sample sizes of at least 30 can be modeled reasonably well by a normal curve, even if the population from which samples are taken is not normally distributed.

   1. Consider a random sample of 50 test scores taken from a population of scores. Should the 68–95–99.7 rule be used to compare the sample mean to the population mean? Why or why not?

   2. Consider a random sample of 20 test scores taken from a population of scores. Should the 68–95–99.7 rule be used to compare this sample mean to the population mean? Why or why not?

d. Consider a sampling distribution with a mean of $\mu_{\bar{x}}$ and a standard deviation of $\sigma_{\bar{x}}$. Use a table of z-scores to determine the probability that a sample mean $\bar{x}$ selected at random from this distribution is:

   1. more than 1.6 standard deviations below the mean

   2. more than 2.3 standard deviations above the mean.

Exploration

Dena's sample of 32 scores has a mean of 529 and a standard deviation of 125. Assuming that these students represent a random sample of the class, Dena can use their mean and standard deviation to estimate the mean and standard deviation of the scores for the entire class.

The mean score on the mathematics portion of the SAT for last year's seniors was 478. Dena would like to claim that this year's seniors did better than last year's class.

Through hypothesis testing, you can determine if the difference between a sample mean and a population mean is expected or not. If the difference is greater than what might be expected due to the predictable variability among samples, the difference is said to be "significant."

a. Formulate the null and alternative hypotheses for the situation described above.

b. Just as any value x from a normally distributed population with mean μ and standard deviation σ can be represented by a z-score, so can any value $\bar{x}$ from a normally distributed population with mean $\mu_{\bar{x}}$ and standard deviation $\sigma_{\bar{x}}$. In this case, the z-score (denoted by $z_{\bar{x}}$) can be determined as follows:

$$z_{\bar{x}} = \frac{\bar{x} - \mu_{\bar{x}}}{\sigma_{\bar{x}}} = \frac{\bar{x} - \mu}{\sigma/\sqrt{n}}$$

Calculate the z-score for the sample mean of 529. Use the sample standard deviation of 125 as an estimate of the population standard deviation.

mathematics note

The **significance level** of a hypothesis test is an arbitrarily assigned probability that distinguishes a statistically significant difference from a chance variation. Traditionally, researchers set significance levels of 0.10, 0.05, or 0.01, then tested the hypothesis at the selected level.

Setting a 0.10 significance level, for example, requires that the sample give evidence against the null hypothesis so strong that this evidence would occur no more than 10% of the time, assuming that the null hypothesis is true. In other words, the chances of making the error of rejecting a true null hypothesis are less than 0.10, or 10%.

The **critical region** represents the set of all values that would lead a researcher to reject the null hypothesis. For example, suppose that a researcher has obtained a positive z-score for a statistic and selected a 0.10 significance level. From the table, the positive z-score associated with an area of 0.10 is 1.28. This value defines the boundary of the critical region, as shown in Figure **14-4.**

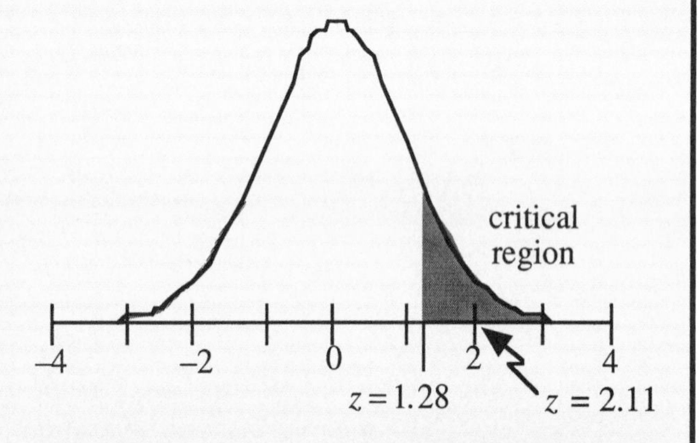

FIGURE 14-4

Critical region for 0.10 significance level.

If the z-score of the individual observation (or sample mean) falls in the critical region, the researcher should reject the null hypothesis. This indicates that the difference between the statistic and the population parameter is not due to predictable variability at the given level of significance.

For example, suppose that a sample of 50 test scores has a mean of 81.5. Is this sample from a population that is different from a population with a mean of 80 and a standard deviation of 5? In this situation, the null hypothesis is that there is no difference between the mean of the population from which the sample is taken and 80.

The sample size is greater than 30, therefore the central limit theorem applies, and the z-score can be calculated as follows:

$$z_{\bar{x}} = \frac{\bar{x} - \mu}{\sigma/\sqrt{n}} = \frac{81.5 - 80}{5/\sqrt{50}} \approx 2.11$$

The critical region for a 0.10 significance level is $z > 1.28$. This indicates that z-scores greater than 1.28 would occur by chance less than 10% of the time. Because the z-score of 2.11 is greater than 1.28, it falls in this critical region as shown in Figure **14-4.** The researcher should reject the null hypothesis at the 0.10 significance level.

If the researcher wanted to test at the 0.01 significance level, the critical region is $z > 2.33$. This indicates that z-scores greater than 2.33 would occur by chance less than 1% of the time. Since 2.11 is less than 2.33, the z-score falls outside the critical region. The researcher should fail to reject the null hypothesis at a 0.01 significance level.

c. Using a 0.05 significance level, determine the critical region for Dena's hypothesis test.

d. Determine whether Dena should reject, or fail to reject, the null hypothesis at the 0.05 significance level. Justify your choice.

e. Based on the results of the hypothesis test, what conclusion can you make?

Discussion 2

a. How does the description of significance given in the mathematics note compare with the ordinary definition of the word *significance?*

b. 1. How does the formula for the z-score of an individual observation (x) compare to the formula for the z-score of a sample mean ($\overline{x}$)?

   2. How is the value of $z_{\overline{x}}$ affected as the sample size n increases?

c. How did you determine the null and alternative hypotheses in Part **a** of the exploration?

d. Describe how you determined the critical region for a hypothesis test at a 0.05 significance level.

e. In what kinds of situations would a researcher select a 0.01 significance level rather than a 0.05 or 0.10 significance level?

f. 1. How did you justify your decision to reject, or fail to reject, the null hypothesis?

   2. Do you think that Dena should claim that this year's seniors did significantly better than last year's class on the SAT? Explain your response.

g. In some hypothesis tests, the critical region is determined by two values, not one. This occurs when the alternative hypothesis states that a parameter is not equal to a given value. In other words, the parameter could be greater than or less than a given value.

For example, to test the null hypothesis, H_0: $\mu = 5$, a researcher must consider possible values for μ that are both above and below 5. If a 0.05 significance level is desired, then the critical region is defined by $z = 1.96$ and $z = -1.96$, because approximately 95% of possible sample means fall within 1.96 standard deviations of μ.

1. Describe a graph of the critical region in this situation.
2. If the z-score for the statistic falls in the critical region, what should the researcher decide?

mathematics note

As computers and calculators have made statistical calculations less arduous, setting an arbitrary significance level has become less common. Today, researchers simply may report a ***p*-value** with their findings (the p is for *probability*).

A ***p*-value** represents the probability of obtaining a statistic greater than (or less than) the observed one if the null hypothesis is true.

For example, consider the sample of 50 test scores with a mean of 81.5 mentioned in the previous mathematics note. The question remains the same: Is this sample from a population that is different from a population with a mean of 80 and a standard deviation of 5?

Rather than assign an arbitrary significance level, however, a researcher might calculate the z-score of 2.11, then determine the corresponding p-value:

$$1 - 0.9826 = 0.0174.$$

h. How does a p-value of 0.0174 support a finding of difference at a 0.10 level of significance, but not at a 0.01 level of significance?

i. How is the magnitude of a z-score related to its corresponding p-value?

j. 1. Describe how you could find the p-value for Dena's hypothesis test in the exploration.

   2. At what significance level(s) would Dena's hypothesis appear to be supported? Justify your response.

k. How would you determine the p-value for a z-score in a hypothesis test like the one described in Part **g** of Discussion **2**?

Warm-Up

1. Consider a situation in which the null hypothesis is H_0: $\mu = 23$ and the alternative hypothesis is H_a: $\mu > 23$. A random sample of 50 items yields $\bar{x} = 23.3$ and $s = 1.1$. Use these statistics to test H_0 at each of the following levels of significance.

   a. 0.05

   b. 0.01

2. Consider a situation in which the null hypothesis is H_0: $\mu = 100$ and the alternative hypothesis is H_a: $\mu \neq 100$. A random sample of 48 items yields $\bar{x} = 99$ and $s = 5.5$. Use these statistics to test H_0 at the 0.10 level of significance.

3. Each of Parts **a–e** below lists H_a, a sample size n, the sample mean ($\bar{x}$), and the sample standard deviation (s). Determine the p-value for each situation, and describe what this value indicates about the significance level of the results.

   a. H_a: $\mu < 14$; $n = 49$; $\bar{x} = 12$; $s = 5.2$

   b. H_a: $\mu > 125$; $n = 144$; $\bar{x} = 128$; $s = 24$

   c. H_a: $\mu \neq 2450$; $n = 100$; $\bar{x} = 2435$; $s = 63.5$

   d. H_a: $\mu < 345$; $n = 58$; $\bar{x} = 339$; $s = 37$

   e. H_a: $\mu \neq 29$; $n = 35$; $\bar{x} = 29.5$; $s = 1.75$

Assignment

4.1 In 1993, 2234 students in the state of Montana took the mathematics portion of the SAT. A random sample of 100 of these students had a mean score of 516 with a standard deviation of 125.

The mean score on this test for students around the nation was 478. Could the governor of Montana claim that Montana students who took this test scored better than students nationally? To make this decision, complete the following steps.

a. State the null and alternative hypotheses in this situation.

b. Determine $z_{\bar{x}}$ for the sample statistic.

c. Decide whether to reject, or fail to reject, the null hypothesis. Justify your reasoning.

d. Use the results of the hypothesis test to state a conclusion.

4.2 The mean score on the mathematics portion of the SAT for one class of 32 students was 529, with a standard deviation of 110. The mean score statewide was 516. A parent would like to know if this class did better on the test than the rest of the students in the state.

a. Formulate null and alternative hypotheses for this situation.

b. Find the z-score for the sample mean.

c. Decide whether to reject, or fail to reject, the null hypothesis. Justify your reasoning.

d. Explain what your decision means in this situation.

4.3 The following table shows the scores for 40 seniors at Washington High School on the mathematics portion of the SAT.

530	610	520	440	490	530	500	480
770	530	520	510	460	450	460	500
420	490	530	500	510	560	540	620
500	600	550	470	580	460	520	530
500	500	540	640	610	450	670	540

a. Determine the mean and standard deviation for this data.

b. The national mean for this test was 478. Assuming that these 40 students represent a random sample of the entire class, do you think Washington High's seniors did better than the rest of the nation? Justify your response.

4.4 A set of scores on a physics exam are normally distributed with a mean of 72 and a standard deviation of 3. Four physics tests are found without names on them. The mean score of the four tests is 77. Is it reasonable to believe that these four tests came from this set of scores?

a. Formulate the null and alternative hypotheses for this situation.

b. Do you think that these four tests came from the physics class with a mean of 72? Explain your response.

4.5 An article in the *Daily News* reported that the mean height of women between the ages of 19 and 32 is 168 cm. In a letter to the editor, one reader insisted that this statement was untrue, arguing that the actual mean is less than 168 cm.

a. State the null and alternative hypotheses for the reader's claim.

b. To test the claim, the reader measured the heights of a random sample of 100 women between the ages of 19 and 32. The mean height in this sample was 164.5 cm, with a standard deviation of 16.2 cm. Find the z-score for the sample mean.

c. Using a 0.10 significance level, decide whether to reject, or fail to reject, the null hypothesis. Justify your reasoning.

d. What does your decision mean in this situation?

* * * * *

4.6 A liquid detergent company claims that their containers are filled with 1500 ml of soap. After analyzing a random sample of 48 containers, a consumer group found a mean of 1488 mL. When the group called the company for an explanation, the customer relations department admitted that the product has a population standard deviation of 47.5 mL. What should the consumer group conclude? Justify your reasoning.

4.7 An elevator has a recommended capacity of 15 people and a maximum load limit of 1200 kg. The masses of the population that uses this elevator are normally distributed with a mean of 75 kg and a standard deviation of 10 kg.

a. What is the probability that a random sample of 15 people from this population will exceed the maximum load limit?

b. What is the probability that a random sample of 16 people will exceed the load limit?

Summary Assessment

In a golden rectangle, the ratio of the measures of the longer side to the shorter side is the number $(1 + \sqrt{5})/2$, or about 1.618. The proportions of the golden rectangle are believed to be particularly pleasing to the human eye. For example, the outline of the Greek Parthenon resembles a golden rectangle, as does the face of each stone block in the Egyptian pyramids. In more modern times, the shapes of credit cards, driver's licenses, and the screens of many graphing calculators also are rough approximations of a golden rectangle.

The table below shows the length-to-width ratios of 30 beaded rectangles used to decorate Crow Indian leather goods:

1.706	1.706	1.704	1.178	1.176	1.175	1.916	1.502	1.919	1.912
1.504	1.499	1.890	1.701	1.894	1.704	1.887	1.698	1.880	1.942
1.159	2.237	1.751	2.242	2.232	1.754	1.748	2.066	2.075	2.070

From this data, does it appear that the Crow Indians also incorporated the golden ratio in their beaded designs? Use statistical analysis to support your belief. Test your null hypothesis at the 0.10, 0.05, and 0.01 significance levels, and report a p-value as well. Assume that the data are normally distributed. **Note:** Use the standard deviation of the sample as an estimate of σ.

Module Summary

* In statistical analysis, there are two types of hypotheses. A **null hypothesis (H_0)** is a statement about one or more parameters. The **alternative hypothesis (H_a)** is the statement that must be true if the null hypothesis is false. The null hypothesis usually involves a claim of no relationship or no difference. When stated using mathematical symbols, it typically contains an equals sign. In many situations, the null hypothesis and alternative hypothesis are negations of each other, but this is not necessarily the case.

* A **hypothesis test** may consist of the following steps.

  1. State null and alternative hypotheses about a parameter of a population.
  2. If the null hypothesis is true, predict what this implies about a sample of the population.
  3. Take a sample of the population and compare the results with your prediction.
  4. If the results are not consistent with the prediction, then you can conclude, with some level of certainty, that the null hypothesis is false and, therefore, reject it.
  5. If the results are consistent with the prediction, you fail to reject the null hypothesis. The failure to reject the null hypothesis does not guarantee that the null hypothesis is true, only that it might be true.

* Whenever a sample is taken of a population about which there is some uncertainty, it is possible that the sample is not representative of the population. Therefore, when performing a hypothesis test by sampling it is always possible to make an incorrect decision about the null hypothesis H_0. The two possible errors are rejecting a true null hypothesis and failing to reject a false null hypothesis.

* The **central limit theorem** states that, even if the population from which samples are taken is not normally distributed, the distribution of the means of all possible samples of the same size will be approximately normal.

  Statisticians generally agree that for $n \geq 30$, the distribution of sample means can be modeled reasonably well by a normal curve. This approximation becomes more accurate as n increases. A sample size of at least 30 is not required if the population itself is normally distributed.

* The mean of the distribution of all sample means, $\mu_{\bar{x}}$, equals μ, the population mean. The **standard deviation of all sample means,** denoted $\sigma_{\bar{x}}$, can be calculated using the following formula:

$$\sigma_{\bar{x}} = \frac{\sigma}{\sqrt{n}}$$

  where σ is the standard deviation of the population and n is the sample size. The value of $\sigma_{\bar{x}}$ is sometimes called the **standard error of the mean.**

- A **confidence interval** for a population mean μ is an interval of numbers in which you would expect to find the value of μ. The 68–95–99.7 rule for a normal distribution implies the following:

  For approximately 68% of all sample means $\bar{x}$, the confidence interval $[\bar{x} - \sigma_{\bar{x}}, \bar{x} + \sigma_{\bar{x}}]$ contains the population mean μ. This interval also can be written as $\bar{x} \pm \sigma_{\bar{x}}$.

  For approximately 95% of all sample means $\bar{x}$, the confidence interval $[\bar{x} - 2\sigma_{\bar{x}}, \bar{x} + 2\sigma_{\bar{x}}]$ contains the population mean μ. This also interval can be written as $\bar{x} \pm 2\sigma_{\bar{x}}$.

  For approximately 99.7% of all sample means $\bar{x}$, the confidence interval $[\bar{x} - 3\sigma_{\bar{x}}, \bar{x} + 3\sigma_{\bar{x}}]$ contains the population mean μ. This interval also can be written as $\bar{x} \pm 3\sigma_{\bar{x}}$.

  The values $\pm\sigma_{\bar{x}}$, $\pm 2\sigma_{\bar{x}}$, and $\pm 3\sigma_{\bar{x}}$ are the **margins of error** for the estimate of the population parameter.

- Any value x from a normally distributed population with mean μ and standard deviation σ can be represented by a **standardized score** or ***z*-score.** A z-score describes the number of standard deviations that the value is above or below the mean. The formula for determining a z-score is shown below:

$$z = \frac{x - \mu}{\sigma}$$

- Any value $\bar{x}$ from a normally distributed population with mean μ and standard deviation $\sigma_{\bar{x}}$ can be represented by a ***z*-score** as follows:

$$z_{\bar{x}} = \frac{\bar{x} - \mu}{\sigma_{\bar{x}}}$$

- The **significance level** of a hypothesis test is an arbitrarily assigned probability that distinguishes a statistically significant difference from a chance variation. Traditionally, researchers set significance levels of 0.10, 0.05, or 0.01, then tested their hypothesis at the selected level. Today, researchers may simply report a p-value with their findings.

- A ***p*-value** represents the probability of obtaining a statistic greater than (or less than) the observed one if the null hypothesis is true.

- The **critical region** represents the set of all values that would lead a researcher to reject the null hypothesis. If the z-score of the individual observation (or sample mean) falls in the critical region, this indicates that the difference between the statistic and the population parameter is not due to predictable variability at the given level of significance. Therefore, the researcher should reject the null hypothesis.

Area under Normal Curve to Left of Z-Score										
z	**0.00**	**0.01**	**0.02**	**0.03**	**0.04**	**0.05**	**0.06**	**0.07**	**0.08**	**0.09**
−3.4	0.0003	0.0003	0.0003	0.0003	0.0003	0.0003	0.0003	0.0003	0.0003	0.0002
−3.3	0.0005	0.0005	0.0005	0.0004	0.0004	0.0004	0.0004	0.0004	0.0004	0.0003
−3.2	0.0007	0.0007	0.0006	0.0006	0.0006	0.0006	0.0006	0.0005	0.0005	0.0005
−3.1	0.0010	0.0009	0.0009	0.0009	0.0008	0.0008	0.0008	0.0008	0.0007	0.0007
−3.0	0.0013	0.0013	0.0013	0.0012	0.0012	0.0011	0.0011	0.0011	0.0010	0.0010
−2.9	0.0019	0.0018	0.0018	0.0017	0.0016	0.0016	0.0015	0.0015	0.0014	0.0014
−2.8	0.0026	0.0025	0.0024	0.0023	0.0023	0.0022	0.0021	0.0021	0.0020	0.0019
−2.7	0.0035	0.0034	0.0033	0.0032	0.0031	0.0030	0.0029	0.0028	0.0027	0.0026
−2.6	0.0047	0.0045	0.0044	0.0043	0.0041	0.0040	0.0039	0.0038	0.0037	0.0036
−2.5	0.0062	0.0060	0.0059	0.0057	0.0055	0.0054	0.0052	0.0051	0.0049	0.0048
−2.4	0.0082	0.0080	0.0078	0.0075	0.0073	0.0071	0.0069	0.0068	0.0066	0.0064
−2.3	0.0107	0.0104	0.0102	0.0099	0.0096	0.0094	0.0091	0.0089	0.0087	0.0084
−2.2	0.0139	0.0136	0.0132	0.0129	0.0125	0.0122	0.0119	0.0116	0.0113	0.0110
−2.1	0.0179	0.0174	0.0170	0.0166	0.0162	0.0158	0.0154	0.0150	0.0146	0.0143
−2.0	0.0228	0.0222	0.0217	0.0212	0.0207	0.0202	0.0197	0.0192	0.0188	0.0183
−1.9	0.0287	0.0281	0.0274	0.0268	0.0262	0.0256	0.0250	0.0244	0.0239	0.0233
−1.8	0.0359	0.0351	0.0344	0.0336	0.0329	0.0322	0.0314	0.0307	0.0301	0.0294
−1.7	0.0446	0.0436	0.0427	0.0418	0.0409	0.0401	0.0392	0.0384	0.0375	0.0367
−1.6	0.0548	0.0537	0.0526	0.0516	0.0505	0.0495	0.0485	0.0475	0.0465	0.0455
−1.5	0.0668	0.0655	0.0643	0.0630	0.0618	0.0606	0.0594	0.0582	0.0571	0.0559
−1.4	0.0808	0.0793	0.0778	0.0764	0.0749	0.0735	0.0721	0.0708	0.0694	0.0681
−1.3	0.0968	0.0951	0.0934	0.0918	0.0901	0.0885	0.0869	0.0853	0.0838	0.0823
−1.2	0.1151	0.1131	0.1112	0.1093	0.1075	0.1056	0.1038	0.1020	0.1003	0.0985
−1.1	0.1357	0.1335	0.1314	0.1292	0.1271	0.1251	0.1230	0.1210	0.1190	0.1170
−1.0	0.1587	0.1562	0.1539	0.1515	0.1492	0.1469	0.1446	0.1423	0.1401	0.1379
−0.9	0.1841	0.1814	0.1788	0.1762	0.1736	0.1711	0.1685	0.1660	0.1635	0.1611
−0.8	0.2119	0.2090	0.2061	0.2033	0.2005	0.1977	0.1949	0.1922	0.1894	0.1867
−0.7	0.2420	0.2389	0.2358	0.2327	0.2296	0.2266	0.2236	0.2206	0.2177	0.2148
−0.6	0.2743	0.2709	0.2676	0.2643	0.2611	0.2578	0.2546	0.2514	0.2483	0.2451
−0.5	0.3085	0.3050	0.3015	0.2981	0.2946	0.2912	0.2877	0.2843	0.2810	0.2776
−0.4	0.3446	0.3409	0.3372	0.3336	0.3300	0.3264	0.3228	0.3192	0.3156	0.3121
−0.3	0.3821	0.3783	0.3745	0.3707	0.3669	0.3632	0.3594	0.3557	0.3520	0.3483
−0.2	0.4207	0.4168	0.4129	0.4090	0.4052	0.4013	0.3974	0.3936	0.3897	0.3859
−0.1	0.4602	0.4562	0.4522	0.4483	0.4443	0.4404	0.4364	0.4325	0.4286	0.4247
0.0	0.5000	0.4960	0.4920	0.4880	0.4840	0.4801	0.4761	0.4721	0.4681	0.4641

Area under Normal Curve to Left of *Z*-Score										
z	**0.00**	**0.01**	**0.02**	**0.03**	**0.04**	**0.05**	**0.06**	**0.07**	**0.08**	**0.09**
0.0	0.5000	0.5040	0.5080	0.5120	0.5160	0.5199	0.5239	0.5279	0.5319	0.5359
0.1	0.5398	0.5438	0.5478	0.5517	0.5557	0.5596	0.5636	0.5675	0.5714	0.5753
0.2	0.5793	0.5832	0.5871	0.5910	0.5948	0.5987	0.6026	0.6064	0.6103	0.6141
0.3	0.6179	0.6217	0.6255	0.6293	0.6331	0.6368	0.6406	0.6443	0.6480	0.6517
0.4	0.6554	0.6591	0.6628	0.6664	0.6700	0.6736	0.6772	0.6808	0.6844	0.6879
0.5	0.6915	0.6950	0.6985	0.7019	0.7054	0.7088	0.7123	0.7157	0.7190	0.7224
0.6	0.7257	0.7291	0.7324	0.7357	0.7389	0.7422	0.7454	0.7486	0.7517	0.7549
0.7	0.7580	0.7611	0.7642	0.7673	0.7704	0.7734	0.7764	0.7794	0.7823	0.7852
0.8	0.7881	0.7910	0.7939	0.7967	0.7995	0.8023	0.8051	0.8078	0.8106	0.8133
0.9	0.8159	0.8186	0.8212	0.8238	0.8264	0.8289	0.8315	0.8340	0.8365	0.8389
1.0	0.8413	0.8438	0.8461	0.8485	0.8508	0.8531	0.8554	0.8577	0.8599	0.8621
1.1	0.8643	0.8665	0.8686	0.8708	0.8729	0.8749	0.8770	0.8790	0.8810	0.8830
1.2	0.8849	0.8869	0.8888	0.8907	0.8925	0.8944	0.8962	0.8980	0.8997	0.9015
1.3	0.9032	0.9049	0.9066	0.9082	0.9099	0.9115	0.9131	0.9147	0.9162	0.9177
1.4	0.9192	0.9207	0.9222	0.9236	0.9251	0.9265	0.9279	0.9292	0.9306	0.9319
1.5	0.9332	0.9345	0.9357	0.9370	0.9382	0.9394	0.9406	0.9418	0.9429	0.9441
1.6	0.9452	0.9463	0.9474	0.9484	0.9495	0.9505	0.9515	0.9525	0.9535	0.9545
1.7	0.9554	0.9564	0.9573	0.9582	0.9591	0.9599	0.9608	0.9616	0.9625	0.9633
1.8	0.9641	0.9649	0.9656	0.9664	0.9671	0.9678	0.9686	0.9693	0.9699	0.9706
1.9	0.9713	0.9719	0.9726	0.9732	0.9738	0.9744	0.9750	0.9756	0.9761	0.9767
2.0	0.9772	0.9778	0.9783	0.9788	0.9793	0.9798	0.9803	0.9808	0.9812	0.9817
2.1	0.9821	0.9826	0.9830	0.9834	0.9838	0.9842	0.9846	0.9850	0.9854	0.9857
2.2	0.9861	0.9864	0.9868	0.9871	0.9875	0.9878	0.9881	0.9884	0.9887	0.9890
2.3	0.9893	0.9896	0.9898	0.9901	0.9904	0.9906	0.9909	0.9911	0.9913	0.9916
2.4	0.9918	0.9920	0.9922	0.9925	0.9927	0.9929	0.9931	0.9932	0.9934	0.9936
2.5	0.9938	0.9940	0.9941	0.9943	0.9945	0.9946	0.9948	0.9949	0.9951	0.9952
2.6	0.9953	0.9955	0.9956	0.9957	0.9959	0.9960	0.9961	0.9962	0.9963	0.9964
2.7	0.9965	0.9966	0.9967	0.9968	0.9969	0.9970	0.9971	0.9972	0.9973	0.9974
2.8	0.9974	0.9975	0.9976	0.9977	0.9977	0.9978	0.9979	0.9979	0.9980	0.9981
2.9	0.9981	0.9982	0.9982	0.9983	0.9984	0.9984	0.9985	0.9985	0.9986	0.9986
3.0	0.9987	0.9987	0.9987	0.9988	0.9988	0.9989	0.9989	0.9989	0.9990	0.9990
3.1	0.9990	0.9991	0.9991	0.9991	0.9992	0.9992	0.9992	0.9992	0.9993	0.9993
3.2	0.9993	0.9993	0.9994	0.9994	0.9994	0.9994	0.9994	0.9995	0.9995	0.9995
3.3	0.9995	0.9995	0.9995	0.9996	0.9996	0.9996	0.9996	0.9996	0.9996	0.9997
3.4	0.9997	0.9997	0.9997	0.9997	0.9997	0.9997	0.9997	0.9997	0.9997	0.9998

module 15

Risky Business

Introduction

Cars and driving play prominent roles in our society, so automobile accidents are everyone's concern. The annual cost of auto accidents amounts to billions of dollars. Often, the cost of even a single accident can be too high for the average family budget. Insurance companies can be used to help with these costs.

business note

Insurance companies provide protection against the costs of accidents in exchange for a fee. The fee for this service is an insurance **premium,** and the contract with the insurance company is an **insurance policy**. The people who pay insurance premiums are **policyholders.**

Figure **15-1** shows an example of a premium renewal notice for an automobile driven by an individual in the 16–20 age category.

SIMMS Insurance Company

Car Policy Number: 542–45983325

Continuous Renewal Policy			Classification	1121
Effective		Expires	Term (Month)	06
05-08	to	11-08	Acc/Viol points	0/0
12:01 A.M. Standard Time			Territory	14

Coverage is subject to the terms of the policy*

Coverage	Limit of Liability		Premium
Bodily Injury Liability	Each Person	$100,000	$362.30
	Each Occurrence	$300,000	
Property Damage Liability	Each Occurrence	$ 50,000	$213.20
Medical Payments	Each Person	$ 5,000	$190.60
Comprehensive	Actual cash value / $100 deductible		$207.50
Collision	Actual cash value / $250 deductible		$262.20
Uninsured Motor Vehicle	Each Person	$ 25,000	$32.70
Bodily Injury	Each Accident	$ 50,000	
		Total Premium	$1268.50
		Previous Balance	$ 0.00
		Premium Charge	$1268.50
		Payment Credit	$ 0.00
		Current Balance	$1268.50

****

*Your premium is based on the following: Principal driver under 21.
If not correct, please contact your agent.

FIGURE 15-1 **Premium renewal notice.**

Discussion

a. How would you calculate the annual premium of the policy in Figure **15-1**?

b. Does this premium seem reasonable?

c. How do you think this premium would compare with the premium for a driver in the 35–44 age category?

d. If the policyholder who received this renewal notice has an accident, do you think that the premium will change on the next renewal notice? Explain your response.

e. What factors do you think are considered by an insurance company when determining an individual's premium?

business note

Bodily injury liability insurance pays for any individual who is injured as a result of the negligent operation of the insured vehicle.

Collision insurance covers the cost of repairing the insured vehicle when the damage is due to its negligent operation.

Comprehensive insurance covers natural damage (by floods, hail, or storms), theft, or vandalism of the insured car.

Property damage liability insurance covers the cost of damages to another person's property caused by the negligent operation of the insured vehicle.

f. Give an example of an accident that would be covered by each type of insurance described in the business note above.

g. What additional information appears on the renewal notice? What do you think this information means?

ACTIVITY 1

Driving an automobile involves risk. Billboards, news stories, and magazine articles provide daily reminders of the hazards of the road. In this activity, you use statistics and probability to simulate the risks of driving.

Exploration

To determine the probability of a policyholder having an accident, insurance companies use accident statistics like those in Table **15-1.** In this exploration, you investigate the importance of considering the number of policyholders when making predictions based on such probabilities.

Table **15-1** summarizes U.S. automobile accident statistics for 2003. The entries in the table are given per 100,000 licensed drivers. For example, the entry in the right-hand column of the third row indicates that there were 6364 accidents for every 100,000 licensed drivers in the 25–34 age category. Of this total, 2081 were in the bodily-injury category, and 4283 were in the property-damage-only category.

TABLE 15-1 ■ *Accidents Per 100,000 Licensed Drivers in 2003*

Age	Bodily Injury (fatal and non-fatal)	Property Damage Only	Total
16–20	4757	10,801	15,558
21–24	3005	5965	8970
25–34	2081	4283	6364
35–44	1722	3495	5217
45–54	1393	2953	4346
55–64	1158	2426	3584
65–74	1002	2730	3732
75 or older	953	1734	2687

SOURCE: Federal Highway Administration, 2004.

a. Use the data in Table **15-1** to estimate the probability that a randomly selected driver in the 16–20 age category was involved in an automobile accident in 2003. Round the probability to the nearest hundredth.

b. Use a random number generator to design a simulation that predicts the driving record of a person in the 16–20 age category during one year.

c. Suppose that an insurance company has n policyholders in the 16–20 age category. While it is not possible to predict exactly how many of these drivers will be involved in an accident during the year, insurance companies need to know the approximate percentage of their policyholders who will have accidents.

   1. Use the simulation developed in Part **b** to model the driving records of different numbers of policyholders for 1 year. Record the numbers of accidents in a table with headings like those in Table **15-2.**

TABLE 15-2 ■ *Simulation Results*

Number of Policyholders	Number of Accidents	Accident Rate
5		
25		
50		
100		
250		
500		
1000		

2. For each row in Table **15-2,** determine the ratio of the number of accidents to the number of policyholders. This is the accident rate. Record these ratios, in decimal form, in Table **15-2.**

d. The percentage of drivers in a specific age group who have accidents will vary from year to year. Assume that each class member's simulation represents a different year for the same age group.

   To see how the accident rate can vary, collect the class data and determine the difference between the smallest and largest accident rates obtained for each value of n.

Discussion

a. Why is it reasonable to use the data in Table **15-1** to determine the probability that a randomly selected driver in the 16–20 age category has an accident?

b. Based on the data in Table **15-1,** how do the driving records of groups in the various age categories compare?

c. What are some limitations of the simulation you developed in the exploration for modeling actual driving records?

d. Compare the accident rates for different numbers of policyholders obtained in Part **c** of the exploration.

e. Describe the trend in the differences between the least and greatest accident rates obtained in Part **d** of the exploration as the number of policyholders increases.

f. Compare the accident rates for each number of policyholders with the probability calculated in Part **a** of the exploration.

g. If you continued this simulation using larger numbers of policyholders, what number do you think the accident rate would approach?

mathematics note

The **law of large numbers** indicates that, if a large random sample is taken from a population, the sample proportion has a high probability of being very close to the population proportion.

For example, it would not be uncommon for a random sample of 10 children from a population with 50% females to contain 8 females and 2 males (a sample proportion of 0.8). On the other hand, it is highly unlikely that a random sample of 10,000 children from this population would contain 8000 females and 2000 males. For large sample sizes, it is much more likely that the proportion of females in the sample would be close to 0.5, the population proportion.

h. Would it be practical for an insurance company to use statistics based on a sample of 100 drivers to determine the probability of 1 driver being involved in an accident?

i. Based on the data in Table **15-1,** the probability that a randomly selected driver in the 16–20 age category had an accident during 2003 is approximately 0.16. Do you think this is a reliable statistic? Explain your response.

Warm-Up

1. Use the following statistics to estimate the probability that a randomly selected member of the population from which the samples were taken will have the given characteristic.

   a. In a random sample of 1084 adults, 813 indicated that they believed there is too much violence on television.

   b. In a nationwide survey of vehicle accidents, a random sample of 64,000 accidents included 41,600 involving property damage of $800 or less.

   c. Among a sample of 90 randomly selected hospital patients, 41 had type O blood.

   d. In a random sample of 750 taxpayers with incomes under $100,000, the Internal Revenue Service had audited 25.

2. **a.** Which estimate in Problem **1** do you believe is the most reliable? Explain your response.

   b. Which estimate do you believe is the least reliable? Explain your response.

Assignment

1.1 Consider the probability that a newborn baby, selected at random, is a girl. Assume that this probability is 0.5.

   a. Design a simulation that predicts the gender of a randomly selected newborn baby.

   b. Use your simulation to complete the following table. Express the proportion of girls to total births to the nearest hundredth.

Number of Births	Proportion of Girls
10	
20	
40	
80	
100	
200	
300	
400	
500	

   c. **1.** Create a connected scatterplot of the proportion of girls versus the number of births.

   2. Graph the line $y = 0.5$ on the same coordinate system. This line represents the probability that a randomly selected newborn is a girl.

   d. Does your graph in Part **c** illustrate the law of large numbers? Explain your response.

1.2 An actuary is a mathematician employed by an insurance company to predict events on which policy premiums are based.

   a. Why is the accident rate important when determining premiums?

   b. Why would an actuary consider a larger group a better basis for making predictions than a smaller group?

1.3 Insurance companies compile accident data from previous years. This historical data is used to determine the probabilities of drivers being involved in accidents in the future. To make predictions, insurance companies treat these probabilities as theoretical probabilities for the current year.

What are some limitations of using the previous year's accident statistics to make predictions about the current year?

1.4 **a.** The following table shows the probabilities that a driver in the 16–20 age category has a bodily-injury accident, a property-damage-only accident, or no accident. All the values in the first row are based on information contained in Table **15-1.** Explain how these probabilities were calculated.

Accident Probabilities				
Age	Bodily Injury	Property Damage Only	No Accident	Total
16–20	0.05	0.11	0.84	1
21–24				
25–34				
35–44				
45–54				
55–64				
65–74				
75 or older				

b. What is represented by the 1 in the column with the heading "Total"?

c. Copy and complete the table using the data from Table **15-1.**

d. Write a paragraph comparing the probabilities of having a bodily-injury or property-damage-only accident as the age of the driver increases. Discuss some possible reasons for the differences in these probabilities.

1.5 As shown in the following graph, the number of fatal automobile accidents in 1992 varied among age categories. One curve displays the number of fatal accidents for every 100 million miles driven. The other illustrates the number of fatal accidents for every 10,000 licensed drivers.

For example, drivers in the 16–19 age category had about 9 fatal accidents for every 100 million miles driven, and about 6 fatal accidents for every 10,000 licensed drivers. In the 65–69 age category, there were about 4 fatal accidents for every 100 million miles driven, and about 2 fatal accidents per 10,000 drivers.

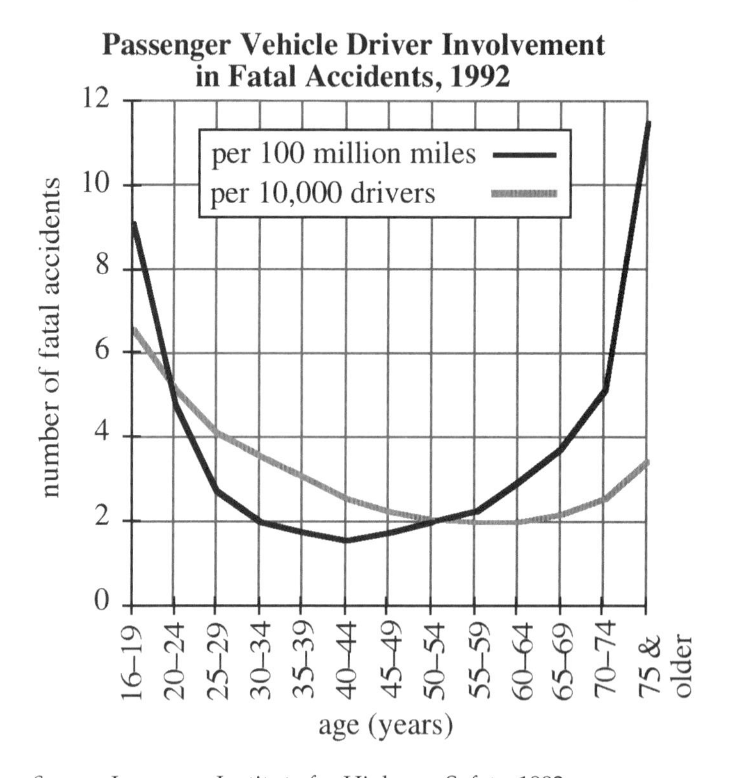

Source: Insurance Institute for Highway Safety, 1992.

a. What statistic in the graph seems to indicate that drivers in the "75 and older" category are better drivers than teenage drivers?

b. What statistic in the graph seems to indicate that teenage drivers are better drivers than those in the "75 and older" category?

c. **1.** Depending on the statistics you select, there are two different age categories with the best driving records. Identify those categories and explain why this is possible.

2. Based on the information in the graph, which age category do you believe has the best driving skills? Explain your response.

d. Using the statistics in the graph, describe the risks encountered over a lifetime of driving. Your answer should include some possible explanations for the changes in risk over time.

* * * * *

1.6 **a.** If a coin was flipped 5 times and came up heads 4 times, would you suspect that the coin was unfair? Explain your response.

b. Create a simulation that models 1000 flips of a coin. Run this simulation 10 times and record the number of times 800 or more heads are counted.

c. If the coin from Part **a** was flipped 10,000 times and 8000 of the tosses were heads, would you suspect the coin was unfair? Explain your response.

The cost of an automobile accident can range from a few dollars to well over a million. Typically, insurance companies pay part of these costs for insured drivers. To obtain benefits, policyholders must file an insurance **claim.** A claim reports the details and costs of an accident and requests payment. The claim value is the amount paid by the company.

If you were involved in an accident, how much might you expect your claim value to be? To answer this question, you will first examine some historical data.

Exploration 1

Insurance companies consider all claims made in a year and use the information from these claims to set premium costs for future years. In this exploration, you examine a method used by insurance companies to compile this information.

a. Table **15-3** below shows 40 bodily injury claims filed with an insurance company in 1990.

TABLE 15-3 ■ *Insurance Claims in 1990, in Dollars*

3,300	15,236	15,461	570
562	175	4,589	1,131
7,200	1,802	4,200	250
888	52	3,563	111
3,900	3,250	2,252	23,898
1,402	290	700	8,550
89	4,300	4,602	388
12,889	5,300	1,244	20,500
20,336	995	13,202	94
410	23,555	4,001	1,452

1. Sort these claim values from least to greatest.
2. Divide the sorted claim values into 10 sets of 4 claim values each. These 10 sets are **deciles.**

b. Calculate the mean of each decile. Record the means in a table with headings like those in Table **15-4** below.

TABLE 15-4 ■ ***Mean Claim Amounts for 1990, by Decile***	
Decile	**Mean Claim Value ($)**
1	
2	
3	
⋮	
10	

c. From 1985 to 1990, the consumer price index increased at an average annual rate of 4.1%. Assuming that this trend continued, estimate the mean claim amounts, by decile, for 1992.

Discussion 1

a. Suppose that an insurance company compiles data for 25 million claims in a given year. Describe the process of finding the mean decile values for that year.

b. If each decile represented 1 million claims, how could you determine the total number of claims in the data set?

c. Describe the model you used to estimate the mean claim amounts for 1992.

Exploration 2

After collecting and analyzing historical data, insurance companies must determine the amount in claims they can expect per policyholder.

a. The information in Table **15-5** summarizes data from approximately 25 million bodily-injury claims and 120 million property-damage claims.

TABLE 15-5 ■ *Mean Claim Amounts in 1992, by Decile*		
Decile	**Bodily Injury ($)**	**Property Damage ($)**
1	125	47
2	378	150
3	753	266
4	1400	389
5	2300	527
6	3550	699
7	5400	936
8	8000	1313
9	13,250	2061
10	24,380	3462

1. Determine the number of property-damage claims represented in each decile.
2. Determine the probability that a randomly selected bodily-injury claim falls in the third decile.

mathematics note

A **random variable** X is a variable that takes on each of its possible values with a specific probability. Given possible values for X of $x_1, x_2, \ldots, x_k$, each has its corresponding probability $p_1, p_2, \ldots, p_k$. The sum of these probabilities is 1.

For example, consider an insurance company that pays $6000 for a bodily-injury accident, $1000 for a property-damage-only accident, and $0 for no accident. A random variable X could be used to represent claim values as follows: $x_1 = \$6000$, $x_2 = \$1000$, and $x_3 = \$0$.

A **probability distribution** for a random variable X assigns probabilities $p_1, p_2, \ldots, p_k$ to the values $x_1, x_2, \ldots, x_k$ for X.

For example, if the probabilities for a bodily-injury accident, property-damage-only accident, and no accident in a given year are 0.08, 0.02, and 0.90, respectively, then the probability distribution for X is shown in Table **15-6.**

TABLE 15-6 ■ *Probability Distribution for X*

Outcome	Bodily Injury	Property Damage	No Accident
Value of X	$6000	$1000	$0
Probability	0.08	0.02	0.90

The **expected value** or **mean** of a random variable X, denoted $E(X)$, is the sum of the products of each possible value of X and its respective probability:

$$E(X) = x_1p_1 + x_2p_2 + \cdots + x_kp_k = \sum_{i=1}^{k} x_ip_i$$

Using the probability distribution in Table **15-6,** for example, the expected value of the claims per insured driver during one year can be found as follows:

$$E(X) = \$6000(0.08) + \$1000(0.02) + \$0(0.90) = \$500$$

b. Table **15-7** shows the probabilities of a bodily-injury accident, a property-damage-only accident, or no accident for a driver in the 16–20 age category. (These are the values you found in Problem **1.4** using the information from Table **15-1.**)

TABLE 15-7 ■ *Accident Probabilities for the 16–20 Age Category*

Bodily Injury	Property Damage Only	No Accident
0.05	0.11	0.84

A claim value selected at random is equally likely to fall in any given decile. Therefore, the probability of a driver having a claim value for a bodily-injury accident in any given decile is $0.05(1/10) = 0.005$. The probability of a driver having a claim value for a property-damage-only accident in any given decile is $0.11(1/10) \approx 0.011$.

Using the 1992 claim values from Table **15-5,** create a probability distribution for the random variable *C*, where *C* is assigned to the set of claim values for a driver in the 16–20 age category. As noted in Table **15-8** below, the claim value is $0 if the driver does not have an accident.

TABLE 15-8 ■ *Probability Distribution for C*

	Bodily Injury		Property Damage		No Accident	
Decile	**Claim ($)**	**Prob.**	**Claim ($)**	**Prob.**	**Claim ($)**	**Prob.**
1					0	
2					0	
3					0	
4					0	
5					0	
6					0	
7					0	
8					0	
9					0	
10					0	

c. Determine the expected value of *C*.

Discussion 2

a. Describe the significance to an insurance company of the value found in Part **c** of the exploration.

b. In Part **b** of Exploration **2,** how many possible values are there for the random variable *C*?

c. Explain how an insurance company might use the expected value of *C* to determine an annual premium for drivers in a given age category.

d. A weighted mean is a representative value for a set of numbers in which each number may be assigned a different relative importance.

For example, suppose that a teacher has decided that each of three research projects should count for 1/5 of a student's final grade, while each of four test scores determine 1/10 of the grade. If a student receives scores of 76, 87, and 92 on the research projects, and 88, 75, 82, and 96 on the tests, the final grade could be calculated as follows:

$$0.2(76) + 0.2(87) + 0.2(92) + 0.1(88) + 0.1(75) + 0.1(82) + 0.1(96) \approx 85$$

Compare the expected value of a random variable to a weighted mean.

Warm-Up

1. Consider an experiment that involves rolling an ordinary six-sided die. The possible outcomes of this experiment are assigned to a random variable X. Create a probability distribution for X.

2. Determine the expected value of X in Problem **1** and describe what this value represents in terms of the experiment.

Assignment

2.1 **a.** The data in Table **15-5** summarizes approximately 25 million bodily-injury claims and 120 million property-damage claims. Estimate the total value of these claims.

b. In 1992, the U.S. population was approximately 256 million. Use your estimate from Part **a** to determine the cost per person represented by the claims in Table **15-5.**

2.2 **a.** From 1992 to 2005, the consumer price index increased at an average annual rate of 2.5%. Given this fact, determine a model you could use to predict claim values in future years.

b. Use your model and the data in Table **15-5** to predict mean decile values for the current year. **Note:** Save your work for use in Problems **2.3** and **2.4.**

c. The table below shows the probabilities of a bodily-injury accident, a property-damage-only accident, or no accident for a driver in the 21–24 age category.

Bodily Injury	Property Damage Only	No Accident
0.03	0.06	0.91

Use this table and the predicted values from Part **b** to create a probability distribution, then find the expected claim value for a driver in the 21–24 age category.

2.3 **a.** Use the predicted decile values from Problem **2.2b** to find a mean bodily-injury claim value and a mean property-damage-only claim value for the current year.

b. Let the random variable C represent the claim values for a driver in the 21–24 age category during a given year. Use the mean claim values from Part **a** to complete the probability distribution for C.

Probability Distribution for C			
Outcome	**Bodily Injury**	**Property Damage**	**No Accident**
Value of C			$0
Probability	0.03	0.06	0.91

c. Determine the expected value of C and describe what it represents to an insurance company.

2.4 In Problem **2.3c,** expected value was found by multiplying each of the decile values by its corresponding probability. Each of these probabilities was determined by dividing a given probability by 10, the number of equally likely outcomes in that category. This method can be represented using the following equation:

$$
\begin{aligned}
E(C) = {} & x_1 \bullet \left(\frac{p_1}{10}\right) + x_2 \bullet \left(\frac{p_1}{10}\right) + \cdots + x_{10} \bullet \left(\frac{p_1}{10}\right) \\
& + x_{11} \bullet \left(\frac{p_2}{10}\right) + x_{12} \bullet \left(\frac{p_2}{10}\right) + \cdots + x_{20} \bullet \left(\frac{p_2}{10}\right) \\
& + 0 \bullet p_3
\end{aligned}
$$

In Problem **2.3c,** expected value was found by averaging the claim values for each category, then multiplying each mean by the given probability. This method can be represented using the following equation:

$$
E(C) = \left(\frac{x_1 + x_2 + \cdots + x_{10}}{10} \bullet p_1\right) + \left(\frac{x_{11} + x_{12} + \cdots + x_{20}}{10} \bullet p_2\right) + 0 \bullet p_3
$$

Explain why these two methods yield the same value.

2.5 In a given year, the probability that a driver in the 55–64 age category is involved in a bodily-injury accident is about 0.01. The probability that a driver in the same age category has a property-damage-only accident is about 0.02. The probability that a driver is not involved in an accident is 0.97.

a. Use the predicted mean values from Problem **2.3a** to create a probability distribution table for drivers in the 55–64 age category.

b. Let the random variable C represent the claim values for a driver in the 55–64 age category during a given year. Determine the expected value of C and describe what it represents to an insurance company.

c. Use your results in Problems **2.3c** and **2.5b** to explain why drivers in the 21–24 age category typically pay higher insurance premiums than drivers in the 55–64 age category.

* * * * *

2.6 Consider a baseball player with a lifetime batting average of 0.315.

a. Assume that the probability this player gets a hit on the next at-bat is $P(\text{H}) = 0.315$. Determine the probability that the player does *not* get a hit, or $P(\text{N})$.

b. In an upcoming game, the player will have four turns at bat. One possible outcome in this situation is HNHH. List all the possible outcomes for the four at-bats and, assuming that they are independent events, determine the corresponding probabilities.

c. Complete the following probability distribution table for the player's next four at-bats.

No. of Hits	Probability
0	
1	
2	
3	
4	

d. How many hits do you predict that this player will get in the next four at-bats? Explain your response.

2.7 According to one math teacher's grading system, group work counts for 20% of the final grade, projects 30%, and tests 50%.

a. A student's scores for the class are shown in the table below. Use this information to determine the final grade.

Group Work	Projects	Tests
78	85	92
95	75	88
82	99	95
75	89	79
98	82	
83	65	
85		
90		
74		

b. Compare this teacher's method of determining final grades to the calculation of expected value.

Whenever you choose to drive, there is a risk of having an accident. The potential costs of an accident—and the law, in many states—motivate most drivers to insure themselves. By insuring a large number of drivers, insurance companies provide a service that allows policyholders to share these financial risks with others.

Exploration

By simulating the operation of an insurance company, you might gain insight into some issues concerning insurance premiums.

Suppose that your class decides to create its own insurance company in which every member of the class is insured for both bodily injury and property damage.

Using statistics from previous years, the class determines that the probability of having a bodily-injury claim for a policyholder in the 16–20 age category is 0.06. The probability of having a claim for property damage only is 0.1. Because the total probability of filing a claim is $0.06 + 0.1 = 0.16$, the probability of not filing a claim is $1 - 0.16 = 0.84$.

To simplify the operation of the company, the class has decided to limit claim payments to the 20 values listed in Table **15-9.** If no claim is filed, the claim value is $0.

TABLE 15-9 ■ *Probability Distribution Table for C*

	Bodily Injury		Property Damage		No Accident	
Decile	**Claim ($)**	**Prob.**	**Claim ($)**	**Prob.**	**Claim ($)**	**Prob.**
1	208	0.006	22	0.01	0	0.084
2	572	0.006	88	0.01	0	0.084
3	1105	0.006	196	0.01	0	0.084
4	2050	0.006	319	0.01	0	0.084
5	3079	0.006	453	0.01	0	0.084
6	4501	0.006	615	0.01	0	0.084
7	6861	0.006	835	0.01	0	0.084
8	9771	0.006	1189	0.01	0	0.084
9	15,266	0.006	1909	0.01	0	0.084
10	26,642	0.006	3567	0.01	0	0.084

a. The class wants to keep insurance premiums as low as possible. To analyze this situation, they use the random variable C to represent the 21 possible claim values.

   Because the expected value of C represents the mean annual claim per policyholder, the class decides to use this value as the annual premium. Determine $E(C)$.

b. Design a simulation of the class insurance company for a one-year period. For each policyholder, your simulation should complete the following sequence of steps:

   1. Determine if the policyholder files a claim during the year.
   2. If a claim is filed, determine if it is for bodily injury or for property damage only. *Hint:* Consider the ratios $0.06/0.16 = 0.375$ and $0.1/0.16 = 0.625$.
   3. If the claim is for bodily injury, determine which of the 10 claim amounts the company will pay. Similarly, if the claim is for property damage only, determine which of the 10 claim amounts the company will pay.
   4. Record the cost of the driver's claim, if any, for the year.

c. Run the simulation once to simulate your driving record for the year.

d. 1. Collect the class data and determine the sum of the claim values for the entire class.
   2. Calculate the claims cost per policyholder for the year.

3. Using the annual premium from Part **a**, determine the profit or loss per policyholder for the year.
4. Determine the total profit or loss for the year for the class insurance company.

e. Repeat Part **c** nine more times, to obtain data for a total of 10 years. Compile the class data for each year. Determine the mean value of each of the following for the 10 simulations:

1. the claims cost per policyholder
2. the profit or loss per policyholder
3. the total profit or loss for the year

Note: Save your work for use in the assignment.

f. Suppose the number of policyholders increases to 100. To examine how this might affect premiums, use your simulation to model the claims of 100 policyholders over 10 years. For each year, determine the mean values described in Part **e** above.

Note: Save the results for use in the assignment.

Discussion

a. What are some of the limitations of your simulation in terms of modeling the operation of an actual insurance company?

b. 1. Why is it not reasonable for an insurance company to set its premiums equal to the expected value of claims per policyholder?

2. Would it be reasonable for the company to set premiums much higher than the expected value of claims?

c. How did your company's ability to pay claims for the class compare with its ability to pay claims for 100 policyholders?

d. A typical insurance company insures a relatively large group of people. What are the advantages and disadvantages of insuring small groups like those in the exploration?

e. Compare the means calculated for the two different groups in Parts **e** and **f** of the exploration. How would you expect this statistic to change for 10,000 policyholders?

f. How does the law of large numbers relate to the data you collected in the exploration?

g. Based on your results in the exploration, what annual premium would you recommend to insure your class only? to insure a group of 100 policyholders?

Warm-Up

1. Insurance companies typically use 65% of the premiums they collect to cover claim costs. This part of the premium is the **pure premium.** Another 30% covers operating costs, or **overhead.** The remaining 5% of the premiums collected represents profit.

   a. Explain why the annual premium used in your simulation is lower than what an actual insurance company would charge.

   b. What premium would a typical insurance company charge in a situation in which the claim cost per policyholder was $512?

   c. Estimate the annual profit for a typical insurance company providing coverage for your class.

2. An insurance company's **loss ratio** is defined as follows:

$$\frac{\text{total claims paid}}{\text{total premiums collected}}$$

   a. Would an insurance company want its loss ratio to be large or small? Explain your response.

   b. Use your responses to Problem **1** to explain why an insurance company's loss ratio is typically 65%.

Assignment

3.1 Imagine that you are employed by an insurance company. The chief executive officer (CEO) requests a report on the predictability of insurance claims. Write a report for the CEO, using the results of the exploration to support your explanation.

3.2 **a.** Use the results of the simulations in the exploration and an annual premium of $788 to find the largest and smallest loss ratio for each of the following:

   1. your class　　**2.** 100 people.

   b. Estimate the largest and smallest loss ratio for a simulation of 1 million policyholders.

   c. Use the law of large numbers and your responses from Parts **a** and **b** to describe some considerations insurance companies might have regarding numbers of policyholders.

3.3 Consider an insurance company with 3500 policyholders. The average annual claim is $707. The probability that a policyholder will file a claim is 9%. Considering the percentages described in Problem **1** of the Warm-Up, suggest an appropriate premium for this insurance.

3.4 The following table shows the annual number of accidents per 100,000 licensed drivers of eight different age groups.

Number of Accidents per 100,000 Drivers			
Age	**Bodily Injury**	**Property Damage Only**	**Total**
16–20	5753	10,022	15,775
21–24	3688	6687	10,375
25–34	2531	4420	6951
35–44	1945	3580	5525
45–54	1757	3432	5189
55–64	1322	2587	3909
65–74	1235	2119	3354
75 or older	1408	2353	3761

The table below shows predicted decile values for insurance claims in the same population.

Decile	Bodily Injury Claim ($)	Property Damage Claim ($)
1	150	100
2	442	255
3	873	361
4	1622	474
5	2591	613
6	3925	795
7	5975	1049
8	8725	1450
9	14,125	2225
10	25,415	3513

a. An insurance company plans to offer coverage for both bodily injury and property damage to this population. Use the data given, along with the percentages in Problem **1** of the Warm-Up, to suggest an annual insurance premium for a 17-year-old driver. Describe how you determined your response.

b. Repeat Part **a** for a 67-year-old driver.

c. Compare the premium of the 67-year-old with the premium of the 17-year-old.

* * * * *

3.5 A life insurance company sells term insurance policies to 20-year-old males that pay $40,000 if the policyholder dies within the next 5 years. The company collects an annual premium of $200 from each policyholder.

The following table shows the probability distribution for X, the random variable that represents the company's income (or loss) per policyholder. In this case, x_1 represents the income if the policyholder dies during the first year (at age 20), while x_6 represents the income if the policyholder dies after the policy expires (at age 26 or older).

Income (or Loss)	Probability
$x_1 = -\$39,800$	0.00175
$x_2 = -\$39,600$	0.00181
$x_3 = -\$39,400$	0.00184
$x_4 = -\$39,200$	0.00189
$x_5 = -\$39,000$	0.00191
$x_6 = \$1000$	p_6

a. Determine the probability that the policyholder will die after the policy expires.

b. Calculate $E(X)$, the company's expected income per policyholder.

c. **1.** Explain why it might be risky for this company to insure only one policyholder.

2. Explain why it is not as risky for the company to insure 10,000 policyholders.

3. How much income would the company expect from insuring 10,000 policyholders?

Research Project

Many insurance companies give discounts for drivers or cars that fit certain criteria. For example, a car with airbags is considered safer than a comparable car without airbags, so a company might offer lower premiums for this feature.

a. Compile a list of the discounts that might apply to you as a driver.

b. Determine the amount that premiums typically are reduced for each type of discount in Part **a.**

c. Comment on the relationship between each discount and the probability of having a claim or the potential value of the claim.

d. Determine the annual premium you would pay—including any applicable discounts—for comprehensive coverage on each of the following types of vehicles:

   1. a sports car
   2. a luxury car
   3. a family car.

Summary Assessment

Cars are not the only possessions that can be expensive to repair or replace. As a result, many people buy insurance for their homes, jewelry, and appliances. Because of the potential for water damage, some even buy insurance for their waterbeds. In fact, it's possible to insure almost anything—from a champion race horse to a concert pianist's hands.

For example, contact lenses are especially easy to lose or damage. Imagine that you own an insurance business that provides coverage for contact lens. Before setting your premiums, you do some research on contact lens claims. Here are the statistics:

- An average of 10 out of every 100 people with contact lens insurance files a claim for damage or loss each year.
- The first decile of claims averages $75.00, deciles 2–7 average $125.00, and deciles 8–10 average $300.

Continue your analysis by completing the following steps.

1. Develop a simulation for annual contact lens claims. Your simulation should utilize a random variable and a probability distribution table. It also should identify mean claim values and be able to model different numbers of policyholders.
2. Use your simulation to compare the mean claim cost per policyholder, and the range in claim costs per policyholder, for different numbers of policyholders.
3. Suggest a pure premium and a full premium for this insurance coverage and describe how you determined these values.
4. Use the results of your simulation and the law of large numbers to describe how the number of policyholders affects your ability to earn a predictable profit.

Module Summary

* The **law of large numbers** indicates that, if a large random sample is taken from a population, the sample proportion has a high probability of being very close to the population proportion.
* A **random variable** X is a variable that takes on each of its possible values with a specific probability. Given possible values for X of $x_1, x_2, \ldots, x_k$, each has its corresponding probability $p_1, p_2, \ldots, p_k$. The sum of these probabilities is 1.
* A **probability distribution** for a random variable X assigns probabilities $p_1, p_2, \ldots, p_k$ to the values $x_1, x_2, \ldots, x_k$ for X.
* The **expected value** or **mean** of a random variable X, denoted as $E(X)$, is the sum of the products of each value of X and its respective probability:

$$E(X) = x_1p_1 + x_2p_2 + \cdots + x_kp_k$$

* Insurance companies provide protection against part of the cost of an accident in exchange for a fee. The fee for this service is an insurance **premium,** and the contract with the company is called an **insurance policy.** The people who pay insurance premiums are **policyholders.**
* **Bodily injury liability insurance** pays for any individual who is injured as a result of the negligent operation of the insured vehicle.
* **Collision insurance** covers the cost of repairing the insured vehicle when the damage is due to its negligent operation.
* **Comprehensive insurance** covers natural damage (by floods, hail, or storms), theft, or vandalism of the insured car.
* **Property damage liability insurance** covers the cost of damages to another person's property caused by the negligent operation of the insured vehicle.
* To obtain benefits, policyholders must file an insurance **claim.** The claim reports the details and costs of an accident and requests payment.
* The percentage of insurance premiums used to cover claim costs is the **pure premium.** The operating costs of a business are its **overhead.**
* An insurance company's **loss ratio** is defined as

$$\frac{\text{total claims paid}}{\text{total premiums collected}}$$

Glossary

68–95–99.7 rule—states that approximately 68% of the total area between the normal curve and the x-axis lies within 1 standard deviation of the mean, 95% lies within 2 standard deviations of the mean, and 99.7% lies within 3 standard deviations of the mean.

absolute maximum (of a function)—the greatest value of the range.

absolute minimum (of a function)—the least value of the range.

absolute value (of a complex number)—the value of r for a complex number $a + bi$ written in trigonometric form $r\cos\theta + ri\sin\theta = r(\cos\theta + i\sin\theta)$, where $r = \sqrt{a^2 + b^2}$; also known as the modulus.

absolute value (of a real number x)—is denoted by $|x|$ and defined as follows: If $x \geq 0$, then $|x| = x$; if $x < 0$, then $|x| = -x$.

acceleration—the rate of change in velocity with respect to time; has both magnitude and direction.

acceleration (due to gravity)—a constant typically denoted by g; on earth's surface, the acceleration due to gravity is about 9.8 m/sec^2 in a direction toward the earth's center.

addition property of congruence—if a, b, and c are any real numbers with $a \equiv b$, then $a + c \equiv b + c$.

additive identity—given a set and the operation of addition defined on that set, the unique element a of the set such that when a is added to any element x, the result is that element x; in other words, $x + a = a + x = x$.

additive inverse—b is an additive inverse of x if $x + b = b + x = a$, where a is the additive identity; the additive inverse of x is denoted by $-x$.

alternative hypothesis—the statement that must be true if the null hypothesis is false; denoted as H_a.

ambiguous case (of the law of sines)—occurs when two non-congruent triangles contain the same given information (the lengths of two sides and the measure of an angle opposite one of these sides).

ampere—unit of electrical current.

amplitude—half the distance between the absolute maximum and the absolute minimum of a periodic function.

angular speed—for a moving point P, relative to a fixed point O, angular speed is the measure of the angle θ through which the line containing O, and P passes per unit time.

annual percentage rate (APR)—the interest rate that, when compounded annually, will produce the same account balance as the advertised interest rate for loans.

annual percentage yield (APY)—the interest rate that, when compounded annually, will produce the same account balance as the advertised interest rate for savings accounts.

area (of an ellipse)—can be calculated using the formula $A = \pi ab$, where $2a$ and $2b$ are the lengths of the axes.

argument (of a complex number)—the angle θ in a complex number of the form $a + bi$ written in trigonometric form as $r\cos\theta + ri\sin\theta = r(\cos\theta + i\sin\theta)$; measured from the positive portion of the real axis to the point (a,b) in the complex plane.

asymptote (to a curve)—a line such that the distance from a point P on the curve to the line approaches zero as the distance from P to the origin increases without bound, where P is on a suitable part of the curve.

asymptote (to a hyperbola)—a line passing through the center such that the distance from a point P on the hyperbola to the line approaches zero as the distance from P to the center increases without bound; the slopes of the asymptotes for a hyperbola are b/a and $-b/a$.

axiom—a statement accepted as true; often describes relationships among terms.

axiomatic system—a mathematical system that contains undefined terms, definitions, axioms, and theorems.

binomial distribution—the probability distribution for a binomial experiment.

binomial experiment—consists of a fixed number of independent trials, where each trial has only two possible outcomes (success or failure), the probability of a success remains the same from trial to trial, and the total number of successes is observed.

binomial formula—$P(r \text{ successes in } n \text{ trials}) = C(n,r) \bullet p^r \bullet (1-p)^{n-r}$, where p represents the probability of success in any one trial; used to determine the probability of obtaining r successes in n trials in a binomial experiment.

binomial theorem—states that the powers of a binomial of the form $(a + b)$ can be found as follows, where $C(n,r)$ is the combination of n things, taken r at a time:

$$(a+b)^n = C(n,n) \bullet a^n b^0 + C(n,n-1) \bullet a^{n-1}b^1 + C(n,n-2) \bullet a^{n-2}b^2 + \cdots + C(n,1) \bullet a^1 b^{n-1} + C(n,0) \bullet a^0 b^n$$

center (of a hyperbola)—the midpoint of the segment joining the foci.

center (of an ellipse)—the intersection of the major and minor axes.

central limit theorem—states that, even if the population from which samples are taken is not normally distributed, the distribution of the means of all possible samples of the same size will be approximately normal; this approximation becomes more accurate as the sample size n increases; for $n \geq 30$, the distribution of sample means can be modeled reasonably well by a normal curve (this requirement is not necessary if the population from which samples are taken is normally distributed).

circle—the locus of points in a plane that are a given distance, the radius, from a fixed point, the center; the standard form of the equation of a circle with center at (h,k) and radius r is $(x-h)^2 + (y-k)^2 = r^2$.

clock arithmetic—an arithmetic in which addition is accomplished by moving clockwise around an n-hour clock containing the digits $1, 2, 3, \ldots, n$, while subtraction is accomplished by moving counterclockwise around the dial; to distinguish the symbols for operations in clock arithmetic from those used in real-number arithmetic, they often are drawn with circles around them.

common logarithm—logarithm of base 10; may be written as $\log_{10} x$, but usually is condensed to $\log x$.

complex conjugates—a pair of complex numbers of the form $a + bi$ and $a - bi$; the sum and product of complex conjugates are real numbers.

complex number—any number in the form $a + bi$, where both a and b are real numbers.

complex plane—a two-dimensional coordinate plane using the horizontal axis as the real axis and the vertical axis as the imaginary axis; complex numbers of the form $a + bi$ are graphed on the complex plane as ordered pairs of the form (a,b).

components (of a vector)—the pair of horizontal and vertical vectors that when added, result in the given vector; the horizontal component of a vector $\mathbf{m}$ is denoted by $\mathbf{m}_x$ (read "m sub x"), while its vertical component is denoted by $\mathbf{m}_y$; using trigonometric ratios, $\mathbf{m}_x = |\mathbf{m}| \bullet \cos\theta$ and $\mathbf{m}_y = |\mathbf{m}| \bullet \sin\theta$, where θ is a directional angle measured counterclockwise from the positive x-axis.

composite function—given two functions f and g, the composite function $f \circ g$, read as "f composed with g" is defined as $(f \circ g)(x) = f(g(x))$; the domain of $f \circ g$ is the set of all values of x in the domain of g such that $g(x)$ is in the domain of f.

composition of transformations—a composition B of transformations B_1 and B_2 is a function whose domain is the domain of B_1 and whose range is the range of B_2; in other words, the composition B is a one-to-one correspondence that maps a preimage point P in the domain of B_1 to an image point P'' in the range of B_2; denoted as $B = B_2 \circ B_1$ (read "B equals B_1 composed with B_2"); this notation implies that transformation B_2 is performed after transformation B_1.

compound interest—interest which is calculated not only on the initial principal but also on the accumulated interest of prior periods.

compound statement—two or more statements joined using the connectives *and* or *or*.

concurrent lines—two or more lines that intersect at a common point.

conditional probability—the probability of an event occurring, given that an initial event, or condition, has already occurred; the probability of event B occurring, given that event A has already occurred, is denoted $P(\mathrm{B} | \mathrm{A})$.

conditional statement—a statement that can be written in the form "if p, then q," where p is the hypothesis and q is the conclusion; also can be written as "p implies q," denoted as $p \to q$; a conditional is false only if its hypothesis is true and its conclusion is false (in all other cases, a conditional is true).

confidence interval (for a parameter)—an interval of numbers in which one would expect to find the value of that parameter; every confidence interval has two aspects: an interval determined by the statistics collected from a random sample and a confidence level describing what percentage of the intervals created by that process would contain the parameter.

congruent (in modulo n)—two numbers are congruent in modulo n if they have the same remainder when divided by n; denoted by the symbol $\equiv$.

conic section—a geometric shape formed by the intersection of a plane with a double-napped cone; the four conic sections are the circle, the ellipse, the hyperbola, and the parabola.

conjugate axis—the perpendicular bisector of the transverse axis of a hyperbola.

conjugate hyperbolas—two hyperbolas that have the same asymptotes.

conjunction—combines two mathematical statements with the word *and;* a conjunction is true only if both statements are true.

connective—a word used to join two statements in a compound statement; the connective *and* corresponds with the intersection of sets; the connective *or* corresponds with the union of sets.

continuous (at a point)—a function is continuous at a point c in its domain if the following conditions are met: the function is defined at c, or $f(c)$ exists; the limit of the function exists at c, or $\lim_{x \to c} f(x)$ exists; and these two values are equal, or $f(c) = \lim_{x \to c} f(x)$.

continuous (over the domain)—a function is continuous over its domain if it is continuous at each point in its domain.

continuous probability distribution—results when the outcomes of an experiment can take on all possible real-number values within an interval.

contrapositive (of a conditional statement)—formed by interchanging the hypothesis and the conclusion and negating both of them; given the conditional "if p, then q," the contrapositive is, "if not q, then not p," denoted as $\sim q \rightarrow \sim p$; a conditional statement and its contrapositive are logically equivalent.

converse (of a conditional statement)—formed by interchanging the hypothesis and the conclusion; given the conditional "if p, then q," the converse is, "if q, then p," denoted as $q \rightarrow p$.

cosine (of an angle)— in a right triangle, the ratio of the length of the leg adjacent to the angle to the length of the hypotenuse.

cosine function—a function that uses the wrapping function to assign a real number t to the x-coordinate of the corresponding point on a unit circle with center at the origin; denoted as $f(t) = \cos(t)$.

coterminal angles—two angles that share the same initial side and terminal side.

counterexample—an example that illustrates a contradiction to a statement; a statement can be proven false by finding only one counterexample.

critical region—the set of all values that would lead a researcher to reject the null hypothesis.

cylindrical coordinate system—a coordinate system that describes the location of a point in space using an ordered triple of the form (r,θ,z), where r is a radius in a polar plane, θ is a polar angle, and z is the directed distance between the point and the polar plane (a positive value for z represents a distance above the polar plane).

cylindrical projection—a projection of the points on a sphere onto a tangent right circular cylinder.

De Moivre's theorem—states that the powers of any complex number $a + bi$ can be found as follows: $(a + bi)^n = [r(\cos\theta + i\sin\theta)]^n = r^n(\cos n\theta + i\sin n\theta)$

deductive reasoning—the process of using a logical sequence of valid arguments to reach a conclusion.

definition—in mathematical proof, a statement that is accepted as true.

degenerate conic section—the intersection of a plane and a double-napped cone to form a point, a line, or two intersecting lines.

degree (of a polynomial)—the value of the greatest exponent of the variable in a polynomial expression.

depreciation—the decrease in an item's value over time.

derivative (of a function)— the instantaneous rate of change in a function $f(x)$ with respect to x; the derivative at the point $(x, f(x))$, denoted by $f'(x)$, is:

$$\lim_{h \to 0} \frac{f(x + h) - f(x)}{h}$$

dilation—a transformation that pairs a point C, the center, with itself and any other point P with a point P' on ray CP so that $CP' / CP = r$, where r is the scale factor; a dilation with center at point C and a scale factor of r is denoted as $D_{C,r}$.

direct proof—a proof that makes direct use of the hypothesis to arrive at a conclusion.

directrix—a fixed line that, along with the focus, defines a parabola.

discontinuous—a function is discontinuous at a point if it does not meet all the conditions for continuity at that point.

discrete probability distribution—a probability distribution in which the set of outcomes is either finite or can have a one-to-one correspondence with the natural numbers.

discriminant—the expression $b^2 - 4ac$ in the quadratic formula, where a, b, and c are real numbers and $a \neq 0$; when the discriminant is less than 0, the solutions are complex and occur in conjugate pairs.

displacement—a change in position in a particular direction.

domain—the set of first elements in a function or relation.

e—an irrational number approximately equal to 2.71828; sometimes called Euler's number in honor of Swiss mathematician Leonhard Euler; the value of e can be represented mathematically as:

$$\lim_{n \to \infty} \left(1 + \frac{1}{n}\right)^n = e$$

ellipse—a locus of points in the plane such that the sum of the distances from two fixed points, the foci, is a constant; the standard form of the equation of an ellipse with center at (h,k) is:

$$\frac{(x-h)^2}{a^2} + \frac{(y-k)^2}{b^2} = 1$$

end behavior—the characteristics of a graph as $|x|$ increases without bound.

equivalent functions—two functions $f(x)$ and $g(x)$ are equivalent if and only if the domain of $f(x)$ is the same as the domain of $g(x)$ and $f(x) = g(x)$ for all values of x in the domain.

equivalent vectors—vectors that have the same magnitude and the same direction.

Euclidean geometry—geometry on a flat surface (a plane); named in honor of the Greek geometer Euclid.

event—a subset of a sample space.

expected value (of a binomial experiment)—the theoretical mean number of successes in n trials; if a binomial experiment consists of n trials and p is the theoretical probability of success on any trial, then the expected value (or expected number of successes) is $n \bullet p$.

expected value (of a random variable X)—the sum of the products of each possible value of X and its corresponding probability (also called the mean):

$$E(X) = x_1p_1 + x_2p_2 + \cdots + x_kp_k \text{ or}$$

$$E(X) = \sum_{i=1}^{k} x_ip_i$$

experimental probability (of an event)—equals the number of times an event occurs divided by the total number of trials.

explicit formula—a rule for finding for calculating any specific term in a sequence.

exponential equation—an equation of the form $y = a \bullet b^x$, where $a > 0$ and either $0 < b < 1$ or $b > 1$.

extraneous root—an incorrect solution that may result from correct algebraic manipulation.

fair game—a game in which the expected payoff equals the cost of playing the game.

family (of functions)—a set of functions that have a common parent; each family member is generated by performing one or more transformations on the parent function.

Fibonacci sequence—a sequence in which the first two terms are both 1 and successive terms are generated by adding the previous two terms; named for an Italian merchant also known as Leonardo of Pisa (ca. 1180–1250).

Fibonacci-type sequence—any sequence in which successive terms are formed by adding the previous two terms; can be defined recursively as $t_n = t_{n-1} + t_{n-2}$ where $n > 2$.

finite geometry—an axiomatic system that, unlike traditional Euclidean geometry, uses a finite number of points.

finite-difference process—the process of finding successive sequences of differences, continuing until the first constant sequence of differences is found.

focus—a fixed point included in the definition of a conic section.

force—a push or a pull in a particular direction; the metric unit of force is the Newton (N).

frequency (of a data item)—number of observed occurrences of that item.

frequency (of electrical current)—the rate at which current alternates; measured in cycles per second; a frequency of 1 cycle per second equals 1 hertz (Hz).

frequency histogram—consists of bars of equal width whose heights indicate the frequencies of intervals.

frequency polygon—formed by the line graph that connects the set of points (x,y), where x is the midpoint of an interval and y is the frequency of the interval; the base of a frequency polygon is the x-axis (if the frequency of the interval containing the greatest or least x-value is not 0, a vertex must be added to complete the polygon).

frequency table—table consisting of two columns that describe data items and the number of observed occurrences of each item.

function—a relation from a domain to a range in which each element of the domain occurs in exactly one ordered pair.

fundamental counting principle—if an event that can occur in m ways is followed by an event that can occur in n ways, then the total number of ways that the two events can occur is $m \bullet n$.

fundamental theorem of algebra—states that every polynomial equation of degree $n \geq 1$ with complex coefficients has at least one root in the set of complex numbers; one consequence of the fundamental theorem of algebra is that nth-degree polynomial equations have exactly n roots in the set of complex numbers.

general quadratic equation—an equation of the form $Ax^2 + Bxy + Cy^2 + Dx + Ey + F = 0$, where coefficients A, B, and C are not all equal to zero.

glide reflection—the composition of a reflection and a translation parallel to the line of reflection.

great circle (of a sphere)—a set of points determined by the intersection of the sphere and a plane that contains the center of the sphere; in spherical geometry, a line is defined as a great circle.

hertz (Hz)—international unit of frequency, represents one cycle per second.

histogram—graph that displays information using rectangles or bars of uniform width and scales with uniform intervals.

homogeneous form (of a point)—when represented as a column matrix, the homogeneous form of a point (x,y) is:

$$\begin{bmatrix} x \\ y \\ 1 \end{bmatrix}$$

hyperbola—the locus of points in a plane for which the positive difference of the distances from two designated foci is constant; the standard form of the equation of a hyperbola with center at (h,k) is:

$$\frac{(x-h)^2}{a^2} - \frac{(y-k)^2}{b^2} = 1 \quad \text{or} \quad \frac{(y-k)^2}{b^2} - \frac{(x-h)^2}{a^2} = 1$$

hyperboloid—surface generated by a hyperbola revolving around an axis.

hypotenuse—the longest side in a right triangle; the side opposite the right angle.

hypothesis test—a process that uses statistical data to reject or fail to reject a null hypothesis.

i—the imaginary unit; $i = \sqrt{-1}$ and $i^2 = -1$.

identity—an equation that is true for all real numbers.

identity transformation—preserves the position, shape, size, and orientation of a figure.

if and only if—when a conditional and its converse are both true, they can be written as a single statement using the words *if and only if,* denoted as $p \leftrightarrow q$, or p iff q (read "p if and only if q"); all definitions may be written as statements using *if and only if.*

image—any subset of points that results from a transformation; if point A is the preimage, then the image of a point A can be represented as A' (read "A prime").

imaginary unit—the complex number i where $i = \sqrt{-1}$ and $i^2 = -1$.

independent events—events for which the probability of any one event occurring is unaffected by the occurrence or non-occurrence of any of the other events; for two independent events A and B, $P(\text{A and B}) = P(\text{A}) \bullet P(\text{B})$; this definition can be extended to any number of independent events.

indirect proof—a proof that begins by assuming that the original statement is false; from this assumption, valid arguments are followed until a contradiction to a known fact is reached; once a contradiction is reached, the assumption must be false; therefore, the original statement is true.

infinity—an unlimited quantity or an amount larger than any fixed value; represented by the symbol ∞.

initial side (of an angle)—when angle measure is thought of as the rotation of a ray, the ray where the rotation begins.

insurance premium—the fee paid in exchange for protection against loss or damage.

interest—an amount earned on invested money, or the fee charged for loaned money.

inverse (of a conditional statement)—formed by negating the hypothesis and the conclusion; given the conditional "if p, then q," the inverse is, "if not p, then not q," denoted as $\sim p \rightarrow \sim q$.

inverse (of a relation)—results when the elements in each ordered pair of the relation are interchanged; the domain of the original relation becomes the range of the inverse, while the range of the original relation becomes the domain of the inverse.

inverse function—if a relation is a function, and its inverse is also a function, then the inverse is an inverse function; the inverse of f is denoted by f^{-1}.

law of cosines—states that the square of the length of any side of a triangle is equal to the sum of the squares of the lengths of the other two sides minus twice the product of the lengths of these sides and the cosine of the angle included between them; in a triangle ABC, $c^2 = a^2 + b^2 - 2ab\cos\angle C$.

law of large numbers—states that the mean of a large number n of independent measurements of a random quantity tends, as n increases, toward the theoretical mean of that quantity; this implies that for very large sample sizes, there is a high probability that the sample mean is close to the population mean.

law of sines—states that the lengths of the sides of a triangle are proportional to the sines of the opposite angles.

leading coefficient (of a polynomial)—the coefficient of the variable with the greatest degree.

leg (of a right triangle)—one of the two shorter sides in a right triangle; a side opposite an acute angle.

limit (of a function)—if the value of $f(x)$ gets arbitrarily close to c as x gets close to a, then c is the limit of the function as x approaches a; this is true if, for every real number e, there exists a corresponding positive real number d so that $c - e < f(x) < c + e$ whenever $a - d < x < a + d$.

limit (of a sequence)—for a sequence $k_1, k_2, k_3, \ldots, k_n, \ldots$, the limit is a number L if for any prescribed accuracy, there is a term k_m such that all terms after k_m are within this given accuracy of L.

linear regression—the linear model that results in the least sum of the squares of the residuals; also called the least-squares line.

locus—the set of all points that satisfy one or more given conditions.

logarithm—in a relationship of the form $b^n = m$, the logarithm of m to the base b is n; denoted symbolically as $\log_b(m) = n$, where $b > 0$ and $b \neq 1$.

loss ratio (in the insurance industry)—the ratio of total claims paid to total premiums collected.

major axis—the longer of the two axes of an ellipse; always contains the foci.

mapping diagram—a method for representing a function between two sets using arrows to indicate the pairings of each element in the domain to its corresponding element in the range.

margin of error—a measure of uncertainty determined by the standard deviation of all sample means for a given sample size, which is denoted by $\sigma_{\bar{x}}$ and calculated as follows, where σ is the standard deviation of the population and n is the sample size: $\sigma_{\bar{x}} = \sigma/\sqrt{n}$; the margin of error for a 95% confidence interval is $\pm 2\sigma_{\bar{x}}$.

mathematical induction—a method of proof that can be described as follows: suppose that for any natural number n, $P(n)$ is a mathematical statement involving n; if $P(1)$ is true, and whenever k is a natural number such that $P(k)$ is true, $P(k + 1)$ also is true, then $P(n)$ is true for all natural numbers n.

mean of a binomial distribution—the product of the number of trials and the probability of a success; in other words, the mean $\mu = np$, where n is the number of trials and p is the probability of a success.

minor axis—the shorter of the two axes of an ellipse.

modular arithmetic—an arithmetic in which addition and subtraction are accomplished in a manner similar to clock arithmetic; a system of modulo n (or mod n) contains the digits $0, 1, 2, 3, \ldots, n - 1$.

modulus—the value of r for a complex number $a + bi$ written in trigonometric form $r\cos\theta + ri\sin\theta = r(\cos\theta + i\sin\theta)$, where $r = \sqrt{a^2 + b^2}$; also known as the absolute value.

multiplication property of congruence—if a, b, and c are any real numbers with $a \equiv b$, then $a \bullet c \equiv b \bullet c$.

multiplicative identity— given a set and the operation of multiplication defined on the set, the unique element c of the set such that when any element x is multiplied by c, the result is that element x; in other words, $x \bullet c = c \bullet x = x$.

multiplicative inverse—d is the multiplicative inverse of x if $x \bullet d = d \bullet x = c$; the multiplicative inverse of any element x (other than the additive identity) can be denoted by x^{-1}; the multiplicative inverse of x also is referred to as the reciprocal of x.

mutually exclusive events—two events that cannot occur at the same time in a single trial; for two mutually exclusive events A and B, $P(\text{A and B}) = 0$.

natural logarithm—logarithm with base e; the natural log of x, where $x > 0$, is denoted by $\ln x$.

negation—the negation of a statement p is the statement "It is not the case that p" or simply "not p,"denoted as $\sim p$; a statement and its negation have opposite truth values.

normal curve—the curve that describes the shape of the graph of a normal distribution; the equation of a normal curve that models a particular set of data depends on the mean and standard deviation of the data.

normal distribution—a continuous probability distribution that is symmetric about the mean and tapers to the left and right like a bell.

***n*th root** (of a non-negative number a)—a number s such that $s^n = a$; the non-negative nth root of a is denoted as $\sqrt[n]{a}$.

null hypothesis—a statement about one or more parameters that usually involves a claim of no relationship or no difference; denoted as H_0.

oblique asymptote—an asymptote that is neither horizontal nor vertical.

one-to-one correspondence—a function between two sets that pairs each element in the domain with exactly one element in the range, and each element in the range with exactly one element in the domain.

one-to-one function—a function such that each element in the range corresponds to a unique element of the domain; in other words, if $f(x_1) = f(x_2)$, then $x_1 = x_2$; one-to-one functions are the only functions whose inverses also are functions.

opposite vectors—vectors that have the same magnitude and directions that differ by 180°.

orientation—a preimage and its image have the same orientation if they have the same sequence of corresponding vertices when read either clockwise or counterclockwise.

parabola—a locus of points in a plane equidistant from a fixed line, the directrix, and a fixed point not on the line, the focus; the standard form, or vertex form, of the equation for a parabola with a horizontal directrix and vertex $V(h,k)$ is $y - k = a(x - h)^2$.

paraboloid—a surface generated by a parabola revolving around its axis of symmetry.

parameter—a numerical characteristic of a population.

parametric equations—a set of equations in which rectangular coordinates are expressed in terms of another variable.

parent function—the preimage for a family of functions, in which each family member represents one or transformations of the parent.

Pascal's triangle—an arithmetic number pattern named in honor of the French philosopher Blaise Pascal; see diagram below.

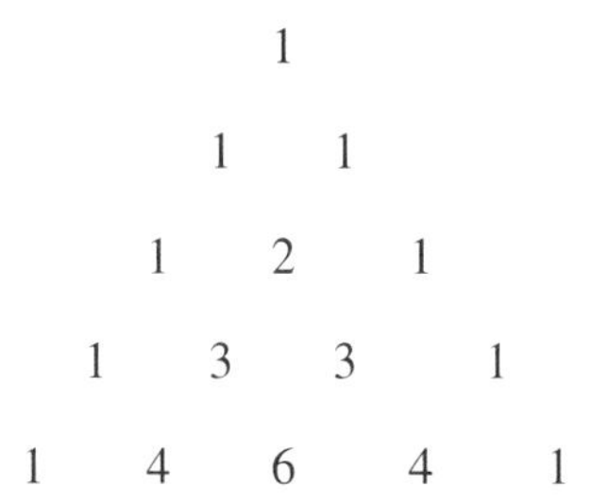

perfect square—the result that occurs when any expression is multiplied by itself.

periodic function—a function in which values repeat at constant intervals.

period—the smallest interval of the domain over which a periodic function repeats.

phase shift—the horizontal translation of a periodic function.

piecewise function—a function for which different parts of the domain correspond with different rules.

plane of symmetry—a plane that divides a three-dimensional object into two parts, each a mirror image of the other.

point of tangency—the point at which a curve and a tangent line intersect.

polar angle—an angle measured from a fixed ray, the polar axis.

polar coordinate system—a coordinate system that describes the location of a point P in a plane using an ordered pair consisting of a radius r and a polar angle θ.

polar plane—a plane containing a polar coordinate system.

polar point—a point on a sphere not on a given line, through which all lines perpendicular to the given line pass; every line on a sphere has two polar points, or poles.

pole (in a polar coordinate system)—endpoint of the polar axis; denoted as O.

pole (of a sphere)—a polar point.

polynomial function—a function of the form $f(x) = a_n x^n + a_{n-1}x^{n-1} + \cdots + a_1 x^1 + a_0$, where a_n, $a_{n-1}, a_{n-2}, \ldots, a_0$ are real numbers and n is a non-negative integer.

population—all of the members of a group about which information is to be gathered.

population mean—a parameter denoted by the Greek letter μ (mu).

population standard deviation—a parameter denoted by the Greek letter σ (sigma); can be calculated using the following formula, where the population has N members represented by $x_1, x_2, \ldots, x_N$:

$$\sigma = \sqrt{\frac{(x_1 - \mu)^2 + (x_2 - \mu)^2 + \cdots + (x_N - \mu)^2}{N}}$$

postulate—a statement that is assumed to be true without proof.

preimage—any subset of points in the domain of a transformation.

principal—an amount of money invested or loaned.

probability distribution—the assignment of probabilities to a specific characteristic that belongs to each possible outcome of an experiment.

proof by exhaustion—the method of examining all possibilities to prove a statement.

pure imaginary number—a complex number $a + bi$ for which $a = 0$ and $b \neq 0$.

pure premium—the percentage of insurance premiums used to cover claim costs.

***p*-value**—the probability of obtaining a statistic greater than (or less than) the observed one if the null hypothesis is true.

Pythagorean theorem—in a right triangle, the square of the length of the longest side (the hypotenuse) equals the sum of the squares of the lengths of the other sides (the legs).

quadratic formula—given a second-degree polynomial equation of the form $ax^2 + bx + c = 0$ with $a \neq 0$, its two solutions are:

$$x = \frac{-b}{2a} + \frac{\sqrt{b^2 - 4ac}}{2a} \quad \text{and} \quad x = \frac{-b}{2a} - \frac{\sqrt{b^2 - 4ac}}{2a}$$

radian—unit of angle measure; 1 radian equals the measure of a central angle whose sides intercept an arc on a unit circle with a length of 1 unit; in general, the measure of a central angle in radians is the ratio of the length of the intercepted arc to the radius of the circle.

radius (of a point on a polar coordinate system)—the distance from the pole to the point measured in the polar plane; denoted as r.

random experiment—an experiment in which the individual outcomes are chance events.

random variable—a variable X that takes on each of its possible values with a specific probability; the sum of these probabilities is 1.

range—the set of second elements in a function or relation.

rational function—a function of the form $r(x) = f(x)/g(x)$, where $f(x)$ and $g(x)$ are polynomial functions and $g(x) \neq 0$.

reflection (in a line m)—a transformation that pairs each point on the line m with itself and each other point P with a point P' so that m is the perpendicular bisector of $\overline{PP'}$; denoted as r_m.

relation—a set of ordered pairs in which the domain is the set of first elements and the range is the set of second elements.

relative frequency—ratio of an item's frequency to the total number of observations in the data set.

relative frequency histogram—a frequency histogram in which the heights of the bars represent relative frequencies instead of frequencies.

relative frequency polygon—a frequency polygon in which the y-values represent relative frequencies instead of frequencies.

relative frequency table—table consisting of three columns that describe data items, their frequencies, and their relative frequencies.

residual—the difference between the y-coordinate of a data point and the corresponding y-value of a linear model.

resultant vector—the sum of any number of vectors; in the tip-to-tail method, the resultant vector joins the tail of the first vector to the tip of the last vector in the sum.

root (of a polynomial)—a solution to an equation of the form $f(x) = 0$; also called a zero; the x-coordinate of each point where the graph intersects the x-axis.

rotation—a transformation that pairs one point C, the center, with itself and every other point P with a point P' that lies on a circle with center C such that $\theta = m\angle PCP'$ is the magnitude of the rotation; a rotation of θ degrees with center at point C is denoted as $R_{C,\theta}$; the value of θ is positive for counterclockwise rotations and negative for clockwise rotations.

rotational symmetry—an object has rotational symmetry about a point if, when rotated through an angle about that point, each point in the image coincides with a point in the preimage.

sample—a subset of a population; typically includes only some members of a population, not all of them.

sample mean—a statistic denoted by $\bar{x}$ (read "x-bar").

sample space—the set of all possible outcomes for an experiment.

sample standard deviation—a statistic denoted by s; can be calculated using the following formula, where the sample has data from n members of a population represented by $x_1, x_2, \ldots, x_n$:

$$s = \sqrt{\frac{(x_1 - \bar{x})^2 + (x_2 - \bar{x})^2 + \cdots + (x_n - \bar{x})^2}{n - 1}}$$

sampling—the process of choosing a subset of a population.

sampling distribution of sample means—a distribution that contains the means ($\bar{x}$) of *all* possible samples of size n from a population; the mean of the sampling distribution of sample means, denoted by $\mu_{\bar{x}}$, equals the population mean μ; the standard deviation of the sampling distribution of sample means, denoted by $\sigma_{\bar{x}}$, equals $\sigma/\sqrt{n}$, where σ is the population standard deviation and n is the sample size.

scalar—a real number.

scalar multiplication—the multiplication of a matrix, vector, or other item by a scalar.

scale factor—the ratio of corresponding sides for two similar figures.

secant—a line that intersects a curve in at least two points.

sequence of differences—a sequence generated from a finite sequence $t_1, t_2, t_3, t_4, t_5, \ldots, t_n$ by taking the differences of consecutive terms.

set diagram—a method for representing a function between two sets using an arrow to represent the rule.

significance level (of a hypothesis test)—an arbitrarily assigned probability that distinguishes a statistically significant difference from a chance variation.

similar—two objects are similar if they have the same shape and the ratios of corresponding lengths are proportional; the ratio of corresponding sides is the scale factor; the symbol for similarity is ~.

simple interest—can be calculated by the formula $I = Prt$, where I represents interest, P represents principal, r represents the interest rate per time period, and t represents the number of time periods.

simple random sample—a sample selected so that each member of the population has the same chance of being included in the sample.

sine (of an angle)—in a right triangle, the ratio of the length of the leg opposite the angle to the length of the hypotenuse.

sine function—a function that uses the wrapping function to assign a real number t to the y-coordinate of the corresponding point on a unit circle with center at the origin; denoted as $f(t) = \sin(t)$.

standard deviation—a measure of spread often represented by the Greek letter σ (sigma) and determined by the following formula, where μ represents the mean and n is the number of items in the set:

$$\sigma = \sqrt{\left((x_1 - \mu)^2 + (x_2 - \mu)^2 + \cdots + (x_n - \mu)^2\right)/n}.$$

See *sample standard deviation* and *population standard deviation.*

standard deviation of a binomial distribution—the square root of the product of the number of trials, the probability of a success, and the probability of a failure; in other words, $\sigma = \sqrt{np(1-p)}$, where n is the number of trials and p is the probability of a success.

standard error of the mean—the standard deviation of all sample means for a given sample size; denoted by $\sigma_{\bar{x}}$ and calculated as follows, where σ is the standard deviation of the population and n is the sample size: $\sigma_{\bar{x}} = \sigma/\sqrt{n}$.

standard position (of an angle)—the position of an angle on a coordinate plane in which the initial side lies on the positive x-axis and positive angle measures indicate a counterclockwise rotation.

statement—in mathematics, a sentence that can be determined to be either true or false, but not both.

statistic—a numerical characteristic of a sample.

stereographic projection—a projection of the points on a sphere onto a plane perpendicular to a given diameter of the sphere.

substitution property of congruence—if a, b, and c are any real numbers with $a \equiv b$ and $b \equiv c$, then $a \equiv c$.

supplementary angles— two angles are supplementary when the sum of their measures is 180°.

tangent (of an angle)—in a right triangle, the ratio of the length of the leg opposite the angle to the length of the leg adjacent to the angle.

tangent function—a function $f(t)$, where t is any real number except an odd multiple of $\pi/2$, defined by the ratio of the y-coordinate to the x-coordinate of the point assigned to t by the wrapping function of the real number line around a unit circle with center at the origin; denoted as $f(t) = \tan(t)$; the tangent function is equivalent to the ratio of the sine function to the cosine function: $\tan x = \sin x / \cos x$.

tangent (to a conic)—a line in the plane of the conic that intersects the curve at exactly one point and contains no points in the interior.

tangent (to a curve)—the tangent to a curve at the point $(x, f(x))$ is the line with the following slope, provided that this limit exists:

$$\lim_{h \to 0} \frac{f(x+h) - f(x)}{h}$$

terminal side (of an angle)—when angle measure is thought of as the rotation of a ray, the ray where the rotation ends.

theorem—a statement proven to be true in all cases.

theoretical probability (of an event)—if each outcome in the sample space is equally likely, equals the number of outcomes in the event divided by the total number of outcomes in the sample space.

tip-to-tail method—a method for adding vectors in which each vector to be added is drawn so that its tail coincides with the tip of the previous vector.

transitivity—a principle by which the true statements "if p, then q" and "if q, then r" may be used to form the valid conclusion: "if p, then r."

translation—a transformation that pairs every point $P(x,y)$ with an image point $P'(x + h, y + k)$; denoted as $\mathbf{T}_{P,P'}$.

translation vector—a vector that describes a translation from $P(x,y)$ to $P'(x + h, y + k)$; can be denoted by the ordered pair $\langle h,k \rangle$, a bold, lowercase letter, or with an arrow.

transverse axis—the line segment joining the vertices of a hyperbola.

trial (in a binomial experiment)—each repetition of a fixed action.

trigonometric form (of a complex number)—a complex number of the form $a + bi$ can be written in trigonometric form as $r\cos\theta + ri\sin\theta = r(\cos\theta + i\sin\theta)$, where r is the absolute value or modulus and θ is the argument.

trigonometric ratios—ratios of the lengths of sides in right triangles.

truth table—a diagram that shows the truth values of a statement for all possible truth values of its parts; the truth table for the conditional $p \rightarrow q$ is shown below.

p	q	$p \rightarrow q$
T	T	T
T	F	F
F	T	T
F	F	T

truth value—the truth or falseness of a statement.

undefined term—a term used without definition.

uniform probability distribution—a continuous probability distribution in which all the probabilities over intervals of equal width are equal.

unit circle—a circle with a radius of 1 unit.

vector—a quantity that has both magnitude (size) and direction; often represented by a bold, lowercase letter, such as vector **m**; the magnitude of a vector **m** is denoted by $|\mathbf{m}|$; also can be represented by the ordered pair $\langle \mathbf{m}_x, \mathbf{m}_y \rangle$, where the first value in the ordered pair is the horizontal component and the second is the vertical component.

velocity—speed in a specific direction.

Venn diagrams—mathematical models that show relationships among different sets.

vertex (of a parabola)—the point of intersection of a parabola and its axis of symmetry.

vertices (of an ellipse)—the intersections of the ellipse and the major and minor axes.

vertices (of a hyperbola)—the intersections of the branches and the segment joining the foci.

wrapping function—a function that pairs each point on the real number line with a location on the unit circle.

z-score—a statistic that describes, for a given value x, the number of standard deviations above or below the mean; calculated using the following formula, where μ is the population mean and σ is the population standard deviation:

$$z = \frac{x - \mu}{\sigma}$$

zero—for a function f, c is a zero if $f(c) = 0$; also called a root.

zero vector—the sum of a vector and its additive inverse.

Selected References

Allendoerfer, C. B., and C. O. Oakley. *Fundamentals of Freshman Mathematics.* New York: McGraw-Hill, 1959.

Alpha, T. R., and D. Strebe. "Map Projections." U.S. Geological Survey Open-File Report 91-553A. Washington, DC: U.S. Government Printing Office, 1991.

American Association of Physics Teachers. *Kinematics and Dynamics of Satellite Orbits.* New York: American Institute of Physics, 1963.

Avital, S., and S. Libeskind. "Mathematical Induction in the Classroom: Didactical and Mathematical Issues." *Educational Studies in Mathematics* 9 (1978): 429–438.

Baker, B. L. "The Method of Differences in Determination of Formulas." *School Science and Mathematics* 67 (April 1967): 309–315.

Barlow, B. V. *The Astronomical Telescope.* New York: Springer-Verlag, 1975.

Bertness, C., et al. "January Calendar." *Mathematics Teacher* 79 (January 1986): 38–39.

Birch, T. W. *Maps Topographical and Statistical.* Oxford: Oxford University Press, 1966.

Blocksma, M. *Reading the Numbers: A Survival Guide to the Measurements, Numbers, and Sizes Encountered in Everyday Life.* New York: Penguin Books, 1989.

Boyer, C. B. *A History of Mathematics.* New York: John Wiley & Sons, 1991.

Brase, C. P., and C. H. Brase. *Understandable Statistics: Concepts and Methods.* Lexington, MA: D. C. Heath, 1991.

Brieske, T. J. "Mapping Diagrams and the Graph of $y = \sin(1/x)$." *Mathematics Teacher* 73 (April 1980): 275–78.

Brieske, T., and J. Lott. "The Motion Geometry of a Finite Plane." *Two-Year College Mathematics Journal* 9 (1978): 259–266.

Broughton, P. "Halley's Comet in the Classroom." *Mathematics Teacher* 79 (February 1986): 85–89.

Brown, L. H. "Discovery of Formulas Through Patterns." *Mathematics Teacher* 66 (April 1963): 337–338.

Brumfiel, C. "A Note on Mathematical Induction." *The Mathematics Teacher* 67 (November 1974): 616–618.

Consortium for Mathematics and Its Applications (COMAP). *For all Practical Purposes.* New York: W. H. Freeman and Co., 1988.

"Crash Problems on a per Mile Basis." *Status Report for the Insurance Institute for Highway Safety* Vol. 27, No. 11 (5 September 1992).

Davis, P. *The Mathematics of Matrices: A First Book of Matrix Theory and Linear Algebra.* Waltham, MA: Blaisdell Publishing Co., 1965.

Day, P. "Day O Ranch: A New American Gothic." *The Ostrich News* 6 (September 1993): 21–26.

Demana, F., B. K. Waits, and S. R. Clemens. *College Algebra & Trigonometry.* New York: Addison-Wesley, 1992.

DeTemple, D., and J. Robertson. *The Calc Handbook, Conceptual Activities for Learning the Calculus.* Palo Alto, CA: Dale Seymour Publications, 1991.

Dossey, J. A., A. D. Otto, L. E. Spence, and C. Venden Eynden. *Discrete Mathematics.* Glenview, IL: Scott Foresman and Co., 1987.

Duenk, L., and C. Tuel. *Understanding Insurance. A Guide for Industrial Cooperative Training Programs.* Blacksburg, VA: Vocational Industrial Education Unit, Virginia Polytechnic Institute and State University, 1986.

Dugle, J. "The Twelve Days of Christmas and Pascal's Triangle." *Mathematics Teacher* 75 (December 1982): 755–757.

Dunham, W. *Journey Through Genius: The Great Theorems of Mathematics.* New York: John Wiley & Sons, 1990.

Egsgard, J., G. Flewelling, C. Newell, and W. Warburton. *Making Connections with Mathematics.* Providence, RI: Janson Publications, Inc., 1987.

Ehrlich, R. *Turning the World Inside Out and 174 Other Simple Physics Demonstrations.* Princeton, NJ: Princeton University Press, 1990.

Eisenkraft, A., and L. Kirkpatrick. "A Topless Roller Coaster." *Quantum* 2 (November/December 1992): 28–30.

Eves, H. *An Introduction to the History of Mathematics.* Philadelphia, PA: Saunders College Publishing, 1990.

Faires, J. D., and B. T. Faires. *Calculus and Analytic Geometry.* Boston: Prindle, Weber & Schmidt, 1983.

Fisher, I., and O. M. Miller. *World Maps and Globes.* New York: J. J. Little & Ives Co., 1944.

Fletcher, P., P. Fletcher, and C. Wayne. *Foundations of Higher Mathematics.* Boston, MA: PWS-Kent Publishing Co., 1988.

Gamow, G. *One, Two, Three . . . Infinity.* New York: Viking Press, 1961.

Garman, B. "Inverse Functions, Rubik's Cubes, and Algebra." *Mathematics Teacher* 78 (January 1985): 33–34, 68.

Gillespie, J., and A. Schupp. "The Role of Speculation and Information in the Early Evolution of the United States Ostrich Industry: An Industry Case Study." *Review of Agricultural Economics* 24.1 (Spring/Summer 2002): 278–292.

Greenhood, D. *Mapping.* Chicago: The University of Chicago Press, 1964.

Guarino, R., and R. Trubo. *The Great American Insurance Hoax.* Los Angeles, CA: Nash Publishing, 1974.

Guillotte, H. P. "The Method of Finite Differences: Some Applications." *Mathematics Teacher* 79 (September 1986): 466–470.

Halliday, D., and R. Resnick. *Fundamentals of Physics.* New York: John Wiley & Sons, 1974.

Hart, E. W., J. Maltas, and B. Rich. "Implementing the Standards; Teaching Discrete Mathematics in Grades 7–12." *Mathematics Teacher* 83 (May 1990): 362–367.

Hewitt, P. *Conceptual Physics.* Menlo Park, CA: Addison-Wesley, 1987.

Higginson, W. "Mathematizing 'Frogs': Heuristics, Proof, and Generalization in the Context of a Recreational Problem." *Mathematics Teacher* 74 (October 1981): 505–515.

Highway Loss Data Institute. *Insurance Special Report A–37.* Arlington, VA: Highway Loss Data Institute, 1991.

Hogben, L. *Mathematics for the Million.* New York: W. W. Norton & Co., 1968.

Joint Matriculation Board. Shell Centre for Mathematical Education. *The Language of Functions and Graphs.* University of Nottingham. December 1985. Joint Matriculation Board. Manchester M156EU.

Kasner, E., and J. Newman. *Mathematics and the Imagination.* New York: Simon and Schuster, 1943.

Kellaway, G. P. *Map Projections.* London: Methuen and Co., 1946.

Kennedy, D. W. *Insurance: What Do You Need? How Much is Enough?* Tucson, AZ: Knight Ridder Press, 1987.

Kleiner, I. "Thinking the Unthinkable: The Story of Complex Numbers (with a Moral)." *Mathematics Teacher* 81 (October 1988): 583–592.

Kleppner, D., and R. J. Kolenkow. *An Introduction to Mechanics.* New York: McGraw-Hill, 1973.

Lauber, M. "Casting Out Nines: An Explanation and Extension." *Mathematics Teacher* 83 (November 1990): 661–665.

Litwiller, B. H., and D. R. Duncan. "Geometric Counting Problems." In *Learning and Teaching Geometry, K–12* 1987 Yearbook of the National Council of Teachers of Mathematics (NCTM). Ed. by M. M. Lindquist and A. P. Shulte. Reston, VA: NCTM, 1987. pp. 210–219.

Lotka, A. *Elements of Mathematical Biology.* New York: Dover, 1956.

McConnell, M. "Brady Couple Feathers Financial Nest with Ostriches." *Rural Montana* 41 (August 1994): 30–31.

Miller, I., J. E. Freund, and R. A. Johnson. *Probability and Statistics for Engineers.* Princeton, NJ: Prentice-Hall, 1990.

Moore, A. W. *The Infinite.* New York: Routledge, Chapman, and Hall, 1990.

Moore, D. S. *Statistics: Concepts and Controversies.* New York: W. H. Freeman and Co., 1991.

National Credit Union Youth Program. *The Big Jump: A Classroom Guide for Teaching Insurance to Teenagers and Young Adults Through Creative Activities.* Madison, WI: National Credit Union Youth Program, 1986.

Neter, J., W. Wasserman, and G. A. Whitmore. *Applied Statistics.* Boston, MA: Allyn and Bacon, 1993.

Nievergelt, Y. "Functions Give Three Points of View on the New Income Tax Law." *Mathematics Teacher* 81(March 1988): 176–180.

Parzynski, W. R. "The Geometry of Microwave Antennas." *Mathematics Teacher* 77 (April 1984): 294–296.

Paulos, J. A. *Innumeracy: Mathematical Illiteracy and Its Consequences.* New York: Hill and Wang, 1988.

Pearce, F. "Licensed to Thrill." *New Scientist* 135 (August 29, 1992): 23–25.

Pedersen, K. *Trivia Math: Pre-Algebra.* Sunnyvale, CA: Creative Publications, 1988.

Pitman, J. *Probability.* New York: Springer-Verlag, 1993.

Pratt, M. M. "Finite Geometries." Master's Thesis, San Jose State College, 1964. pp. 124–133.

Priestley, W. M. *Calculus: An Historical Approach.* New York: Springer-Verlag, 1979.

Pulfer, W. "Make Up a Story to Explain the Graph." *Mathematics Teacher* 77 (January 1984): 32–35.

Ranucci, E. R. "Fruitful Mathematics." *Mathematics Teacher* 67 (January 1974): 5–14.

Robinson, J. H. *Astronomy Data Book.* Plymouth, Great Britain: David & Charles Newton Abbot, 1972.

Rosen, K. H. *Discrete Mathematics and Its Applications.* New York: Random House, 1988.

Rowntree, D. *Statistics Without Tears: A Primer for Non-Mathematicians.* New York: Scribner's, 1981.

Runion, G. E., and J. R. Lockwood. *Deductive Systems: Finite and Non-Euclidean Geometries.* Reston, VA: National Council of Teachers of Mathematics, 1978.

Salisbury, D. F. *Money Matters: Personal Financial Decision Making with the Pocket Calculator.* Englewood Cliffs, NJ: Prentice-Hall, 1982.

The School Mathematics Project. *Living with Uncertainty.* Cambridge: Cambridge University Press, 1991.

Seymour, D., and M. Shedd. *Finite Differences: A Pattern-Discovery Approach to Problem-Solving.* Palo Alto, CA: Creative Publications, 1973.

Simmons, G. F. *Calculus Gems.* New York: McGraw-Hill, 1992.

Sincich, T. *Statistics by Example.* San Francisco: Dellen Publishing Co., 1987.

Smart, J. R. *Modern Geometries.* Pacific Grove, CA: Brooks/Cole Publishing Co., 1988.

Snyder, J. P. "Map Projections—A Working Manual." U.S. Geological Survey Professional Paper 1395. Washington, DC: U.S. Government Printing Office, 1987.

Sokal, R. R., and R. F. James. *Biometry.* San Francisco: W. H. Freeman and Co., 1969.

Swadener, M. "A Finite Field—A Finite Geometry and Triangles." *Two-Year College Mathematics Journal* 5 (1974): 22–25.

Taffel, A. *Physics: Its Methods and Meanings.* Boston: Allyn and Bacon, 1981.

Travers, K. J., W. F. Stout, J. H. Swift, and J. Sextro. *Using Statistics.* Menlo Park, CA: Addison-Wesley, 1985.

Trinklein, F. E. *Modern Physics.* New York: Holt, Rinehart and Winston, 1990.

Triola, M. F. *Elementary Statistics.* Reading, MA: Addison-Wesley, 1992.

U.S. Department of State. *Addressing the Safety Issues Related to Younger and Older Drivers: A Report to Congress.* Washington, DC: U.S. Government Printing Office, 1993.

Van Dyke, F. "A Concrete Approach to Mathematical Induction." *The Mathematics Teacher* 88 (April 1995): 302–307, 314–318.

Verhille, C., and R. Blake. "The Peg Game." *Mathematics Teacher* 75 (January 1982): 45–49.

Vilenkin, N. *Stories about Sets.* New York: Academic Press, 1969.

Vonder Embse, C. "Graphing Powers and Roots of Complex Numbers." *Mathematics Teacher* 86 (October 1993): 589–597.

Wallace, E. C., and S. F. West. *Roads to Geometry.* Englewood Cliffs, NJ: Prentice-Hall, 1992.

Walton, K. D. "Imagine That!" *Consortium* 40 (Winter 1991): 8–9.

Withers, P. "Energy, Water, and Solute Balance of the Ostrich—Struthio camelus." *Physiological Zoology* 56 (October 1983): 568–79.

Wood, E. F. "Self-Checking Codes—An Application of Modular Arithmetic." *Mathematics Teacher* 80 (April 1987): 312–316.

Zerfass, G. *Mathematical Induction: A Resource for Teaching in the High School Classroom.* Glenview, IL: Glenbrook South High School, 1992.

Index

D

E

F

G

N

O

P

T

U

V

W

Y

Z